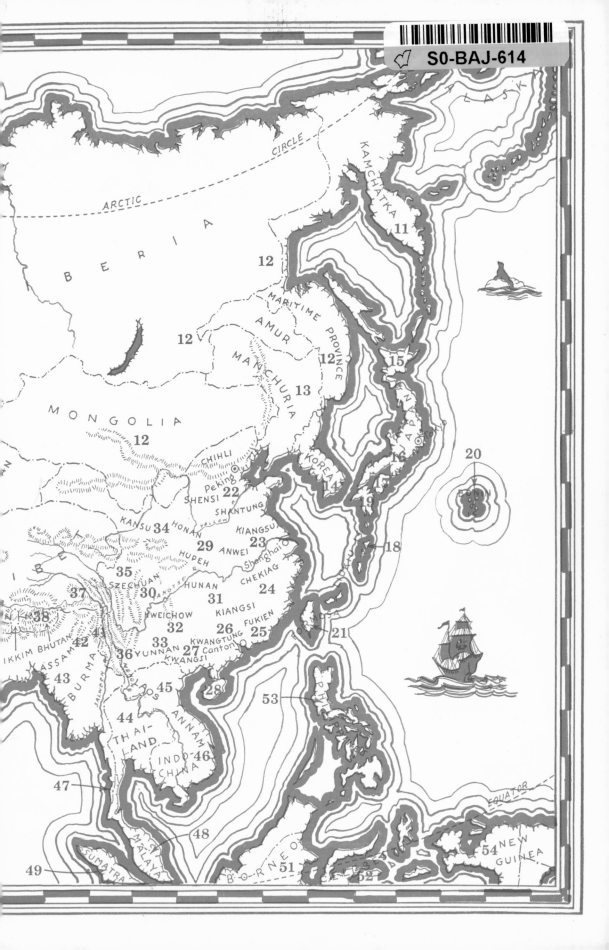

RHODODENDRONS AND AZALEAS
(Second Edition)

THE MACMILLAN COMPANY
NEW YORK · CHICAGO
DALLAS · ATLANTA · SAN FRANCISCO
LONDON · MANILA

IN CANADA
BRETT-MACMILLAN LTD.
GALT, ONTARIO

RHODODENDRONS AND AZALEAS

THEIR ORIGINS, CULTIVATION AND DEVELOPMENT

BY

CLEMENT GRAY BOWERS

WITH ILLUSTRATIONS IN COLOR BY

FRANCK TAYLOR BOWERS

AND

CLEMENT GRAY BOWERS

AND PEN DRAWINGS BY
THE AUTHOR

SECOND EDITION

NEW YORK
THE MACMILLAN COMPANY

TO MEMORIES OF

ƒ.ɪ.ß.

THIS BOOK IS INSCRIBED
BY THE AUTHOR

PREFACE TO THE SECOND EDITION

THIS book was originally produced a quarter-century ago. The fact that it has endured for so long, with an increasing demand for its republication, is very gratifying to the author.

In the intervening years great changes have been wrought in the extent to which members of the genus *Rhododendron* have become used and understood. The tremendous expansion of rhododendron culture on the American West Coast from a comparatively obscure status twenty-five years ago to one of dominance in 1960 is an example in point. Other changes have included such matters as the increased activity of hybridists both here and abroad, as well as a fundamentally better knowledge of the different sorts and their suitability for special purposes. Equally important is our newer knowledge of propagating techniques, physiological and ecological factors, soil and water relations, and several other vital phenomena.

Naturally, a considerable amount of updating has been required for the new edition. In order not to destroy the character and atmosphere of the work, as few alterations as possible have been made, although certain whole chapters have been rewritten. Most of the descriptive matter regarding species and hybrids remains unchanged, but the hardiness and merit ratings, especially of those imperfectly known in 1935, have been radically altered. And for clearer coordination the present volume has been divided into three parts—the living plant, the descriptive material, and the compiled data.

It should be repeated that this is primarily a horticultural book and not a work in systematic botany. The author has had no extensive rhododendron herbarium conveniently accessible, and he has designed the work to be horticulturally useful, although enough technical material is included to make the book of some value to the scientist as well as to the gardener.

After several years' work in the congenial climate of Long Island, circumstances forced the author to remove to a very cold region of upstate New York where the soil, water, and temperature are rather antagonistic toward plants of this genus. He has thus been able to appreciate some of the difficulties as well as the advantages encountered by growers over a wide range of conditions.

vii

If consideration for some of these factors has colored the pages of this book, as compared with other works written by those who garden in natural rhododendron-growing areas, he hopes that the information given may benefit those who need it and may not appear irrelevant to those more fortunately situated. For similar reasons, certain practices, now regarded as obsolete in some quarters, have been allowed to remain because of their continued serviceability elsewhere. This book is designed to be useful over a wide territory.

It will be recognized, of course, that in any work dealing with so broad a group of plants no one author can completely encompass the whole field in his personal experience. Ranging from the tropical to the arctic, much material has been assembled from afar. In doing so, the author has not only traveled much and observed broadly, but has also made use of published material, plus information collected orally from growers and specialists. Wherever feasible, credit has been given and references cited in the text. But in many instances, especially where duplications have existed, it has been impossible to recognize everyone who has helped in this compilation.

The author, therefore, wishes to acknowledge his debt to many friends, colleagues, and co-workers from far and near who in one way or another have assisted him. He appreciates the cooperation he has received from individuals and institutions at home and abroad, as well as the continuing interest of many who helped in the original work. At the present time he especially wishes to mention the scientific staff of the Royal Botanic Garden at Edinburgh, Scotland, including the late Sir William Wright Smith, Dr. John MacQueen Cowan, Dr. Harold R. Fletcher, Mr. H. H. Davidian, Mr. James Keenan, and other staff personnel. Others include Mr. William T. Stearn of the British Museum of Natural History, Mr. Francis Hanger and others from the Wisley Gardens of the Royal Horticultural Society, as well as a number of British and Dutch nurserymen and hybridists. In America, the list is too numerous to repeat, but special credit is due to Dr. Henry T. Skinner of the United States National Arboretum, Dr. Edward P. Breakey of the Western Washington Experiment Station, Mr. Paul Vossberg, Mr. Frederic P. Lee, and other members of the American Rhododendron Society, and the continued close cooperation of several others who are named in the original preface.

CLEMENT GRAY BOWERS

April, 1960

PREFACE

THIS book is concerned with the practical use of rhododendrons and azaleas in North America and elsewhere.

It has developed from a project in plant breeding begun nearly ten years ago when the author undertook certain technical investigations within the genus *Rhododendron*. One of the first steps in any scientific problem is to assemble the known facts regarding the subject. In this instance it soon became apparent that very little up-to-date knowledge concerning this group of plants was accessible, so the author was forced to secure the needed information, little by little, from literally hundreds of sources. This has been drawn from scattered scientific papers, old records, reference books, texts, periodicals and from experienced individuals. Finally, additional observations and experiments had to be made first-hand before the needed data were secured.

It was with the thought of preserving the information thus assembled and of making it available to others who might use it that the present book was designed. Recently, and chiefly in England, considerable information concerning the botany of the genus has appeared, through the botanic gardens and the publications of the Rhododendron Association. A large and rather recent work, *The Species of Rhododendron*, covers the technical descriptions of the species, but is scarcely adapted for popular horticultural use. The author has felt that such detailed taxonomic work embraces a field in itself and that matters of identification and classification, already covered in taxonomic works, need not be repeated here.

This book has been written, therefore, from the viewpoint of the practical horticulturist rather than from that of the systematic botanist. An emphasis is placed upon growing and reproducing the plants, caring for them under all sorts of conditions and obtaining improved forms by means of breeding. Demonstrated facts in physiology, pathology and genetics have been recognized. The illustrations have been made with the object of conveying the natural effect of the species as garden plants rather than of classifying them. Living plants rather than herbarium specimens have been employed so far as possible in making observations. Such matters as hardiness, color, form and garden merit have been stressed. Naturally, also, American climatic and soil requirements have been emphasized, although the volume is adaptable for use wherever rhododendrons are grown.

The author has employed many devices to clarify, simplify and shorten the material for the benefit of the amateur and the busy practical grower. References are provided so that additional sources of information may be consulted by the student. Specialized material is confined to the footnotes, tables and charts.

Sources of special data have been mentioned at various places in the text, and the author here wishes to express his deep appreciation to the friends who have so graciously aided in furnishing this information, as well as to all others who, in one way and another, have been helpful during the preparation of this work. He is greatly indebted to Mr. Henry Hicks, Mr. E. H. Costich and their associates, for highly valued technical information and for the use of their facilities. The author wishes to thank, also, Dr. L. H. Bailey and Dr. Edgar Anderson for their kindly interest in the work as a whole. Special acknowledgment, with sincere thanks, is also made to Dr. A. B. Stout, Dr. Lewis Knudson, Dr. Clarence E. Kobuski, Dr. Richard P. White and Mr. A. H. Nehrling for critically reading portions of the manuscript. Technical aid was rendered by Mr. I. B. Solberg and Mr. H. R. Sebold.

Due to the interest of Mrs. Harold Irving Pratt and Mr. Henry W. deForest, Mrs. Winthrop W. Aldrich, Mr. John S. Ames, Mrs. Robert Bacon, Mrs. S. V. R. Crosby, Mrs. Francis Crowninshield, Mrs. Bayard W. Cutting, Mrs. Ernest B. Dane, Mr. Henry F. duPont, Mr. Pierre S. duPont, Mrs. Childs Frick, Mrs. Edwin Gould, Mr. Harry G. Haskell, Mrs. Walter B. James, Mrs. Walter Jennings, Mrs. Gustav E. Kissel, Mr. Frederick S. Moseley, Mrs. Frederic B. Pratt, Mrs. John D. Rockefeller, Jr., Mrs. Samuel A. Salvage and Mrs. Carll Tucker, it was made possible to illustrate the book extensively by including the entire set of colored plates and line drawings prepared by the late Franck Taylor Bowers and the author. The author wishes to express his deep appreciation to this group of patrons of horticulture.

He dares to hope that his book may merit in some degree the interest bestowed upon it by one and all of those mentioned in this preface, and that it may bring to the people of America a new beauty and added contentment through a broader knowledge of these regal plants.

CLEMENT GRAY BOWERS

December 4, 1935

CONTENTS

CONTENTS

NOTES ON THE ILLUSTRATIONS

Except where otherwise noted, the colored figures are reproduced here at a scale of approximately two-thirds their natural diameter, while the line cuts of inflorescence types are approximately one-third diameter and the cuts of flower forms two-thirds diameter. Twenty-two of the colored drawings were made by the late Franck Taylor Bowers and six by the author, who also did all line drawings and maps.

COLOR PLATES

Following page   78

CATAWBA HYBRID 'MRS. CHARLES S. SARGENT'

This vigorous and beautiful red hybrid has remained supreme for many years as the most satisfactory red rhododendron for New England and other cold regions where special hardiness is required. It has commonly been sold in the trade as 'Mrs. C. S. Sargent,' but such usage is undesirable owing to possible confusion with a less meritorious clone called 'C. S. Sargent.'

RHODODENDRON MAXIMUM

Introduced into England in 1736, this American species was the first rhododendron to be grown in the English-speaking world by gardeners, although *R. ferrugineum* from Switzerland appears to have been cultivated on the Continent a few years earlier.

RHODODENDRON JAPONICUM VAR. AUREUM

This is the yellow form of the fine hardy species from Japan.

RHODODENDRON CAROLINIANUM VAR. FOLIATUM

This variety is distinguished from the type species by its long-jointed form and greater height, not by the color, as one might assume from this picture. This color, with its yellowish tinge in freshly opened buds, is found in strains of the regular species as well as in this variety.

RHODODENDRON ARBORESCENS VAR. RUBESCENS

Another variant in the wild is this pink form of the normally white *R. arborescens.* Both this and the typical form make splendid garden plants. They are hardy and heliotrope-scented.

CATAWBA HYBRID 'CATAWBIENSE ALBUM'

A splendid white hardy rhododendron, sold as a named clone and possibly of hybrid origin rather than a variant of the natural species. For many years this clone has remained one of the best among the "ironclad" rhododendrons.

RHODODENDRON VISCOSUM

A very hardy American azalea with spicy fragrance, which blooms late in the season (July in the north).

RHODODENDRON HYBRIDS

1. 'Mrs. Ashley Slocock,' an apricot-colored hybrid of *R. campanulatum*. Not recommended for sub-zero climates. 2. 'Tan,' one of the Dexter Hybrids, sun-tanned flesh color. 3. 'Mariloo.' This is the form of the Mariloo group that is grown at the Wisley Gardens of the Royal Horticultural Society. It is a big luscious pure yellow, a hybrid of *R. lacteum*. Probably not hardy. 4. 'Betty Wormald,' one of the best large-flowered British hybrids, now becoming popular elsewhere if the climate is not too cold. 5. Catawba Hybrid 'Everestianum,' an old clone which still remains deservedly popular. It has frilled petals, a bluish lilac color and is among the "ironclads" in hardiness. 6. 'Sappho,' an old-time hybrid with a strong, interesting color pattern of dark maroon on white. Not entirely hardy in the north, but unique and handsome. 7. 'Purple Splendour,' a violet-purple British hybrid, not entirely hardy in sub-zero climates, but the best purple hybrid. 8. 'Britannia,' perhaps the brightest and best of the red commercial rhododendrons now available on the market, but not hardy enough to be grown in the American northeast except in the most sheltered gardens. It originated in Holland in 1921. The petals have a very shiny surface. 9. 'Keay Slocock,' a hybrid of *R. campanulatum,* characterized by yellow flowers and bright orange-vermilion buds. Like others in its class, it is not recommended for very cold climates except experimentally.

The illustrations on this plate are reproduced at approximately one-third their natural diameter. Drawn by the author from specimens in Great Britain and America.

Following page 142

CATAWBA HYBRID 'LADY ARMSTRONG'

One of the time-honored sorts for cold climates.

RHODODENDRON JAPONICUM IN ITS NATURAL VARIATIONS

This shows the wide range of variation that comes from seeds of *R. japonicum,* a very hardy Japanese sort related to *R. molle.*

INDIAN HYBRID AZALEA 'PRESIDENT COMTE OSWALD DE KERCKHOVE'

A well-known clone used as a florists' potted plant. The typical form is shown at the left, the other flower displaying a prominent chimera or "bud sport" that commonly occurs on some variegated azaleas.

RHODODENDRON CAROLINIANUM VAR. ALBUM

A pure white form, compact and very hardy, which is rather distinct from the typical species and deserves to be used wherever an early-blooming evergreen plant with a neat, compact habit and desirable flowers is required.

CAUCASICUM HYBRID 'BOULE DE NEIGE'

This resembles a Catawba Hybrid, with which it is related, but it blooms about ten days earlier and is of rather low, compact growth. To avoid damage from lacewing flies, this should not be planted in the full sun. Hardy.

GHENT HYBRID AZALEAS

The clones 'Daviesii,' 'Coccinea Speciosa,' and 'Pucella' shown in the illustrations are century-old sorts which, with others, have stood the test of time and are generally hardy in sub-zero climates. However, they do not enjoy the warm dry weather of summer and need plenty of water during that season. Under proper culture, the azaleas of this class are among the best flowering shrubs in existence.

RHODODENDRON ATLANTICUM IN WHITE AND PINK FORMS

This little species is to the American deciduous azaleas what the Kurume azalea is to the azaleas of Japan. It is only 18 inches tall, is quite floriferous and has stoloniferous roots. Its broad spreading growth makes it adaptable for use in foreground plantings. Drawn by the author.

RHODODENDRON ROSEUM AND R. NUDIFLORUM

Many of the wild azaleas of the American northeast are natural hybrids or intermediate forms of these two species. One of these intermediates appears in the top figure.

CONTENTS

HALFTONE ILLUSTRATIONS

the graft has "taken" and the union has formed. The upper portions of the stock plant have been cut away and the scion is functioning in their place. The twine will soon be removed. Photographs by courtesy of Mr. Montague Free and *House and Garden,* the copyright owner.

THE TECHNIQUE OF HAND POLLINATION

In Figure 1, the anthers containing pollen are being removed from the flowers of *Rhododendron maximum* before the buds open. The anthers are simply pulled off by means of forceps. The flower cluster is then bagged (as in Figure 4) and allowed to remain until the flowers would normally be in full bloom and the stigmas sticky. Then the bag is removed and pollen is applied to each stigma as in Figure 2. In the picture, pollen from a small capsule is being applied by means of forceps. The pollinated flower cluster is then placed under a bag again, as shown in Figure 3. Figure 4 shows how the bag is fastened on by means of a wire paper clip, the cross being recorded on a wooden tree label attached to the stem as shown.

A JAPANESE AZALEA GARDEN

Low but unclipped specimens of azaleas belonging to the Obtusum subseries are used to cover the banks of this pool in Japan, where broad drifts of color are produced by this means. Several Japanese sorts are fairly hardy in America, while one native American species, *Rhododendron atlanticum,* is a dwarf of only 18 inches and is noteworthy for floriferousness and complete hardiness in climates where the temperature goes to zero in the winter.

RHODODENDRONS AND THEIR KIN ON A RESIDENTIAL PROPERTY

An excellent use of rhododendrons is here exemplified in the base planting by Mrs. W. C. Corkran at her Short Hills, New Jersey, home "Boxley." The photograph is here reproduced through the courtesy of Mrs. Corkran and the *American Home.* Mr. Richard Averill Smith, photographer. Azaleas, vaccinium, mountain laurel and other heaths and broad-leaved evergreens may easily and effectively be combined with rhododendrons in favorable situations around the home grounds.

A FORTY-YEAR-OLD CATAWBA HYBRID

An old rhododendron, grown as a specimen on the lawn of a Long Island estate, develops a formal character combined with immense size, which renders it an impressive sight at all seasons, especially when in bloom. The Catawba rhododendron carries its flower trusses out beyond its foliage, so that the leaves do not conceal the flowers and thus a showy effect is produced. *Rhododendron maximum,* blooming later in the season, develops new foliage in the spring which partially conceals its flowers. Photograph copyright by J. H. McFarland.

RHODODENDRONS IN THE HEART OF A GREAT CITY

Tiny back-yard gardens such as this are to be found in the busiest sections of Manhattan. While city conditions are none too favorable for any plants, rhododendrons and azaleas fare better than many other species because of their ability to thrive in partial shade. Good plants, intelligently cared for, kept clean and supplied with plenty of moisture, are considered necessary for success. This garden is by Annette Hoyt Flanders, Landscape Architect, and the photograph is by Mattie Edwards Hewitt.

THE USE OF CLIPPED AND DWARF AZALEAS IN JAPAN

Many of the Japanese species of the Obtusum subseries are naturally of low, spreading growth and in mild climates they are semi-evergreen. The Japanese gardeners plant them to cover banks and obtain broad sweeps of color by this means. Their use, also, in Japanese gardens approximates rock-garden usage. For formal effects or as ornamental features for the foreground, they are often clipped, with either flat or rounded tops. Some of the clipped bushes in the Japanese garden shown in Figure 1 are azaleas. The bush at the base of the twisted pine trunk in Figure 2 is also a clipped azalea. Azaleas are used to cover the bank at the water's edge, Figure 3, and are blooming at the same time as the wistaria on the arbor.

CONTENTS

AN AZALEA GARDEN IN NEW ENGLAND

This Cape Cod garden is glorious in late May with its many azaleas and rhododendrons. The bush in the foreground is a rather typical specimen of the Torch Azalea, *R. Kaempferi,* and illustrates the extreme floriferousness of this species when well grown. Azalea gardens are by no means confined to the south, and wonderful effects may be secured in the colder regions by the use of properly chosen hardy species. Plants varying from dwarfs of 18 inches to fairly large shrubs of 12 or 15 feet may be found among the hardiest species of azalea. Photograph copyright by J. Horace McFarland.

MAPS

The numerals on the maps indicate geographical regions that are referred to as the natural habitats for certain groups of species.

PART I

THE LIVING PLANT

CHAPTER I

INTRODUCING THE GENUS RHODODENDRON

RHODODENDRONS and azaleas are remarkable plants. There is every indication that in the future they will be used and appreciated much more generally than they are at present. In regions like the British Isles, where the climate is very congenial, these plants already occupy a very important place in ornamental horticulture. America, although possessing several fine native species, is only at the beginning of her rhododendron development.

To catch a glimpse of their possibilities one has only to look at the wealth of new rhododendrons and azaleas now available to gardeners who live in mild climates. Much of the material used abroad is worthless, of course, to those in the excessively cold, hot or dry regions of America and elsewhere, whose efforts are hampered by the harsh environment. But new things are in the offing for the more severe climates and new knowledge is beginning to eliminate some of the hazards of cultivation in not-too-friendly localities.

While we look hopefully toward the future, we should not forget that we already possess a quantity of good material—a quantity and variety far greater than commonly realized—which is well adapted to regions such as those of the northeastern United States and which may be utilized if we will but take advantage of it. So while we are waiting for the good things of the future, let us avail ourselves, in the meantime, of the several excellent things immediately at hand.

As I begin, let me explain that wherever in this book the word "rhododendron" is used in a general way, it is my intention to include the azaleas within this term. As I shall explain later, there are botanical reasons which make it difficult to do otherwise. Of course, azaleas will be designated separately whenever occasion demands it.

This is, as I have said, a remarkable group of plants. From the arctic and the tropics they come to us, a galaxy of living forms from pygmies of a few inches to giants of 80 feet in height, with a range of colors which defies even the roses. These plants are remarkable for several reasons. First, because they

3

will grow in certain shady places where other plants fail. Next, because they demand an acid soil solution—something abhorrent to many of our agricultural crops and, for that reason, formerly associated in mind with waste land. They are remarkable also because they can be made to grow in great cities, under the shadows of skyscrapers, and will tolerate such conditions better than ordinary plants. They are remarkable for their idiosyncrasies, such as the curious movements which their leaves perform in cold weather. They are remarkable because their blooming season can be made to extend from April to August if a wise choice of early and late sorts is made. They are also remarkable for the evergreen character of many, for the number and variability of the species and for the facility with which they may be crossed.

But most of all, rhododendrons and azaleas are remarkable for their beauty. Gorgeous when in bloom, they are also handsome in their foliage and branching habit when they are out of bloom. The true rhododendrons, always green, are praised for their sturdy form and bold foliage, while the azaleas make up for their lack of winter foliage by producing an extra abundance of glittering, dazzling blossoms when blooming time comes around. A group of blooming rhododendrons or azaleas under the somber canopy of a grove of old trees becomes as gleaming jewels when touched by a filtering sunbeam. When in bloom there are no plants more gorgeous than these. Surely, if the rose is the queen of flowers, the rhododendron, in its stately majesty, is the king of flowers!

Looking over the old books, and even some of the modern foreign trade lists, one can find the rhododendrons and azaleas, along with *Kalmia, Vaccinium* and other related items, listed under this one large heading AMERICAN PLANTS. It is only recently that western China has become known as the world's greatest home of the genus *Rhododendron*. Heretofore, the United States held that position in the popular imagination. This was because most of the species introduced first, including the parents of the first hybrids, were natives of North America. Our species were the pioneers.

In view of this fact, it is a curious commentary that in many parts of the United States today where rhododendrons and azaleas grow wild, comparatively few people know them even by name. In some places these wild shrubs are known only under various homely names and are scarcely considered as subjects for ornamental planting. Near my home, for instance, beautiful azaleas have long been abundant in the countryside and should be used extensively in gardens; yet few people have thought of cultivating them. What an anomaly it is that Americans should know so little about these plants, while the gardeners of other countries use them so much—especially in England where not one species is native! Until recently there had been almost no breeding of rhododendrons in the United States, compared with that in England, Holland and

Germany, where thousands of exquisite hybrids have been produced. Now, however, American breeders are quite alert.

There are several different kinds of rhododendrons. First there are the large, leathery-leaved species which are familiar as the hardy, evergreen sorts, having their flowers in big, round trusses. Then there are other evergreen forms, many of them from the tropical rain-forests, less familiar to us and useful only as greenhouse plants. There are the epiphytic kinds which anchor themselves to trees after the manner of certain orchids. Then there are the highly colored tropical rhododendrons such as the Javanicum group, coming from Malaya and the islands of the sea and grown as ornamentals under close, hot-house conditions. On the other extreme are the dwarf Lapponicums and their allies from the arctic regions and the snow-capped mountain ranges and alpine meadows of western China. In the Azalea series there are likewise several categories. The deciduous forms, familiar as the native azaleas of the eastern United States, comprise one group. Then there are the hardy Japanese species, some of them semi-evergreen and inclined toward dwarfness, coming in several sizes of flower and plant. A group closely allied to the latter is that commonly grown in greenhouses for their flowers and popularly known as Indian Azaleas.

And so we have all sorts of things within the genus *Rhododendron*. Perhaps no person has ever seen them all or even their approximations. Most of us are familiar with only one or two main groups, the kinds that are near to us. The azalea of my own childhood was the lovely, fragrant *R. roseum* which the old soldiers used to carry on Decoration Day and which were known locally as "Mayflowers." People in the neighborhood used to say that they could not be grown in cultivation. What a joy it is now to have them growing luxuriantly in my garden and to realize that the old taboo, if it ever existed, is no longer in force against the culture of these woodland flowers.

And now a word about the place rhododendrons occupy in the classified scheme of things. When speaking of rhododendrons, we often call them "ericaceous plants." This expression refers to the family *Ericaceae* to which the rhododendrons and azaleas belong. Along with them in this family are certain other relatives, such as the mountain laurel, the wintergreen, the blueberry, the trailing arbutus, the Scotch heather and others too numerous to mention. A common name for the *Ericaceae* is the heath family and ericaceous plants are sometimes called "heaths." The name *Ericaceae* is derived from the genus *Erica,* another member of the family.

Members of the heath family are widely scattered throughout the world and occupy an important portion of the earth's surface. They are distinctive in their love for an acid soil and, hence, do not often grow in soil that is used for common agricultural crops. Although they are often placed in the class of "poor land plants," they are, nevertheless, as fastidious about soil conditions in their own way as other plants are in theirs.

The word "rhododendron" comes from the Greek ῥοδόδενδρον, which literally means "rose tree." The rhododendron of the ancient Greeks, however, was the oleander (*Nerium*) and our own rhododendrons were not cultivated in Europe, so far as we know, until the eighteenth century A.D.

Chapter II

RHODODENDRONS AS ORNAMENTAL PLANTS

Given a proper background, rhododendrons and azaleas may be as beautiful as any ornamental plants in existence. Like everything else, they need a suitable setting in order to display the full value of their charms, but, placed in such a setting, there are few things to compare with them. Certain gardens, such as the one at Magnolia-on-the-Ashley, near Charleston, S.C., give evidence of this in the fame which has come to them. If popular approval be a measure of beauty, then little else need be said regarding the beauty and effectiveness of such plantings.

Since I am not a landscape architect, it would ill become me to discuss planting design. I do not want to make the mistake of so many garden writers who without knowledge of the elements of composition seek, nevertheless, to give directions concerning matters they are incompetent to discuss. Moreover, special circumstances alter cases, so that it is unwise to attempt the giving of directions except in a general way.

There exists, however, the obligation to say something honestly descriptive of the uses to which rhododendrons and azaleas may be put, referring especially to the uses which best suit their cultural requirements and which tend toward the most satisfactory effects. This is an important consideration, aside and apart from any thought of actual landscape design, because no plant can be beautiful if it is sick, unthrifty or out of its proper environment. I would also call attention to the wide extent to which these plants, as woody landscape materials, offer possibilities for the trained designer of gardens and grounds, as well as for the amateur who plans his own place.

Considerations of shelter, soil or other growing conditions sometimes determine the site of a rhododendron planting without regard to preferences in the matter of appearance or effect. Where such circumstances prevail, a planting should be made in the place where the plants will thrive and an effort made to harmonize the surroundings with the planting. More often, however, the site where rhododendrons will grow the best is also the place where they appear to greatest advantage. This, I think, is especially true of the "true" or evergreen rhododendrons. These plants are somewhat more sensitive to exposure than are the azaleas and, for best results, should have the semi-shelter of a partially wooded situation. Their deep green foliage, also, looks better in such an environment than in any other location, especially when standing in front of an evergreen background. When they bloom, their flower trusses are tremendously enhanced if seen in such a setting.

This suggests another matter: the behavior of rhododendron leaves in winter. All the evergreen rhododendrons of America as well as many from China will roll up their leaves and point them downward in response to the stimulus of cold temperatures. This does not become a serious factor unless the temperature drops to 15°F. or lower, but on cold mornings a rhododendron planting assumes a peculiar and not attractive appearance if the curled-up leaves are seen silhouetted against a very light background, such as a white wall or a bank of snow. If, on the other hand, the rhododendrons are standing against a background of hemlocks, pines or any other dark or green material, this curling of the leaves is quite unnoticed. Hence, this matter should be considered when a site for rhododendrons is being chosen.

For the same reason, it pays to carefully plan all plantings of rhododendrons which are in a foreground and are to be seen at close range, because, by careful planning, the unattractive curled leaves can nearly always be rendered inconspicuous. If other green plants, such as conifers, kalmia or additional broad-leaved evergreen species with non-curling leaves, are interplanted here and there among the rhododendrons, the curling of the leaves, in plants growing close to the observer's eye, may be very successfully camouflaged. Considering, also, that the leaves do not curl except in the coldest weather, and then usually only at morning and evening, one can not regard this foliage behavior as a very serious objection. But, to forestall any possible criticism from the super-sensitive, it is always well to avoid planting the evergreen rhododendrons directly in front of light walls or in a close-up foreground position unless some ameliorating feature is provided. The person who scorns rhododendrons because of their winter effect need not hesitate to use them if he studies their background requirements thoroughly.

But for one situation in which rhododendrons need to be planted with special care, there are a dozen in which they may be used without restraint. They are almost universally fitting in a woodland or naturalistic setting. Here they obtain the shelter they desire and here the wild species, whose colors sometimes clash with architectural features and artificial light, may be used with impunity. Although the lilac-magenta color of the wild forms of *Rhododendron catawbiense* and some other species does not always suit the fastidious, it has a place, nevertheless, and this place is in the woodland. Surrounded by green foliage and dark shadows, with no other colors to clash against it, the natural coloration of the Catawba rhododendron finds an environment where it is truly delightful. The secret lies in its relation with other colors. It may be combined with white, yellow or green, but looks "dirty" beside brighter hues.

There are probably no flowering plants which excel the rhododendrons and azaleas for use in an evergreen garden. They are especially adapted for use in combination with conifers and frequently accompany them in nature. Not only do the rhododendrons with their dark foliage appear to great advantage with such plants as hemlocks, pines, yews, junipers and spruces, but they derive a considerable benefit from the association by reason of wind protection. It is a combination of great usefulness in formal garden designs where clipped evergreen hedges and various other coniferous materials may be employed with rhododendrons and azaleas to create a harmonious effect throughout the year with the addition of richly colored flowers during the blooming season. Whenever flowers are desired in an evergreen garden the several species of rhododendrons and their close allies, the kalmias, are able to furnish continuous bloom for a period of more than two months if a careful selection is made of overlapping species and varieties. Even the deciduous azaleas have the capacity of blending well with the surrounding conifers and may well be employed in an evergreen garden, giving added interest to the planting and furnishing an abundance of color hard to duplicate with any other materials. Their autumn foliage, also, harmonizes well.*

While unsurpassed for naturalistic plantings, rhododendrons and azaleas can be equally good when formally used in strict architectural designs, either classical or contemporary. Planted in regular beds, they may be formalized by enclosing in a clipped hedge or raised curb. Incidentally, this is a satisfactory way of handling them in raised peat-beds where the natural soil is unfavorable or where aeration and drainage are poor. A mulch may be hidden by a surrounding taxus hedge. Where some of the compact and dwarf species can be grown, these in themselves are useful as edging plants. Certain of the larger azaleas, such as *R. Vaseyi*, may even be used as clipped hedges.

In England, blooming rhododendrons and azaleas, balled and burlapped, are lifted from nursery beds and placed temporarily in window boxes or formal beds, the roots being plunged in peat moss. After the blooming period has stopped, they are returned to the nursery. Such plants are extremely effective

---

* When laying out a mixed planting of deciduous and evergreen materials, it is a practice of landscape architects to first place the evergreen materials, making a perfectly balanced composition of them alone, and then locate the deciduous materials among them. In this way "spottiness" of the evergreens in winter is avoided.

as bold color notes in public places. Such uses in America have been overlooked for too long.

Rhododendrons and azaleas may be used in many places about the garden and grounds of a residence. They do not necessarily need to be planted in the shade, although that is where they are especially useful. Wherever they are not too greatly exposed to the sun and wind they are generally appropriate and decorative. On the edge of a lawn, under the partial shade of large trees, rhododendrons are quite successful. Along the borders of an estate, in large parklike areas and on the banks of ponds and streams they find a suitable and fitting environment. Around the shady spots of a residence lot they often produce charming effects and the azaleas and smaller-leaved rhododendrons may be used against the north or east side of a small cottage. Where the large-leaved species are too coarse or heavy, the deciduous sorts and finer-leaved evergreen species are useful. I shall later speak more fully concerning the conditions which they need for best growth.

In addition to their uses about the grounds of residences, estates or parks, rhododendrons also have other uses of a more formal nature, such as the adornment of large public buildings. Where large masses of green are desired beside the entrances to buildings or in courtyards—situations where often the sunlight is limited—rhododendrons and conifers may be used together to create imposing effects. Similarly, too, the use of rhododendrons and azaleas in formal gardens is entirely satisfactory provided the plants employed are of a compact, formal habit and not too naturalistic in appearance. Plants of this type are not difficult to find in the genus *Rhododendron* and among its close allies. For background planting, a bushy habit of growth is not essential, but for foreground planting in a formal garden, only the dwarfish, thick, bushy sorts should be used. There are many different types and sizes to be had, both in species and in individual varieties. Some of the dwarfer sorts, such as the Alpine Rose hybrids and certain forms of *R. carolinianum,* are almost laurel-like in habit. A clonal variety called 'Boule de Neige' and other hybrids and *R. caucasicum* are likewise very compact, while the dwarf form of *R. catawbiense* from Mt. Mitchell, variety *compactum,* fills all the requirements of a naturally low-growing race. Among the azaleas, the Japanese sorts are excellent for formal effects, because of their round, twiggy character and they possess the additional virtue of being able to endure clipping. This includes, besides the naturally dwarf Kurume and obtusum sorts, the hardier forms such as *R. Kaempferi, R. poukhanense* and *R. mucronatum.* Where the climate is suitable, a great quantity of dwarf and semi-dwarf species newly introduced from the Orient may be used. I might add that planting for formal effect does not necessitate the exclusive use of low or dwarf rhododendrons. Old specimen plants of large size, provided they are of a symmetrical and rather compact form, are especially valuable in formal gardens.

I have been surprised many times to see rhododendrons enduring the hard life of a city backyard or the cramped quarters of an apartment-house court-yard. I cannot imagine that any plants can enjoy these conditions and how long rhododendrons will persist I do not know, but I have seen plants which have been growing with apparent success in the heart of New York City for more than five years. It seems probable that such plants would require rather frequent syringing and perhaps actual washing of the foliage to remove ac-cumulations of dust and soot, but the fact that rhododendrons (and Kalmia, too) will live in spite of such conditions suggests that they are exceedingly useful plants for difficult places of this nature.

Perhaps the main reason why rhododendrons will succeed in great cities is their tolerance of shade. On the shady side of buildings, in courtyards where the sun seldom penetrates, in woodlands or beneath shade trees, rhododendrons can be made to live happily if they are protected from adverse factors, such as the drying effect of cellar walls or the competition of shallow tree roots. Per-haps they find the "canyons" between skyscrapers similar to their native ravines and woodland dells. They do not bloom so freely in constant shade as when enjoying partial sunlight, yet they actually enjoy a certain measure of shade and are sufficiently tolerant of it to endure situations where other plants would fail. But they must be good plants, well cared for and adequately watered.*

Where rhododendrons are grown in open situations, care should be taken to

* City conditions are often characterized by atmospheric dryness and this, of course, is very injurious to rhododendrons. I would not advocate the use of rhododendrons or their kin in cities unless the plants were good to start with and well taken care of after planting. They must be kept clean, properly irrigated and in a suitable soil at all times. One may find numerous failures with rhododendrons in cities because of the lack of these essentials. And it may be true that certain other plants, such as *Ilex crenata* and *Pieris,* are even more satisfactory as broadleaf evergreens for city use. But observation leads me to believe that azaleas and rhododendrons, properly chosen and cared for, are among the few plants that may be con-ceived to have a definite usefulness in urban surroundings. One hesitates to recommend any plants, outside of privet and ailanthus, to the dweller in the heart of a great city, but I feel that ericaceous plants are worth a trial where one is prepared to properly attend to their needs.

Unfortunately, a large share of the rhododendron plantings in some large cities comprises poorly collected native material which has not been cut back, nursery grown or properly planted. Added to this, its subsequent care is often entrusted to janitors or other employees who know little about horticulture. The soil and moisture conditions are likewise frequently bad. Under such conditions, it is little wonder that one frequently sees dead or dying rhodo-dendron plantings. This is false economy, often the result of competitive prices among con-tractors. Any plant in a city needs extra care and should be in a good vigorous condition to start with. To insure such conditions, it is better to have fewer but better plants.

It might be added that an interesting use of rhododendrons and azaleas in the tiny city garden is found in tubbed specimen plants, often fine but tender sorts such as Pink Pearl, which may be plunged in the ground during the mild portion of the year and taken inside a greenhouse or conservatory during the winter.

see that they are furnished with abundant water during the warm, dry months of summer and that the foliage is sprayed with a proper insecticide to control the small sucking insects in hot weather. The lace bug and aphis are not serious pests and, when plants are grown in the shade, they scarcely appear at all, but if the evergreen rhododendrons are grown in positions where they get the full sunlight all day the foliage seems to exude small quantities of sirup which attracts these little insects. It is not difficult to control them, but this extra effort, along with extra attention to watering, makes it easier and more satisfactory to grow rhododendrons in partial shade if one has the option of choosing either sun or shade.

Nowadays, varieties of rhododendrons are available in clear, bright colors, so that no one need avoid these plants if he does not like magenta and bluish tinges in his garden. Pure whites, clear pinks, deep rose colors and dark reds are available in true rhododendrons of reliable hardiness. If other colors are desired, azaleas may be included, for the combination of rhododendrons and azaleas in a mixed planting is perfectly feasible and often very beautiful. When azaleas are included, almost any color in the spectrum may be obtained in plants that are hardy and desirable. Some of the most colorful garden effects I have ever seen have been combinations of rhododendrons with azaleas blooming at the same time. The whole yellow range is represented, comprising orange, lemon, cream, apricot, bronze and many of the art shades; vermillion, scarlet, maroon and purple are in the red group. If one wishes to go outside the "iron-clad" hardy types, he may find almost any color except bright blue in the newly discovered species from Asia. Eventually, many of these new colors will, it is hoped, be worked into evergreen hybrids of hardiness, which, of course, will materially increase the usefulness of the genus.

I have often wondered why azaleas are not more extensively grown in America. Many of the species are admirable plants, coming in all sorts of colors. They have a tremendously long season of bloom, one species following another from earliest spring to midsummer. They are lovely in texture and line. Many of them are fragrant. Different species are available for warm or cold climates. Almost all of them make attractive ornamental shrubs. When well grown, our native American species make handsome garden plants, becoming thick, well-formed, floriferous shrubs, quite unlike the often sparse, scrawny objects that we see in the woods.

There are certain uses to which azaleas are better adapted than are the ever-green rhododendrons. One of the great advantages of the hardy, deciduous azaleas is that, in the North, they are somewhat easier to grow than the true rhododendrons. Owing to their deciduous character and innate hardiness some of them can withstand more exposure to wind and weather in winter and hence can be employed in many situations where rhododendrons would fail. Some azaleas appear to be more tolerant of alkalinity than the common American rhododendrons, notably *Rhododendron roseum* and *R. japonicum* which are decidedly easier to grow in such regions as central New York.

Probably no flowering shrub is more showy than the azalea. It, too, will endure partial shade and, like the rhododendron, is useful in shady places, but luxuriant bloom can not be expected without a certain degree of sunlight; in fact, azaleas ought to have a little more sun than evergreen rhododendrons, and they can endure much more. In spite of the showiness and brilliant coloration of their flowers, there is a fineness of texture about azaleas which removes them from all suggestion of crudeness or garishness. This makes them most useful about small properties where some rhododendrons are too heavy. They appear to best advantage, perhaps, when set before a background such as that recommended for the evergreen rhododendrons—dark, shadowy foliage. A sunlit opening in a somber grove is the setting *par excellence*. But they are more adaptable than rhododendrons to some adverse sites. Because azaleas have a very interesting branching habit, they may be planted against a light background with perfect fitness. Some of them are quite dwarf and are among the most useful members of that rare but much-sought-for group of smallish deciduous shrubs which do not grow above 4 feet tall and which, for this reason, are of extreme usefulness in foreground and foundation plantings. Moreover, the higher growing azaleas may be easily restrained by clipping back if this is needed to keep them from growing out of scale. Some of the azaleas, too, are attractive in the autumn when their leaves become brightly colored. All require plenty of moisture in summer.

If you have a wood or shaded coppice try making it gay with azaleas. Such an azalea garden is easy to construct, relatively inexpensive and immeasurably effective at blooming time. The corner of a wood, a little thicket of small trees, the shady banks of a brook or a small clearing in the forest will furnish just the conditions needed for the construction of a little garden, naturalistic, Japanesque or otherwise. If the trees and bushes are too numerous, clear some of them out and replace with azaleas. Surrounded with a fence, equipped with a rustic gate, a crude stone walk and perhaps a rustic garden-house, you need nothing else, save plenty of azaleas, to make the place delightful. And the American azaleas are sufficiently hardy to make such a layout entirely practicable in many places where the growing of evergreen rhododendrons is not considered feasible. On small properties such a shady site may be easily constructed by moving in a few small trees.

Another use for azaleas is in situations where the low-growing sorts act as ground-cover materials. This is a usage particularly employed by the Japanese, but is worthy of more general application. The banks of streams, garden slopes, rock gardens and other small areas are planted to azaleas which form a twiggy mass about 18 inches high and which is utilized mainly for its foliage, although sheets of color are obtained at blooming time. The Japanese species, some of which are relatively hardy and many of which can be kept dwarf by clipping (a favorite Japanese practice), are especially useful for this kind of work. Two of our own species, *Rhododendron atlanticum* and *R. roseum,* are dwarfish and tend to be stoloniferous, so that they offer possibilities for this.

In regions where the dwarf species of the Lapponicum series and their allies can be grown, the alpine rhododendrons offer a new and exceedingly promising opportunity for rock garden development. One strain of *R. racemosum* has already proved hardy in cold regions and many other species have been tried. It is entirely probable that the future will see a number of selected clones or hybrids available for use as rock garden subjects.

Mention should be made of the very great usefulness of some of the hybrid azaleas as greenhouse subjects. Their presence in the floral shops for many years has familiarized us with most of them. There are many points in their favor and the commercial florists are again returning to the culture of the azalea as it was in the days before the plant quarantine prevented their importation from Europe. There are other azaleas and rhododendrons which have special uses as conservatory plants, some of the most gorgeous being the hybrids of the Javanicum series, little seen in this country. Semi-hardy sorts may be tubbed and carried over winter in pit greenhouses, then returned outdoors in summer.

In mild regions, such as England and the Pacific coastal areas of the United States, the possible usefulness of rhododendrons and azaleas exceeds anything I have even suggested in the foregoing remarks. The enormous number of species, their wide diversity in all sorts of ways, their overlapping seasons of bloom and their adaptability to different purposes make possible their use in an almost limitless measure.

In concluding my discussion of the usefulness of rhododendrons and azaleas as ornamental plants, I should not fail to state that hardy species and varieties, once established and of flowering age, require very little care thereafter. The application of a mulch of leaves once or twice a year, and ordinary attention to obvious needs, constitutes about all the care needed. This, of course, is a paramount reason why these plants are to be recommended as being of wide usefulness.

Finally, it should be remarked that both rhododendrons and azaleas have an interesting sphere of usefulness as cut flowers for decorative purposes. This seems to have been a neglected field. To be sure, their keeping qualities are not of the best and the flowers may at times be a bit fragile for shipment and for the purposes of the commercial florist's cut-flower work. And then, too, one does not want to cut branches off his ornamental shrubs unless he has an abundant supply to draw from. But where flowers are abundant and where the cutting is done so as to avoid the removal of too much flowering wood, rhododendron and azalea flowers may be used satisfactorily and with striking effect in the creation of beautiful floral arrangements. Their interesting branching habit is not the least of their charms and there are probably no other hardy flowering shrubs—not even the roses!—that may be used with such colorful and effective results in the interior decoration of one's house.*

Mixed arrangements of bright colored rhododendrons and azaleas are among the most effective of cut flowers for decorative purposes, especially when such an arrangement is placed in a large, wide brass or black receptacle and "staged" in a telling spot. The deciduous and evergreen sorts harmonize perfectly. Strangely, the purple and lilac shades, so common and so much criticized among the Catawba rhododendrons, become tremendously effective when placed in a mixed arrangement with the yellow and orange shades of the flame or Mollis azaleas. Effective, too, are individual specimens or naturalistic groups done in the Japanese manner where the rugged stem-character of these plants is of great decorative value. The flowers may be used with or without leaves, as desired.

The main drawback in the use of azaleas and rhododendrons as cut flowers is the tendency of the flowers to drop off after they have been open a day or so. This may be overcome and the flowers sometimes kept for a week or more, it is said, by placing a drop of thin gum arabic into the very center or throat of every flower, using a small dropper with which to apply the gum. This adhesive material causes the corolla to stick firmly to the calyx, with the result that the water-connections of the corolla are retained and the flower does not wilt for a long time. This practice is used for material in flower shows and might be applied to potted plants as well.

---

* For years we have annually cut good-sized sprays of the Mayflower Azalea, *Rhododendron roseum,* which we have in abundance, without detriment to the plants and with telling effect in our home. Arranged in an old-fashioned blue and white Spode tureen, a bouquet of *R. roseum* will remain fresh for several days and impart a delightful spicy scent to the whole room. Lest this shock the super-sensitive, who are accustomed to frown upon the decorative use of material which needs protection by law to prevent its extermination in the wild, let me hasten to say that you need not despoil a woodland colony of azaleas to gain cut flowers, since you may grow these same flowers so easily in your own backyard. And let me add that if you own a woodland well stocked with azaleas, there is little chance of seriously injuring the plants if you do your cutting intelligently and moderately. It is the wanton vandalism of an ignorant public that destroys such things as our wild azaleas, not their intelligent utilization.

CHAPTER III

RHODODENDRONS IN THE WILD

THERE is an amazing number of different rhododendrons in the world. In a recent authoritative work, about 850 species of rhododendron were listed. This figure does not include subspecies, varieties or clones, of which there are hundreds and possibly, if all were known, thousands. In view of the natural variability of rhododendrons, it seems probable that some of the kinds now classed as species will some day be reduced to geographical forms or botanical varieties. On the other hand, a good many other species probably remain undiscovered. They occur in all sorts of obscure places, many of which have not yet even been explored. So we can look for rearrangements in our list of the wild species as our knowledge increases, and the only thing we can be certain of is that the number of different kinds will still remain relatively large. Many of them are now very new.

It should not be imagined that all these wild species, or any considerable portion of them, are good, handsome plants for the garden. Probably, after cultivating and testing, a great many of them will be discarded as horticulturally worthless. In some series there will be no representatives of value for garden or greenhouse; in others, perhaps only one species to a series; and in most of the good series, there will always be two or three species which rank far above their associates in horticultural value. While many of the mediocre kinds may be relegated to the gardens of collectors and botanical institutions, there will undoubtedly come out of the mass of new things some noteworthy rhododendrons which, either directly or through their hybrids, will take their places among the best of our future garden plants. The possibilities are tremendous and only time will tell.

At the present moment we find ourselves in a peculiar situation. There are literally hundreds of new species of rhododendron being introduced into cultivation, most of them total strangers to the average gardener. These plants come from various parts of the world. Let us briefly examine their native habitats,

16

see where and how they are distributed and under what conditions they grow. We can by this means gain a better insight, perhaps, into the cultural requirements of rhododendrons and into their possibilities.

They come to us, these rhododendrons, in a myriad of forms, colors and sizes from many scattered parts of the globe, almost entirely from the northern hemisphere. The extent of their distribution is simply astounding. From the frozen moorlands, the cold arctic tundras, the hills and ravines of the temperate zones, the lofty ranges of the mighty Himalayas, the rain-forests of Burma and the dark, tropical woodlands of the East Indies, rhododendrons come to us in a variety of types that is amazing. The great rhododendron center of the world is western Yunnan, in southwestern China, where some 200 species have been found within one small area.

Rhododendrons are found sparingly in central Europe and the Caucasus. They occur more abundantly in the eastern United States, a few even growing in eastern Canada. They are represented, but not numerous, on the Pacific coast of North America. In the arctic the species are few, but they are practically circumpolar in their distribution. In eastern Asia the number of species is nearly the same as in the eastern United States. A great concentration exists, however, in the region of the Himalayan Mountains and spreads southward down the Malay peninsula and out into the islands of the Pacific. One species reaches Australia, but aside from this there are none in the southern hemisphere.

As a rule, the rhododendrons are either mountain, forest or arctic plants. A few stragglers may be found outside such districts, but their predominant characteristic, as a genus, is their fondness for uplands or forests. The alpine types are similar to the arctic types, both being dwarf and generally well protected by snow in the winter. Some of them live in arctic or alpine marshes, but these, and a few other exceptional members, are all that could be considered fond of swamps or bogs. Ordinarily, rhododendrons do not wish to stand in water or in soil that is soggy, although they distinctly enjoy a cool, moist soil. Like orchids, they prefer aeration about their roots, provided it does not produce a dry condition.

In considering the habitat of wild species, we should always remember that it is not the forests, the mountains or the soil *per se* that produces the natural development of these plants, but that it is the combination of conditions produced by these environmental things that does it. For instance, I have seen an excellent native growth of *Rhododendron maximum* in a wooded Rhode Island bog, near sea level; yet it is not ordinarily a bog plant, nor even a lowland plant. *R. maximum* is primarily a mountain plant, yet it is found in the lowland bog— an environment which suits its needs fully as well as that of a mountain ravine. In cultivation, the shady side of a building may sometimes produce the desired ecological condition as effectively as a group of forest trees, while the garden hose, used intelligently, may substitute for the mountain shower.

One hears about lime-loving rhododendrons. Apparently, certain species in western China do grow about limestone cliffs. At present, it is difficult to determine how much alkalinity, in terms of measured values, these plants will endure, but the inference is that these rhododendrons are not actually lime-*loving*. They probably can tolerate a somewhat higher degree of alkalinity than their brethren. In the limestone regions of western New York *Rhododendron maximum* and *R. roseum* may be found. A few inches underneath is a limestone soil, but the surface soil in which they are growing is full of organic matter and tests definitely acid. These plants do not *love* lime at all (although *R. roseum* can endure with less acid than some); they are merely surface-rooting and grow entirely in the thin mat of acid leaf-mold which overlies the alkaline soil. I think it can be said that nearly all rhododendrons prefer an acid soil and that most of them demand it.

The great rhododendron regions of the world are places of copious moisture. Rhododendrons abhor drought, be it from lack of water, lack of atmospheric moisture or the drying effect of winds. If there be great heat, it must be accompanied by moisture. If there be intense cold, which in itself is drying, the plants are either protected by a blanket of snow or located among other protective plants in a sheltered forest where the extremes of temperature do not penetrate. The soils in which they grow are generally well mulched by natural agencies, thus being protected against the elements. Fogs, especially in summer, are frequent in most important rhododendron regions, while in western China summer rains are exceedingly abundant. Rhododendrons are never found in arid regions.

There are two main localities in Europe where rhododendrons occur. The easternmost is the area of the Caucasus mountains and the region of the Black Sea, spilling over into Asia Minor.* The Caucasus is the home of a few species that are too little known and too little used at present, since they possess valuable qualities of hardiness. Those of the Black Sea region are well known, but are not particularly desirable. The second main region of Europe is that of the Alps, including the Transylvanian area. Here the so-called "alpine roses" occur.

In North America the great concentration of species occurs in the Appalachian mountains, reaching its main focus in western North Carolina. The genus spreads out, however, and extends into all the states along the Atlantic sea-

---

* Marked Region 1 on the map. These and the other regions referred to in this chapter may be found designated by appropriate numerals on the maps which comprise the endpapers of this book.

board and north into Canada, going so far, with one arctic species, as Labrador. It covers the states contiguous to the Appalachian mountain system and extends throughout the southeastern United States, but does not go southward, so far as known, into Mexico or Central America. In those Latin-American regions, as in South America, the genus *Befaria,* a relative, replaces *Rhododendron.*

The species of the northeastern United States and the Appalachian mountain regions have to endure a climate in which the winter temperature reaches zero Fahrenheit and, in the north, considerably lower. *Rhododendron maximum, R. canadense, R. roseum, R. viscosum, R. nudiflorum* and possibly others occur in localities where the temperature occasionally goes to −30°F. or below. In western North Carolina, however, the temperature seldom goes below zero. Most of the Appalachian species are able to endure sub-zero temperatures in winter without injury. Snow occurs throughout most parts of these regions, but it is by no means certain that the ground will be covered by a protective layer of snow all winter. In summer the temperature often exceeds 80°F. and periods of comparative dryness, but not drought, are not uncommon. Summer fogs mitigate these dry periods.*

Professor C. S. Sargent, writing of *R. catawbiense* around Roan Mountain, N.C., said the soil is a "rich, black vegetable mould, varying from 18 inches to two feet in depth. Although saturated with moisture, as small springs are common, the surface soil is perfectly drained, being underlain by coarse gravel mixed with large stones. Abundant atmospheric moisture, for rarely a day passes without clouds settling over the summit of the Roan, increases the vigor of the plants." He went on to say that under these conditions of good drainage, atmospheric moisture and protection from high winds "they can support excessive winter cold, as the temperature on the summit of the Roan has been known to fall in winter to 30° below zero, while ice probably forms during every month of the year except July and August."

Oaks are much associated with rhododendrons and azaleas in the eastern United States. Pines and hemlocks are the leading conifers and perhaps next to oaks, they are the trees most associated with rhododendrons. In general, it may be said that the American rhododendrons occur in conditions of semi-shade, although in many parts of the North Carolina mountains the tall rhododendrons and kalmia, both 20 feet high, themselves furnish considerable

---

* In Asheville, N.C., the rainfall totals about 40 inches per year, normally distributed without great unevenness. Freezing temperatures obtain between December and March. The lowest temperature recorded is −6°F. and the highest 96°F. In 1929 there were 120 clear days and 245 cloudy ones. The relative humidity at 8 A.M. during the summer averaged 90%; at noon, 55%; and at 8 P.M. 71%. At certain points in the mountains the humidity and fog are greater than indicated by these figures. Although rhododendrons occur on both light and heavy soils, the soil of these mountains is relatively light. In acidity tests, its Hydrogen-ion concentration ranges from pH 4.6 to 5.4.

shade. In these mountains and in the Catawba river region the trees associated with rhododendrons are chiefly oak, with a good deal of maple, *Betula lenta,* chestnut and other hardwoods, besides two species of hemlock, balsam spruce, *Cornus florida* and much *Vaccinium* and *Kalmia* among the shrubs, *Gaultheria, Epigaea* and other ericaceous ground-covers grow on the forest floor.

The species of the middle Atlantic coastal region grow in comparative low-lands and generally on rather light soil among oak woods and other conditions of semi-shade. In general, they are not subjected to quite the cold weather of the Appalachian and northern groups, but are generally hardy when cultivated in the north.

The species represented in the southeastern United States are chiefly azaleas. Here the winters are milder and the summers warmer than in the mountainous districts. Many of the plants occur along the edges of streams or in swamps or woodlands where moisture is readily accessible during the warm weather. Rain-fall is copious throughout the spring growing season and the climate is often humid. There is some frost in winter, but no zero temperatures occur and there is little freezing. One rare evergreen species, *Rhododendron Chapmannii,* occurs on the lowlands of northern Florida.

The single species of the Rocky Mountains occurs in high altitudes and is neither amenable to culture in other regions nor attractive enough to justify the effort of growing it, according to reports.

The climate of the Pacific coastal area is mild throughout the year. In the north, especially, the rainfall is abundant and there are no extremes of high or low temperature. In the south, there may be a dry season in summer. In the Puget Sound region the climate is moist and mild and is said to resemble the climate of England. It is probable that most of the rhododendrons which grow in England will succeed well in this locality.

The arctic species are low shrubs, a few inches high, which lie buried in snow during a large part of the year. *Rhododendron lapponicum* is practically cir-cumpolar, if the closely related form, *R. parvifolium,* be considered its Asiatic representative. *R. lapponicum* is found in northwest Sweden, Swedish Lapland, Norway, Labrador and even in the United States, occurring on Mount Wash-ington, N.H. *R. glandulosum* occurs in Alaska, while *R. camtschaticum* is found in the arctic regions of both Siberia and Alaska, extending south to an island off the coast of British Columbia. Until spring is well advanced, these species are well protected by snow. They are said to be difficult to cultivate in other climates.

The regions of northeastern Asia join the arctic regions and may be con-sidered almost a part of the arctic. Kamchatka is not distinguishable from the arctic in so far as its rhododendrons are concerned, while the mountains of eastern Siberia and Mongolia have species of similar character. The species of eastern Manchuria are less dwarf, but are necessarily very hardy.

The rhododendrons of the Korean peninsula are similar both to those of Manchuria and to those of Japan. The Korean species are of a hardy nature. Korea is of the latitude of central Japan and is a land which extends into the sea, where fogs are said to be common.

Japan is a land of many azaleas and, it might be added, her azaleas do much better in the cold portions of the United States than do the species from China. Of course, not all the Japanese sorts are hardy in the north, even in Japan, since one cannot expect plants from a naturally warm climate to succeed under more rigorous conditions. But parts of Japan have a climate not unlike that of America, so such azaleas as *Rhododendron japonicum,* and *R. Kaempferi,* as well as the rhododendrons *R. Metternichii* and *R. brachycarpum,* find a congenial home in the eastern United States. Of the other Japanese species which are not reliably hardy north of New York City, *R. mucronatum* and *R. obtusum* in their various forms are important. It is not enough to merely say that a species comes from Japan; we must know where it comes from in Japan if we wish to estimate its probable hardiness.

We hear a great deal nowadays of Chinese rhododendrons. It must be remembered that China is a vast country and that all its rhododendrons, even those from western China alone, are by no means confined to one area. Indeed, there are some sixteen geographical areas into which the Chinese rhododendrons must be divided. We may group these areas, however, into about three large regions in which conditions can be said to be markedly different. First, is the northern region, including Mongolia and Manchuria and the eastern provinces which lie north of the Yangtze river. Here we have but very few species and, in *Rhododendron micranthum* and *R. dauricum,* they are widely distributed. This is in contrast to the situation in Yunnan, where there are many species, but narrowly localized. The hardiness of the species in the northern area is equal to or greater than those of Korea and northeastern Asia. There is a good deal of affinity between these species and those of Japan. The climatic conditions are severe and plants from these parts, therefore, can be expected to survive under difficult conditions of culture.

A second region comprises eastern and central China, extending southward into the hill country south of the Yangtze, but keeping east of the Himalayan region. The species here, although growing at much lower altitudes than in the west, are, in many cases, subject to more actual exposure, because there is neither the protection of snow in winter nor the influence of the monsoon. Hence, species from this region, particularly in its northern part, such as Hupeh and eastern Szechuan, are frequently much hardier than those from the high altitudes of the west. Summer rains are abundant, however, and few of these species tried have succeeded in the northern United States. Azaleas are plentiful in this region. Travelers speak of the brilliant color effects produced by the azaleas along the hilly country near the Chinese coast. Fortune wrote that "the yellow *Azalea chinensis* (*R. molle*) seemed to paint the hillsides, so large were its flowers and vivid the colors," while E. H. Wilson said of *R. Simsii* that "in many places it is extraordinarily abundant, and in May whole hillsides are red with its colors."

As indicators of the hardiness of the species found in Hupeh and the hills of eastern and central China, we may cite *Rhododendron Fortunei, R. discolor, R. Fargesii* and the azaleas *R. molle* and *R. Simsii,* which occur in parts of this region. Only in favored spots north of Philadelphia will the species cited succeed well in the eastern United States. They are promising, however, for regions south of this area and all of them do well in England. *R. auriculatum,* a notable August-blooming species, is from this region of Hupeh. The species from the southern provinces of the area, such as Kwangtung, Hongkong, Hainan, eastern Yunnan and Kweichow cannot be expected to be so hardy as those from Hupeh and eastern Szechuan.

A third region comprises western China, especially the southwestern provinces. and is not complete until the species from Tibet, Sikkin, Nepal, Bhutan and northeastern Upper Burma are included, since these are all connected in a general way. Indeed, we may include the whole western and Himalayan district in this category, but, if we were to be exact at all, we should have to subdivide the region again into several parts. The region is full of local differences and, as for the species, they are quite closely confined to definite localities, not becoming widely distributed.

The northernmost province of the western region is Kansu. Here the number and distribution of the species is strictly limited, but they are relatively hardy and might, perhaps, be classed with some of the species of the northern region.

The remaining regions in western China and contiguous areas may be subdivided into two general climatic areas. The first area comprises the Tibetan Marches, western Szechuan, eastern Tibet and the eastern Himalayan region which have many species in common.* Western Yunnan and Upper Burma form another area whose species have no common representatives among those of the first area. The Tibetan Marches represent a region of wet summers and dry winters, while the Yunnan-Upper Burma district is a region of wet summers and wet or snowy winters, having perpetual precipitation under the influence of the monsoon. Captain F. Kingdon Ward contrasts these two regions

---

* This area is marked as Regions 35, 37 and 38 on the map, while the Yunnan-Upper Burma district is marked 36 and 41.

by describing their appearances near a place in the Assam Himalayas, where the two districts occur in close proximity. "Ascending from the Tsangpo," he says, "through thickets of Triflorum, Souliei and Taliense species, into forests of Grande, Barbatum, Thomsonii and Lacteum species, one emerges at 11,000 feet into the alpine region. Here the wealth and variety of rhododendrons is simply astounding. By the middle of June they are all in flower together, and the traveller is well repaid for his trouble in that gorgeous sight. They form seas of sulphur, carmine and rose pink; rivers of purple Lapponicum flow into lakes of brick-red, lemon and snow-white Anthopogon; strains of cherry-brandy Glaucum are splashed over a satiny lining of pink and mauve cherry-blossom Glaucum; clumps of merry little pouting Campylogynums, pink and plum-purple, are plastered like swallow's nests against the grey cliffs, and pools of canary-yellow Trichocladum glow from the brown grass slopes. Along the snow-fed streams, the twin flowers of a royal purple Saluenense nod in rising spate. Not twenty miles away to the northwest, on the other side of the Tsangpo, is a similar range of mountains. Here the alpine region begins at 14,000 feet, but the open moorland is covered just as thickly with rhododendrons. Instead of twenty or thirty species, however, they number just three."

This difference, Ward continues, is due not to summer conditions, since these are similar, but to winter conditions. The species in the first region are buried under snow for eight months, while the snow protection lasts only five months in the latter region. The longer dormant period seems to favor a greater variety of forms. The species which grow in the dry-winter region have to withstand lower temperatures, for they may never be buried under snow at all, the snow acting as a protective blanket and assuring a constant temperature of only a few degrees below freezing, with the added assurance of protection against drying. Theoretically, at least, the dry-winter species should prove hardier under our conditions of cultivation than those which demand a snow blanket and a four months' working period only.

Another important point concerning the general region of western China and its contiguous areas is the type of growth in relation to altitude. It is a region of high mountains and deep valleys, with amazing differences in altitude within short distances. At lower altitudes the rhododendrons are small, scattered and inconspicuous, says Captain Ward. "With increasing altitude they gradually increase in size and numbers. Higher yet they begin to dominate and to form forests, either by themselves or with bamboo or *Abies*. It is in the middle zone that the biggest tree rhododendrons flourish. These occur in the temperate rain-forest, where it is always moist and dark. As conifer forest begins to gain the upper hand, the rhododendrons diminish in size again and become more gnarled; on the other hand, they increase in number and variety. Towards the upper limit of *Abies* and larch they tend to form entire forests by themselves, usually consisting of a few, sometimes only one, species. Higher yet, this forest dwindles to a dense, gnarled scrub, almost impossible to penetrate. Finally, on the open moorland above the tree limit, they grow like heather, forming an immense association composed of several species." These carpet-forming alpine plants grow with full exposure to the sun and with moisture percolating around their roots: cool roots and moderate sunshine above.

Western China is, as I have said, the great rhododendron center of the world. Some 220 species have been listed from western Yunnan alone, according to the classification adopted in this book. Other areas have fewer species, but the total of the Sino-Himalayan area is tremendous. The species may be put into five groups, as follows: tropical, forest, scrub, alpine and very dwarf or table-top species. Since vegetation varies in different regions, no definite altitudes can be given, but the forest species generally occur below 10,000 feet. Nothing in this forest class can be considered as more than half-hardy, even in England.

The Muli range in western Szechuan and the Tibetan Marches are reported as regions of considerable limestone. They also belong in the dry-winter class. The Lapponicum series is most prominent in these regions. A wet summer followed by drought, cold in winter and warm in spring, seems to be the climate which these Chinese Lapponicums enjoy.

The rhododendron season lasts from mid-April to mid-June in northwestern Yunnan, melting snows furnishing moisture at that time. Northeastern Upper Burma adjoins southwestern Yunnan and the species and conditions in the two areas are very similar. The Burmese frontier is "a region of lofty mountains, deeply dissected by innumerable rivers," says Ward, who continues: "Owing to unceasing and heavy rainfall the mountains are everywhere covered by a rich forest." The annual rainfall approximates 140 inches and during the summer the mountains are enveloped in clouds for weeks at a time. Snows in winter last five months above an altitude of 10,000 feet.

Captain Ward describes the rhododendrons of northern Burma. At the lower levels are epiphytic species of the Maddenii series and similar groups—greenhouse species with us. Higher up is the temperate rain-forest, where mighty oaks, magnolias and other trees grow, with scattered tree rhododendrons among them. As higher elevations are reached the conifer-rhododendron forest is attained. Epiphytic species are now rare. The rhododendron trees attain considerable size and, Ward notes, the large species all grow in deep shade. "It may easily be imagined what a riot of color the forests of the northeast frontier are in early spring," says Ward. And again, "the rhododendron trees themselves, aflame with blossom, standing beneath a canopy of big timber." Higher up, the alpine species predominate, as in western China.

The species of Indo-Malaya are generally considered soft. The Javanicum hybrids and their allies are typical warmhouse plants and, while interesting, have never attained much horticultural importance. They have little affinity with the hardier species and, considered as a group more or less by themselves, are largely omitted in this work.

In general, the horticultural significance of rhododendrons as *species* is less than that of the superior *individuals* within those species, because great variation exists within the natural populations. Inconstancy in details is ever present. Seedlings often fail to come true because of genetic instability. One should always be aware that a species of rhododendron constitutes a somewhat mixed population and that merit awards, granted to superior individuals, do not always represent typical or average plants.

As the Himalayan species extend southward, their places are taken by relatives better adapted to warm conditions, so that a continuous distribution of rhododendrons occurs southward through Burma and Siam, extending to Indo-China, the Malay peninsula and out into the islands of the East Indian group. Here many of the species become epiphytic, attaching themselves to the trunks of trees, like orchids. This is a region rich in rhododendrons and one which has not yet been sufficiently investigated to permit of a very definite horticultural knowledge of the species found there.

Chapter IV

SOME GENERAL OBSERVATIONS ON RHODODENDRON CULTURE

We have seen where and how rhododendrons and azaleas grow in the wild. Now we come to the practical problem of growing them and their hybrids in our gardens.

I wish to make it apparent at the outset that the growing of rhododendrons and azaleas is easy, pleasant and not fraught with extraordinary difficulty. This is the actual truth where knowledge and discreet observation go hand in hand. I might even say that in certain localities rhododendron growing is almost foolproof. But I shall not say that these plants can be grown satisfactorily in *all* places with the utter disregard of care and knowledge implied in some of the optimistic catalogue announcements and magazine articles that I have recently encountered.

Rhododendrons are not hard to grow, but they are peculiar. They have certain definite and rather violent likes and dislikes—several of them. While they may be grown with no concern whatever in natural rhododendron regions, certain important adjustments are often necessary in other places, without which they absolutely refuse to be happy. And these adjustments are not always easy to discover. Then, there are differences in varieties. Some may grow in Philadelphia with the utmost ease and would require more consideration in Boston, and perhaps be unable to survive at Buffalo, N.Y. Such results may not be due entirely to varietal characteristics, but the matter of environment and culture may enter the problem as well. Hard and fast rules can not always be laid down.

We should not forget, too, that there are certain large areas in the United States, such as the arid regions of the west and the wind-swept plains, where the environment is so unfriendly to rhododendrons that they would not ordinarily be expected to thrive without great and extraordinary protection. I would not claim that they should be attempted in such places as other than experimental subjects. In speaking of rhododendron culture, therefore, I am discussing the question as it exists in those regions where rhododendrons or azaleas have, to some extent at least, been grown or where they might conceivably be expected to survive without extraordinary measures. These regions are somewhat larger than popularly supposed, for the culture of rhododendrons might well be extended considerably beyond its present limits.

If we are going to grow rhododendrons we should not be blind to the peculiarities both of the plants and of the climate. If, in our locality, rhododendrons and their kin thrive naturally and are common materials in the gardens of the people, we need take little thought of their needs other than to copy the successful practices of the neighborhood and let nature do the rest. There are many such regions. On the other hand, there are countless numbers of other places where special measures, although usually simple ones, must be taken to insure success.

The eccentricities of rhododendrons are several. First, there is the matter of soil acidity—or the abhorrence of "lime," as many people call it. This matter is sometimes popularly stressed so far beyond its rightful place that the uninitiated are led to believe it the complete sum and total of successful rhododendron culture. It is not. There are several other factors just as important, although we will grant, of course, that proper soil acidity is absolutely essential. In other words, acidity is not solely *the* essential factor; it is only one of the essentials. Other factors of equal importance in ordinary garden culture are the questions of organic matter in the soil, site and water relations.* We need to recognize that the oft-made statement that rhododendrons will thrive in any soil not containing lime and in any site but on a south slope, needs modification in most parts of the country.

What the requirements of rhododendrons are and how we may successfully provide for them in practical horticulture will be the theme of the next few chapters. The several matters involved will be taken up separately. Before doing this, however, we should become aware of how these several factors work together in harmonious relationship to bring about successful growth.

Of the various factors involved—site, soil, climate, moisture, organic matter, nutrients and variety or species grown—we can not say that one is individually of paramount importance, for no one is independent of the others. If any one be wrong or deficient, then that one, for the moment, assumes chief importance, because it becomes a limiting factor and inhibits the action of all the others. All are inter-dependent and inter-related. When everything goes properly, they stand in a position of mutual balance and harmony—that delicate balance which exists in all the phenomena of living things! True, an acid soil is essential to

* Under special laboratory conditions, these factors can be altered, but in ordinary garden culture they are all equal determiners of success or failure.

the health of most rhododendrons in garden culture, and yet, no matter how favorable the soil reaction, the plant may utterly fail if placed in a physically unsuitable soil—possibly a stiff clay with little or no organic matter to furnish moisture, aeration and a permeable physical structure for the roots to work in. I have seen tragedies of this sort occurring through ignorance of anything other than the belief that "rhododendrons will grow in any soil so long as it is acid."

We may take a hint of the rhododendron's preferences from a study of its wild conditions. These have already been outlined in a general way, and they will be further alluded to in subsequent discussions of specific conditions. This may give us, in general, a conception of the sort of treatment rhododendrons, and in a broad way ericaceous plants, enjoy. But I wish to caution the reader against taking too literally the wild environment as a model for cultural methods and accepting it as the best or ideal standard. This is not true to any great extent, for growth under wild conditions is often not to be compared with what is possible under good garden culture. And, after all, it is the result under garden conditions that we are seeking. So let us take whatever hints we can from nature, accept what proves by trial to be most satisfactory and finally adopt whatever method, natural or artificial, produces the best actual results in our gardens.

In further pursuit of this subject, let me observe that, in the wild, the plants are often scrawny, ill-formed, sparse of bloom and slow of growth. They are growing under conditions of strict competition. When we take them into our grounds we carefully remove all competition and we give them special attention, special food and often special irrigation. In most instances, we could not even approximate woodland conditions in our gardens if we wanted to. Naturally, we must adapt our methods to the responses of the plants under the particular set of conditions obtaining in the garden. This presupposes that we use our observational faculties instead of slavishly trying to imitate nature.

For many years American gardeners have cultivated their rhododendrons with no fertilization other than could be derived from occasional applications of leaf-soil, an exceedingly slowly available form of fertilizer. This was in keeping with the practice of imitating natural conditions. Now they are awakening to the fact that rhododendrons can and do utilize chemical and organic fertilizers as successfully as any other plants and that growth can be increased manyfold by their application. They have learned that it was not the plant nutrients, but unfavorable chemical reactions that caused troubles with this practice in the past and they are now learning how to circumvent this hazard. This is an instance where it has paid to depart from nature and embrace experimentation.

There was a time when rhododendron growing was considered difficult. In those days one seldom saw rhododendrons in quantity except on large estates where expert gardeners could attend them. There seemed to be something mysterious about their requirements which few people understood and which gave these plants a reputation for aloofness. Yet, wild members of the genus grew and thrived in almost desolate places. After a while certain significant facts were discovered regarding the soil requirements of these plants. Later, other facts were unearthed. Now we can say there is no longer any excuse for regarding the culture of rhododendrons as difficult or mysterious. Knowing a few of the main facts, one may proceed with a good prospect of success.

Since the first edition of this book was published in 1936, the possibilities of growing rhododendrons and azaleas in new places have been greatly expanded as a result of such experimental work, as is indicated above. You will now find some of these plants in such unexpected places as Missouri, Kansas, Nebraska and Texas—growing, of course, under very special conditions but, with proper care, making life endure. However, this should not be accepted as evidence that they are generally as "foolproof" in such localities as some advertisers would have us believe.

In the following chapters the various matters of culture will be discussed under their respective headings. I am aware, of course, that in localities where soil and climatic conditions are already quite favorable—and this includes certain rather large regions along the Atlantic seaboard—much of this discussion is superfluous. On the other hand, there are many, many growers, and prospective growers, whose gardens are not blessed with a naturally good rhododendron environment. I propose, therefore, to make my discussion complete enough to guide them adequately on the proper road toward success.

CHAPTER V

SITE AND SHELTER

THE first item to consider in choosing a site for a rhododendron planting is, I believe, protection from strong wind. Some kinds will tolerate more wind than others and probably some of the northern deciduous azaleas, such as *Rhododendron roseum,* will stand so much wind that this factor need not be seriously considered. But all the evergreen species and many of the others need at least a little protection from sweeping winds, both in winter and summer, while some of the hardy azaleas, which stand the winter winds undismayed, will succumb to the hot, dry winds of summer. I believe that any rhododendron or azalea will do best if given some wind protection.

Another consideration affecting the choice of site is the matter of sunlight and shade. Ordinarily, rhododendrons will tolerate a relatively large amount of shade. This makes them useful in such situations. They prefer not to have complete shade, however, and rejoice in a speckled interplay of sunlight and shadow or else a site which gives them full sunlight only during a part of the day. They do not like a position against a dry, hot south wall where the mid-day sun beats down upon them in its full intensity, nor do they enjoy a position on an exposed south slope unless an extra amount of water is provided to keep their roots cool and moist. Given proper attention of this sort, rhododendrons may be grown with moderate success in many open situations with full exposure to the sun, but it should be emphasized that under such conditions they should be adequately mulched, watered and sprayed. The inference is that if you can provide this special attention you may grow rhododendrons almost anywhere. If, however, you find it inconvenient to watch them closely and are apt to neglect them, the safe thing to do is to plant them where they will get at least a little shade at some time during the day. For the average amateur or home owner, the best course to follow is to plant them in partial shade if possible. This gives them better protection, prevents insect visitations and possibly has other advantages.*

* There is some evidence that shade, may be of benefit to the internal constitution of rhododendrons, enabling them to assimilate iron better than in full sun, where adverse photochemical reactions may possibly inhibit cell processes. This is a theoretical assumption, however, based upon the behavior of other genera.

Good sites are not always available, yet a satisfactory place for rhododendrons or azaleas can usually be found somewhere on a residence property. In more than a few cases this will be a site which is unfavorable for other plants. On the north or east side of a building rhododendrons can generally be used to advantage. In courtyards, inside the corners of hedges, for background effects or, if correctly used, for foundation planting the evergreen and deciduous rhododendrons may be employed. One of the best places is around the borders of a property or in a shady corner of the lawn, provided the plants are not directly under a tree which has surface-feeding roots. Some properties abound in opportunities for the use of rhododendrons, while other properties may have very few favorable sites. But, figuring that every building has a shady side, we may generally conclude that unless some unfavorable feature exists, such as strong winds or competing tree roots, a suitable site may be found for at least a few rhododendrons or azaleas on nearly every property.

Trees are a natural source of shade for rhododendrons. But it should be emphasized that not all kinds of trees are equally useful. Some, indeed, should be avoided. Maple trees of any kind are generally unsuitable, mainly because of their far-reaching surface roots which enter the rhododendron beds and overrun the delicate roots of the rhododendrons. Trees of this type also consume all the available supplies of moisture and nutrients in the surface soil. The shade of maples, too, is exceedingly dense and the leaves, when fallen, decompose with great rapidity and become alkaline more quickly than the more enduring leaves of oaks. I have, however, seen rhododendrons and azaleas growing near maples successfully, so that this, although not advised, is not entirely impossible. Elms, also, have surface feeding roots which have to be guarded against, although their shade is not so dense as to be injurious. If one wishes to take the trouble he may systematically cut away the invading roots from such trees every year, but this involves digging a trench three feet deep around the rhododendron plantation or else laying a concrete wall. Even with these precautions, tree roots will sometimes come up through the bottom of the bed from deeper-lying roots below.

Oaks and conifers are the trees which are preëminently suitable for growing with rhododendrons. Any kind of oak is excellent. Oaks have deep roots, sometimes tap roots, and a rhododendron can be planted alongside an oak with impunity.* The shade of oak trees is not dense, but open and airy, and the leaves are fibrous, long-enduring and make the finest sort of acid leaf-soil for rhododendrons.

* If there should ever be any root-robbery caused by the competition of oak trees, it could be overcome by the application of water and fertilizers. But with maples, elms and similar gross-feeding trees, root-robbery cannot be so easily fought, because the tree roots actually invade the rhododendron soil and displace the rhododendron roots.

Nearly all the conifers are very suitable, indeed, and furnish a good bit of extra protection because of their evergreen foliage. I shall speak of them later as windbreaks. Trees of the rose family, such as the apple, cherry, crataegus and amelanchier, seem to make satisfactory associates for ericaceous plants. Chestnuts, where they still grow, are suitable. The dogwoods are good as well as being artistically effective; *Cornus florida* blooms with *Rhododendron carolinianum* and makes an effective combination. Birches and beeches, while condemned by some, are endorsed by others and with these, as well as with other hardwood trees, much, I think, depends upon whether the trees are so placed that they are actually robbing the rhododendrons of needed moisture and minerals. If the site and the trees are so arranged as to preclude direct competition, I see no reason why almost any kind of tree could not be made to serve. Naturally, however, it will save bother if the rhododendrons be planted only among neighbors that are known to be friendly.

If a suitable site is not already available on a property, one may often be created without much difficulty. For shade, a person may sometimes move in fair-sized trees or even large bushes. Although this is sometimes costly, it is not always, if properly handled, so difficult or expensive as one might imagine. At my own home I transplanted, in April, some six-foot white pines from a pasture lot. A good ball of earth was taken and left undisturbed about the roots and no skilled labor or special machinery was needed. These trees make an excellent windbreak now and in a few years will furnish overhead shade, since they are growing rapidly. With skilled workmen, large trees may be moved successfully to furnish overhead shade or a background for rhododendrons when immediate effect is necessary. The increased valuation of a properly planted property will often more than pay for the total expense of bringing in good-sized trees.

For protection against sweeping winds, one may establish plantings of conifers which will furnish adequate protection at all seasons. A thick planting of deciduous shrubbery is also effective in breaking the main force of the wind. As for conifers, it seems superfluous to say that only those species which can endure the wind should be employed as windbreaks. These are mainly the rather large-growing kinds which in the north comprise the pines, spruces and firs. Small white pines, well feathered-out at the bottom, are easily transplanted and do satisfactory duty as windbreaks. I am told that they may be satisfactorily clipped and thus kept within bounds if planted near a building or otherwise employed where small stature is demanded. They should be clipped back in July, with only one inch of new leaf-growth left. The Douglas fir, *Pseudotsuga Douglasii,* is another hardy evergreen that may be clipped. So also with the Norway spruce to some extent. The hemlock, of course, when compactly

grown, can not be excelled and is beautiful when clipped. Unfortunately, however, the hemlock is not very resistant to wind. Where it can be used as a background for rhododendrons it should be grown, because the two combine well,
and it will stand as much wind as any rhododendron. It can be made to simulate
boxwood by clipping. A relatively small and more slowly growing species is
the Japanese yew, *Taxus cuspidata*. It is a fine species and thrives excellently in
central New York's cold weather, but it cannot usually be obtained in plants
large enough to be effective as windbreak material. There are a number of other
conifers which may also be used; some of the larger ones can be adapted to
restraint by clipping to keep them in scale.

In choosing a site free from wind, attention should be given to the little
currents which whip around corners of buildings and pass between or over
obstacles. If you will inspect the fresh, light snow on a windy day in winter,
you will notice that it is blown off in certain places and piled up into drifts in
other places. The little spots where the snow always blows off are places to
avoid when planting rhododendrons; or else wind currents should be eliminated
by the use of windbreaks. You may plant your rhododendrons on the leeward
side of a building, but if you get them too near a windy corner the wind, whip-
ping around, will eddy and swirl in such a way as to hit the plants as badly as
if they were placed on the windward side of the house. I have seen one rhododendron killed in this way, while another plant, exactly like it, survived uninjured only ten feet away.

Waterside planting is sometimes desirable. Rhododendrons look well on the
banks of ponds, streams and other bodies of water and they often derive considerable benefit from the atmospheric moisture and the equalization of temperature prevailing in such a site. Water, too, occurs in ravines and other topo-
graphical depressions where shelter is provided by higher surrounding land. The
combination of water and trees furnishes a good site for rhododendrons and I
well remember how a certain plantation of Ghent azaleas seemed to thrive when
grown in such a situation. Low frost pockets should be avoided, however.

When necessary to give rhododendrons special winter protection, a tent of
burlap serves quite satisfactorily. One may devise a cover of this sort to fit his
own particular needs. For an individual plant, four feet or so tall, I have found
that a piece of chicken-wire, or any wire mesh, placed around the plant in the
form of a cylinder and covered with burlap, makes an excellent tent. Two sides
of the cylinder are brought together at the top to form a ridge which sheds
snow and ice. Coarse burlap or Hessian cloth is used to admit a little light.
A long stake or iron pipe is driven into the ground and allowed to go up the
side of the cylinder, to which it is attached. This furnishes anchorage and
prevents the cylinder from blowing over. While this simple device does not keep

out low temperatures, it is exceedingly effective in bringing plants through the winter without injury. Green burlap may be employed if desired. Construct the tent about the time that the ground first freezes, or even earlier.

An entire bed of rhododendrons may be covered by building a rough wooden fence around it and covering the sides of this fence with burlap. If the bed is not more than six feet wide, lath hot-bed shades may be put across the top and these then covered with burlap. The shades give support to the top burlap during heavy snowstorms. If the bed is more than six feet wide, boards may be laid across at six-foot intervals and the lath shades laid on these. If you live in a climate where such protection is necessary, it is well to design your rhododendron plantation so that it may be easily covered.

The boughs of pines, hemlocks or other evergreens are often used to shelter rhododendrons and are one of the best protections. They may be laid over the plants or stuck in the soil and allowed to lean up against the plants or they may be used in other ways. Cut boughs of pine or hemlock may also be tied up with posts and wire or boards to form a sort of temporary wattle fence around the plantation and, by reason of their dark green character, are not objectionable to look at during the winter.

A wooden box, with a burlap window on one side, has been used successfully, or a barrel with both ends out has been similarly used for the protection of a valuable plant when such a specimen is not too large. Sometimes stakes are driven around a plant and burlap is wound around on these stakes. And where the plants are not too large, a deep coldframe furnishes excellent protection, but this, of course, applies only if the plants are moved in and out for winter. So-called pit houses may be used for tender sorts.

Lath houses are in successful use by many propagators of rhododendrons and have been found to be very satisfactory for wintering-over plants which are slightly too tender for open sites. They have also been used in warm climates for reducing the heat of the sun and conserving moisture. At Cornell University it has been found that a number of species of rhododendron much too tender for ordinary outdoor growth are successfully carried through the winter in ground beds inside a lath house. Ornamental lath houses are now coming into vogue and may be attractive in design, though inexpensively built. While they are mainly intended for use in warm climates, there is no reason why they should not be equally useful in cold climates, where this measure of protection will permit rhododendron fanciers to grow some of the more beautiful but delicate species. Rather heavy "stucco" lath should be used and the structure may be covered with creosote, whitewashed or painted. One of the great advantages of lath houses is that they conserve moisture and prevent excessive heat in summer, as well as furnish protection in winter, thus providing conditions for better growth throughout the year. Probably the improved summer growth is a factor which makes for better winter hardiness. They are used in Missouri.

The use of a mulch in protecting rhododendrons is an important subject, but it will be considered later in the chapter dealing with planting and maintenance.

In summing up the subject of sites and shelter for rhododendrons, few rules of thumb can be applied, because so much depends upon local conditions. We might, however, summarize briefly the more important points in the following way:

In choosing a site, first strive to attain the following ideal conditions:

1. Select a site free from sweeping winds, but with good air drainage.

2. Make sure that it is not a hot, south slope which will become dry and parched in summer or against a hot, dry wall.

3. Most rhododendrons prefer semi-shade. Some sun is desirable, but alternate sun and shade is considered the very best. Azaleas will endure more exposure than rhododendrons, but can not endure drought. "High" shade is good.

4. Planting near trees having surface-feeding roots, such as maples and elms, should be avoided, because of root competition. Oaks and pines are considered desirable.

If your property does not include an ideal site, or you wish to create special conditions, you may adopt the following amendments:

1. Trees or bushes may be moved in to act as shelter against wind or sun. The use of artificial windbreaks is also feasible.

2. Plants may be grown successfully in spite of unfavorable winter weather if protected by burlap tents or lath houses.

3. Plants will grow in total shade, but will not bloom profusely nor grow so vigorously as in partial sunlight.

4. Plants may be grown successfully in complete sunshine or in rather dry sites if given irrigation and the soil moisture is maintained by means of mulching.

5. Encroaching tree roots may sometimes be kept from interfering with nearby rhododendrons by cutting off the roots annually or by constructing a sunken concrete wall, or using a sheet of metal as a barrier in the soil.

Probably no ordinary grower of rhododendrons need ever go to the length of adopting more than one or two of these suggested amendments. If he needs to, however, he can overcome nearly all of the adverse features of an inhospitable site by trial and persistent observation. The rest of us can nearly always find a suitable site for our rhododendrons or else prepare one without too much trouble.

As for the dwarf and alpine rhododendrons, which are new to American gardens, it seems evident that the stereotyped cultural methods are incapable of producing the desired results and that either a modified cultural technique or different climatic conditions from those of the American Atlantic seaboard are needed for success. It is probably too soon to prescribe recipes. An account of some of the work being done and results achieved is given, however, in other places in this book.

It is possible to grow a few rhododendrons and azaleas outdoors in unfavorable climates if special methods are used. In Missouri, where intense summer heat and parching air often prevails, rhododendrons are successfully grown in the partial shade of buildings or lath houses, in sawdust beds properly enriched with nitrogenous fertilizers and well protected from excessive hot sunlight.* It should be observed that water must be applied to the soil itself and not to the foliage of the plants, since repeated overhead spraying induces leaf fungus.

Alkaline water presents a problem more serious than ordinarily realized. This makes rhododendron-growing difficult in some regions. Water from rain or snow is generally good if it falls directly and does not percolate through alkaline soil on its way to the rhododendron bed. But even in some regions where acid-loving plants grow naturally, water coming from deep wells in the underlying rocks may be so "hard" from the presence of alkaline mineral salts that it will quickly neutralize a good acid rhododendron bed if used for irrigation. Unsuitable water is one reason why these plants fail in certain cities. The principal way to overcome this handicap is to mulch the plants so heavily that rainwater is stored and held in the mulch, reducing the need for artificial watering.

Air drainage is of utmost importance in certain spots. Do not locate your planting in a depression where frost collects, but place it at least on a slight elevation or slope if possible. The matter of microclimate is exceedingly important when choosing a site for planting. The influence of small differences in environment is sometimes striking. At the Cornell Experiment Station we found a difference of 14°F. on a still, cold morning in winter in the temperature of a cold pocket on the valley floor and that of the crest of a nearby hillside only about one-quarter mile distant. Such a difference, or even less, can mean the difference between life and death for many plants, especially those of marginal hardiness. This factor is also something to watch with regard to flower-bud damage by frosts in either spring or fall. Good air drainage, by locating on a slope, will usually prevent such trouble.

* Seevers, Harry B. "Rhododendrons in the Midwest" (American) Rhododendron Yearbook, 1945, p. 41, and 1946, p. 21. Portland, Ore.

CHAPTER VI

SOIL AND NUTRITION

HAVING chosen a site for rhododendrons or azaleas, the next matter is to provide a suitable soil for their proper growth and maintenance. Unless one is growing rhododendrons extensively, the question of soil is not an insurmountable obstacle, for one can always create, without much difficulty, an artificial soil mixture that will be suitable for a few plants if he is compelled to do so. In many localities, however, very little alteration is needed to make the native soil suitable for ericaceous plants.

The matter of acid soil has now become a watchword among all gardeners who even consider rhododendrons and their kin. Acidity, of course, is a question of first importance. Many expert gardeners realized years ago the benefits of peaty soils for these plants. The significance of acidity, however, was little appreciated by horticulturists until it was called to the attention of people in this country through the notable researches of Dr. F. V. Coville and his associates on blueberries and other heaths, beginning some years ago.

While the main facts of acidity are well known, some of the underlying features of the problem should be known in order to properly comprehend the whole question.

Rhododendrons and all other plants of the heath family demand an acid soil solution for successful life. The common expression is that rhododendrons abhor lime. While this is true in the common, literal sense, it is not a complete statement, because some other active chemical base, such as sodium or ammonium, in a form which can neutralize an acid soil or render it alkaline, might have the same deleterious effect as lime. Actually, a little lime in a non-active form of the element calcium is an indispensable component of the rhododendron's tissues and is absolutely essential for the life and growth of all plants. In the form of calcium nitrate, in the New Jersey sand culture experiments, it proved quite harmless to rhododendrons. But as an active alkali it is quite toxic, and there is some evidence that calcium *per se,* in some forms, may create an imbalance that is harmful.

We might now go a step further and note what happens when rhododendrons are placed in an ordinary alkaline soil. They become pale and chlorotic—a condition strangely resembling anaemia in humans—and they finally dwindle and die of chlorosis. We believe this is connected with a failure of the plant to assimilate iron. In an alkaline solution, the iron in the tissues becomes unavailable to rhododendrons through a chemical change and the plant becomes ill because it cannot use the iron which is needed in its vital functions.* In the last analysis, therefore, the matter becomes a question of iron and not one of lime. That, at least, is a present opinion of some physiologists.

The statement that rhododendrons hate calcareous soils still holds good; also that an acid soil is desired. We need to avoid fresh manure which contains much ammonia in an active form, although in old manure, in ammonium sulphate and in certain organic fertilizers the ammonium is not injurious as an alkali, if not applied too liberally, and is useful as a fertilizer. The common chemical fertilizer sodium nitrate has proved definitely toxic to rhododendrons in tests. Potassium nitrate and calcium nitrate, on the other hand, seem beneficial.

The amount of acidity needed by rhododendrons for best results is that which, when measured, is designated as between pH 4.5 and 5.0.† This is the

---

* The rôle of iron is not entirely clear, but it may act in plant cells in a manner not unlike its action in the blood of animals. It is perhaps connected with the oxidation-reduction processes or it may act as a catalyst. At any rate, it must be in solution, and not in an insoluble state, to act. Iron that is ferrous in the presence of an acid becomes ferric when the pH is increased, in the latter state becoming insoluble and dropping out of the solution in the form of a metallic precipitate. So far as the plant is concerned, it thus becomes utterly unavailable and useless. Spencer and Shive (1933) suggest that, in addition to iron deficiency due to precipitation, there may also be a direct effect of high pH values on the absorbing and assimilating power of the plant. The relation of iron availability to organic matter will be noted later.

We cannot overcome alkalinity by applying iron, beyond a limited degree, although Shive was able to grow *Rhododendron ponticum* successfully at nearly the neutral point by frequently spraying the plant with iron as ferrous sulphate, and chelated iron does even better.

† The acidity or alkalinity of a solution is measured as Hydrogen-ion concentration and is recorded in "pH values," in much the same manner as temperature is recorded in "degrees Fahrenheit." The actual meaning of Hydrogen-ion concentration or its symbol "pH" need not concern us here, since we are interested merely in its practical use in measuring acidity. On the "pH scale" the neutral point is pH 7.0. Below this neutral point is the acid side; above it, the alkaline side. Thus, pH 6.0 is mildly acid and pH 8.0 mildly alkaline. The optimum point for rhododendrons, namely, pH 4.5 to 5.0, is well on the acid side. Acidity and alkalinity have also been recorded in degrees of "specific acidity" and "specific alkalinity," but these terms have not attained general use. A comparison of the two scales follows:

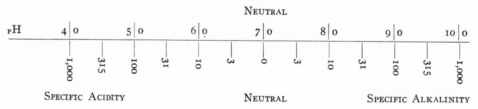

range of concentration commonly found in the places where rhododendrons grow wild and is a good mark to aim at. In most instances noted, the pH value can go as low as pH 4.0 with no bad effects. Where plenty of organic matter, such as peat, is present, the value can go up to pH 5.5 with no injury, but this can not be expected unless organic acids be present. Above or below the points mentioned injury or, at least, mild inhibition will begin to occur, becoming greater as the distance increases away from the point of best results.

This brings up the question of organic matter in the soil, which is closely related to acidity. By organic matter, I mean such things as peat, leaf-mold, old roots, decomposing wood or the remains of other vegetable or animal tissues— in short, the sort of material spoken of as "humus." Such substances are often fibrous and contribute by their physical properties an open, spongy, water-retentive structure to the soil. Chemically they are very complex and are constantly changing as they pass through the successive stages of decay. They are chemically very valuable to rhododendrons because of the organic acids which they liberate. These organic acids, among other activities, form compounds with iron which remain in solution at a higher "pH" than the inorganic or metallic salts of iron. When plenty of acid-forming organic matter is present, therefore, rhododendrons ought to grow successfully in a slightly more alkaline soil than otherwise. Were it not for the organic matter, we could probably not grow ordinary rhododendrons at all in soils testing above pH 5.0. For this and other reasons the value of organic matter is so great that, in my opinion, it should be relied upon as the main source of acid in soils which require acidifying treatment, in preference to inorganic salts.

All organic matter, however, is not necessarily desirable for rhododendrons. Certain of the commercial humus preparations are alkaline in reaction and also, with mucks, are sometimes of a physical nature that becomes soggy and undesirable. There are quickly decomposing things, such as maple leaves, which, although acid at first, soon become alkaline. The same condition exists with ordinary garden compost or, in fact, with almost any plant material after it reaches an advanced state of decomposition.* Even oak leaves, when very fully decomposed, will lose their acid character, but they, and certain other sub-

---

* Coville, F. V. in L. H. Bailey's "The Cultivated Evergreens" (1923), pp. 336–431. "Fully decomposed leaves form a true leaf-mold, black in color and neutral or alkaline in reaction, in which rhododendrons and other acid-soil plants will not grow. . . . A sharp distinction should be made between half-rotted oak leaves and the ordinary compost of leaves with manure, garden soil and garden trash. Such a compost is neutral or alkaline in reaction and should not be used on acid-soil plants."

It has been noted (Rhod. Assn. Yearbook, 1934) that a toxic condition seems to occur in soil where rotten tree stumps have formerly stood. Although I have never observed this phenomenon (and some American experience might indicate otherwise), it might be that the toxicity attributed to dead tree roots is due to the alkalinity of their final state of decomposition.

stances, such as peat, rot so slowly that they remain acid for a long time and, if fresh supplies are added annually as a mulch, the acid condition of the soil may be successfully maintained.

The two most useful sources of acid organic matter are half-rotted oak leaves and peat. There are several kinds of peat. The commercial product is usually a dried bog-peat, of which several kinds are on the market. This may be imported from Holland, Sweden or Germany (Dutch peat, Swedish peat, German peat, granulated peat, peat moss, etc.) or it may be native sphagnum peat, Michigan sedge peat or other similar material. While these are usually acid, they do not always run uniformly and the purchaser should ask for peat that is definitely acid. Another form of peat is the so-called "upland" peat, which is simply an accumulation of half-rotted vegetable remains comprising the upper layer or mat occurring on well-drained acid soils. Often it is a brown fibrous mat of oak leaves, 2 to 20 years old, such as is commonly found around laurel or huckleberry plants. The remains of roots, stems and leaves, laced together into a persistent, fibrous layer, forms this upland peat on acid soils, but it does not occur on limestone soils because of the rapid decomposition of these materials under alkaline conditions. Upland peat, or any of the other acid peats, is entirely suitable for rhododendrons. Spent tanbark is another organic acidifying substance of considerable promise as a mulch for rhododendrons.

In the northeastern United States it is found that the native peat soils usually contain a high percentage of other decaying materials which cause rapid disintegration of the mixture. On the other hand, most peat moss imported from Western Europe is more nearly pure, is packed more tightly and endures much longer. Generally, therefore, we have found the imported baled product superior and more economical in the long run than the American peat moss.

I have discussed the chemical benefits of peat, acid leaf-soil and other organic materials. In addition to these, there are certain physical benefits to be derived from such organic matter. Their fibrous nature and water-retaining capacity provide the soil with the spongy structure needed for aeration and drainage without the danger of drying-out. Many failures mark the attempt of would-be rhododendron growers who are solicitous to see that their soil is acid, but who overlook the need of a soil physically adapted to their plants. While rhododendrons can be grown very successfully under laboratory conditions without any organic matter at all, they will not do so under garden culture unless special provision is made to compensate for this in some other way. The use of a peaty soil is still the most practicable means of insuring the proper physical condition. And peat moss provides good insulation to keep rhododendron roots from touching unfavorable soil below. The leaching effect is downward in regions of abundant rainfall, so that plants are relatively safe from alkaline soils in lower strata.

Rhododendron rootlets are very fine and commonly grow near the surface of the soil. They must not be allowed to dry out and they prefer to be kept cool and relatively moist. At the same time, there need to be liberal quantities of air spaces through the soil and ample provision for the drainage of surplus water. A soil containing much fibrous, organic material automatically provides just these conditions. If there is any benefit in root fungi, such conditions also promote their development. The feeding roots work in this surface layer and seldom reach the lower soil. Like a sponge, this fibrous soil absorbs a tremendous amount of water and retains it tenaciously, at the same time permitting a circulation of air through its interstices. We should remember that some members of the genus *Rhododendron* are epiphytes, living on tree trunks like orchids, and that probably all of them, except the few which appear to be swamp-loving, need this aeration near their roots and dislike a water-logged soil. The proper kind of organic matter provides all these physical conditions when it is incorporated in the soil.

While this somewhat extended discussion of the chemical and physical needs of rhododendrons may seem complex, we can quickly and simply peg it all down with one or two brief, practical conclusions.

A proper rhododendron soil for the ordinary garden is acid (preferably testing pH 4.5) and contains a high percentage of peat, half-rotted oak leaves or other acid, fibrous organic materials. Such a soil automatically takes care of all the fundamental physical and chemical requirements of the plants. Provision must be made for maintaining this acidity and organic matter, which is usually accomplished by the annual application of an acid-forming mulch, such as oak leaves or pine needles.

I shall now present some rules and recipes for the use of the practical gardener. Let me say, however, that there is no *best* rule. Gardens and soils vary enormously and what fits one situation best may give mediocre results in another. The old system of trial and error is still the surest way to obtain accurate information. Here are a few suggestions, however:

1. First test your soil to determine its pH value.*
2. If it tests between pH 4.5 and 5.5 and obviously contains plenty (say 50%

* There are several effective and inexpensive testing outfits on the market, and the operation of making a test is so simple that any person can easily do it. Colorimetric outfits, which depend upon the color changes in reagents, are obtainable for as little as $2.00. The Lamotte, Sudbury, Wherry and Morgan test-kits, and perhaps others, are of this general type. Other outfits depend upon electrometric readings and are more expensive, but quite accurate. A rough determination, however, is usually sufficient for most horticultural work. Experiment stations, Farm Bureaus, colleges and similar institutions are usually equipped to make soil tests for growers if required.

by volume) of acid organic matter, such as peat, leaf or vegetable remains of a fibrous nature, and if ericaceous plants are naturally occurring on it, then the soil is probably all right with no further treatment. Rhododendrons will generally succeed in soil where huckleberries (*Vaccinium*) grow, but such soil may be very shallow, so that it is necessary to add peat in order to obtain sufficient depth for planting.

3. If the soil tests over pH 5.2 or 5.4, add peat (or ericaceous top-soil, such as the soil from oak woods) until it tests pH 5.0 or less. If over pH 5.5, use at least 50% peat in the soil mixture. In definitely neutral or alkaline areas, rhododendrons are best planted in beds of pure peat or acid woods-soil containing half-decomposed leaves. Any such material or mixture is suitable, provided it is acid, but best results attend the use of soil from oak woods or acid peat. Upland peat is usually not obtainable in neutral or alkaline regions. Take care that the acidity is not neutralized by irrigation with "hard" water or the drainage from adjacent alkaline soils, masonry walls and the like.

4. Sandy soils are much better than clay soils, but rhododendrons will grow upon either. If the sand is of an alkaline quality, such as certain creek and river sands, it had better not be used in soil mixtures directly in contact with rhododendron roots. Coarse, sharp quartz or silica sand, neutral or acid, is excellent and may be mixed with peat up to 50% by volume. Clay soil should never be used in appreciable quantity, and clay loam or silt should not exceed 25%. Very fine sand, such as sea-sand, is likewise unsuitable, being too fine for adequate drainage. Heavy clay presents difficulties. You cannot just dig a hole in clay and plant a rhododendron therein with satisfactory results, no matter how good the immediate soil. Water must drain out of the hole.

5. The use of a soil amendment to promote acidity is practicable and successful, but should supplement and not replace organic matter. Common directions have been to use aluminum sulphate for this purpose, one-half pound to one square yard of surface, but this practice is now disapproved, because aluminum residues are regarded as toxic. Sulphur is much preferred today as the acidifying medium. Ordinary flowers of sulphur are used and may be mixed into the soil to a depth of eight inches when the bed is being prepared, and then allowed to set for two to six weeks before planting. More sulphur is required to acidify small soil particles than coarse ones, so that, while it takes ¾ pound of sulphur to lower the pH one degree in sandy soil, two or three times that amount is required for loams, and treatment of heavy clays is usually not feasible at all. In fact, one would not grow rhododendrons in heavy clay anyway, for physical reasons. When using sulphur, one should be sure that underdrainage is good. Never use sulphur on poorly drained soil; it may prove toxic. Where rhododendrons are already established, surface applications of sulphur

may be made, but one pound of sulphur per 100 square feet is the maximum dosage per application, and it should not be repeated within four weeks. Other acidifying substances are usable, such as dilute solutions of tannic acid applied through a watering pot. Since certain fertilizers, such as ammonium sulphate, leave an acid residue, soil should be tested periodically. It is possible to have it too acid as well as too alkaline.

6. It is a good practice to dig a test hole one foot or more deep, fill it with water and find out whether the water disappears within an hour. If not, the soil is poorly drained, hence, poorly aerated, too.

A few additional observations are pertinent. If peat is used it should be regarded as a soil constituent, never as a top-dressing to be applied over the surface and left uncovered. Peat should be shaded from the sun and wind by a leafy mulch to prevent it from becoming dry and corky. A dry surface of peat moss sheds water like a duck's back, but if kept moist it will absorb and hold rainwater like a sponge. Then, too, surface peat invites surface rooting, which is bad. In poor soils, beds of pure peat moss are suitable. On heavy clay soils, raised beds of peat will provide drainage. But where peat is used alone, it should be supplemented by fertilizers. Imported European peats are more durable than the domestic products, which often contain rapidly disintegrating top-layer ingredients.

One should not become confused by statements regarding lime-tolerant azaleas or rhododendrons, growing in soils of high pH. These things are all possible under laboratory conditions and in some other very special circumstances. Recently *R. occidentale* in California was found growing wild with its roots in soils above pH 8.0.* The soil was of low calcium content and of very unusual nature, with relatively high iron and magnesium ratios. It has been noted, too, that acid-loving plants will live when grown experimentally in soils of pH 8.0 if fed with chelated iron. While calcium is an essential element for plant growth and may be present as a harmless salt in soils, one must regard the carbonate form (limestone) as harmful. Also, it is nonsense to say that rhododendrons may be grown on "any lime-free soil." What is meant is that rhododendron soils should contain "no free lime." Nor is "any" soil (a heavy clay, for instance) physically or biologically suitable for them, even if chemically corrected. However, "limestone" soils are difficult to deal with.

The use of chelated iron, or Sequestrene, for the correction of iron deficiency, is effective. Iron deficiency is most often manifested by chlorosis (pallor or yellowing) of the foliage, although the same symptoms may indicate other troubles, such as nitrogen deficiency, virus disease, unthriftiness from

* Leiser, Andrew T. *R. occidentale* on Alkaline Soil. Roy. Hort. Soc. Rhod. & Cam. Yearbook *11*:46-51. London, 1957.

other causes, or even a too-acid soil as well as a too-alkaline one. The chemical may be used either as a foliage spray for quick local effects or as a soil amendment for more permanency, or for both. Sequestrene NaFe Iron Chelate comes as a dry powder to be dissolved in water according to directions on the package. As a foliage spray or soil drench, about two teaspoons of the powder per gallon of water is recommended for azaleas and rhododendrons. For applications to the soil around plants two feet high, apply the equivalent of one teaspoonful of the powder for each plant; or two teaspoonsful for plants three feet high; and one tablespoonful for larger plants. For big plants one may pour the solution into several shallow holes in the soil around the plants.

Very recently some new research work has been reported concerning the antagonism between rhododendrons and lime.* It has been difficult to separate the effect of calcium *per se* and the effect of an alkaline soil, and this paper makes such an attempt. Like the azaleas in California, rhododendrons were grown by the investigator successfully on alkaline soil where the pH was raised by the use of magnesium carbonate instead of calcium carbonate. Here the base and not the pH seems to be the important factor. He also analyzed the leaves of rhododendrons and found that they contained relatively low levels of magnesium, potassium and phosphorus and high levels of iron and manganese in comparison with the leaves of other kinds of plants. The level of calcium, however, was comparable to that of other plants, which would not ordinarily be expected on normal rhododendron soils where the calcium content is almost always low. This suggests that rhododendrons possess greater facility for collecting calcium than do other plants. Therefore, they may take up too much, so as to create a serious imbalance when grown on calcareous soils. It is possible that this excess of calcium induces deficiencies of other elements, such as the trace elements iron and manganese, the symptoms of which appear on the leaves as an interveinal (marbled) chlorosis or a general yellow pallor. Since calcium and magnesium are antagonistic to each other, only a little calcium is taken up on soils which are high in magnesium, so that the plants are enabled to survive although the acidity may measure pH 8 or more.

In this connection, it is noted also that the leaves of deciduous trees growing in calcareous regions may contain far greater percentages of calcium than those of trees grown elsewhere. Such leaves, when used as a mulch, are probably capable of contributing unwanted lime to the soil. This, then, is an additional handicap to those who are seeking to grow ericaceous plants in regions of calcareous soil.

After providing the proper soil, with its required acidity and organic mat-

* Tod, Henry. Rhododendrons and lime. Roy. Hort. Soc. Rhod. & Cam. Yearbook *13:*19–24. London, 1959.

ter (if it needs such attention), and taking care of other obvious necessities such as drainage, many growers conclude that no further consideration of soils is needed. Indeed, the common practice in America is to duplicate, as near as possible, the soil of the native woodlands and give the rhododendrons no fertilization beyond what they obtain from the decomposing leaves or peat applied as an annual mulch. This practice works fairly well and is comparable to conditions found in nature. But the nutrients contained in the mulch or peaty soil become available very slowly, so that the plant does not make vigorous growth and often assumes a relatively inactive state or "checked" development. Peat alone has almost no nutritional value whatever and needs to be supplemented by an active fertilizer.

It has been found that nutrients in the form of more readily available chemicals may be safely applied to rhododendrons and azaleas and that the plants will respond to the right kind of fertilizers with great celerity. Given the proper diet, rhododendrons are as responsive to the stimulus of fertilizers as are any other plants. This has recently been demonstrated by several different growers, using a variety of fertilizing materials. The advantages of such artificial feeding are that it induces quick development and provides better foliage, a more luxuriant appearance and a generally improved state of health. The time-saving element is especially important, because large plants are costly, but, with rapid development, smallish plants may be made to assume large size at a great saving of expense. This is important in commercial production and in breeding new varieties.

It cannot be said that the matter of fertilizers has been worked out as yet in completeness. Several growers have found materials which, applied as fertilizers, produce highly satisfactory results under their conditions. Perhaps none of these are suitable for universal application, because of the local differences in soils. They are, however, of sufficient promise to warrant careful trial. Where one fails, another may succeed. I shall give some of these in the form of recipes, with notes regarding their use.

One of the most successful users of mineral nutrients was Mr. Charles O. Dexter of Sandwich, Mass. He obtained marvelous rapidity of growth, combined with sturdy development, in his plants. In my opinion, his success was due quite as much to careful methods as to his fertilizers. Besides this, he had a well drained, acid, sandy soil and a climate especially congenial for rhododendrons. He used peat and decomposing oak leaves liberally in combination with his fertilizer. His plants obtained a very liberal supply of water, without, however, the slightest tendency toward sogginess. He also provided conditions of semi-shade. Most important of all was the meticulous care with which he attended to the common needs of his plants, never permitting them to become checked in development through crowding, drying out or disease, and maintaining a steady, uninterrupted rate of vegetative growth throughout the season. Mr. Dexter's formula is as follows:

1 part potassium nitrate (KNO_3)
2 parts superphosphate (acid phosphate, $CaH_4(PO_4)_2$).

Apply one trowelful (about ½ pint) of the dry mixture to each 3-foot plant. Other sized plants proportionately. Never use this fertilizer later than the month of May—a rule which may well be followed in the use of all fertilizers on rhododendrons or azaleas which are grown outdoors and which must be permitted to stop growing and "harden off" in late summer if they are to successfully endure the subsequent winter. Mr. Dexter's soil tested pH 4.3.

The addition of organic materials in the fertilizer formula is probably desirable in many cases. Dr. Richard P. White has employed the following formula and finds that it works very well on the rather light sandy soils of southern New Jersey. It has the advantage of containing an organic form of nitrogen which becomes available gradually as the plant uses it. The proportions are as follows:

tankage	1,000	lbs.
ammonium sulphate (NH_4SO_4)	150	"
magnesium sulphate $(MgSO_4)$	200	"
muriate of potash (KCl)	150	"
bone	500	"
	2,000	lbs.

This should be applied at the rate of 1,000 lbs. per acre (about 6½ ounces per square yard) in the spring.

Ordinary commercial fertilizers, unless especially devised for rhododendrons, should be avoided, since many contain toxic substances such as sodium nitrate or lime or are otherwise unadapted for use with ericaceous plants. Wood ashes are likewise undesirable. Some organic fertilizers, however, which are marketed under proprietary names, are not objectionable. Cornell University reports favorably upon the use of Clay's Fertilizer, an English preparation, for ericaceous plants. Recently fertilizers have appeared upon the market which are specially advocated for rhododendrons and there will probably be more of these as time goes on. While unable to report upon the action of these, the general assumption may be made that commercial products advertised as especially adapted for ericaceous plants will be suitable for use on rhododendrons and azaleas, although, in all probability, somewhat more expensive than a home-mixed product where large quantities are needed.

Dr. Coville investigated the possibilities of certain acid, organic, nitrogenous materials as fertilizers for ericaceous plants, going so far as to feed his blueberries on buttermilk,* which he found suitable but high in calcium. Cottonseed meal proved a more practicable material and the following special acid fertilizer was devised and recommended † for use on blueberries and cranberries, and probably rhododendrons, to be applied at the rate of one-eighth to one-fourth of a pound per square yard:

cottonseed meal	10 lbs.
acid phosphate (superphosphate, $CaH_4(PO_4)_2$)	4 "
sulphate of potash (K_2SO_4)	2 "

Animal manures are constantly used on rhododendrons by some growers and are probably all right if the acidity of the soil is maintained. Some English nurseries and certain American establishments advise the careful use of old, well-rotted manure in the soil mixture for rhododendrons. The special character of the local soil and its actual behavior when applied with manure to rhododendron plants should govern, to a large extent, its use. Obviously, manure of any kind must be used with great discretion, because of its alkaline reaction. It should never be used when fresh, as it contains ammonia in a very active alkaline form. Although I can not vouch for the use, safety or value of barnyard manure in all circumstances, I have seen it employed with peat, sand and loam in the preparation of nursery beds, with apparently good effect. I do not feel, however, that it is sufficiently safe on all soils to recommend its general use to amateurs for either rhododendrons or ericaceous plants of any kind, except as an experimental measure.‡

Good decomposing woods soil, preferably from an oak wood, contains a mild supply of available nutrients and, while it does not furnish the quick stimulation of an active fertilizer, is often sufficiently rich to support good growth

* Coville, F. V. Buttermilk as a fertilizer for blueberries. Science 64:94-96. 1926.

† Coville, F. V. The effect of aluminum sulphate on rhododendrons and other acid-soil plants. From the Smithsonian Report for 1926, p. 381.

‡ A little experimentation, using combinations of manure with strongly acid substances, such as peats and organic acids, would perhaps reveal a mixture that could be generally recommended as a safe and effective fertilizer. It seems evident that ammonia, which is present in manure, is the form of nitrogen which rhododendrons like the best. An English recipe, presented here with the proviso that it be accepted only experimentally, is as follows: "The ground should be thoroughly trenched to a depth of 2 feet or more . . . replacing it with . . . one-third fibrous loam, one-third peat and one-third natural soil, with a sprinkling of well-rotted leaf mold (*probably acid leaf-soil is better.—C.G.B.*). Fresh stable manure should be avoided, but some well-rotted cow manure should be added, care being taken to keep it well away from the roots when planting. A topdressing or mulching of the same can be given annually or biennially in May with advantage." Acid peat is often employed as a litter for poultry-houses, and the question has come up as to its value, when combined with the poultry droppings which it acquires in use, as a rhododendron fertilizer. Experiment alone can tell how such a material will work, but its application is worth trying.

unaided. If a person has a wooded plot where ericaceous plants grow naturally, the soil from such a place is almost certain to be suitable. Beds filled with acid woods soil, about one foot deep, make excellent places for young rhododendrons, provided the under-drainage is adequate.

Where a nitrogenous fertilizer alone is needed to stimulate leaf-growth, a dilute solution of ammonium sulphate (NH_4SO_4) may be applied to the soil. I have successfully used this upon young rhododendron seedlings in the greenhouse at the rate of one level tablespoonful of the dry salt to about 12 quarts of water, applied through a watering-pot. Frequent and very dilute applications are probably more effective than stronger doses, and the user must be exceedingly careful, when applying ammonium sulphate, not to get it too strong, because it is an extremely concentrated substance and will easily burn the plants if too strong. The dry salt may be applied very sparingly over the mulch on larger plants growing outdoors, but here again care is needed to avoid burning. It is also sometimes incorporated with oak leaves in compost heaps, as it hastens the decomposition of the leaves and also adds nitrogen to the mixture.

Some basic research on the nutrition of rhododendrons was made some years ago in New Jersey by Doctors Shive, White, Spencer and their associates.* The plants were grown from seed to bloom on nothing but clean quartz sand and fed on chemical solutions by a continuously flowing apparatus, which kept the nutrient solutions constantly dripping on the sand. Many different combinations of chemicals were tried, all of them being composed of different proportions of the following inorganic salts: mono-potassium phosphate (KH_2PO_4), magnesium sulphate ($MgSO_4$), ammonium sulphate ($(NH_4)_2SO_4$) and calcium nitrate ($Ca(NO_3)_2$). The chemicals used were not anhydrous, but carried their usual molecules of water. No organic materials whatever were used. Despite the apparently unnatural character of the growing media, results from the best cultures were remarkable, with plants of *R. ponticum* growing from seed to five feet in height, and blooming in two years.

Nutritional deficiencies can produce symptoms resembling disease infections on the leaves, especially of seedlings. Soluble chemicals, such as ferrous sulphate and also certain trace elements, sprayed on the leaves, can be directly absorbed by the plant to correct chlorosis (pallor) and other deficiency troubles as an emergency measure, but the effect of foliar feeding is temporary. If the condition is to be permanently adjusted, the needed substances must be applied to the soil itself. It is interesting to note that well-nourished plants of vigorous growth resist winter injury better than impoverished plants, yet late summer

* Spencer, E. L. and J. W. Shive. The Growth of *Rhododendron ponticum* in Sand Cultures. Bulletin of the Torrey Botanical Club 60:423–439. 1933.

growth may delay ripening-off in the autumn. So feed your plants to make them grow well, but do it in the spring.

Sawdust has been used as a soil constituent quite successfully, but only where its use is accompanied by the extra application of nitrogen. Soil organisms which break down sawdust by rotting it also exhaust the available nitrogen supply in the process. High-nitrogen fertilizer or ammonium sulphate should be applied with the sawdust, or the plants will become chlorotic.

The presence of root fungi, or mycorrhizae upon the roots of rhododendrons and azaleas has been noted as a customary condition. I have observed the mycelium within the cells of root tissues, as well as abundant hyphae about the outside of the roots. Statements have been made that rhododendrons and certain other members of the heath family are benefited in one way or another by the presence of these microorganisms. Values have been ascribed to them as nitrogen-gatherers and as vehicles for the absorption of water and mineral salts. It has been stated that rhododendrons have no root hairs and that they derive their water from the soil through the helpful assistance of these root fungi. Causes of failure in growth have been cited as due to unhappy fungous conditions. In some instances the very presence of a mycorrhiza has been interpreted as of indispensable value in that these fungi live with their hosts in a state of dependent symbiosis. Such extreme views are hardly correct and were successfully refuted by Dr. Lewis Knudson,* who demonstrated that *Calluna* seedlings could be successfully germinated and grown in sterile cultures in the total absence of any kind of fungus whatever. He went on to grow rhododendron seedlings in fungus-free cultures. Indeed, cultures without a mycorrhiza actually surpassed the others.

But in a state of nature fungi seem to be definitely associated, and the exact nature of their relationship, i.e., as to when or how they may be beneficial and when they may perhaps turn around and become definitely pathogenic, is still vague. There is some evidence to support the view that the successful culture of rhododendrons and azaleas may involve also the successful culture of the mycorrhizae which inhabit (or inhibit) their roots. A correct answer to this question might also answer the riddle of why ericaceous plants do not thrive in certain localities. Although rhododendrons may be made to grow on pure quartz sand or in culture tubes in a laboratory, it would seem that a high content of organic matter in the soil is highly desirable under garden conditions. Besides its obvious physical and chemical advantages, this would presumably be of biological value, too, in that it offers a favorable medium for the fungi.

Apart from what has been said above concerning azaleas which have been

* Knudson, L., in The New Phytologist *32*(2) : 115–127. London, 1933.

found growing on soils of unusually high pH values, it has been noted that certain species do possess a bit more tolerance toward lime than other species. *R. roseum* is one of these, frequently occurring in calcareous regions. These and others, however, are usually found growing in pockets or surface layers of leaf mold or other organic matter, acid in reaction and uninfluenced by the nearby limestone.

Light and the process of photosynthesis play quite as important parts in plant nutrition as do the elements derived from the soil. The light and shade relations of rhododendrons are of great significance. The high light requirements of cuttings under mist culture have been noted.* Experiments in Holland have also established the fact that young plants under glass will continue in active growth through winter if given supplemental light, thus doubling their usual size, so that hybrid seedlings of the Catawbiense type were bloomed as quickly as 33 months from seed.† It is normal for rhododendrons and azaleas to grow until a terminal bud is formed, when growth is temporarily checked. If the bud is removed or supplemental light is given, growth will presently be resumed until the next terminal bud is formed. Photoperiod was found to be the most important factor in breaking this bud dormancy and speeding the growth cycles from one flush of growth to the next. Under long days at about 60°F. the number of growth periods was increased. In experiments on *R. catawbiense* in Michigan ‡ it was found that continuous illumination may cause malformed or sterile flowers, and similar effects were noted in my own experiments with spring-forced plants of *R. maximum* at the Cornell Experiment Station in 1949. In the latter case, although early bloom was secured, the sex organs of the forced flowers appeared non-functional when subjected to pollination. Several other interesting results were noted in the Michigan experiments. The best results appeared to come from 16-hour illumination and a temperature of 60°F. Short days will cause the rhododendron plants to become dormant and ripen-off, while long days will keep the plants in a vegetative condition and prevent ripening-off. Subsequent treatment of the plants with cold temperatures to test their relative hardiness indicated that the short-day treatments produced cold-resistant plants, while the plants given long days suffered cold injury. Plants under an eight-hour photoperiod failed to grow. Those over 16 hours developed a leggy appearance and malformed shoots, with fewer buds developing into shoots. The combination of day-length and temperature would thus seem to have a bearing upon ripening-off and consequently

* See p. 119.

† Doorenbos, J. Shortening the breeding cycle of Rhododendron. Euphytica 4(2) :141–146. 1955.

‡ Davidson, Harold and C. L. Hamner. Photoperiodic responses of selected woody ornamental shrubs. Quar. Bull. Mich. Agr. Exp. Sta. 40(2) :327–343, illus. East Lansing, 1957.

upon the matter of winter hardiness. This is discussed further in Chapter IX, where I have noted that plants in northern New York, where winter comes early and is steady, will endure much greater cold without bud injury than those in southern New York where intermittent temperatures interrupt the ripening-off process in autumn. Latitude may also be a factor. Britain, which is in the latitude of Labrador, has very short autumn days, favoring prompt and complete ripening-off. Northwestern Scotland, which is in a very high latitude, is noted for its subtropical rhododendrons.

A statement frequently made, especially in Britain, is that certain not-so-hardy species "require some shade." The inference, of course, is that shade is synonymous with protection. This requires qualification. A canopy of trees can certainly ward off injury from late spring frosts, a constant hazard in Britain, and this is probably the usual implication. Shade might also assist in the ripening-off process or in the maintenance of a mulch. It is true, also, that some species need winter shade to prevent growth activity from starting on warmish winter days, and, in summer, shade is needed for protection against undue heat and dryness. Wind-shelter is needed, too.

But there are other situations where shade is a drawback. Deciduous azaleas which grow naturally on cool mountain tops in full exposure, grow sparse and leggy under heavy shade and fail to bloom well. Those in lowlands bloom best when on the edges of woods rather than inside the woods. The natural habitats of *R. catawbiense* and *R. carolinianum,* as well as the azaleas *R. calendulaceum* and *R. Bakeri,* for instance, are more often than not on the open "bald" tops of mountains, where the air is cool and the light very bright indeed, but with fibrous, spongy soil underneath. *R. maximum* and *R. minus* seek less exposure and are perhaps more shade-tolerant, but there may be a complete absence of bloom when grown in too-shady places.

I think it may be said also that as one goes north, less and less shade is needed, particularly for azaleas. Trees seem to be needed to provide shade from the full hot sun, especially in the South, or on any slope that faces the full-day sun, but in the northern climates a few hours of sunlight every day may be essential. And in almost any situation, high shade, such as that provided by tall trees, is the best kind that can be found.

Interesting growth responses in various plants from treatment with gibberellic acid have been noted in recent experiments. Little work has yet been reported on rhododendrons, but Cox * has found it effective on young seedlings of *R. burmanicum* in Scotland. Five applications of Gibberellin during May at six-day intervals induced marked stem and leaf development, although with temporary loss of dark green color soon after application. No results

* Cox, E. H. M., in Roy. Hort. Soc. Rhod. & Cam. Yearbook, p. 93. London, 1958.

have yet been reported from treatment of blooming-sized plants, nor as to reproductive responses. Ticknor * working at the University of Massachusetts has found that gibberellic acid applied to rhododendron seedlings may increase the rate of growth of some species (and not of others), but the type of growth produced is undesirable and stimulation is temporary. Supplemental light, however, proved to be a good growth stimulant.

Almost any number of additional recipes for feeding or treating rhododendrons may be found, many of which are good. But to sum up, one may say that nitrogen is important and that rhododendrons like theirs in the form of ammonia. Thus, ammonium sulphate and rotted untreated manure remain good sources of this element. Beyond feeding, it is increasingly apparent that the physical texture and structure of the soil is as important as its chemical nature in promoting healthy growth. Oxygen is needed at the roots, but without drying. No rhododendron or azalea can succeed where soil aeration and drainage are inadequate. To produce these conditions in unsuitable soils, peat moss remains the very best soil amendment and should be regarded as a soil ingredient, not as a mulch. It combines chemical buffering with physical benefits. Pure peat may be used alone where necessary if supplemented by fertilizers, and the use of a raised bed of peat is probably the best practicable means of solving a heavy-soil problem.

* Ticknor, Robert L. Gibberellic acid—its effect on the growth of rhododendron seedlings with and without supplemental light. Quar. Bull. Amer. Rhod. Soc. 12(2) : 78-80. 1958.

CHAPTER VII

PLANTING AND MAINTENANCE

AN EXPERIENCED rhododendron nurseryman or qualified expert can transplant rhododendrons and azaleas at any time of the year and do it successfully if the ground is workable and the conditions not too severe. Commercial men are constantly selling and planting. This, however, implies that the right sort of material be used, a good ball of soil be taken, proper protection given and skillful care rendered after planting. To transplant at a hazardous time of the year is not recommended to inexperienced beginners, for too many details are involved. The best thing for amateurs or ordinary gardeners to do is to plant at the most favored times of the year. By taking an extra large ball of soil, keeping the roots wet for two days while out of the ground, and then watering well after planting, however, plants may be moved in winter, it is said, with little loss. The replacement records of at least one large nursery verify this statement.

All things considered, the safest time to plant rhododendrons in the north is the early spring. In New York and New England, the month of April seems especially suitable. In certain other places, autumn planting seems to be preferred. Local conditions sometimes determine the most advisable practices, and one can generally be safe if he follows the system used by those of his neighbors who are successful. My belief is that all rhododendrons should be planted in the spring, or, in certain places, in the fall, unless necessity demands that the work be done at some other season. In the spring, the plant is starting upon its most vigorous season of growth and can accommodate itself to its new situation without the hindrance of cold or drought. The moist spring weather favors the plant in preventing undue loss of moisture through transpiration before the roots have established water relations with the soil. In commercial production, nurserymen generally arrange their schedules so that the transplanting of rhododendrons from frame to row in the nursery will occur in the spring.

Rhododendron and azalea plants may be transplanted with no injury whatever during the height of their blooming season, if they bloom in the spring

53

months. Plants in bud are retarded somewhat by the process of moving and, consequently, their date of flowering may be slightly delayed. The late flowers of such plants have furnished me, in more than one instance, with fresh pollen for use in hybridizing after the normal blooming period for the species had passed.

Perpetual Mulch　Of Oak Leaves

Root Ball

Peaty Soil Mixture
pH 4.0-4.5

Garden Soil At Least Slightly Acid In Reaction

ONE SATISFACTORY METHOD OF PLANTING

Especially adapted for regions where rhododendron growing is none too easy, but where the surrounding soil is well drained. The perpetual mulch of loose leaves may be held in place either by a low wire edging or by dwarf shrubs (as shown). The broken lines indicate the ultimate extent of the roots if not crowded, thus illustrating the need of proper acidity, not only in the special soil mixture, but also in the surrounding garden soil.

Next to spring, late summer or early fall ranks best as a time for the transplanting of rhododendrons. The plants are then dormant and, if proper precautions are taken to see that they are supplied with sufficient water, they will not suffer from the operation. They should be well protected during the following winter, with good wind protection, especially for the evergreen species.

Perhaps the most unfavorable time to plant rhododendrons is in the hot, dry weather of midsummer, when the dry, scorching winds are apt to remove water from the plant tissues faster than it can be replaced. Shelter from the sun, protection from the wind, mulching and the application of water as needed are necessary at such times. Another unfavorable season is midwinter, when the evergreen sorts may suffer from dryness and exposure. It is also unreasonable to expect good results when rhododendrons are moved in early summer (late June and early July), during the middle of their season of active growth, although the operation can be accomplished if skill and care be used.

Those who are fastidious often put a layer of granulated peat about the roots of the rhododendron plant in order to furnish ready moisture at all times.

FAULTY PLANTING TECHNIQUE

Left: What may happen if too broad a root ball is taken up, especially with species like *R. carolinianum* which have long straggling roots. Right: Improper planting. The plant is set too deeply and the soil is mounded up over it, both being improper practices.

This practice seems to pay, in that the plant is not checked during the dry weather. The peat, being spongy, absorbs a great deal of water and thus helps to keep the roots cool and the plant supplied with moisture when the overhead supply is diminished. When setting out young plants which have been grown in the moist atmosphere of a greenhouse or coldframe, a handful of peat, dropped in the bottom of the hole, is valuable in preventing a check in vegetative growth due to the change in water relations of the plant. This is a good practice at all times. So, also, is the custom of putting a little water in the bottom of each hole when setting out the plants. Cinders are also placed in the bottoms of holes when the underlying soil is alkaline.

Except in heavy, "hardpan," poorly drained or alkaline soils, I question the value of deep trenching in the planting of rhododendrons. In their native habitats, rhododendrons and azaleas often grow upon a comparatively shallow layer of leafy soil, with an unbroken layer of heavy, consolidated soil immediately beneath. Of course, they prefer a well-drained, mellow soil under them and this should be provided in cultivation. Although naturally shallow feeding, the roots would doubtless go deeper and benefit thereby if the soil below were specially prepared for them. I do not think, however, that rhododendrons of medium size can benefit greatly by having the soil prepared below a reasonable depth of 18 inches or so, excepting, as I said, where special preparation is needed for drainage or the maintenance of acidity. Good drainage is essential for proper aeration of the soil, and excellent results are secured where the underlying soil is sandy or gravelly. Sites where water naturally collects should be avoided. Where exceedingly heavy soils exist, it may be advisable in cases to install tile under-drains. Well drained hillsides make satisfactory sites.

It should be emphasized again that most rhododendrons and azaleas will not thrive when planted in an undrained hole, no matter how good a soil mixture is placed alongside their roots. The hole becomes just a water-logged reservoir, shutting off the essential oxygen supplies needed by the roots. In heavy clay or alkaline soils a raised bed is recommended and may be worked into either an architectural or naturalistic design. The bed may be made entirely of pure peat moss, spread about 12 inches deep on the surface of the soil, or a gravel base may be put underneath the peat moss, with the latter acting as a buffer and keeping the rhododendron roots from contact with the alkaline soil below. Since drainage is downward, the peaty soil will be unaffected by the substrata. The peat moss will supply both aeration and drainage while acting as a moisture-retainer and a chemical buffer, too. The edges of a raised bed may be bordered by a low clipped hedge (see Chapter II), a low wall, another planting, or an architectural device, or soil may be filled in around it and graded up to it in such a way as not to prevent drainage. Or it may be unnecessary to use any edging, especially if the edges of the peat bed are graded down to the ground level.

If the plant is large and comes with a deep ball of soil on its roots, the hole must be proportionately large (see illustration, page 54). Dig the hole considerably larger than the ball of earth, and throw out all the soil, so that a quantity of fibrous rhododendron soil or peat can be put in all around the ball. Plenty of room should be left for the development of the roots and growth of the plant, because frequent transplanting is not desirable. Once established, rhododendrons are best left to remain in their permanent sites. The feeding roots of rhododendrons, compared with those of other common shrubs, are exceedingly minute. Their delicacy demands that they be disturbed as little as possible. Transplanting should be accomplished without rough handling or the shaking of soil from the roots.

Young plants may be lifted carefully with a spade, disturbing the soil as little as possible. Medium sized plants, that is, plants having root-balls not over two feet in diameter, may be lifted after a circular cut has been made around them to define the edge of the ball. Such plants should be removed carefully and placed gently on a burlap square. The diagonally opposite corners of the square are then brought together over the ball and tied tightly, thus surrounding the ball with a tight bandage which holds it firmly in place. The coarsely woven fabric called Dutch burlap or onion sacking is superior for this purpose, because it ties tightly and remains that way. Plants dug and shipped in this manner are known in the trade as "balled and burlapped" or "B & B." *

Very large plants must first have a trench dug around the circumference of their roots, a tree-moving canvas applied tightly to the ball of earth, and then be pulled up on a flat platform in accordance with the technique of tree moving. Plants having root-balls of two feet or more across, and weighing 150 to 200 pounds, may be moved in the following way, suggested by Comber.† After digging a trench around the plant, thrust two crowbars underneath, and with them lean the plant over. Never use the stem as a lever. Take about eight feet of rope, double it, place it beneath the ball of roots about eight inches apart, and let the bush back upon it. "Twist the ends of the rope on either side, so they can be held in one hand, with the other free to steady the plant. Two men can now lift it comfortably into any conveyance, out again, or adjust it in the hole, lowering or raising it as required." The rope may be pulled out without disturbing the plant after it is set. This method will save labor where only a short haul is to be made and the plant does not have to be out of the ground long. Large plants may be handled by machinery.‡

Old garden ground, which has been manured and cultivated and which raises ordinary flowers well, is often unsuitable for rhododendrons and should be all removed when the hole is dug. If not too alkaline, some of it may be replaced after mixing with peat or similar acid media. It is always well to test the soil before planting.

Consideration should also be given to protecting the soil from alkalinity in other ways. Water used for irrigation is frequently "hard" and this will almost always neutralize an acid soil ultimately. Where such a danger is present, it is wise to keep the plants mulched rather heavily during the growing season so that the soil moisture is conserved and little or no artificial irrigation is neces-

---

* With good-sized plants, the burlap covering is sewed on, instead of being tied. The sewing is done with a regular steel packing needle and tough twine.

† Comber, James. Rhododendrons for medium-sized gardens. Yearbook, Rhododendron Association (London), 48–53. 1933.

‡ For an account of methods used in moving large rhododendron plants see: Savill, Sir Eric H. The Collection of Rhododendron Species in Windsor Great Park. Roy. Hort. Soc. Rhod. & Cam. Yearbook 8:16–23. London, 1954.

sary. This same principle obtains in greenhouse culture, where potted rhododendrons may be plunged in peat and very little water need be applied directly to the plants. While rainwater itself is generally the best sort of water that can be obtained, it sometimes becomes alkalized and is then injurious to acid-loving plants. I have spoken of drainage from adjacent alkaline soils. Another source of alkalinity is the lime in masonry or cement. Rain, beating against the brick or stucco wall of a building, will run down the sides of the wall and into the soil, carrying with it enough dissolved lime from the masonry to alkalize the soil around the foundation of the building. If rhododendrons or other ericaceous plants are used around the foundations, they will be endangered by this alkaline drainage from the masonry wall. This possibility, therefore, should be considered whenever such plants are used for foundation plantings and appropriate means should be employed to prevent the alkaline water from running into the rhododendron soil. The excretions of animals will also render a soil alkaline or toxic and have been observed to cause the death of rhododendron plants. The repeated application of alkaline spray mixtures, or the residues of chemical fertilizers all have the capacity to make the soil alkaline ultimately.

Some persons consider that it is not worth while to attempt the growing of rhododendrons in regions where the subsoil is naturally alkaline or where a heavy clay prevents good drainage. While this may be true in some places, it is not always true that rhododendrons are beyond the reach of gardeners in a limestone region. At Rochester, N.Y., where the soil tests pH 7.5 or more, the rhododendrons and azaleas planted by the late John Dunbar in Highland Park are famous. This plantation is a shining example of success attained in spite of highly unfavorable natural conditions. Mr. Dunbar chose a gently sloping, well drained location, sheltered from sweeping winds by the topography and by trees. Peat beds were constructed by excavating the native soil to a depth of from 2½ to 3 feet. The subsoil was a sandy gravel, containing lime. The beds were then filled with an acid soil of a peaty nature taken from a nearby swamp. Old cow-manure was mixed liberally in the surface. "Rhododendrons planted in this preparation began to root immediately, grew with vigor and flowered splendidly." Since the plants are grown in the open, a water system is available to irrigate them in dry weather. They are mulched heavily in winter, and the annual addition of a layer of half-rotted leaves maintains the acidity of the soil.* This plantation is now 60 years old and is still thrifty. While the native soil, in this instance, tests around pH 7.5, Mr. Dunbar thought the method might not be so successful at pH 8.0.

* Dunbar, John. Experience at Rochester. Standard Cyclo. of Hort. 5:2935. 1916. Also, Bailey, L. H. The Cultivated Evergreens, p. 345. 1922.

Unless the native soil is naturally quite suitable, it is frequently more satis-factory to place the plants in "made" beds than to plant them as isolated indi-viduals. In acid soil up to pH 5.5 or so, all that is usually necessary is to spade up the soil to a depth of 18 inches, mix in some peaty material or half-rotted leaf-mold, or both, and thus obtain a soil mixture that is both acid and fibrous. Beds filled with ericaceous woodland soil a foot deep make excellent places for young rhododendrons. A combination of loam, sand, leaf-mold and peat, in about equal proportions, is a good soil medium. Other soil mixtures, and, of course, the use of manure and fertilizers, are discussed in the previous chapter. Peat beds have long been used at the Royal Botanic Garden, Edinburgh, and beds of pure peat moss, 12 inches deep, are presently being employed for azaleas at the Cornell Experiment Station where the soil is a heavy calcareous clay and the water alkaline.

In planting rhododendrons, the crown of the plant (the place where the main stem and upper roots meet) should not be buried, but should be placed just beneath the surface of the soil. A good rule is to set the plants at the same depth at which they were formerly growing. If the plant does not seem to be placed deeply enough, cover the soil with leaf-mold, peat or a mulch, rather than using additional soil. Set the plant in firmly, but, beyond what is needed for firm anchorage, there is probably no virtue in stamping the roots in or tread-ing upon them heavily in planting. Such a practice seems unnecessary and likely to injure rather than benefit the delicate roots. But, of course, the plant must be firmly anchored. In doing this, do not press down on the roots themselves, but press the surrounding soil.

When the plants come from the nursery, the balls of soil should be moistened and planting should proceed as soon as possible. If heavy burlap is on the ball, it should be removed. Thin burlap may remain. After planting, the plants should be well watered and should not be allowed to become dried out while establishing themselves in their new home. Do not keep the soil sodden, how-ever. Be sure that all labels are removed which may constrict and girdle the growing branches. At the same time, see that a proper label, preferably a per-manent one of copper or zinc, is applied to the plant for the sake of an accurate record. A thin piece of sheet copper, upon which you can make embossed letters by writing with a metal stylus or a nail, makes one of the very best and most permanent plant labels. Careful gardeners who have many plants often make diagrams of their plantations, so that any plant can be identified when the label is gone.

After the rhododendrons are planted, they should be mulched. This is not necessary with spring plantings, but is always a desirable practice, for it helps to insure proper moisture during the summer and prevents the development of weeds. After a young plant is a foot or more tall, it is large enough to have its roots protected by a leafy covering on the surface of the soil. It is an excellent practice to maintain a mulch around the plants at all seasons of the year. It should not, of course, be so heavy as to become soggy. And, if it becomes "caked" or too compact, it should be loosened up. But the use of a proper mulch conserves soil moisture to such an extent that artificial watering is unnecessary, which is a tremendous advantage in regions where only "hard" water is available, besides saving considerable labor. The labor saved, also, in weed prevention is strongly in favor of the summer mulch. In summer, the plants are constantly protected against the drying effect of the sun, the wind and high temperatures if the soil be mulched. And, of course, in winter the mulch is a very effective protection against early frosts, quick changes in temperature and the heaving of frozen ground.

Various kinds of mulches are used, but oak leaves are always considered the mulch *par excellence* for rhododendrons. These may be spread over the surface of the soil loosely in the autumn to a depth of 12 inches in cold regions (although 6 or 8 inches will suffice in most places) and allowed to remain all winter. By spring they will have become matted down to a depth of 3 or 4 inches and, if not too closely matted, may be left in place all summer, during which time they will gradually disintegrate. When autumn comes again, a fresh application may be placed on top of them. Except in very formal situations, the leafy mulch does not appear objectionable.

In some cold regions, the plants are almost buried in leaves for the winter, the leaves being kept from blowing away by an inconspicuous girdle of chicken-wire stretched around the borders of the bed. In spring, the wire is taken down and all but the lower three inches of leaves are removed; the remaining leaves are worked into the surface soil. As will be noted later (see diagram, page 54), an edging of low shrubs will serve to keep a leafy mulch on a rhododendron bed, as well as to conceal it.

Oak leaves are not always available, or the supply is insufficient. The leaves of other deciduous trees may be used, but many of these decompose so rapidly that they soon lose their fibrous nature and also become alkaline. Maple leaves are of this type and also have the disadvantage of packing down so tightly that if they are not raked loose occasionally they will cut off the proper aeration of the soil beneath them. Therefore, if deciduous leaves, other than oak, are used, they should be watched carefully and removed by spring before they become alkaline.

Granulated peat is useful as a mulch, but sometimes becomes very dry on the surface, so that rain will run off rather than soak in. A few leaves or a sprinkling of soil over the surface will remedy this condition. Sedge peat, also, is excellent. The peats have the advantage of appearing less unkempt than a leafy mulch. Pine needles are highly recommended by some growers. Spent tanbark has possibilities of being one of the best; it contributes enough tannic acid to be of real chemical benefit, but, perhaps, is not yet out of the experimental stage. Old, hardwood sawdust has been used successfully as a mulching and acidifying substance; it is best if it has lain outdoors in the weather for several years before being used. It is best to add nitrogen with the sawdust (see p. 49). Other plant residues have been recommended. Bracken, cut and applied in July, is advocated in England. The stiff stems of certain herbaceous plants are said to be useful as a winter mulch.* Buckwheat hulls should be avoided. One ingenious nurseryman devised a method of using shredded cornstalks as a winter and summer mulch.† I have had no reports from persons who have used tar or plastic "mulch paper" as a mulch for rhododendrons. It might be beneficial, but, of course, would not have the chemical and nutritive advantages possessed by pure vegetable residues and there is a possibility of its being injurious by cutting off the aeration of the soil. Besides this, it is, for rhododendrons, neither durable, cheap nor handsome.

Probably some of the alpine rhododendrons should be handled differently from the ordinary sorts. Mr. G. G. Nearing considers that the dwarf alpines should not be covered, and that some should be in full sun both summer and winter, with the all-important provision, however, that water be within reach of their roots at all times. He approves of mulching them with stones the size of an egg, packed around the plants after setting them in moist but well drained acid soil, away from winds. The Lapponicums especially, he says, need a wet but well drained soil and will endure full sun and heat if water is copiously supplied. His observations indicate that these dwarf species cannot endure a dry soil.

The soil around rhododendron plants should never be hoed or cultivated. The delicate roots grow near the surface of the soil and are endangered if the soil is stirred with an implement. If a leafy mulch is used, no common weeds will be troublesome. When weeds do appear, they may be pulled out easily by hand, as the peaty soil is loose and does not hold them firmly. Weeds, of course, are competitors for water and mineral salts and are to be exterminated when

* See Nearing, G. G. Horticulture. 6:51 (Feb. 1), 1928.
† Plants two feet high were mulched with dried stalks of common maize (cornstalks) which had been passed through a corn-shredder. This furnished protection in the winter and eliminated the necessity of an overhead sprinkling system by conserving moisture in summer. It has the advantage of being cheap and plentiful wherever corn can be grown. Mr. P. M. Koster originated this method.

they appear. Prevention by means of a mulch is by far the best method of dealing with weeds.

In some localities, especially where the water is "hard" or alkaline, the soil should be tested at regular intervals to determine its acidity. Whenever the Hydrogen-ion concentration gets above pH 5.5, the soil should be acidified by one of the methods outlined in the previous chapter. In such situations, apply as little hard water as possible, depending upon rains and the conservation of soil water by means of the mulch to furnish an adequate moisture supply. When raising young seedlings, it is sometimes possible to secure enough suitable water by collecting rain-water in a barrel or tank. Rain-water is as neutral as distilled water and is entirely satisfactory. Watch for other things which might modify the condition of the soil and guard against these, and the ever present "unknown" factor, by testing the soil once or twice a year.

It is frequently stated, and probably with good reason, that rhododendrons should enter the freezing weather with plenty of moisture in the soil. A soaking rain before the ground freezes is said to be requisite to a successful wintering. Unless copious rains occur in autumn, therefore, the plants should be watered artificially. Mr. Dexter observed that plants copiously watered in the fall passed through the severe winter of 1934 with much less injury than those which were not so watered.

No definite rule can be followed as to how near a tree rhododendrons may be planted. Trees differ in the extent of their root systems as well as in their power to antagonize rhododendrons. It is part of the task of maintenance to see that seriously competing tree roots are kept out of rhododendron plantations. Rhododendrons will grow in the presence of competing roots, but probably not at their best.

Rhododendrons are often planted near trees in order to insure shade. Deep-rooted trees, such as oak, offer little trouble, but those having surface roots, such as maples and elms, offer serious problems. A method of guarding against encroaching roots is to dig a trench around the rhododendrons, on the side toward the tree, and insert a sheet of old corrugated metal or roofing to act as a barrier against tree roots. Most trees draw water from the surrounding soil, so be sure that rhododendrons growing near trees, whether protected or not, receive adequate water whenever they need it.

If a heavy mulch is not employed where rhododendrons are used for foreground or formal plantings, ground cover plants are sometimes grown among the rhododendrons or in front of them (see diagram, page 54). Perhaps the most harmonious and suitable are the small ericaceous plants, and there are so many of these that one need scarcely look for anything else. Most of these may be combined with a light mulch. They are valuable in shading the soil at all times of the year and help to keep a light, leafy covering from blowing off the beds. Of the rhododendrons which may be used for this purpose, dwarf forms, such as *R. racemosum* (which comes in a hardy strain), are excellent. In formal plantings, a low evergreen hedge surrounding the rhododendron beds will formalize the planting as well as conceal the mulch.

The pruning of rhododendrons is generally restricted to the removal of dead or unthrifty wood. Except for the so-called "tree rhododendrons," such as *R. Falconeri*, most species will endure severe cutting-back. At the Arnold Arboretum old Catawba hybrids with stems two inches in diameter were cut back to within 12 inches of the ground and new shoots from below soon replaced them. Woody stems which are not vigorous, because of age, winter injury, or any cause which checks growth, seldom develop or support good growth later on. Stems which remain half-dead might better be removed. Then, by good care, feeding and watering, or even moving to a better site, the plant should be encouraged to replace such wood by new vigorous growth. In such manner a non-vigorous plant may be rehabilitated, unless it is inherently unfit for the environment. Some plants growing under marginal conditions seem to require this cutting-back treatment. One should always try to keep Ghent and Mollis azaleas vigorous by cutting out senile wood and encouraging its replacement by new shoots from the ground. Mollis azaleas in eastern America seem to need this treatment; otherwise old wood, which is more tender in winter, dies and the plants dwindle. So keep the new wood coming. Cutting-back may also be used to restrain plants which have grown too large. Old plants collected in the wild should also be cut back and regrown.

Mixed plantings of large and small rhododendrons are practicable, as well as the use of other genera in a border with rhododendrons. Ericaceous plants are eminently suitable, because they enjoy rhododendron conditions. Herbaceous plants are usable, too. Large blue squills (*Scilla nonscripta*), as well as forget-me-nots (*Myosotis*), are used effectively with deciduous azaleas. *Lupinus perennis* occurs wild with *R. roseum*. *Mertensia virginica* makes an attractive azalea companion, too. Some lilies appear to enjoy rhododendron conditions. A list of possible ground cover materials appears on page 64.

Do not use the rake or hoe around rhododendrons or azaleas. Pull the weeds or cut them off, but do not stir the soil. More of these plants are ruined by tidy gardeners than die of neglect. Fine old specimens are suddenly ruined by new owners or ignorant plantsmen who rake away the mulch and expose to heat, cold, dryness, and mechanical injury the delicate feeding roots, which lie near the surface. Rhododendron roots are quite unlike those of roses, fruit trees and other common garden plants. Let the leafy mulch remain throughout the year. If oak leaves appear untidy or tend to blow off, use a layer of pine needles instead. Or you may conceal the mulch by a low hedge or edging around the rhododendron bed to hide and hold it.

GROUND COVERS AND LOW PLANTS FOR USE AMONG RHODODENDRONS AND AZALEAS

Ericaceous Plants *

Andromeda glaucophylla
Arctostaphylos uva-ursi
Calluna vulgaris
Chiogenes hispidula
Chimaphila maculata
Daboecia cantabrica
Epigaea repens
Erica (in variety)
Gaultheria procumbens
Gaylussacia brachycera

Ledum groenlandicum
Leiophyllum (in variety)
Leucothoë catesbaei
Leucothoë axillaris
Loiseleuria procumbens
Pieris floribunda
Rhodothamnus chamaecistus
Vaccinium (evergreen sorts)
Vaccinium angustifolium
Vaccinium vacillans

Non-ericaceous Woody Plants

Aronia arbutifolia
Chamaedaphne calyculata
Cornus canadensis
Cotoneaster horizontalis, etc.
Daphne cneorum
Euonymus radicans and *E. vegetus*
Galax aphylla
Hedera helix
Ilex glabra

Lonicera Henryi
Lycopodium (in variety)
Lysimachia nummularia
Mahonia (in variety)
Mitchella repens
Pachysandra terminalis
Pyxidanthera barbulata
Shortia galacifolia
Vinca minor

Herbs

Asarum canadense
Erythronium (in variety)
Goodyera pubescens
Hepatica triloba, etc.
Iberis sempervirens
Lilium (in variety)
Lupinus perennis

Mertensia virginica
Myosotis palustris
Orchids, hardy (in variety)
Parochetus communis (for California)
Thalictrum (in variety)
Trillium (in variety)
Viola (in variety)

Ferns

Many kinds available

* All ericaceous plants listed are evergreen except *Vaccinium angustifolium* and *V. vacillans*, which are deciduous.

CHAPTER VIII

THE CHOICER SORTS

GIVEN everything that proper site, soil and care can provide, there is yet another basic factor which determines success with rhododendrons. This is, the
kind of plant which is grown. The proper choice of clones, varieties and species
with reference to the climate in which they are to be grown is exactly as important as any other consideration. All of them are not "just rhododendrons";
even among common kinds, some are much better adapted to your situation
than others. No matter how good the other conditions, if a variety is entirely
unadapted to a certain climate, there is no use in trying to grow it there successfully.

It is not difficult to find the kinds of rhododendrons and azaleas which are
hardy in your region. Lists are available, some of which are included here.*
Then, too, the experiences of your neighbors should prove helpful in determining what to choose or avoid. The main thing is to recognize the need of a
guide in planting, rather than to plant indiscriminately—that is, if you live in
a cold region, for in a mild country much leeway is possible. There is considerable diversity in the hardiness of different varieties in a cold climate.

Taking the natural species, we may distinguish those which are exclusively
greenhouse plants, those which are tender outdoors, those which are perfectly
hardy in cold climates, and various other intermediate grades of hardiness in
between these extremes. Obviously, one does not expect a species from a warm
country to succeed outdoors in a cold climate. The natural habitat of a species,
then, gives us, at the outset, a rough guide to its hardiness. Coupled with horticultural experience, this knowledge provides a fair *a priori* means of telling
whether or not a given species can be expected to succeed in a given place.

With the hybrids, however, our judgment must be based solely upon horticultural experience. Of course, there are instances where, with the parentage
known, the hardiness of a hybrid can be predicted, but wherever there is a complicated ancestry with several species involved—and the common rhododendron

* See Chap. XXIV.

65

hybrids have such an ancestry—prediction is impossible. In most of these hybrid races we find all kinds of individuals, ranging through the whole scale of hardiness. We can make general statements concerning the hardiness of certain strains or races, based upon group averages, but individuals will constantly appear which depart widely from the average and may approach or even exceed the extremes of their progenitors in one direction or another. When we deal with hybrids, therefore, we need to know the hardiness of each particular individual or clone in a mixed race.

In many instances, the only sure way to ascertain the hardiness of a plant, either species or hybrid, is by its actual behavior under local growing conditions. Fortunately, horticultural experience has provided records of this to a very great extent.

Other considerations besides hardiness are also involved in any discussion of the choicer sorts. In compiling a classification it is necessary to give, instead of a single list, a series of lists of plants for various locations and purposes. What determines a good plant is its suitability, not in one character, but under a whole set of conditions.

The elements of personal taste, fashion and prejudice also enter into any discussion of a "best" group of plants. Tastes differ among persons, as well as between groups of people in different nations, different environments or separated by a gap of years. I am reminded of the statement made by a friend whose good taste and artistic judgment I hold in deep esteem. Said this friend recently, upon returning from a trip, "I saw a quantity of flowers of hybrid rhododendrons that seemed to me too hideous for sight, but they came of important parents and so were gushed over and even commended." Here, apparently, the sense of newness had run away with the judgment of those who thrilled over the novelties.*

In compiling lists of preferred kinds, I have been guided not solely by my own judgment nor by that of any other one person. I have taken, instead, data gathered from a variety of sources and am presenting it in tabular form as a series of lists.

Starting with the so-called "ironclad" clones of the evergreen rhododendron which are reliably hardy in New England and the northeastern United States, I present a list prepared in 1926 by the late Dr. E. H. Wilson from observations and data covering many years' experience at the Arnold Arboretum in Boston. A similar list had been previously prepared (1913) by Professor

---

* Every hybridist or introducer of new rhododendrons should paste in his hat the following motto, derived from the writings of Henry de Vilmorin, the celebrated French plant breeder: "The greatest virtue of a plant breeder is to be severe toward his own creations and not easily to become enthusiastic over their real or supposed merits."

Ralph W. Curtis. Since their publication, I have checked over these lists and rechecked them many times as I have traversed the colder portions of the country. At all times I have found them to be very reliable and consistently useful, and I can mostly concur that these represent the best time-honored clones for all-around usefulness in the sub-zero regions of the American Northeast. There are others probably just as hardy, and a few new sorts, which might be added to the list, but few that are superior for the climate and purpose. This list and others will be found in Chapter XXIV.

A few comments on individual clones might here be made. Perhaps the most meritorious red-flowered clone for this cold region is 'Mrs. Charles Sargent,' often known in the trade as 'Mrs. C. S. Sargent,' an old Waterer hybrid. This is hard to excel for size of flower, vigor and hardiness in the cold regions. My favorite among the older whites is the clone known as 'Catawbiense Album,' which may be a hybrid and not the true botanical variety of that name. I think it may be equalled, and perhaps surpassed, by a new clone derived directly from the wild and being introduced as 'La Bar's White,' not yet generally available. 'Roseum Elegans' and 'Lady Armstrong' are very attractive rose-colored clones, and 'Atrosanguineum' is deep red and valuable for its somewhat earlier blooming date. For early bloom as well as foreground planting, the somewhat lower-growing 'Boule de Neige' is a white clone without a peer among the hardy sorts, but suffers from lace-bug in summer if given full sun. For tall background effects and late bloom, the white Maximum hybrid 'Album Elegans' is highly suitable. 'Henrietta Sargent' has a flower almost identical with that of 'Mrs. Charles Sargent,' but is much more compact, slower growing and dwarfer in habit. 'Purpureum Grandiflorum' and 'Purpureum Elegans' are both very effective deep lilac-colored sorts, while 'Everestianum' is another good purplish-lavender clone with prominently yellow-spotted flowers and attractively frilled petals. Of course, the finest purple flower is that of 'Purple Splendour,' but this is not hardy enough to recommend in zero climates. So it is with many more of the newer kinds, mostly bred abroad, which have better colors than most of those mentioned here. Yet these old "ironclads" are by no means to be despised for they are husky, floriferous, nicely formed and excellent insofar as their range of colors goes. If I were asked to name the best six among these readily available sorts for cold climates, I would have difficulty in making the choice but would be tempted to include the following, about in the order named: 'Mrs. Charles Sargent,' 'Catawbiense Album,' 'Lady Armstrong,' 'Boule de Neige,' 'Atrosanguineum' and 'Everestianum.' I would wish to include 'Roseum Elegans' and 'Purpureum Grandiflorum' also, and I have seen 'Charles Dickens' equally good, but think it a slower grower than the rest. Some growers consider that 'Caractacus' should be added to this list.

Coming to the natural species for sub-zero regions, one may quickly eliminate several as not truly choice, and others which are imperfectly known. Among the real evergreen rhododendrons, *R. Smirnowii* is excellent if you get a good plant and not an inferior seedling. The wild forms of *R. catawbiense* are generally floriferous and may be considered excellent when used in places where their lilac-purple flowers will display their true beauty against green backgrounds, or with white, cream or yellow associations, rather than alongside brighter-colored reds and pinks which tend to make the purplish Catawbas look sad and dull by comparison. These same comments apply to ever so many other wild species of rhododendron in all succeeding categories which happen to have this wild anthocyanin lilac color, for this particular hue is by all odds the most common color in the genus.

Dealing further with *R. catawbiense,* we should note that this species not only is a parent of most of the old-time "ironclad" hybrids, but has a few interesting variations in its natural state, and some of these variants could be regarded as truly choice. Very rarely, it produces a white-flowered mutant, a botanical variety correctly called *R. catawbiense album* Waterer. Yet the original Waterer introduction under this name is really a clone tinged pink in the bud and perhaps a hybrid, because it is prone to produce purple-flowered seedlings, even in controlled crosses with other whites. Other white-flowered individuals have subsequently been found in the wild. During the 1930's the late Mr. Powell Glass of Lynchburg, Virginia, discovered a form in the Blue Ridge Mountains, which, though faintly pink in the bud, becomes pure white upon opening. In its seedling progeny, this has come to be known as 'Glass White,' and Mr. Gable has made some good crosses from it. More recently, a very superior white wild mutant, without a trace of pink, was found by Mr. Russell Harmon of La Bar's Nursery, and this is being propagated vegetatively as a clone under the name of 'La Bar's White.' It is recommended as a really choice white rhododendron of the "ironclad" class.

Rhododendron catawbiense also produces a variant race, from Mt. Mitchell, North Carolina, which is constantly dwarf, about three feet tall at maturity. This is highly recommended.

Rhododendron maximum would be better esteemed everywhere if its superior forms were more generally recognized and used. In America one sees quantities of its rather unvigorous and sometimes non-flowering plants brought in from the wild by collectors. Even when properly collected, cut back and regrown, many plants of this species, especially from its northern range, are inherently inferior to its better forms. Abroad it is practically unknown. Although it was the first rhododendron to be introduced there (1736), I doubt if an authentic plant of *R. maximum* is to be seen in England today. Actually, this species, in good examples, bears rounded, well-formed trusses of flowers nearly two inches across and of considerable beauty. Typically, it has pink buds and pink-tipped flowers, reminding one of apple blossoms, but it frequently is pure white. Its color is sprightly and free of the purplish cast of *R. cataw-biense,* but it is seldom as floriferous as this species. Opening late in the season, its flowers are often obscured by new leaf growth. *R. maximum* may almost always be identified by its elongated bract-like scales at the base of its buds. Its more vigorous forms grow in the Blue Ridge Mountains and southward. Certain individual plants, especially some excellent whites, are worthy of being propagated as clones and given "fancy" names. The way to obtain superior individuals is to select them in nurseries at blooming time. Impartially judged in comparison with many new and popular species, *R. maximum* in its best forms is still a very fine rhododendron.

Rhododendron brachycarpum is a little-known but desirable species from the Orient. It is hardy and is useful as a parent of hybrids.

The American *Rhododendron carolinianum,* a lepidote species, is smaller and earlier to bloom than either of the preceding. It is excellent for the American East. Its behavior in Britain, however, is disappointing. Its light purplish-pink color tends to vary in intensity from year to year with changes in ecological conditions, but its compact white form, var. *album,* which is relatively common, is more stable, and is considered by some to be superior to the species itself. An occasional faint tinge of yellow is sometimes seen in the bud or freshly opened flower (see color plate following page 78). A related species, *R. minus,* which, despite its name, is frequently much taller, blooms six weeks later.

Among the dwarfer sorts which may be regarded as "ironclad," the Alpine Rose hybrid clones 'Laetevirens' (syn. 'Wilsoni'), as well as 'Myrtifolium', are excellent compact plants, valuable for their foliage rather than for their flowers. One of greater floral value among the dwarfish species is *R. racemosum,* which is very desirable except that it may not be fully "ironclad."

Some deciduous azaleas will withstand much colder temperatures than any of the preceding evergreen rhododendrons, and in many sub-zero climates these, rather than the other species, should form the main basis of rhododendron culture. These deciduous American species have remained inadequately known and too faintly appreciated by growers in the cold regions of northeastern United States and eastern Canada. They might be used to great advantage in places where rhododendron growing is considered taboo because of cold winter temperatures.

Of these, the choicer sorts are the best forms of *Rhododendron roseum,* the diverse forms of *R. calendulaceum,* the strong-growing *R. Vaseyi* (including its white form, which is extra good), and such others as *R. arborescens* and

R. viscosum. Along with these, such Asiatic species as *R. japonicum* (near *R. molle*), and *R. Schlippenbachii* should be included. *R. mucronulatum,* a deciduous rhododendron from Korea, should be added where the weather remains cool enough in early spring to keep it from making too-early bloom; otherwise it may get nipped by late frosts. *R. poukhanense* (syn. *yedoense*) is the only azalea of the Obtusum subseries which can be regarded as winter-hardy to —20°F., but where the temperature does not regularly descend much lower than —10°F. (Boston and Rochester) the fine Japanese species *R. Kaempferi* is unexcelled. This latter is one of the truly choicest azaleas for moderately cold climates.

The Ghent and Mollis hybrid azaleas are of the greatest excellence for certain cold climates and, again, are not sufficiently recognized. My first choice rests with the Ghents, which, although smaller in flower size, are much more durable and frequently more showy. They all need adequate water during the early summer, but will endure severe winter temperatures if they have grown well in summer. They probably do better on their own roots than when grafted. The newer hybrids (such as the Knap Hill and Exbury strains) have much larger flowers, but involve the addition of other kinds in the hybrid complex and may not all be hardy enough for the coldest regions. Some appear hardy, however, and their future looks very bright. Some are magnificent and seem to be hardy in sub-zero climates.

Turning to somewhat milder climates in America, such as those near water on the New England coast where boxwood will survive, we may extend all of the above lists considerably. In this grouping we would include the metropolitan regions of New York City and Philadelphia, plus the state of New Jersey and comparable climates elsewhere. Here the winter temperature may occasionally touch zero, but does not linger there. The preferences noted above, including the "ironclad" list, still maintain good status. One may now add several more of the old Waterer-hybrid type of rhododendrons to the preferred list, although few will actually be superior to the ones already mentioned, except as they may extend the season of bloom or bring in additional color patterns. There is room here, however, for the testing of several *A*-hardy clones of British origin and especially some new hybrid races, such as the American Dexter hybrid rhododendrons of the Fortunei series. These latter are now mostly unnamed and unavailable except as mixed seedlings of varying merit, but will undoubtedly have great effect upon the future of rhododendron growing in these regions, since they are equal in appearance to many of the best-regarded hybrids in existence. They still need richer colors and more winter-resistance, especially among their yellow-tinged sorts; also, too many have floppy trusses and a too-open habit of growth. But excellent individuals are being found for introduction as clones and more will surely follow. It is important to choose only the best and avoid ordinary Dexter seedlings.

In the matter of species, there are a number of new ones which may be included in addition to those recommended for the colder areas. A considerable list could be compiled of those species which some people think may survive temperatures to 10 or 15 degrees below zero. Of the unfamiliar sorts, such a list would comprise a dozen Lapponicums, five members of the Taliense series, and one or two members each of a dozen other series in addition to those already in use. The question which arises here is: How good are they?

Perhaps all rhododendrons are good when compared with the rank and file of woody plants in other genera. But when compared with one another—and there are some 900 species—some are certainly better than the rest. When reading the description of almost any rhododendron species that is unknown to you, it is easy to build up a fanciful picture of its possibilities. Collectors, especially, are prone to become enamoured of new names, and unless the new thing is really quite inferior it has been possible, in the past, to find committees who will recommend merit stars for it. After much labor and waiting, you may finally discover that the new species is just another purplish flower, good enough perhaps, but no better than the old reliable "ironclad" that you have known for years. Yet there are certain superior species, and within species, otherwise mediocre, there may be superior individuals. And what is superior elsewhere may not be so good in your climate. As time goes on, only the superior sorts, in the sense of being well-fitted to the purpose, will remain in cultivation. And these, in many instances, will be selected clones and not just ordinary seedlings. This is particularly true within groups of borderline hardiness, where only an exceptional variant will be able permanently to endure a given climate.

Of those on the list, *Rhododendron auriculatum* is a fine, white lily-like thing that blooms in August, after you have waited for twelve or fifteen years for the first flower. *R. caloxanthum*, which makes a three-foot plant with light yellow flowers, will be very worthwhile if hardy in this region, but it is not sufficiently tried to be recommended generally. *R. Keiskei* delights some people with its very light yellow, smallish, azalea-like flowers, while others consider it too inconspicuous to be good either as a rhododendron or as an azalea. *R. racemosum* does better here than in the colder zone; it is praised as a dwarfish plant with pink flowers. *R. russatum* is perhaps the best garden species in the Lapponicum series, and if it should prove reliable here, it will be excellent to plant in masses for covering slopes. Its best color forms produce an effect of blue-violet, thicker and a bit dwarfer than a Kurume azalea and with smaller flowers, but covered with bloom. As a rock garden subject, *R. campylogynum* is interesting but not spectacular. It makes a thick, mound-like little plant, a foot or so in height, with sparse, nodding flowers curiously unlike a rhododendron. If you wish to experiment in warmer spots with additional species of exotic rhododendrons, there are many that are better than these, but adapted for regions slightly warmer in winter.

In the azalea list, there is a wealth of material, mostly clones, for this region where boxwood will survive. A vast array of Japanese azaleas is available, along with hybrids of the Obtusum subseries, and since they all propagate readily from cuttings these kinds are easily obtained. There are literally hundreds of worthwhile azaleas that will thrive from Cape Cod to the Lower South, mostly evergreen or semi-evergreen. In the United States, the greatest azalea-breeding project in history has been conducted under government auspices by Mr. Benjamin Y. Morrison, who has introduced over 400 clones of Glenn Dale azaleas, originating near Washington, D.C. It is too soon for an accurate appraisal of the choicer sorts for each locality, but it can be said that Morrison has produced outdoor-growing garden azaleas equal in excellence of bloom to good greenhouse or florists' sorts.

Besides the Glenn Dales, which seem to encompass almost everything, there are the time-honored Kaempferi and Kurume hybrids, the various forms of *R. mucronatum* and a galaxy of other things. These all seem well suited to that portion of America where winter temperatures do not often descend to the zero mark. There is no telling how far their range might be extended if they were planted in warmish spots and given special protection. There are so many good azaleas in this class, and so much depends upon personal taste, that I consider it fairly hopeless to attempt any evaluation of clones as to individual excellence. Besides, more are being introduced every year and the "best" ones of today are replaced by those of tomorrow. The fact that they are now being used lavishly in the parks and gardens of the American East Coast and southward to create spectacular effects is bound to bring the best azaleas to public attention and give everyone a chance to evaluate them on his own behalf. Abroad they are less common, the only considerable planting in England being the very broad plantation of Kurume azaleas in Windsor Great Park.

As for the natural species of azalea, in addition to the list given for sub-zero temperatures which is still valid for this warmer zone, we may now add *R. mucronatum* and *R. pentaphyllum,* both of which are fine things. *R. atlanticum* is native to a part of this region and has considerable value. And there are the several species that have gone into the new hybrids, all allied with the Obtusum subseries.

Proceeding now to milder regions south of Philadelphia and including Maryland, Virginia and the Southern Highlands, we encounter climatic conditions where the useful species and hybrids may be presumed to coincide with some of those recommended for Great Britain, Holland and the American West Coast. In the American East, however, we have to reckon with hot summer temperatures—something not encountered in the other territories mentioned. This seriously handicaps most evergreen rhododendrons along the seaboard south of Baltimore, except where the severity of the summer heat is mitigated by water or other local conditions. However, this does not bother the Obtusum azaleas too much.

Inland, especially in or near the mountains where summer conditions are cooler and more moist, the natural conditions for native species are at their optimum and this is the habitat of the best American kinds. It may be expected that around western North Carolina and southward to the Great Smoky Mountains, spots can be found where many more kinds of British and Asiatic hybrids and species might be grown than are presently found there in cultivation. This area, therefore, is one of potential development, and experiments with new materials are justified. In this area one could speculate with such fine subjects as 'Britannia,' 'Betty Wormald,' 'Cynthia,' 'Mars' and a few others of *A* or *B* hardiness (British rating), and with a number of species. There is presently very little data on these for the American East, but there are instances of success near Baltimore and in the Virginia piedmont.

In the American Lower South, the Oriental azaleas reach their greatest glory, while the true rhododendrons diminish to the vanishing point, except in higher altitudes. Most spectacular are the large-growing Indian azaleas of old Belgian origin, derived from several species, among which *R. Simsii, R. phoeniceum* and *R. mucronatum* are included. Other kinds, grown under glass in the North, are satisfactory garden subjects in this area. This includes Kurume azaleas and a number of other races. A few native species of less showy character, wild in the Southeast, are also adapted to this situation, but ordinary evergreen rhododendrons, with the possible exception of *R. Chapmanii* from Florida, do not flourish at low elevations. It might be worth-while, however, to experiment there with Malayan and tropical species under shade.

In the American Pacific Northwest most of the British hybrids and Asiatic species will succeed admirably. From northern California, through Oregon and Washington along the coast to British Columbia, the climate and soil is as satisfactory for these plants as any that may be found anywhere. Except for the tender kinds, such as those of the Maddenii series and others which will grow at San Francisco but not in Oregon, one may expect success with the hybrids, both commercial and fancy, now growing in Great Britain, Holland and Germany, as well as with the popular kinds of Chinese and Himalayan species. This embraces an enormous list of possibilities, most of them much better than the "ironclad" list for the Northeast.

In Great Britain one has to differentiate between the rather lush conditions of the South and West and the more rigorous, and sometimes calcareous conditions of the East. There are the warm, sheltered gardens and the more exposed gardens. The insular climate of the British Isles differs sharply from the continental climates elsewhere. Late spring frosts are treacherous in Britain and may occur in mid-May, so that hardiness is sometimes reckoned with reference to late spring development more than to minimum winter temperature-resistance. But much of Britain is admirably suited for rhododendrons and they have been grown there in cultivation for so long that British experience and data on the subject are voluminous. Therefore, one may safely rely upon the determinations made by the Royal Horticultural Society as to how the various species and hybrids fit into the different conditions of temperature, exposure and site. A number of the old Waterer hybrids are still very good and to be recommended for difficult places, because of their universal reliability. Besides these, many of the later commercial sorts are to be especially pointed out as valuable for a good show of flowers and vigorous growth, in contrast to some of the fanciers' sorts which may be unique but lacking in certain of these characters. There are hundreds of species and clones meriting special distinction, and no special effort will be made here to choose a few that may be best. Some consideration will be given, however, to the personal tastes by listing here the published favorites of a couple of British authorities on the subject whose preferences differ radically. Since experience with new things alters original conceptions, the reader is advised to keep abreast of current changes by consulting the publications of rhododendron organizations in his own region. In Britain the *Rhododendron Handbook* issued every few years by the Royal Horticultural Society is a better guide than most reference works, since it undergoes periodic revision and considerable changes are made in ratings from time to time.

In Holland and in adjacent parts of Western Germany, climatic conditions are not so mild as those in Cornwall or western Scotland, the favored parts of Britain. But the Dutch and German (Oldenberg) hardiness ratings vary only slightly from those of the British. While these ratings might serve for the American Southern Highlands region, too, the British and Continental hardiness and merit ratings must be regarded as entirely unreliable when applied to the American East. Also in Eastern Germany, as around Dresden, the climate is more severe and a different set of recommendations is given.

As intimated above, when it comes to determining the choicer sorts from a list so extensive as that available for Great Britain, or even the Dutch and

German lists, it becomes a matter of personal taste in picking out a few. A listing similar to that of the British is presently being prepared by the American Rhododendron Society, and other pertinent data are published for Germany in the Yearbook of the Deutsche Rhododendron Gesellschaft in Bremen. These are prepared by committees. It is anticipated that the new international registry will eventually serve the purposes of all.

One sometimes hears conflicting testimony regarding the merits of different kinds of rhododendrons, because tastes vary and some points are subject to controversy. Although one may hear arguments pro and con, there is no validity to the claim that natural species are superior to hybrid plants or vice versa. Good individuals are good, no matter where they occur, and it is largely a matter of how and where the plants are to be used, along with the personal preferences or prejudices of the talker or writer, that actually determines their merit. It may be said of nearly all rhododendron species or seedlings that they are mixed populations where the average or "run-of-the-mill" seldom equals the quality of a highly selected specimen when it comes to real excellence. Certainly, I have seen plants of pure natural species that are as fine in most respects as some of the best hybrids. But such are almost invariably superior individuals selected out of a group of less-valuable seedlings. Hybrids, also, are similarly picked from scores or even hundreds of competitors. In my opinion any outstanding plant, whether of wild or hybrid origin, if worthy of special distinction, should be separated from the common herd, given a special cultivar name and propagated vegetatively as a clone. Once in this category, it matters not a whit whether the plant exemplifies nature's wild product or the effort of some plant breeder.

In judging the horticultural value of any rhododendrons, much depends upon how well they are chosen for the purpose in which they are to be used. There are certain places where small, sparse or unselected plants fit well into a naturalistic setting. Hybrids have their special uses, too. Some hybrids have magnificent flowers, but a frightful habit of growth. Others are fanciers' pets, good mainly in a flower show, but unhardy, unthrifty, sparse or unbeautiful otherwise.

By and large, the better rhododendron for showiness and reliability is the commercial hybrid. I agree that it is often more hardy, more floriferous, more cosmopolitan and more thrifty than most unselected species. Yet, even today, some of the more prized and highly starred fanciers' sorts, both hybrids and species, are entirely unsuited for growing outdoors except within a very narrow climatic range where very special conditions prevail. No such plant could be a commercial success. Yet such fanciers' rhododendrons have a definite place and purpose. After all, the main thing in evaluating the horticultural worth of any rhododendron is that it be thrifty, good looking and well adapted to the use for which it is intended at the place where it is grown.

A few recommended lists, set up especially for definite geographical areas, are presented in Chapter XXIV. The author has not wished to make recommendations except on the basis of prolonged and critical observation and also with reference to the tastes of different people. Consequently he has drawn upon the advice or published writings of others for some of the data presented herewith. In every such instance, the source is given.

CHAPTER IX

HARDINESS *

SOME readers will have no occasion to consider the question of hardiness. I do not wish to burden those who already grow rhododendrons easily with details which might make the consideration of rhododendrons seem difficult or irksome, so all are hereby warned that they may skip this chapter, unless they are interested in the theoretical aspects of the subject. There are others, living in less favored climes, however, to whom the matter of hardiness will seem the sole determiner of success or failure with rhododendrons. It is for these latter that this chapter is written.

In most discussions of the subject of hardiness in plants, particularly among amateurs, a certain amount of time is always wasted and misconceptions engendered by the failure of the discussants to recognize certain basic facts underlying the subject. My purpose in writing this chapter, therefore, is to bring out a few of these underlying points in order to clarify some phases, at least, of the problem and furnish a groundwork for intelligent observation. I shall not attempt to solve the problems involved (for who, indeed, can do it?), and shall endeavor to avoid technicalities in so far as it is possible.

Perhaps nothing in plant science is more elusive than the question of hardiness. It is not a simple quality that can be tied down to one thing, described definitely and then dismissed in an off-hand manner. It consists, rather, in the successful balancing of a set of inter-related conditions, the cumulative effect of which is to make for either success or failure in the life of the plant. Many of its phases still defy scientific investigation, and theories change as, from time to time, new facts are unearthed. We can not speak of hardiness, therefore, with any degree of finality. We can only point out certain known features along the road and trust, thereby, to avoid some of the pitfalls.

What the gardener wants to know is how he can make plants live outdoors with no special fuss. He knows the outdoor performance records of some of

* A considerable amount of further material on hardiness is included in Chapter XXIV. Also see table on p. 230.

his plants. Perhaps there are others, and better ones, which are just outside his grasp. How can he bring them through?

In the first place, he should define hardiness and know what he is talking about when he uses the word. There are several kinds of hardiness: resistance to winter cold, to drought, to disease, to exposure of various kinds—in general, the ability of a plant to adapt itself to its environment. In common practice, if a plant fails to start growth in the spring, the gardener says that it died during the winter and that its death was due to "winter-killing." This, at least, is a common practice in the north. Winter-hardiness, therefore, is the term commonly implied when gardeners in cold regions speak of hardiness, for most plants which die in those localities do so in the winter.*

Now, when a plant dies there are certain things that we should always investigate before we condemn such a plant for tenderness. We ought to find out, if we can, exactly what caused its death. This may be a simple matter or not, as the case happens; sometimes it will be impossible. Let us consider some of the factors that might be involved.

First, the possibility of disease. In rhododendrons, this is a serious factor only in very young plants, but, among plants in general, more than a few of the failures ascribed to tenderness are nothing but cases of disease, in which the winter-hardiness of the plant had no part whatever. Fungus diseases, especially, run rampant during the cool, moist weather of autumn and spring, and the subsequent death of plants, occurring during the dormant period, is too easily and carelessly laid at the door of "winter-killing." Seedlings over-wintering in coldframes are sometimes seriously affected by disease, but, as I mentioned, it seldom is a factor in rhododendron or azalea plants which have reached blooming size. The fact that some diseases are inconspicuous, being no more than a rotten spot on the base of the stem, leads to the misconception that winter-tenderness caused the death.

Similar, but slightly more obvious, is the effect of injury from insect attack. Such injuries, occurring during the autumn or winter, may easily be mistaken for deaths due to winter cold. Grubs, working in the soil, may injure the underground portions and cause death without mutilation of the visible parts of the plant. So, also, the attacks of borers. Small, sucking insects, such as thrips, mealy-bugs and so forth, can produce injuries which will kill a plant without the serious mutilation of its visible parts. Again, these injuries are mostly confined to young plants in the nursery.

Poor growing conditions or unfavorable soil relations can cause the death

* As noted in Chapter XXIV and elsewhere, "hardiness" in Britain often means bud-resistance to late spring frosts. Hardiness must also be interpreted with reference to local sites as well as to broader geographical areas.

Catawba Hybrid 'Mrs. Charles S. Sargent'

Rhododendron maximum

Rhododendron japonicum var. aureum

Rhododendron carolinianum var. foliatum

Rhododendron arborescens var. rubescens

Catawba Hybrid 'Catawbiense Album'

Rhododendron viscosum

Rhododendron Hybrids

of a plant at any time. Plants weakened by unthrifty growth during the summer may be rendered susceptible to winter injury when, inherently, there is nothing actually tender about their constitution or that of the race to which they belong.

This brings up the physiological aspects of hardiness and tenderness. In discussing this subject, we should first take note of the fundamental processes that are going on within the plant itself. These are the vital phenomena of growth and nutrition which must constantly proceed if life is to be sustained.

The layman hears a great deal about how fertilizers aid plant growth, but he seldom hears anything like this said about sugars. He would not think of putting sugar on his plants to make them grow; this, truly, would be ridiculous! Yet, sugar plays an important rôle in the growth of all plants. Sugars and starches (collectively called the carbohydrates) are the very staff of life to plants. Like humans, plants get most of their energy and do all their work through sugars, starches, fats and proteins. Their tissues are largely composed of carbohydrates (35–45%), only 5% being made up of the minerals which they obtain from the soil and which you apply as fertilizers. The remainder of the plant is made of water (50–60%). Carbohydrates and water are, therefore, the main components of a living plant.

Animals differ from plants in that the animals have to eat their carbohydrates ready-made, while the green plants possess the power of manufacturing their own carbohydrates. The green cells of the plants are little factories where this manufacturing process takes place. Under the influence of light, carbon dioxide from the atmosphere enters the leaves through minute holes called stomates and gets into the cells where it is dissolved in water and made into a sugar solution by a chemical process called *photosynthesis*. With this sugar solution as a basis, starches, cellulose colloidal derivatives and other cell-building materials are formed and can be translocated to other parts of the plant through the action of a special kind of conduit system which permits of the movement of water and foodstuffs from one place to another within the plant. It is through this same system that water and mineral salts move upward from the roots.

With this in mind, one can readily discern that water is exceedingly necessary in the growth of a plant. Great quantities are constantly being used as a solvent, as a medium of transportation, as a cooling medium in warm weather, and for other purposes. Light is also a factor, since photosynthesis can only proceed under its influence. Temperature, likewise, is involved, since the vital processes, like chemical reactions, are directly affected by heat and cold.

Enormous amounts of water are constantly passing through a living plant

---

Rhododendron Hybrids Illustrated Opposite: 1. 'Mrs. Ashley Slocock' 2. 'Tan' 3. 'Mariloo' 4. 'Betty Wormald' 5. 'Everestianum' 6. 'Sappho' 7. 'Purple Splendour' 8. 'Britannia' 9. 'Keay Slocock'

when it is in active growth and some even when it is dormant. Just as carbon dioxide is taken in through the small stomates in the leaves, so water is passing out through them; in the form of vapor, of course. The stomates act like little chimneys, which constantly draw the water vapor out of the plant tissues. They have the power of opening and closing automatically under certain stimuli. The amount of water lost by a plant is amazing. No figures for rhododendrons are available, but it has been estimated that one 25-year-old apple tree will lose one gallon of water per minute during a sunny day. The stomates are mostly located on the under side of the leaves. A stream of water, so to speak, is thus constantly passing through the plant, from roots to leaves and out, whenever the stomates are open and active. This loss of water as vapor through the stomates is called *transpiration*.

Plants outdoors, although nominally dormant, are far from lifeless in the winter. This is especially true of the evergreens. Dr. Raymond Wallace * has measured photosynthesis in evergreens during the winter and finds them very active, even at temperatures far below that of frost. He has not yet measured the activity of rhododendron leaves, but in *Kalmia* he finds photosynthesis proceeding normally down to only a few degrees above zero Fahrenheit. Whether or not this is important in the consideration of hardiness remains to be seen.

These experiments, and others, indicate that, although plants are not in active growth, at least insofar as appearances go, they are nevertheless doing a number of things during the cold months. If they are manufacturing sugars, taking up water and losing water, all of these activities may bear relationships to their hardiness. There are so many things yet to be learned that it seems dangerous to theorize. It is worth while to remember their possibilities, however, and to recall again that the quality of hardiness may be affected by one or several factors.

Let us consider the water relations of a rhododendron in winter. Cold air has a drying effect—it is desiccating. This alone would tend to withdraw water from the plant tissues, thus, if proceeding too far, drying out the cells to the point of injury. Coupled with this is the effect of wind, in which every stomate acts like a chimney and the loss of water is especially rapid. If the ground water be frozen, it is probably difficult for a plant to replenish the supply of water lost from its tissues, and thus the danger of death or injury from drying is imminent. I do not doubt that much winter injury is due to this drying out of the tissues, where the actual freezing of cells is not concerned at all. Associated with this withdrawal of water from the plant tissues during low

* Wallace, Raymond H. The photosynthetic activity of evergreens in winter. Paper presented before the Ecological Soc. of America, Amer. Assn. Adv. Science, Dec. 30, 1932.

temperatures are certain physio-chemical changes which may be of profound significance.*

The winter leaf movements of many of the evergreen rhododendrons furnish interesting evidence of the physiological activity which goes on in these plants during the cold weather. Under the stimulus of cold temperature (20°F. or lower), the leaves curl up and hang close to the stems, rolling themselves tightly inward, thus leaving only the upper surface exposed. The leaf petioles bend downward also, bringing the leaves close to the stems, with their tips pointing downward instead of outward. Whenever the temperature rises, the leaves uncurl, the petioles unbend and the leaves resume a normal, horizontal position. Take a curled-up leaf into a warm room and it will uncurl, before your eyes, in a few moments. This phenomenon, formerly called thermotropism or thermonasty, was investigated in 1899 by the late Professor J. W. Harshberger † who concluded that the leaf movements were probably brought about by translocations of water within the leaf tissues in response to temperature changes. Professor Harshberger observed that the probable value of the thermotropic movements to the rhododendron plant lies in the conservation of internal water from loss through transpiration. Thus, according to Professor Harshberger's theoretical conception, the plant protects itself against winter weather by curling its leaves.

The fact that the curling of the leaves may, in some instances, be a factor in protecting the plant from winter injury seems borne out by subsequent observations.‡ *Rhododendron ponticum* is notoriously tender in the eastern United States at New York and northward. Observing a mixed planting of *R. ponticum* and hardy Catawba hybrids in cold weather, it was noted that, on cold mornings when all the hardy rhododendrons showed pronounced curling of the leaves, *R. ponticum* showed no response to the cold whatever, the leaf blades remaining fully open and flung out broadly in their summer position. In the spring, brown necrotic lesions (dead areas), characteristic of winter injury,

---

* Not only is water lost through atmospheric dryness, but, at low temperatures, proteins are thrown out of the cell solution and water is withdrawn from the protoplasm, forming ice crystals within the cells or in the intercellular spaces. This injury is associated with the withdrawal of water. "Hardening-off" increases the amount of water remaining unfrozen and prevents the disintegration of the protoplasm. Some authorities consider that the presence of increased sugar prevents the precipitation of proteins and makes the protoplasm more retentive of water, thus markedly increasing the hardiness of the plant. The ability of the plant to produce colloidal materials which hold the water against freezing is doubtless an important consideration in determining its hardiness.

† Harshberger, J. W. Thermotropic movement in the leaves of Rhododendron maximum. Proc. Acad. Nat. Sci. Philadelphia, pp. 219–224. 1899.

‡ Bowers C. G. Thermotropism and tenderness in Rhododendron ponticum. Florists Exchange 78(15):31. 1 fig. Dec. 12, 1931.

appeared around the margins of the leaves of *R. ponticum,* giving unmistakable evidence of their inability to withstand low temperatures. The hardy hybrids, some growing upon the identical *ponticum* roots from which suckers with badly injured leaves arose, were entirely uninjured. The inference is plain that the curling of leaves is a protective process and that *R. ponticum* was injured because it did not respond.*

Still more recently a Japanese scientist, working on *Rhododendron micranthum* in Manchuria, made some detailed investigations on their winter leaf movements which, he says, are due primarily to translocations of water and, hence, are properly hygronastic rather than thermotropic in nature.† He maintains that wind and atmospheric moisture have little effect upon the movement which, as noted above, is mainly a protective action against mechanical rupture due to freezing and against desiccation at low temperatures.

Besides the direct effect of water relations upon winter hardiness of rhododendrons, the amount of sugar in the cells doubtless exerts a great influence. It has been demonstrated that a fairly high concentration of sugar in the cell solution of other plants induces resistance to cold in several ways. One of these is in its beneficial effect in making the protoplasm more retentive of water. Then, too, as water is removed from the cells to form ice in the intercellular spaces, the remaining sugar becomes more concentrated and, hence, increasingly effective in preventing freezing. The dissolved sugar depresses the freezing point of the cell contents, working in much the same manner that alcohol, glycerine or honey does when it prevents freezing of the radiator solution in an automobile at low temperatures. The more concentrated the sugar solution, the lower temperature it will withstand without freezing. The "hardening off" of plants in the autumn is characterized by an increase in the sugar concentration within the plant cells and is, as we shall see later, a matter of probable

* It should, by no means, be inferred that the lack of thermotropic response, although associated with tenderness in *R. ponticum,* is a universal cause or evidence of tenderness in rhododendrons or other broad-leaved evergreens. Certain very hardy species, such as *Kalmia,* show little or no curling of the leaves. Conversely, many rhododendrons which are quite tender show marked leaf curling in response to cold temperatures. Obviously, this phenomenon is only one of many factors which may, at times, have a bearing upon hardiness.

† Fukuda, Yasona. Hygronastic curling and uncurling movement of the leaves of *Rhododendron micranthum* with respect to temperature and resistance to cold. Japanese Journal of Botany 6:191–224. 14 figs. Tokyo, 1932.—Spongy parenchymatous tissues beneath the leaves form a framework which easily broadens or narrows with gain or loss in turgidity. This change in the size of the cells is due to the swelling or contracting of the plasma and may be stopped by anæsthesia. Water thrown out of a cell in which the plasma membrane has contracted may flow into the veins and intercellular spaces, allowing the cell to change its size and shape, which, in turn, causes the leaf to curl. The more concentrated the cell sap, the more easily the leaves will curl, so that in winter, when the sap is concentrated, curling takes place much more readily than in summer when the sap is dilute. Plants vary in the ability of their plasmic membranes to contract in response to cold temperature, so that this feature, as much as the actual leaf curling, may be a factor influencing hardiness.

importance. Just how well these general principles apply to rhododendrons has probably not yet been fully worked out.

Most important is the tendency for starch to change to sugar, and vice versa, when the temperature drops or rises. We have mentioned the importance of these physio-chemical changes, which probably, after all, are the most fundamental factors in questions of hardiness. The capacity of a plant to adapt itself to cold is doubtless mainly an inherent quality.

Any rhododendron should be properly ripened in the fall before it is permitted to go through the winter outdoors in a cold climate. New growth is full of water, with a very low concentration of sugars and colloids. Hence, new growth freezes easily. Plants develop soft tissues quickly as soon as growth starts in the spring when, with plenty of water and stored-up carbohydrates available, they first burst forth into activity. Gradually, as summer approaches, this growth slows down, new leaves become mature and function as sugar manufactories, the sugar solution (and other materials making up the material within the cells) becomes more concentrated and the wood becomes hard. By the end of the summer, growth has entirely ceased (except in greenhouses or in mild climates) and the plants enter their resting period, becoming practically dormant as cold weather approaches. This slowing up of growth is greatly influenced by the gradual decrease in available water during the summer months. In warm weather, both the atmosphere and the soil are much drier than in the spring. The sun is still high and photosynthesis goes on with even greater production of sugars than in the spring, for new leaves are now functioning. Due largely to an insufficiency of water (if the plants are kept "on the dry side" in late summer), new tissues are not built, so the sugar accumulates. Thus, the plant enters its resting period well furnished with hard wood and concentrated sugars and other carbohydrates to withstand the rigors of winter.

Active growth late in the summer not only means that the new, young tissues will probably be frozen during the ensuing winter but also indicates a lowered sugar concentration throughout the whole plant. Hence, in cold climates it is well to see that active growth stops by midsummer and is not resumed until the following spring. If the plant is supplied with an unusual amount of water or fertilizers during the summer months when it would normally be "hardening off," the active, vegetative condition of growth is prolonged into the late summer and autumn. In cold climates, therefore, it is usually unwise to irrigate rhododendrons during the late summer and earliest autumn beyond their absolute requirements for maintenance. Where a mulch is used, no artificial watering is usually necessary except in the event of serious drought. An exception to this rule may be found, perhaps, in the Ghent azaleas, which seem to require summer watering. Otherwise, rhododendron plants should be kept "on the dry side" from the first of August until after the first hard frost. After this frost, however, and before freezing weather sets in, all rhododendrons and azaleas should, and must, be watered copiously to insure that the soil becomes thoroughly moist before the plants enter the winter. At this late season, the weather is so cool and the plants are so fully in their resting state that there is no danger of new growth starting. Considerable importance is attached to this late autumn watering by experienced rhododendron growers. Mr. Dexter reports that his plants which were very thoroughly watered just before freezing weather set in, passed through the severe winter of 1934 with much less damage than those other plants which he did not especially irrigate. His observations include several American and Asiatic species, so that the general benefits of this practice would seem established.*

The minimum cold temperature for flower bud survival is not a definite figure. Twenty degrees below zero finds all the flower buds dead on *R. catawbiense, R. maximum,* and hybrids in southern New York State. Yet in northern New York, near Saranac, and in northern New England, authentic records show that it may be −30°F. (and some say −40°F.) *on the plant* without flower bud injury. It is supposed that ripening-off in the fall is completed early in the North because of short days and steady, cold air, while farther south intermittent warm days in late autumn keep the plants active. Damage often occurs in late November and December, before ripening is complete.

The value of a good mulch is hardly to be overestimated in winter. Rhododendron rootlets are delicate and are located very near the surface of the soil The soil around them is generally well aerated. Violent changes or extremes of temperature, alternate freezing and thawing, the drying effect of cold air and wind, as well as other atmospheric conditions, might easily penetrate to the roots of a rhododendron which is not protected by a mulch. A hard frozen soil, too, might be relatively impervious to the free water which becomes available during winter thaws, when, with temporary warmish weather, it is supposed that most evergreen plants become somewhat active and require such water. Besides all its other values, such as exist during the growing season, a fairly heavy oak-leaf mulch, applied late in the autumn, is a wonderful protection to rhododendrons in winter, being a valuable insulating medium against both heat and cold as well as a reservoir of moisture.

The age of a rhododendron plant has something to do with its hardiness. If the plant be five or six years old, it has perhaps reached a point where its true hardiness may be accurately judged, but if younger than this it may be subject to winter injury because of its youth, even though it be of a hardy variety or

* See Nearing, G. G. Wintering tender rhododendrons in the northeast. Quar. Bull. Amer. Rhod. Soc. 8:39–41. 1954.

species. All rhododendrons, and especially azaleas—even the hardiest—are tender when very young. As they become larger and develop more woody tissues, they become more resistant to cold and drought. A plant quite tender at one or two years may be perfectly hardy after it becomes four or five years old. A common mistake, I believe, in the testing of new species is to expose the plants to harsh conditions at too young an age to allow of a fair estimate being made.

A certain type of tenderness is associated with old plants or those which are not in a vigorous condition. Such plants, sometimes collected specimens which were not cut back and re-grown in the nursery, may start dying at the top. This may occur at any season, but is noticeable especially in the spring after a severe winter. All the old wood above the base may die or, in other cases, none may die but all may be unthrifty. Such a condition seems associated with the inability of the inactive tissues, especially those of the old, woody main stem, to resume active vigor and deliver the needed water and nutrients for the support of vegetative growth further up. Such old tissues are probably so lignified and otherwise so constricted that they are physically incapable of admitting the passage of enough liquid material to support active top-growth. Moreover, the vascular cells of slowly growing, half-starved plants, never having had to transport large quantities of material, are probably not built to accommodate rapid or luxuriant growth. Perhaps the best remedy for this condition is to remove the unthrifty wood by cutting the plant back almost to the base and allowing new shoots to start from the ground, replacing the old stem with vigorous new ones.

That the vigorous stems are hardier than the inactive ones seems to be well established by observation. This might seem to contradict the statement previously made that the young, rapidly growing tissues are tender. But there is no contradiction, because the youngest tissues are of very soft structure, while the vigorous stems of mature plants are well hardened before winter but very active in the growing season. The inability of inactive or unthrifty plants to withstand severe winter cold was strikingly demonstrated during the phenomenal winter of 1933–1934, when temperatures in the northeastern United States dropped to unheard of low points. Many thriftless plants were killed to the ground, and inactive branches on other plants were likewise killed, while vigorous plants or actively growing branches withstood the winter temperatures much better. Temperatures in the author's garden went as low as 35° below zero Fahrenheit, at which practically all flower buds, except those on the azaleas, were killed and many of the hardy evergreen seedlings reduced to the ground. Such temperatures are below the normal range of even the hardiest species, but the unthrifty plants suffered the most. The flower bud appears to be the part first injured by the cold. As for the woody parts, these would seem to follow the course indicated for certain other woody plants whose response to cold temperatures has recently been investigated. The results in those cases showed that the heartwood is first injured and that the cambium, at the periphery of the stem, is affected last. So many considerations enter the subject that it seems idle to speculate upon probable causes until we possess more definite scientific knowledge. Superficially, it seems reasonable to assume that a plant which has a poor root system, whose vital processes are not functioning well or whose vegetative vigor has been drained by the overproduction of bloom, insect attacks, disease organisms or other inhibiting agencies, is ill equipped to perform the physical and chemical work needed to get it through a severe winter. An ailing plant will often hang on to life through the growing season—or through several seasons—to die finally during the winter, for rhododendrons are slow to die and often need the shock of winter to kill them ultimately. On the other hand, the normal slow growth, characteristic of some varieties and some environments, does not predispose a plant to winter injury.

Although the temperatures went to 20 degrees below zero in Mr. Dexter's Cape Cod garden in 1934, many of his plants belonging to species elsewhere considered rather tender survived the ordeal. Of course, flower bud injury was prevalent. Many factors enter such a situation, but in Mr. Dexter's case there are several which appear significant. The great vigor of his plants (which he feeds liberally, but never fertilizes after May), the careful watering in late autumn, adequate mulching, protection from sweeping winds, shade from the winter sun, avoidance of cold air "pockets" and drafts, and possible local climatic advantages (such as slowness of temperature drops) probably all combined to the advantage of the plants. A notable factor was the importance of immediate site. Sometimes a distance of only ten feet, as it influenced exposure or air currents, was sufficient to spell success or failure in the life of a half-hardy or fastidious species. The periodic occurrence of warmish days during the winter, at which times absorption of water from the soil is possible, may also have been a factor.* Extreme fluctuations of temperature within a short period (a week) are always dangerous to plants.

Summer conditions constitute another cause of failure which is sometimes erroneously laid at the door of winter tenderness. I have noted that the "dwindling" of the Ghent and Mollis azaleas seems to be mainly caused by summer

---

* It is questionable if one or two very cold days, say −20°F. in a climate where the temperature seldom goes below zero, is a reliable test of hardiness at that minimum temperature. Long continued cold, or even two successive years of abnormally low temperature, is probably much more destructive than a single "cold wave." Without further evidence I would not consider it proper to assume that a species or variety which had endured a given low temperature on one or two abnormally cold occasions was capable of withstanding the climate of a place where such low temperatures are customary.

heat and dryness, both soil and atmospheric. Some of these varieties, of course, are actually winter-tender, but others apparently stand severe winter weather and thrive if given proper moisture in summer. The question in this case, therefore, is one of drought resistance rather than of hardiness against winter cold.

The matter of drought resistance is perhaps somewhat correlated with winter hardiness and, like the latter, varies with species. Certain rhododendrons come from natural habitats much drier than others. In checking over the Chinese species which have been tested in the United States, I find that several of the most promising ones are those that come from the dry side of the mountains, rather than those from the regions of copious moisture. This relation holds, even when the dry regions are farther south and warmer. Perhaps the correlation is not absolute, but the drought-hardy species will, I predict, prove more winter-hardy in America than the species from moister, though possibly colder, regions.

A form of winter injury, of the utmost importance in England and in certain mild regions elsewhere, is the freezing of tender growth by late spring frosts. Warm days, followed by cold nights and killing frosts, will catch the early developing buds, especially of the early flowering species. This is not such a factor in the northeastern United States, where warm spring weather does not ordinarily arrive until danger of frost is over. For this reason, some of the hardiness figures for species and varieties determined by the experience of growers in England are misleading when applied in America. For example, certain early blooming sorts expand their flower buds in mid-winter in the British Isles, and are often killed before the flowers open by the occurrence of a cold wave there. Such plants are classed as somewhat tender in the list of the Rhododendron Association of England. Yet when grown in the United States, some of these same species will not bloom until spring is actually at hand and, being otherwise perfectly hardy, they may be grown with entire satisfaction over here. This explains such an anomaly as that of *R. Schlippenbachii*, which, though classed *C* in the British list, is so hardy in America that it deserves a rating of even hardier than the British *A*. Any species which develops either flowers or foliage in the very early spring may be subject to the same limitations.

Properly to understand the underlying causes of frost injury to early-flowering species in late winter or early spring, we need to explain the distinction which exists between the *rest period* and *dormancy* in plants. Although these may occur simultaneously, they should be regarded as two separate phenomena. Nearly all plants normally experience some period in the year during which vegetative growth is practically at a standstill, regardless of weather conditions. Most hardy rhododendrons enter such a period in autumn. This is properly called the rest period. During this time the plants will not ordinarily grow or bloom, even if placed in a greenhouse and given summer temperatures. Probably the evergreen species always remain somewhat active, but all undergo at least a season of partial rest. As soon as the rest period is completed, however—and this varies with different species and varieties—the plant is capable of growing and blooming. If the plants are located outdoors and the weather is cold or unfavorable when the rest period is completed, the plants will remain dormant until favorable weather arrives. But as soon as a warmish day or two occur, all plants that have fully completed their rest period will immediately become active. Some plants complete their rest period very quickly and are capable of becoming active again the moment the rest period is passed. Thus, *R. dauricum* and its ally, *R. mucronulatum,* are over their rest period by January and are ready to begin blooming as soon as their dormancy is broken by a rise in temperature. *R. maximum,* on the other hand, has a very long rest period and is not affected by warm spells in winter or early spring. Should warm temperatures occur in January, probably *R. dauricum* would become active and later be injured by a succeeding cold wave, while *R. maximum* would be unaffected and hence uninjured. The rest period is controlled by inherent causes and not influenced by environmental factors, while dormancy is purely a state of inactivity due to an environment unfavorable for growth.

It has been shown * that the cell sap of a rhododendron reaches its greatest concentration in December and January, with a sharp let-up the moment spring growth commences. While the sugar is concentrated, there is less danger of injury, but as quickly as the first spring growth begins the solution becomes less concentrated and possibly other chemical changes occur. The early spring growth, therefore, is in danger during the cold nights which follow warm days in certain localities, so that plants which have a short rest period are especially subject to injury of this kind, since they are not held in check until the weather is safe. Such plants are often perfectly satisfactory in very cold regions where continued low temperatures keep them dormant long after the rest period is completed and good spring weather is assured. This is the case with many species in the northeastern United States. In milder regions, however, warm days in January, February or March, followed by freezing weather, may prove disastrous. This, as noted, is a common complaint in parts of England and in certain localities in the United States.

In a previous chapter I discussed at length the subject of hardy and tender varieties. This, of course, is a matter of the greatest practical importance, because definite species and varieties are inherently tender, hardy or intermediate,

* Fukuda, Y. (See reference p. 82). *R. micranthum* in Manchuria.

as the case may be. It would seem as if many improved forms might be developed in the future by breeding for hardiness. In our hybrid races, certain tender species have been incorporated which contribute little or nothing to the advantage of the strain and which add tenderness to the hybrid race. Such species as *Rhododendron ponticum,* it seems to me, might be eliminated from the Catawba hybrid race with great benefit to the race. I suspect, also, that *R. luteum* does little good and much harm (from the American standpoint) to the Ghent azaleas by reason of its inherent tenderness.

The matter of adaptation also plays a part in determining how well a plant or species will succeed in cultivation. Species growing wild in foreign lands are often out of tune with the local climates in which cultivation is attempted. It is conceivable, for instance, that a species from the arctic or from the higher Himalayas might be naturally adapted only to a short growing season and would wear itself out or fail to make the necessary preparations for a cold winter if grown where the season is longer. It might also require a constant supply of water, such as comes from melting glaciers. Then, too, such other ecological features as long-continued snows *versus* "open" winters, bright but cool sunshine *versus* intense heat or cloudiness, heavy summer rainfall *versus* hot, dry weather—such contradictory conditions as these are the things which make it difficult to grow exotic species in America. Britishers can do much better than those of us who live on the American Atlantic seaboard, because the climate of England is more equable than ours with its extremes of heat and cold. The fact that a species endures zero weather in Szechuan does not necessarily mean that it will survive a winter in New York, for conditions other than temperature enter into the setup. On the whole, adaptation to a given climate is an inherent quality and may be altered or improved upon only by selective breeding or by hybridization.

Now, as a practical conclusion, there are several things which in theory and practice would seem to be desirable when persons wish to grow rhododendrons in regions where the plants are not already well adapted to the climate. Let us enumerate some of them:

1. See that the plants stop growing in mid-summer and are properly "hardened-off" in the fall. To do this, withhold water in August and do not apply any fertilizer after the month of May. Protect against warm sun in late autumn.

2. Give the plants plenty of water late in autumn, just before the ground freezes.

3. See that the plants are adequately mulched.

4. Provide good wind protection and air drainage.

5. Furnish shade and shelter, as outlined in Chapter V. Where extra protection is needed, evergreen boughs, a burlap covering or a burlap tent is excel-

lent, for it permits some light but gives good protection in practical use. Cover your plants early, rather than late in the autumn. Lath shades, lattice houses, hot-bed sash or other devices may be used. Try to admit a little light. A wooded location is desirable and this is the shelter recommended for the rain-forest species when grown in England.

6. Watch out for insects and, if the plants are young, for disease.

7. General vigor and thrifty growth, during the proper season, induced by good soil and environmental conditions, aid hardiness.

8. All rhododendrons and azaleas are tender when very young.

9. Some individuals in a species or race are hardier than others. Try to obtain the hardy ones.

10. Observe your plants closely and they will teach you best how to care for them.

CHAPTER X

THE KIND OF PLANTS TO USE

RHODODENDRONS and azaleas in the trade come under several different categories. Some are collected from the wild and sold without cutting back; others are collected, cut back and re-grown in the nursery before being sold; some natural species are raised in the nursery or at home from seed collected in the wild, others from seed out of mixed garden collections, and still others from the seed of hybrids. Among those raised as seedlings are those which come from unprotected, open-pollinated seed and those that have been pollinated by hand under controlled conditions to insure authentic parentage. Last are the clonal varieties or choice strains which have been propagated by layering, grafting, cutting or division.

In order to give the reader an idea of the relative merits of these different kinds of plants, it seems worth while to say a few words about what may be expected from each type. The amateur often buys his rhododendrons on price and size alone, and it is well that he should consider the long-term values of what he is getting. Plants from any of these classes may be absolutely satisfactory under appropriate conditions, but they differ markedly. Hence, their value and effectiveness depend entirely upon their suitability for a given purpose.

Plants collected from the wild and sold or placed in gardens directly without cutting back or re-growing in a nursery depend upon two factors for success: the vigor of the plant and the way in which it is handled. Material of this sort is constantly being used in America, but the plants must be well selected and the job competently done if the result, in the long run, turns out as well as could otherwise be expected. If improperly handled, the plants may die almost immediately, but, on the other hand, some plants will linger on for years without ever becoming thrifty, vigorous or beautiful. Such results are discouraging to the owner and should be avoided by care in the selection of good plants and by competent digging and transplanting. I do not wish to discourage the use of this system, which is relatively economical and results in the planting of thousands of good, successful rhododendrons every year, but I do wish to emphasize that hazards are present.

Plants in good, vigorous condition should be chosen. It is better to choose a young, vigorous plant of small or medium size rather than a large plant if the latter is not in active growth. Plants growing wild are often in a semi-active or "checked" condition; they have grown very slowly, perhaps, for years, due to lack of fertile soil and to the general conditions of competition surrounding them. During this time their tissues have become thick and hard, their water-conducting cells may be of insufficient capacity to accommodate vigorous growth and, more often than not, they are somewhat scrawny in appearance and scant of foliage. Placed in a garden where growing conditions are better, such plants may start from new buds at the bottom and eventually make new vigorous wood which will supplant the older parts of the shrubs. One cannot expect, however, that the old wood will ever become rejuvenated and assume an active growing condition. In very old plants a large crown of buds, coming up from the roots at the surface of the soil, is present at the base of each plant. Buds from this crown or "burl" will easily start into growth and make active, new tissues. Where such a burl is present, therefore, an old plant is as good as a young one.

Sometimes the old wood of a collected plant is desirable, because of its picturesque quality, in the design of naturalistic or Japanesque settings. There is always some danger, however, that inactive plants of this type will not be vigorous enough to accommodate themselves to their new environment. If you find yourself in the possession of an old plant which fails to do well after moving, it is probably best to cut it back and let new wood come from the base.

In some localities where rhododendrons grow wild, casual persons, who know little or nothing about rhododendron culture, will rip up wild plants and peddle them in nearby cities at low prices. If the work is done by someone who is careful and a good ball of soil is left about the roots of each plant, the results may be satisfactory, but, more often, such care is not given and failure ensues. Such a plant is never a bargain, no matter how low the price, for, when it does live, it often is so badly injured that years are required before it can be brought into healthy shape. I have observed that many such plants will survive for a year or two, making almost no growth whatever, and then finally die.

A better system for handling collected plants is that which is practiced by some of the foremost nurserymen-collectors. The plants are dug up in the wild and taken to a nearby nursery. They arrive in the nursery before becoming dried or wilted and are placed under good growing conditions in a nursery row where they eventually are cut back to within a few inches of the base.* The

* Some experienced authorities consider the best practice is either to grow the plant for one year in the nursery row before cutting back or to cut it back while still standing in its native habitat and not moving it until a year later. The idea of transplanting and cutting down immediately is not looked upon with favor by these persons.

young buds around the base then start into active growth and produce a new, vigorous, bushy top. New root growth is also initiated to replace the long, trailing root system of the wild plant with a compact ball of roots. It requires about four years of growth in the nursery to produce a fine specimen plant from a cut-back, large wild plant. The rejuvenated plant, however, is in fine, active growth and possesses a healthy, compact ball of roots which greatly facilitates subsequent shipment and transplanting. There can be no doubt but that the cut-back specimen is infinitely better equipped to live and flourish in the garden than is the plant which is dug and shipped directly from the collecting grounds. Cut-back plants may be obtained in all sizes and are usually worth the additional price, which is not much over that of an uncut plant. When the wild, American species are desired, therefore, the cut-back, nursery re-grown plants are the ones which are advised. This applies to the azaleas as well as to the evergreen species. The plants in nature are apt to be scrawny and not floriferous.

Plants raised from seed collected in the wild are excellent and represent the best available type of seedling material. Generally seedlings of native American species are not raised in nurseries, because collected plants are cheaper to obtain. Some of the rarer species, however, are regularly grown from seed and this practice will doubtless be extended as it becomes harder to obtain collectible stock * and as special races or varietal strains are isolated. With the natural species from foreign countries, the seed which comes directly from the native habitat is, next to hand-pollinated seed, the very best medium of propagation. Where seed can be obtained directly from the wild, therefore, it is to be preferred over seed from plants growing in collections, since it is usually true to type and is not contaminated by cross-pollination with other species.

Plants produced from seed taken from specimens which are growing in gardens, in mixed collections or in situations where they are not isolated from the pollen of other sorts blooming at the same time are becoming rather common. Such plants are not to be relied upon as true representatives of the type without investigation, for many of them bear little or no resemblance whatever to the specimen plant from which the seed was taken although, on the other hand, a great many such plants are perfectly authentic specimens. In their anxiety to

* No alarm need be felt as to the ultimate destruction of the native American species by collectors, in so far as the common sorts are concerned. Much of this collecting is done upon government-owned land and a systematic cropping system is being established by the U.S. Forest Service. The only danger of extinction faces colonies of these plants which are situated on private land or in the neighborhood of large cities and in other populous districts where acts of vandalism occur. In such districts, therefore, the plants should be protected by stringent state and local laws in order to prevent the destruction of native stands and to preserve the natural beauty spots which they help to create. There is need, however, of legislative restriction of the collecting of rare species and the forcing of nurserymen to propagate these from seed.

obtain plants of the rare, new species from the Orient, growers have taken seed pods from any plants which were available and have sought to reproduce the type through these seeds. Moreover, a considerable quantity of such seed is being marketed as well as what is being disseminated by exchange among amateurs. Seedlings are being grown and sold under the names of the species from which the seed has come. Some of the resulting plants are not true to type at all. When two different species or varieties are in bloom at nearly the same time, the insects carry pollen from one to another and the resulting seeds are largely of hybrid origin instead of being true progeny of one given plant. Moreover, self-pollinated seed, if it does occur, is apt to result in weak seedlings. More often, however, self-pollination does not occur at all (or, at least, self-fertilization does not ensue) and the only seeds produced at all are of hybrid origin. Owing to a phenomenon of sterility, which will be discussed in a later chapter, less chance exists for true seedlings than for seedlings which are the result of a cross with some other plant. Seed, therefore, from unprotected or, as they say, open-pollinated flowers should not be regarded as reliable unless backed up by a true-to-name guarantee. Seedlings from such seed might, on occasion, be actually better than those of the true species, but one can never be sure that they will resemble the parent at all. With many such chance hybrids in gardens, under the specific names of their seed-parents which they do not always resemble, a great deal of confusion is sure to result regarding the true nature of some of the rare wild species.

If propagators realized how easily protection and hand-pollination might be accomplished, few of them would bother with the uncertainties of open-pollinated seed. By taking two plants of a given true species and pollinating the flowers of each with pollen from the other, an abundance of good seed, assured of coming "true," can be produced. Sometimes several hundred seeds will occur in one seed-pod which has taken only a moment to pollinate. The resulting seedlings can usually be depended upon to reproduce the parental characters as well as those commonly found in the wild.* Plants produced in this way are not, at present, on the market to any extent, but will doubtless be produced in the future when growers realize the great advantages of the method. Plants from hand-pollinated seed are, next to those propagated vegetatively, the most reliable ones to buy. The technique of pollination is described in Chapter XVIII.

Hybrid seedlings are also available in the market and have certain advantages as well as disadvantages. One can expect them to be, on an average, somewhat superior to the wild sorts in color, although the wild color pre-

---

* As will be noted later, hybrids and special forms cannot be depended upon to come true from seed, even when hand-pollinated.

dominates in perhaps 75%, more or less, of the seedlings. Certain strains will produce more, others less, of desirable colors. Very few individuals arise from open-pollinated hybrid seed of the Catawba rhododendrons which are as good as those of the "best dozen" hybrid clones,* and yet colors better than the wild type are of common occurrence. Another advantage is that the vigorous, nursery-grown seedlings are usually in a better vegetative condition than collected plants. On the other hand, the hybrid seedlings are extremely variable in all characters, including hardiness, and consequently some may not be able to adapt themselves to a severe climate unless the plants have been raised from the beginning in such an environment, in which case the weaklings will have perished before the plants reach a marketable age. If one can go to a nursery and pick out the plants he desires while they are in bloom, or if he can purchase them graded and guaranteed as to color, then the use of hybrid seedlings is a very desirable practice. Seedlings have an advantage over grafted plants in being on their own roots and usually in being of a bushy habit, permitting several stems, rather than one, to arise from the roots.

Certain hybrid clones make better parents than others and it is also assumed that, from definite combinations of parents, a consistently higher percentage of good hybrid seedlings than the average may be obtained. Experiments are now in progress to isolate some of these combinations and determine what parents, if hand-pollinated, will produce the highest percentage of good colors in the progeny. Up to the present, very few hand-pollinated hybrid seedlings are available in the trade, but this method has distinct possibilities for the future.

Outside the raising of seedlings and the collecting of wild plants, the only other method of obtaining rhododendrons is by vegetative propagation. Some choice hybrids and many rare forms are reproduced in this manner. These comprise plants that are layered, grafted, divided or rooted from cuttings. Ordinarily, a plant reproduced in this way is the most reliable duplicate obtainable of any given sort, because it is, in reality, simply a piece of that original individual and, therefore, identical with it in hardiness, color and all inherent characters. As a means of insuring the finest colors, plus the advantages of hardiness, vigor and so forth as rarely occurs in an exceptional individual, there is nothing so good as a plant produced in one of these asexual ways. These varieties are usually named and, as such, are known as clones or clonal varieties.

The choice of whether the plants be layered, grafted, divided or raised from cuttings will depend largely upon the species and also upon the preferences of individual growers and buyers. There is little choice in the matter, provided the plants are well rooted and healthy. Personally, my preference among the

* See list, Chap. XXIV, p. 445.

evergreen rhododendrons is for plants that have been propagated on their own roots, but there are those who will advocate the grafted sorts with even greater fervor. My reason for favoring layered plants, or cuttings and divisions where they can be obtained, is that these plants are on their own roots and hence can be permitted to develop from more than one main stem, giving the whole plant a round, bushy appearance and insuring that no "suckers" of an unattractive under-stock will come up, even if the top becomes killed. Cuttings of the evergreen rhododendrons are beginning to appear in the trade and there is no reason why these will not be equally as good as layered plants. Cuttings of azaleas have long been used.

More recently, progress in the propagation of evergreen rhododendrons and deciduous azaleas from cuttings has enabled buyers to secure "own-root" plants in America more readily than before. As will be discussed in another chapter (see page 117), not all kinds are equally amenable to propagation by these means, but more and more plants are becoming available in this way and experience elsewhere indicates that they are satisfactory.

In conclusion, a word should be said about the advantages of picking out your own plants. If you live near a nursery, it will pay you to visit the establishment when the rhododendrons or azaleas are in bloom and choose at that time the plants you wish to buy. You will not only be better satisfied with the material you receive, but you will also be able to obtain more for your money. For instance, by the careful choice of desirable individuals among collections of mixed seedlings, you will often be able to obtain colors, in these cheaper grades, that will serve your purpose as well as the more costly hybrids. Sometimes, too, as in the native *Rhododendron calendulaceum,* you will find colors nearly as good as the best hybrids, but with the advantage of better adaptation.

Chapter XI

SOME PREVENTIVES OF TROUBLE

ENOUGH has been said, in previous chapters, to indicate those conditions which rhododendrons and azaleas prefer. Given such conditions, most rhododendrons which have reached the blooming age will have little excuse for not thriving. When good rhododendron growing conditions are maintained, there are relatively few enemies to bother, except, of course, among very young seedlings, in which only the professional propagator or the fancier is interested.

When non-success does occur, however, it is often difficult to diagnose the cause. Sometimes it is a combination of several unfavorable conditions. Again, rhododendrons are sometimes slow to die, so that a primary underlying cause may be past and gone by the time the plant finally falls victim to death from a secondary trouble. It is only too evident that there are still some important factors yet undiscovered in rhododendron culture. Barring direct injury, or that which occurs through the agency of insect pests or diseases, however, there need be little fear of trouble if the growing conditions are good. In other words, prevention, rather than treatment, should be the watchword. It is much easier to do this than to find the cause of a trouble and nurse the plants back to health after it occurs. To recall the principal points brought out in previous chapters concerning the requirements for successful rhododendron culture, let us recapitulate very briefly, putting some of the major requirements into a list of "ten commandments" for the rhododendron grower:

1. An acid soil is necessary.
2. Plenty of organic matter in the soil, and this of the right type to furnish acid, minerals, fiber and root protection.
3. A well drained and well aerated soil, without the least dryness.
4. Protection from sweeping winds, but avoiding frost pockets.
5. Protection from extremes of heat and cold.
6. Adequate water relations, soil and atmospheric.
7. No competition, especially from tree roots.
8. A constant mulch, of proper character.

97

9. Species and varieties which are naturally adapted to the climate and the site.

10. Protection from insect pests and plant diseases.

A compilation of data concerning the various insect pests and plant diseases known to affect rhododendrons or azaleas is presented in Chapter XX, with recommendations of control measures. The other points on the list have already been discussed in detail. If non-success occurs, the cause is usually attributable to failure under one or more of the above ten headings.

Of the pests and diseases which might attack a fairly mature rhododendron plant (that is, a plant of blooming age), most are controllable, once recognized, and are nothing to become excited about. The serious diseases practically all occur when the plants are under two or three years of age and so are not of concern except to the man who happens to be raising seedlings or very young plants. It has been very rare, in my experience, to see any good-sized plant die of disease. For the benefit of the propagator, however, and others who may wish to know something about the prevention of disease and insect troubles, I shall make a few general observations concerning their behavior and give suggestions about avoiding them.

If your young plants are dying or look thriftless, do not be too sure that the trouble is due to cultural conditions. It might be disease. Propagators are sometimes too prone to ascribe the failure of their young stock to conditions of soil, water, temperature, sunlight or some other ecological factor, when the underlying cause is a fungus or an insignificant sucking insect. I would not discount the effect of good nursing, good soil and proper conditions, for these are often the determiners which induce or prevent pests. But when the tissues of a young plant are invaded by a hostile organism, something more than good growing conditions is necessary to overcome the trouble. Hence, I would advise all propagators of rhododendrons and azaleas to familiarize themselves with the symptoms of the various types of injury which occur on these plants, so that troubles may be seen, recognized and controlled as soon as they manifest themselves.

The best way to handle all pest troubles is by prevention. There is no substitute for the observant eye of the gardener which watches the individual plants day by day and sees their trouble at its inception. Once a diseased leaf is seen, it should rightfully be burned up at once, although few growers can ever watch their plants so closely as to practice this rigid sanitation. No infected plants, litter or dead leaves should be left in or around a bed, or in the walks or under the benches of a greenhouse. Such are the sources of disease infection and the over-wintering of insects.

Promptness in taking care of diseased plants is essential. Small, spotted areas, or other marks of disease, are sometimes left to remain, because only one or two plants are affected or because the spots, being small, are not considered of much consequence. Such areas are the loci from which diseases can spread to more serious proportions. One diseased plant can produce enough spores to inoculate a whole houseful, and, as such spores can be carried everywhere by air currents and insects, the disease may become widely distributed in a short time. The sudden appearance of disease in a whole bed or bench of seedlings can usually be traced to some small, initial infected area where spores were being produced some time in advance of the general onslaught. It is obvious that the grower should take immediate means to offset the spread of a disease, by spraying, eradication or some other method, as soon as he finds the first plants infected.

Practically all the disease organisms reported on rhododendrons and azaleas are of fungal nature. A fungous disease is a low form of plant life which derives its support from a host plant upon which it is parasitic. A fungus does not produce seeds, but it produces spores which are small particles, about the size of pollen grains, which float about in the air and when alighting in a favorable spot on a plant (or, in some cases, in the soil where a plant grows) germinate and grow. Fungi are also disseminated by contact: when their rootlike mycelia touch a plant, they grow into the cells of that plant.

To illustrate how fungous diseases act and how a fungicide protects the plant against them, let us consider what occurs in the case of a common leaf-spot disease. Suppose that a spore alights on the surface of a leaf. Perhaps a drop of water, from rain or dew, is present and the spore gets into this. It germinates in a very short time, sending out a fine root-like process which dissolves its way through the cell walls, by excreting an enzyme which digests those walls, and enters the cells of the leaf. This mycelium, as the root-like structure is called, invades one cell after another, developing into an extended mass of strands among the leaf tissues. The fungus derives its nourishment from the invaded cells, killing them as it advances. A brown spot, which is nothing but an area of killed cells in the center of infection, develops and is visible on the leaf. If conditions continue favorable for the fungus, the mycelium enlarges its feeding area, advancing from one cell to another until it spreads all over the leaf, coalesces with some other leaf spot or goes to some vital part where the food supply is cut off by the death of tissue and the entire leaf, or perhaps the whole plant, dies. At a certain stage of development, fruiting bodies appear and produce great quantities of spores which, in turn, carry the disease organism to other plants.

A fungicidal spray, such as Bordeaux mixture, cannot reach the mycelium which is buried within the plant tissues, and, consequently, it has no power to kill or arrest the disease which has already invaded the plant tissues. All that the fungicide can do is to protect uninfected areas, the healthy leaves and stems, by preventing the development of spores which alight in those areas. When such spores start to germinate, the fungicide with which the leaf is coated comes in contact with the delicate, sprout-like process which emerges from each spore and kills it. With this in mind, one can readily understand why the spray should be regarded as a preventive rather than a cure, because the fungicide is effective only when it reaches healthy tissue before the spores germinate. It should also be emphasized that spores often like to germinate in droplets of water and frequently work on the under sides of leaves. Hence, it is important to see that the fungicide reaches the under surfaces of leaves.

Bordeaux mixture is a time-honored fungicide, useful and effective on rhododendrons and azaleas. It may be applied as a liquid spray or as a dry powder by means of a dusting apparatus. If used as a powder or "dust" it should be applied when the foliage is wet in order to stick to the foliage and form a protective film. It has the undesirable quality of being light in color and leaving a whitish residue on the leaves which is sometimes objectionable where the plants are in use as ornamentals. Accordingly, another copper fungicide has been devised which leaves no visible residue and which may be used as a substitute for Bordeaux mixture. One product of this nature goes under the trade name of "Coposil." Sulphur, in various forms, is also useful as a fungicide. Perhaps the best form of sulphur for rhododendrons is ordinary dusting sulphur, applied as a dust. This is merely a very finely-ground form of sulphur flour. Do not apply Bordeaux or sulphur on warm sunny days.

Insect pests may be divided into two general classes: those which suck and those which chew. The most common sucking insect is the lace bug (sometimes erroneously called the lace-wing fly), which is decidedly worse when the plants are grown in the sunlight and is seldom a menace to plants grown in the shade. Certain varieties, such as the Caucasicum hybrid 'Boule de Neige,' are especially susceptible to this pest. In greenhouses, the common greenhouse pests, thrips, mealy-bug and aphis are real enemies, but may be controlled in the usual way by nicotine, pyrethrum or rotenone combination sprays and by fumigants. Contact insecticides for the sucking insects and stomach poisons for the chewers are the general rule. Grubs and borers are especially hard to find before the damage is done. Several new and improved insecticides are now available.

In the prevention of both insects and diseases, nothing is so successful as the systematic spraying of young seedlings in beds, frames or in the greenhouse by regular weekly or bi-monthly use of appropriate fungicides, insecticides and fumigants. For this work, combination sprays, which control both insects and diseases, are especially convenient. Several such products are on the market.

This systematic attention prevents enemies from gaining a foothold by exterminating them when they first appear, often before they become apparent to the eye. This, of course, need not be practiced except with young seedlings or in other situations where a possibility of attack exists. With older plants, a seasonal treatment, to prevent lace bug or other prevalent pests, applied when needed, is usually sufficient. But lace bug is seldom troublesome if the plants are grown in the shade, as it works mainly in sunny spots. Indeed, many rhododendrons are so happily situated that they never require spraying or treatment of any sort.

I have already spoken of some of the physiological troubles, such as chlorosis from an alkaline soil, winter injury and difficulties due to an improper site. The symptoms of an alkaline soil are a general yellowing or pallor of the foliage and the inability of the plant to grow or appear thrifty. Winter injury of the foliage produces typical dead areas around the margins of the leaves. If the injury occurs to the stem or roots, the whole top dies at once. When bark cracks, due to winter injury or other causes, fungous disease organisms sometimes enter the cracked area, near the surface of the soil, and soon girdle the main stem, killing the plant. Young rhododendrons, mainly, are the sufferers from this type of injury.

Some troubles, simulating disease, as for instance dead areas around leaf-margins or blotches on leaves of seedlings, may result from nutritional deficiencies. In the absence of definite evidence of pathogenic infection, it is well to try feeding with a complete nutrient. Foliar feeding, with solutions containing trace elements, is certainly a worthwhile experiment in cases where nutritional imbalance seems indicated. Solutions are sprayed on the leaves in accordance with directions usually supplied by the manufacturer. Certain new materials for foliar feeding, such as chelated iron, are now on the market.

Hard water generally contains calcium or other alkaline salts which can cause changes in soil acidity to a surprising degree. For young seedlings under glass, where only a small amount of water is required, it is often possible to collect enough rain water from the roof to use on the plants.

A word of caution should be said concerning the use of high-potency spraying materials. If the time-honored solutions, such as nicotine sulphate and dilute Bordeaux mixture, are effective in controlling the pests on your rhododendrons, do not use the newer materials at all. The danger is that the higher potency of new sprays not only kills the pest, but kills natural control agents too.

CHAPTER XII

PROPAGATION FROM SEED

FOR species and varieties which reproduce themselves satisfactorily from seed, there is no other method of propagation so good as this. Given proper attention, seedlings can be raised in considerable numbers with comparative ease. There is also some advantage in seedling plants, because they have root systems of their own which permit the development of a bushy, many-stemmed habit at the base and freedom from the restraint of a graft union. A disadvantage is that seedlings are apt to be uneven in type and quality.

For best results the seed should be taken from desirable plants. If the flower can be hand-pollinated at blooming time, using pollen from some other good individual, the result will be better than the use of self-fertilized seed or that produced by the indiscriminate mixing of blooming varieties by the bees. Considering that one flower will sometimes bear as many as four hundred seeds, a few minutes spent in hand-pollinating will yield large returns, both in the quality of seed secured and in the saving of time between seed and bloom.*

The usual seed, however, is not from hand-pollinated flowers, but is ordinary insect-pollinated seed taken from plants either in garden collections or in the wild. Commercial seed is generally of this type and is obtained without special selection of the parent plants. It bears the label of the plant that bore it and, as noted elsewhere, may be the product of an insect-made cross with some other neighboring species which happens to bloom simultaneously with its seed parent. Seed collected from the wild, however, is seldom of hybrid origin, and is generally a result of matings within the species and will vary within typical limits. If trueness to a species type is desired, one should, accordingly, aim to se-

* This statement implies that two parents of demonstrated compatibility and power to produce desirable seedlings are used. As noted elsewhere, there are certain combinations of varieties which work together especially well as parents, while others, as good in appearance, do not produce good seedlings. Such matings can be determined only by experience. See Chapter XVI.

cure seed that has been collected from wild plants growing in their natural habitat.

Rhododendron seed will remain viable for about two years if kept at ordinary room temperature, but it is best when fresh. Numerous seeds fail to germinate after one year's storage, and the viability of any declines sharply after that time.

The seed capsule ("pod") should be collected as soon as it begins to lose its green color and become yellowish or brown. This color transformation takes place very rapidly and is soon followed by a splitting of the capsule and discharge of the seeds, so that one must watch for it with some care.

The seed capsules of most rhododendrons are ripe and should be collected, in northern regions, at the time of the first "killing" frost in autumn. A few kinds, such as the Caucasicum hybrid clone 'Boule de Neige,' ripen from three to four weeks earlier than the average, so one must watch for them, else the capsules will split open and the seeds will be lost. In New York the earliest varieties ripen about September 1st, while the Catawba hybrids and the native azaleas do not split their capsules until nearly the first of October. This ripening season is, I understand, somewhat earlier than in England.

After being collected the seed capsules should be stored for a few days in a dry place, during which time those that are still green and moist may have a chance to dry out. At any time thereafter the seeds may be removed from the capsules. An easy way to accomplish this is to gently crush the dry capsules under a rolling-pin or cylinder of round pipe, then sift the material through a screen which will remove the coarse particles of chaff. The finest, dust-like chaff may be removed by sifting through a very fine screen. The dry seed may be kept in envelopes or bottles at room temperature if not planted immediately. Rhododendron seed is relatively fine in size and light in weight. Some seed, as in the Carolinianum series, is considerably smaller than the average. Rhododendron seed may be obtained from dealers in tree seeds, private gardeners, nurserymen, collectors and, by exchange, from amateurs and fanciers.

Perhaps there is no "best" method of sowing the seed. In every instance, much depends upon the situation, the facilities available and the materials at hand. In the north, it is almost necessary to have a small greenhouse or heated frame, although a Wardian case will sometimes suffice and I have seen excellent plants started in sunny windows. Coldframes are required for young plants during cold weather until they are more than a year old.

I shall mention several different methods, but will first outline a complete schedule, following the traditional course of operations as formerly employed by the majority of growers in America. Mr. C. O. Dexter, who was unsurpassed as a propagator of rhododendron seedlings, planted seed as soon as possible after January 1st. He used wooden "flats" (shallow boxes) having open spaces one inch wide between the slats that form the bottom. Owing to these unusually wide openings, he had to place a screen of ¼-inch wire mesh in the bottom of the flat to keep the soil from washing out. Also flats were made with wire mesh over the entire bottom in place of bottom boards, and worked well. He then placed a layer of clean coal cinders or slag over the wire mesh to hold in the soil but to permit of free drainage through it. The soil mixture consisted of 1 pail (about 10 quarts) of sifted, leafy soil from oak woods (which is of a light, sandy consistency and has an acid reaction of about pH 4.5), to which he added a little sand (not over 25% by volume) and two or three handfuls of granulated German or Dutch peat moss. The sand he used was not alkaline in nature.

This soil mixture is placed loosely in the flat, levelled off and then pressed down gently but evenly. Ground sphagnum moss is prepared by rubbing dried green sphagnum through a wire mesh screen. Some of this is then sifted over the surface of the soil in the flat—enough to make a light covering. The seeds are then sown broadcast, directly on top of this sphagnum. After sowing, the seeds are only half covered by sifting a very light additional coating of ground sphagnum over them. The soil should be watered thoroughly at planting time, but only very seldom afterward until germination takes place. Only a fine "rose" (spray-head) should be used on the watering can. The temperature during this period should be 60°F. at night and from 65° to 70°F. during the day. The seeds will require from 16 to 20 days for germination. After germination, the surface of the soil may be allowed to dry off every day, and when the spring sun becomes too hot, the greenhouse glass should be lightly shaded. With so much sand in the soil mixture and abundant provision for drainage in the flats, much water can be applied to seedlings raised under Mr. Dexter's technique without danger of overwatering. It is essential that they do not become too dry.

More recently, the use of ground sphagnum moss alone, in a flat or other container, has been urged. It is wetted, and the seeds are then sown on top, covering with a glass plate or plastic tent. Damping-off fungi do not start on green sphagnum. This method is now preferred.

Some growers prefer to water the soil mixture in the flat or seed-pot before the seeds are sown, thus avoiding danger of washing them away. Others use sub-irrigation by setting the flats or seed-pots in a pan of water and allowing the moisture to creep up to the surface of the soil by capillarity.

The matter of temperature for germination is relatively important. I have found that seeds left in a temperature of less than 55° or 60° require a long time in which to germinate. In trials where the temperature has been allowed to fall to 40° on cold nights, no germination whatever occurred until spring weather brought night temperatures of 60° or more. Much failure in germination is due to the temperature factor; the thing is deceptive, because the seeds require a relatively higher temperature for germination than is commonly believed to be optimum for the culture of the older plants. The late Mr. T. D. Hatfield, after failures in a cool house, subsequently had great success in raising and transplanting his rhododendron seedlings in a *Cattleya* house where seedling orchids were also raised.

If only a few seeds of each kind are to be sown, earthenware seed-pans or three-inch clay pots may be used instead of flats or seed-boxes. In such a case, the container should be half filled with broken potsherds, washed cinders, stones or other coarse material to furnish quick and efficient drainage. The soil mixture is then added and the sowing is made as previously described.

Some growers prefer to use the surface covering of ground sphagnum and cover the flats or seed-pans with panes of glass also. Others place the flats or pans in an enclosed, moist frame, such as a grafting case or a sunken, sash-covered bench. In either instance, the surface is kept warm and moist until germination has occurred, after which air is gradually admitted.

The seed and young seedlings should be kept moist, but the soil should never be permitted to become sodden. As soon as the first rough leaves are formed—that is, the first true leaves following the cotyledons—the seedlings should be "pricked out" and transplanted into flats or "pans" containing fresh soil of the same mixture as that used for germination, spacing the plants about one inch apart in rows. If a rapidly growing species is used, a slightly greater distance between plants may be allowed.* The seedlings are about ¼-inch tall when this operation takes place. The transplanted seedlings should be kept in the same warmish, rather moist atmosphere which they received during germination, and should be kept in an active growing condition, without being allowed to receive a "check" at any time. Much of the success of Mr. Dexter and other good propagators can doubtless be attributed to the fact that at no time are his plants allowed to "stand still," but are kept continuously in active growth. The application of a good plant food (which does *not* contain nitrate of soda) is an aid toward this maintenance of vegetative vigor. I have used

* As practical propagators know, it is not feasible to space the young seedlings so far apart that the plants cannot utilize the moisture in the spaces between them, as this results in a sodden condition and possibly weed or fungus growth in these unoccupied areas. Besides, such a practice would be wasteful of greenhouse space in mid-winter. It is much better, therefore, to first space the plants one inch apart and later transplant to two inch intervals, using fresh soil each time, than to "prick" them off in January into a space large enough to support them in August. The same principle applies to repotting, where small shifts, rather than large ones should be made and care taken not to use too large-sized pots. The fresh soil added at each transplanting or shifting, also, is of great benefit in stimulating growth and preventing the establishment of disease invasions.

ammonium sulphate in frequent but dilute applications: one tablespoonful in 12 quarts of water, applied through the watering can. Mr. Dexter used one part of potassium nitrate to two parts of super-phosphate, applied lightly or mixed in the soil. At Cornell, a product called Clay's Fertilizer has proved successful. There are doubtless other readily available preparations, rich in nitrogen, which may be used to stimulate growth in the young seedlings. The main thing is to keep them "going."

The plants should not be allowed to crowd one another or their growth will be checked. As soon as they have become large enough to shade the surface of the flat, they should be again transplanted into another flat, where they should be spaced two inches or more apart each way. The same sort of soil is used.

Growth in seedlings, as in older plants, takes place mainly before July, with very little after that time, so it is necessary to encourage as much growth as possible during the early spring months. By the time of the second transplanting, growth has begun to slow down unless artificial light is used which will be discussed later.

In commercial production, the young plants in flats are often kept in the greenhouse until the first of August, although the flats may be set into cold-frames in May or June if desired. In any event, they are kept somewhat shaded, either by lath shades or by paint on the greenhouse glass, and are kept moist throughout the spring and early summer. Protection from hot, dry winds is essential. If kept indoors, the house should be made as cool and moist as possible, the walks and sash being frequently wet down to lower the temperature and provide atmospheric moisture. Gradually more and more air should be given the seedlings. If insects or diseases appear, spraying or dusting must be resorted to. I have spoken elsewhere of Bordeaux mixture, fumigation and the various insecticides. Frequent and systematic applications of preventives are more to be desired than control methods.

By August first the flats of plants should go outdoors if they have not already been put there. At this time all shade should be removed and they should be given full sunlight. Gradually, water should be withheld and the plants should go "on the dry side" to harden their tissues against winter injury. Of course, they should not be allowed to dry out, but irrigation should be lessened. The plants have now stopped elongating, but may thicken up somewhat and be more bushy. They should not be permitted to develop late growth, unless they are to spend the winter indoors, for this will keep them tender too long. During late July, August and September the plants should be kept sprayed or dusted with Bordeaux mixture, sulphur or copper fungicides as protection against certain fungous diseases, notably leaf-spot troubles such as *Exobasidium,* which become very active in late summer and early fall, causing the death of young seedlings in frames. The foliage should be kept covered with a protective spray from the last of July through the following fall and winter.

In October the azaleas should be potted up and brought back into the green-house for the winter or else placed in a very deep and well protected pit. Azaleas are more tender when young than are the hardy rhododendrons, such as those of the Catawba type. Certain half-hardy evergreen species, also, had better come indoors. But the hardy evergreen rhododendrons may be kept outdoors in covered frames all winter. During the cool autumn months, they should be covered with a sash and the addition of a straw mat during cold nights. On pleasant days, the plants should be uncovered, ventilated, allowed to receive sunshine and watered if too dry. When freezing weather starts, about December in the north, a covering of hay eight or ten inches deep should be placed over the sash (not on the plants themselves!) and allowed to remain all winter. The hay may be forked aside and the sash raised for ventilation on sunny days during the winter to guard against excessive dampness. As spring approaches, the open periods should be gradually lengthened.

In March, when the sun has become stronger and spring is definitely in the air, remove the hay covering and let the sunlight into the frames, ventilating when necessary to avoid over-heating and supplying water as needed.

Early in May the young rhododendrons, now three inches or so tall, may be removed from their flats and planted in open ground or nursery beds. These beds are about 5½ feet wide, with plank sides like coldframes to hold a mulch and support lath shades. The young plants are set in rows running across the bed, about six inches apart in the row, with an eight-inch space between the rows. The soil of such a bed should be finely prepared to a depth of 12 inches or more, should be excellently drained and is best composed of peaty loam and sand, or a combination of peat, light loam and sand. Plain fibrous woodland soil is often very good, especially when somewhat sandy or peaty. Not so much sand needs to be used in the beds, however, as in the seed-flats, for the plants are larger and require more moisture and nutrients. It is desirable to keep the plants in the semi-shade of lath during times of intense heat and dryness, so the current practice is to keep the beds covered by lath shades from the time the plants are set out in May until midsummer. Ample water should be provided during this time. During late summer the lath shades should be removed altogether and the plants again put on the "dry side" in preparation for winter. They should not go into the winter dry, but should be kept somewhat dry during August and September to prevent tender late growth and force early ripening and "hardening off" of the wood. The plants should have a good soaking just before cold weather begins and after the danger of late growth is past.

In October many growers consider that the plants should be mulched well, preferably with oak leaves, almost but not quite burying the entire plants with the leafy blanket. Other growers do not employ a mulch but use special or patent coldframes and other methods instead. It is a good practice to spray with a fungicide just before applying the mulch. Where the mulch system is used, four to six inches of loose hay should be applied directly over the mulch in late November or December. If tree leaves are abundant, I am somewhat of the opinion that the use of six or eight inches of additional leaves might be preferable to hay for this purpose. In regions of heavy snowfall, it is desirable to replace the lath shades over the mulch in order to keep off the weight of the snow which would otherwise cause the hay or leaves to form a tight, smothering mat over the young plants. If azalea seedlings are left outdoors this second winter, they should be very carefully protected. They are hardy enough to withstand some cold now, but are still more tender than rhododendrons and protection in frames may still be desirable.

The following spring, when cold weather is past, the hay or part of the leaves should be removed, but the leaves underneath should remain all summer as a mulch. They not only help to insure a uniform moisture condition about the roots, but also keep down weeds. If the plants grow fast and become crowded, they may be transplanted, but they are usually kept in the nursery beds until the following year, thus passing two winters in the same situation. It is still best to furnish some overhead shade during the late spring and summer months.

In the autumn they are mulched again with leaves and perhaps some hay, and are sprayed if danger of disease is present. At this age, however, the danger of death from leaf-spot is not so serious as with younger seedlings.

In May of the following year the plants, now a foot or 18 inches tall, should be removed from the nursery bed and planted in permanent nursery rows. The same sort of soil is now used as that recommended for mature rhododendrons and azaleas. Some growers prepare their soil by spading in peat moss with the naturally acid fibrous soil, if this occurs on the site. Several large growers take advantage of sparsely wooded areas by utilizing these for their rhododendron nursery rows, as the young plants appear to thrive better if they receive this protection from the hot sun and drying winds. A wooded area furnishes some protection of this sort both summer and winter, and also renders lace bug and some other pests less troublesome. The shade should not be dense, however, and the direct competition of tree roots should be avoided so far as possible. Neighboring trees doubtless rob the rhododendrons of some moisture and minerals, yet I incline to believe their advantages outweigh these handicaps. Again, by careful management and clever planning, rhododendrons may be placed near enough to receive the benefits of trees without coming into much competition with them. Careful attention to the water requirements, through mulching or irrigation, and the use of suitable fertilizers ought to overcome most of the disadvantages of this system.

Many nurseries grow their plants in full sunlight after they are put in the regular nursery rows. If this is done, attention needs to be given to proper irrigation or heavy mulching, in order to escape injury from drought. Lace bugs also may injure the appearance of the foliage. Plants properly grown in full exposure are apt to be somewhat denser than those grown in shade and often have more flower buds. A little shade, however, is generally considered desirable and this may be provided in open nurseries by the use of lath shades 2½ feet or so above the plants mounted upon light, inexpensive iron fence-posts. In other cases, permanent lath roofs, seven feet above ground, are constructed. Complete lath houses are excellent for young seedlings and are used by some of the best propagators. Some growers favor close planting, with a fence around the outer rows of the plot as protection against winter winds and exposure. Inside the plot, the plants protect one another by their closeness.

Mulching with leaves, shredded cornstalks, old sawdust or some other material is desirable both summer and winter, with oak leaves topping the preferred list. Weeds should be removed by pulling and not by digging or cultivation, which disturbs the shallow-rooted plants.

Fertilizers may be used advantageously and these should be such as are recommended in Chapter VI, chosen to best fit the needs of the situation. The formulas of Mr. Dexter and Dr. White are both in successful use for young plants outdoors.

Some propagators prefer to sow their seeds, especially of azaleas, as soon as ripe in the fall. This schedule brings the plants to the "pricking-off" stage about January first. They can then utilize the entire spring season, from January to July, in one long period of uninterrupted growth, attaining considerable size before growth slows down in midsummer and autumn arrives. The increased size promotes greater hardiness, with the result that certain azaleas, if well developed, are capable of remaining outdoors in frames or pits throughout the ensuing winter instead of being carried over in a greenhouse. This system is useful, therefore, where greenhouse space is limited. It also has possibilities as a method of securing maximum growth in a minimum of time.

A laboratory method, in connection with the sand culture experiments of the New Jersey Experiment Station previously referred to, consists of sowing the seed in pure sand, keeping it moist and supplied with mineral nutrients by a special system of automatic irrigation. This, at present, is a bit too complicated for the layman to attempt, but the results have been surprisingly good and its ultimate commercial application seems not entirely impossible.

Since the above directions were written some years ago covering the orthodox methods of seed-sowing, experimenters who have dared to depart from the time-honored recipes have come up with a few new techniques which may save labor and make success more certain. We now have many gadgets, ranging from artificially lighted, thermostatically controlled, automatically watered Wardian propagating cases to simpler soil media and tricky new fungicides.

Morrison * and others at Washington, D.C., have found it entirely feasible to sow rhododendron seeds on chopped or shredded green sphagnum moss and leave them closed up in a moisture-saturated atmosphere for weeks at a time. The seeds germinate and grow without any soil and, since the sphagnum is not susceptible to ordinary fungous infection, the seedlings are in no danger from damping-off or molding. Also, the labor and hazards of watering are reduced. A flat, a seed-pan or a pot is prepared with nothing but chopped sphagnum moss lightly packed in it. This is topped off with a thin surface layer, a quarter-inch or so, of sphagnum moss which has been rubbed through a quarter-inch screen. The flat is then placed in a pan of water to soak as long as necessary to become thoroughly wetted. After removal and draining off of all free water, the rhododendron or azalea seed may be sown on the surface and left uncovered. A pane of glass is then placed over the top of the flat to keep out the air, and one sheet of newspaper is kept on top of the glass until the seed germinates. No watering will be needed for a month or so, for the glass prevents drying. When it finally needs water, the flat is again set in a pan of water and thus sub-irrigated without the use of any overhead application. The seedlings may be pricked out and transplanted when they are large enough, but will remain alive for a year or so in the sphagnum if left over. No feeding is necessary until transplanting.

Another adaptation is the use of glass or plastic refrigerator boxes with covers for smaller lots of seed. These can be used instead of a covered flat, but just remember that they have no drainage, so do not water them at all after planting.† Pure granulated peat moss gave best results in these tests. Seedlings raised in a closed, moisture-saturated atmosphere, of course, must be very carefully "weaned" to the outside air after they are transplanted. This is effected when transplanting, by putting them into pots, pans or flats which can be kept in a closed case or otherwise covered at first, then gradually lifting the cover, a little at a time, and letting more and more air touch the plants until they are in free air.

---

* Morrison, B. Y. The Glenn Dale azaleas. Am. Rhod. Soc. Yearbook 5:3. 1949.
† Nisbet, F. J. Simplified seedling production. Quar. Bull. Am. Rhod. Soc. 5:160–163. 1951. Also, Hanger, F. E. W. A note on plastic containers. Roy. Hort. Soc. Rhod. Yearbook 7:97–98. London, 1953.

A most significant development, however, has been the use of a new fungicide which can be combined with the use of this closed-up seed-chamber idea. This permits plants to be grown from seed to almost any size, if desired, using regular soil mixtures whenever necessary and without fear of fungous damage in a closed atmosphere. Where fungus might not infect seedlings growing in pure sphagnum, the time comes when they must be put into soil containing humus and other plant food. This fungicide, known as Vancide 51, possesses an enduring residuary action, so that its potency will remain for months if applied to plants kept in a closed vessel. Ordinary soil mixtures will mildew in a few hours if kept in a closed, moist atmosphere, but the presence of the fungicide will prevent all fungous development for long periods. In the experiments by Knudson and Mott at Cornell, wide-mouthed Mason jars with lids were half-filled with peat moss. This was thoroughly wetted with a solution of Vancide 51 (5 cc. of the chemical to 1 liter of water). The liquid surplus was then poured off and the jars were left open for 24 hours to permit the escape of gases. Then rhododendron seeds were sown on the surface of the peat moss (with or without a sprinkling of quartz sand over them), after which the glass lid was replaced on the jar. Placed in a suitable temperature (70°F. is about optimum for germination, 60°F. for subsequent growth), the seed will germinate promptly and grow in the saturated atmosphere of the closed jar without watering or the need of any attention whatever until transplanting size is reached. With such a method, seeds may be started in one's living-room window with no fuss of watering or bother of attention for weeks. This is a boon to the amateur who wishes to grow seedlings.

A worker, whose material was used in the original experiments, has applied the same method with complete success, when using plastic containers instead of fruit jars. He suggests that for larger-scale seed sowing, as well as for subsequent transplanting, deep flats, boxes, or a plastic tent be used, covering them to maintain a closed and moisture-laden atmosphere, and applying the fungicide to prevent the damping-off troubles that often cause so much mortality during the first year or so of a seedling's life. The saving in labor is considerable, too, and the benefit which the plant derives from having a uniform moisture condition in the soil and air cannot be denied. Here, as noted above, all seedlings grown in a closed atmosphere must be gradually acclimated to the open air. A Wardian case is valuable for this operation. Extra artificial light helps young seedlings.

Only an experimenter with very few and valuable seeds would need to resort to laboratory germination of rhododendron seed in sugar-agar-nutrient media, but this can be done successfully with rhododendron seed, using the techniques devised by Knudson for orchid seed germination in sterile culture-tubes. Knudson did this many years ago with seeds of rhododendron and other ericaceous plants, but I have employed it recently in a very practical way and have reported upon it.*

A covering of polyethylene plastic film, the so-called "plastic tent" method, either in small or large units, fits well into the propagation of rhododendrons by seed or by cuttings. Results in both these techniques are described by workers at the Arnold Arboretum, who first applied them to certain uses.† For amateurs, a deep flat is filled with the rooting medium and a wire frame fitted over it for a framework to support a damp cheesecloth covering. Over the cheesecloth is fitted a sheet of semi-transparent polyethylene film large enough to tuck under the sides, ends and bottom of the flat. Large units, built on greenhouse benches, are designed on the same principle. The plastic retains moisture but admits a certain amount of aeration. Once watered and filled, no further attention is needed for some time.

Sphagnum moss (the acid bog plant) has peculiar qualities of resistance to fungi and also seems able to support young seedlings to and beyond the pricking-off stage without the application of any fertilizers, fungicides or other treatments. Its several uses in propagation have been described in a recent publication.‡ Dried sphagnum will absorb up to twenty times its weight in water and will retain it, while still allowing good aeration within its interstices. The time will come, after transplanting, when the seedlings require feeding and gradual exposure to the open air. A peat and sand soil mixture, plus liquid fertilizer, is recommended.

One very important factor, not previously stressed, which applies to all young plants grown in a closed atmosphere, such as under a pane of glass, in a jar or plastic box, or by the plastic tent method, is the matter of light and shade. While high light is desired, hot sun should be carefully guarded against. Keep your seedlings shaded when the sun is warm. Otherwise, without adequate ventilation, a very hot temperature will be built up under the enclosure, and this will injure or destroy the young plants.

Other media for the germination and growing of rhododendron and azalea seedlings have been used. These include such materials as leaf-mold, woods soil, upland peat, and various mosses. These have been largely replaced by the methods described above, of which the sphagnum-moss method appears most promising.

*Bowers, Clement G. Rhododendron seed germination in agar nutrient solution. Nat. Hort. Mag. *33:206–207.* 1954.

† Lipp, L. F. New methods in plant propagation. Arnoldia *13:61–67.* 1953. Also, Coggeshall, R. G. Polyethylene plastic—its application to the propagation of hardwood cuttings. Arnoldia *14:57–63.* 1954.

‡ Creech, John L., R. F. Dowdle and A. O. Hawley, Farmers Bulletin #2085, U.S. Dept. of Agric., Washington, D.C. 1957.

CHAPTER XIII

VEGETATIVE PROPAGATION

ALL *means* of propagating rhododendrons and azaleas, except from seed, come under the head of vegetative or asexual propagation, which may be described as the perpetuation or multiplication of an individual by cuttings, layers, grafting, division, budding or any other means in which sexual reproduction has no part. Sorts necessarily propagated in this way are called clones, and, as noted elsewhere, differ from seed-propagated varieties by being composed of plants inherently identical with one another, whereas each member of a seedling population is a separate individual and hence not genetically identical in all respects. Vegetative propagation is used for all rhododendrons and azaleas which do not come sufficiently true from seed. This includes nearly all the hybrids, as well as many of the choice, selected natural individuals. Since most of our finest garden forms belong in this category, vegetative propagation is of great practical importance, especially in commercial production. Plants which may be propagated in this way are the only ones eligible for plant patents under the United States patent regulations.

Layering is employed extensively in propagating evergreen rhododendrons and some deciduous azaleas. It has been a favorite commercial method of production in England and to some extent in America. Its advantages are that layered plants, being on their own roots from the outset, may be permitted to develop new shoots freely from roots around the base. These give the mature plants a round, shrubby, well-feathered-out appearance at the base which makes them look better than those with a single stem, and are useful for protection. Another advantage is freedom from suckers arising from the grafting stock, which sometimes overgrow and ruin grafted plants. A further advantage is that, if the tops are killed, new shoots coming from below will be true to type. A disadvantage of layering is that many stock plants three feet or more tall must be used for the process, and these are often difficult to obtain if the stock is new or limited in quantity. The process of layering also requires one more year than that of grafting. And it is said that layering is not successful in all cases.

I shall discuss the process of layering as practiced by certain American commercial nurserymen with evergreen rhododendrons. On hand are stock plants of the desired clones, which have been kept in vigorous growth the previous year, so that they are in luxurious condition when propagation is started. Stock plants need not be more than three or four feet tall, but they should have many branches in order to provide numerous points for layering. Plants which have been pinched back when young to induce branching make excellent stock plants.

The stock plant is laid down in nearly a horizontal position, with its ball of roots covered by ordinary rhododendron soil, which may be mounded up some-

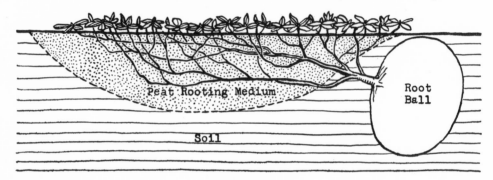

LAYERING

Diagrammatic cross-section showing a method used in laying down a stock plant for propagation.

what as shown in the accompanying diagram. All the branches are carefully spread out in a flat, horizontal plane, like a fan, and these are embedded in a mixture of peat and sand, 50% each by volume. The lower leaves of the branches are removed and the upper portion of each branch which is to be rooted is pegged down with a forked stick as illustrated here. A notch is cut in the stem, about three inches down from the terminal end of each branch (by making a single slanting cut about halfway through the stem). Above the notch, the twig is turned upright with the leaves coming out of the soil. Everything except these leaves and the tips of the branches is covered up with the sand and peat mixture. The layering is done under high lath shades supported by posts, which permit a person to walk around under them as in a sort of arbor. The stock plants are laid down in regular rows. The accompanying figures show a plant in horizontal and vertical cross-section as laid down.

The plants are layered in July and August and are left undisturbed throughout the following two winters and the intervening summer. In the spring of the second year, about 18 or 20 months after laying down, roots will have been formed above the notches on the layered twigs. The stems can then be cut off at the notches and the new plant thus severed from the stock plant can be grown on independently. It requires two years or so in the nursery after the plants are rooted before the new plants reach merchantable size. The old stock plants can be salvaged and, after growing two or three years longer, will again be fit for use in layering. A large plant will yield from 100 to 700 layers.

A STOCK PLANT

as seen from above, after it has been laid flat and spread out in a fan-like manner for layering. The branchlets to be layered are slit and pegged down at the locations indicated by the cross-lines in the above diagram.

Where only a few plants are needed and it is not desired to injure the stock plant, layering offers a means of propagation available to the amateur. In good soil, a branch, usually a lateral or drooping one, may be bent down, notched, pegged to the soil, covered and rooted as a layer. Sometimes a tall ungainly plant may be made to bush out by layering its lower branches around it. If layered in summer, the rooted branch may be severed from the main plant in about 20 months. A flat stone placed over each layer will help to keep it in place. The stock plant is not disturbed.

Layering has been much used in England for propagating deciduous azaleas on their own roots. Stock plants are grown on sandy soil, plus peat, and kept well fed for vigorous vegetative growth. In the spring of the first year, an old stock plant is cut down to within six inches or so of the ground and many new shoots are encouraged to grow from its base. When these new shoots have grown one season, a mound of sandy, peaty azalea soil is built over the plant, almost burying the new shoots and leaving only their tips showing. This is done in the autumn. The moisture within the soil of the mound must be kept steady and not permitted to dry out. During the second year the shoots will form roots inside the mound. In the spring (now the third spring), the mound is cleaned out to the original ground level, the newly rooted shoots are detached from the mother plant and set out into nursery rows. The old mother plant, now cut down, is again allowed to grow new shoots, repeating the process, or is sometimes allowed one year of rest in between. At every operation, the old stock plants produce an increasingly large number of new shoots, so that one very old mother plant may produce a crop of a hundred or more rooted layers in every three-year rotation. In spite of this, layering is often considered a somewhat slow method of propagation compared with that from cuttings.

Propagation of many kinds of rhododendrons by *air-layering* has accompanied the development of plastics. This method is especially good for those who have limited facilities and a small amount of material. It is applicable to either true rhododendrons or to azaleas. A shoot of one-year-old wood is selected at a time when the new growth above it begins to ripen, which is usually in summer. This year-old wood is cut with a short upward incision, making the knife-stroke just deep enough to accommodate some root-inducing powder. Then a pack of moist sphagnum moss (one handful) is wound around this incision and the whole is wrapped in a sheet of polyethylene plastic, tied at top and bottom with rubber bands. By autumn, roots should have formed in the sphagnum moss. after which the rooted shoot may be severed from its parent plant and potted up separately or placed in a bed of peaty soil. In either case, the new plant should be carried on in a greenhouse (cool: 50° to 60°F.) and not allowed to dry out until well established. The following spring it may be planted outdoors.

Propagation by *cuttings* is a method regularly used for a number of rhododendron groups. Azaleas, particularly those of the subseries Obtusum, the Javanicum group and many of the Lapponicums, Triflorums and other Asiatic species, root from cuttings quite readily. The common hardy evergreen sorts, on the other hand, and the deciduous azaleas require special methods. Recent advances in the techniques of propagation by cuttings have resulted in so much success with these more difficult subjects that this form of propagation is now being used more and more. Except in the case of certain difficult-to-root individuals, these new methods are rapidly superseding the old grafting practices, especially since disastrous fungous diseases have made the growing of *R. ponti-cum* understock hazardous.

One of the pioneer experimenters in the rooting of evergreen rhododendrons from cuttings, especially the Catawba hybrids, was Mr. G. G. Nearing of Ridge-wood, New Jersey. In the early 1930's he perfected a special patented cold frame for rhododendron propagation. This has been described in the literature.* A feature of this and most other recommended cutting treatments for rhodo-dendrons is that the frame faces north and is protected against summer sun-shine. Again, rhododendrons under this method appear to root more readily with little or no heat. Almost invariably, growth-inducing plant hormones increase rooting, although there is a decided difference in sensitivity of in-dividual clones of rhododendrons in response to the treatment they receive and to the various strengths and kinds of root-inducing hormones used in the process. This applies to deciduous azaleas as well.

No attempt will be made here to describe in full the various methods of root-ing rhododendrons from cuttings. A great deal of experimental material has been reviewed by Bridgers † in his research report, as well as many precise observations on the anatomical structure and physiological responses of rhodo-dendron stems. Besides the work of Nearing, conducted without a heated green-house, some very successful propagation using a greenhouse has been carried on by other experimenters. Mr. Paul Vossberg of Westbury, New York, who has not yet published his data, has been rooting rhododendron cuttings very suc-cessfully for some time on a commercial scale and has perfected techniques of his own. One gathers that Mr. Vossberg varies his chemical treatments to suit individual clones, or groups of clones, and that very diligent nursing care, plus careful attention to nutrition, light and timing, are essential parts of his pro-cedure. For evergreen rhododendrons, ripened softwood cuttings of the current season's growth are used. Another commercial propagator who roots rhodo-dendron cuttings in a greenhouse is James S. Wells, whose work has been fully described.‡ Using hardy hybrids, he cites twelve critical operations in the process, *viz.* proper timing, type of cutting, making the cutting, wounding, hormone treatment, rooting media, inserting the cuttings, bottom heat, hu-

* Nearing, G. G. and C. H. Connors. Rhododendrons from cuttings. N.J. Agr. Expt. Sta. Bull. 666, 1939. Also Baldsiefen, Warren. Successful rhododendron propagation without a greenhouse. Quar. Bull. Amer. Rhod. Soc. 7:46–52. 1953.

† Bridgers, B. T. Studies of factors inhibiting the rooting of rhododendron cuttings. Quar. Bull. Amer. Rhod. Soc. 6:186–205, 1952; and 7:11–28, 1953. Portland, Ore.

‡ Wells, James S. Propagation of rhododendrons from stem cuttings. Roy. Hort. Soc. Rhod. Yearbook 7:74–82. London, 1953. Also the reader is referred to the entire chapter 27 in Mr. Wells's book, *Plant Propagation Practices* (Macmillan, 1955), and especially pages 280–290. Clones differ as to optimum date for making cuttings; slim cuttings from side shoots are pre-ferred; wounding to expose larger areas of cambium to action of rooting hormones is desirable; 100% atmospheric humidity and maximum light intensity are special points.

midity, temperature, light and after-care. Since clones differ in their responses, each kind may require a special balance, says Wells. Flower buds are removed, but leaves are not removed or reduced by halving unless they are too many or too large.

The *mist-culture* or "fog" method of maintaining saturated atmospheric moisture in the cutting bench of a greenhouse should be described at this point. Owing to the success of this technique, some of the older methods will become obsolete as mist-culture becomes standard procedure in the rooting of cuttings as above referred to. The basic principle underlying this process consists in the maintenance of a steady, high level of relative humidity over the cuttings while forming roots, plus the control of water relations, including transpiration, throughout the period. A very significant day-length and light factor is present, too. Roots will form eventually if the cuttings can be kept "fat" and turgid. Mist-culture bears some resemblance in principle to the plastic-tent method of maintaining atmospheric humidity over seedlings. Despite the constantly high moisture content of the whole setup, there is remarkable freedom from damping-off troubles.

I shall first mention the methods followed in commercial practice which Mr. Wells has described quite fully in his above-cited book. Working with ordinary evergreen rhododendrons, he uses greenwood cuttings taken in late summer or fall (September or November) and wounds these cuttings heavily by removing a thin slice from one side of the base of each cutting for about 1½ inches, using a sharp knife or razor blade. The cut is made only to the cambium layer, no deeper. The cuttings are then treated with a root-inducing hormone. Wells uses the powdered form, 2% indolebutyric acid in 98% talc, and covers the wound well. He uses a rooting medium consisting of 90% peat and 10% sand, and it is essential that the cutting bench be very well drained, because of the almost constant application of water over it. Water-supply pipes are rigged up over the bench, and small fognozzles are inserted at two-foot intervals or sufficiently close to cover all plants with a heavy fog of fine water vapor. Water valves regulated by an electric time-switch turn the water off and on at set intervals. The air temperature is always kept above 50°F. and the water temperature is about the same. Cuttings usually root in from four to six weeks.

Perhaps the system used by Dr. Henry T. Skinner, Director of the U.S. National Arboretum in Washington, D.C., deserves more detailed comment. It has been conspicuously successful in rooting deciduous azaleas, such as the Ghent and Mollis hybrids and the native American species. Also, it is a method that can be used by almost anyone having a small greenhouse and a non-alkaline water supply. The apparatus is somewhat similar to that used by Wells. A well-drained cutting-bench is fitted with a smallish water pipe running horizontally down the middle of the bench at a height not more than two feet above the cuttings. Along this pipe, "Florida" nozzles are spaced at intervals so that the mist will just cover the bench evenly. Above this are electric lights for extra illumination. A low curtain, plastic or otherwise, is hung like a shower curtain along the side of the bench next to the aisle to ward off draughts and splash. The soil medium under mist is a mixture of sand and peat—several other media have been tried. Automatic operation by an electric time-clock cuts the mist off and on. The intervals between "off" and "on" are set apart just far enough to keep the plants covered continuously with a moisture-laden atmosphere, but no more than this, because soluble nutrients will leach out of the plant cells and be lost under continuous drenching. The length of these intervals will vary with season and temperature, but are always relatively short. For instance, the mist may be in operation for only six or eight seconds, then shut off for four minutes before repeating. Thus an almost continuous fog is thrown about the plants, and yet they are not drowned in water. The air is simply not allowed to get dry and the cuttings are kept moist.

Illumination while under mist and also in subsequent after-care is a very essential part of Skinner's technique, and this seems to furnish an answer to a serious problem. Some growers who have attempted mist-culture report that mist-propagated plants possess brittle roots and are mere water-shoots, very difficult to carry on when subsequently transplanted or potted up. Successful mist-propagators reply that such a situation results mainly from inadequate light—extra light is needed to keep things in balance and will produce firm, satisfactory plants. Obviously, too, mist-culture would not be feasible in places where the water supply is "hard," because of the presence of alkaline salts.

For deciduous azaleas, and possibly for true rhododendrons, too, mist-culture permits one to take cuttings much earlier in the season than otherwise, and this is an advantage. All azalea cuttings are first treated with indolebutyric acid. Relatively young cuttings placed under mist in the late spring (June) will not need artificial light, because strong daylight and long days prevail at that season. But immediately thereafter cuttings of deciduous azaleas must be kept under lights continuously while under mist. Right after they come out of the mist the young rooted cuttings should be put into a peaty soil mixture and followed immediately with full light, using electric illumination all night. Some cuttings would proceed without this, but for difficult sorts such as 'Fannie,' on which growth is checked by the early formation of terminal buds, continuous supplementary light is essential.

Subsequent growth will be good if a peaty soil is used and if full light is given. After the cuttings are well rooted, potted up and/or hardened off adequately, they should be given shade-house treatment to protect them from too-hot sun or too-cold air until the plants are ready for growing in the open garden. The transition from peat-culture to normal garden conditions should be gradual. This statement also holds true in the acclimating of Holland-grown stock after importation and to any other peat-grown plant. Having been grown in peat, it will suffer a setback if not continued on peaty soil and gradually weaned into its new situation.

It is this writer's belief that there is nothing inherently wrong with rapid or forced culture under mist or in peat or in forced seedling production, provided that adequate light is given and proper precautions are taken to insure firm growth and a gradual hardening-off period. The warning should be repeated here, too, that all azaleas and most rhododendrons are quite tender when small anyway, gaining in hardiness only as they develop in age and stature. Unfortunately, not all growers are careful to observe these principles in the sale of commercial stock.

If *leaf-and-stem cuttings* were entirely successful, they would have the advantage of permitting more plants to be propagated from limited stock—something that is needed in the slow-moving multiplication of rhododendrons, especially new and valuable clones. Dr. Skinner * has made a type of leaf cutting in which not only the leaf-blade and entire petiole is included, but a portion of the attached stem, too, with a dormant bud. It is necessary to have the bud, because this is where the new stem will form. The critical elements are, first, to make roots develop before the leaf material disintegrates, and, second, to break the dormancy of the bud. Well developed leaves, taken early from the current season's growth, are used, plus petioles and three-quarters of an inch of stem bearing a good axillary bud. This is treated with a root-inducing powder and buried shallow in a suitable rooting medium. With some rhododendrons this method is successful, but not others.

With such rhododendrons as *R. catawbiense* and *R. maximum* as they grow wild in the Carolina mountains, a large burl is formed near the base of each old plant. If the top of the plant is cut down, burned off or injured above ground, numerous new shoots, from previously dormant buds, begin to grow out of the burl. If the burl were taken up and divided, it is probable that its several parts would each develop into a separate plant. This form of division is a unique form of vegetative propagation, probably little known.

Real propagation by *division* is practiced with at least one species, *R. atlanticum,* a deciduous azalea which is unique in having a stoloniferous root system. It sends up shoots here and there, which may be cut off and grown as separate plants. *R. pemakoense* and *R. radicans* have similar possibilities.

Until recently *grafting* was the popular method of vegetative propagation

* Skinner, Henry T. Leaf-and-bud cuttings. Nat. Hort. Mag. *3*:19. Washington, 1954.

for rhododendrons in America. Lately, however, heavy losses due to infection of stock plants with *Phytophthora* and other fungi have caused growers to search for other methods. Discovering new techniques in the raising of own-root plants from cuttings, the growers are now turning to these other methods as commercial procedures. Nevertheless, grafting is still very useful, especially for plants that do not make their own roots readily, or where the roots lack vigor or where special requirements are faced. One very valuable use of grafting has been its application to limited stocks of imported scions when received in America by air mail from foreign countries. Owing to United States plant quarantine regulations, it is generally forbidden to bring in plants from abroad having soil on their roots. It has been found feasible and permissible, however, to import scions for grafting. Developments in transoceanic air transportation have made this method so convenient and practicable that new hybrid clones and other selected plants can be shipped as scions and grafted after arrival. This has made it possible for American growers to develop stocks of new foreign varieties despite the strict quarantine. The American Pacific Coast is climatically favorable for the growth of British material and hence is the chief user of imported kinds. Grafting is also used advantageously in the propagation of large florists' azaleas, grown under glass, which are said to do better when grafted than when on their own roots.

The species which has long remained in most favor as a grafting stock for evergreen rhododendrons is *Rhododendron ponticum*. In early life, at least, it is presumably somewhat more vigorous than the native *R. catawbiense* and certainly more so than *R. maximum,* and is supposed to work better in the grafting operation than most other species. Vigorous seedlings of *R. catawbiense* are sometimes used, however, and also seedlings of *R. maximum,* the latter being quite slow to grow but more resistant to fungous disease. A clone known as 'Cunningham's White,' an old hybrid presumed to have been a cross between *R. caucasicum* and *R. ponticum,* which roots very readily from cuttings, has been used as a grafting stock quite extensively in Germany and is highly regarded. While the other grafting stocks are raised from seed, this clone can be rooted quite easily from cuttings of ripened wood taken in August and held overwinter outdoors in a cold frame, the roots being formed by spring. These own-root plants are then grown on for another year, by which time they are of suitable size to use as grafting stock.

Certain disadvantages of grafted rhododendrons are apparent. One of these is the occurrence of shoots, or suckers, from the understock, which grow up to compete and become confused with the grafted clone. In America, this seldom happens north of Long Island, because the cold climate of the Northeast usually kills the above-ground parts of *R. ponticum,* the usual rootstock. I cannot feel that *ponticum* understock impairs the hardiness of a grafted plant, however, because its tenderness seems to be a leaf characteristic and not anything affecting the root or scion directly. But there is some reason to believe that the understock commonly used for the grafting of deciduous azaleas does adversely affect the ability of the plant to make vigorous vegetative growth in summer, thus impairing its winter hardiness.

When grafting is done upon *Rhododendron ponticum,* seedling plants are commonly raised for this purpose. They are sown indoors in the usual way and are handled exactly as prescribed for seedlings in general. In cold climates they are always overwintered indoors, growing either in pots, flats, benches or in ground beds. Given proper care, they develop rapidly. They should be given high lath shade or other protection from hot sunlight during the warmest months. During September and the other autumn months they should be watched closely for leaf-spot disease, to which *R. ponticum* is especially susceptible during cool, moist weather. If this trouble appears, it may be checked somewhat in the greenhouse by turning on the heat and drying the air. Bordeaux mixture as a spray helps to protect healthy foliage against infection.

When the plants are about two years old they will be about one foot or so tall, with main stems the size of a lead pencil. They are then of proper size to graft. The plants should be potted during the previous summer or fall, usually in three-inch to four-inch pots, and permitted to become established. If potted in September or earlier, they should be ready to graft by December or January.

Some growers consider an ideal propagating house to be one having only two aisles, with a six-foot bench between them in the middle of the house and a three-foot bench on either side against the outer walls. The grafting-cases ("sweat-boxes") are constructed on the center bench, where light is abundant and bottom heat is not lowered or condensation of moisture increased by proximity to the outer walls. The side benches are then used for grafting stock and for the grafted plants after removal from the cases. The type of house actually used, however, is more often dictated by convenience or necessity, although a smallish house is considered necessary unless the larger structure is specially designed for propagating purposes. In all cases, provision should be made for shading the glass and also for securing adequate atmospheric moisture, all of which are most easily controlled in a small house.

The grafting-cases themselves may be about 12 inches deep with close-fitting sash cut to fit the top and hinged at the back. When closed, the sashes are level, except where provision is made for removing the drip of condensed moisture which collects on the lower side of a sloping-roofed case. More recently, propagators have been experimenting with plastic coverings and other materials as substitutes for glass.

Heater pipes under the bench beneath the grafting-cases provide bottom heat. Four inches or more of peat moss or similar material is placed in the bottom of the case to furnish a medium in which to plunge the pots. When in operation the temperature of the grafting-case should be kept steadily as near to 58° or 60°F. as possible. The house itself should run at about 50° at night. The latter is the right temperature for the young understock plants before being grafted.

The stock plants should be about the diameter of a lead pencil at the point where the graft is made. Seedlings often run unevenly, and when some of the plants are of insufficient size these may be kept indoors over winter and grown on for another year before using. January is a favorite month in which to graft rhododendrons. The scions may be cut at that time from plants growing outdoors, but if the weather is cold the scions should be brought indoors and put in a cool, dark place to adjust themselves and thaw out before being used.

There are several possible types of grafting, but the veneer graft and the side graft are the ones most used. For a veneer graft, select a stock plant and scion, the stems of which are as near the same size as possible. Use a very sharp knife and make a cut into the main stem of the understock about an inch or two above the rim of the pot in which it is growing (see accompanying figures). This is the lower cut and should go about one-third through the stem. Then start about one and one-half inches above and make another cut downward until it joins the first. Take a scion with a stem of about the same size and trim it to fit the cut which has been made on the stock. In doing this cutting, first note the way the foliage turns on the scion and then cut stock and scion so that when joined and laid in the grafting-case the best leaves will face the glass. The cuts should not be made at too sharp an angle, as about one and one-half inches should be allowed and the cut should not go more than one-third of the way through the stem, as previously noted. The cuts on stock and scion should match as nearly as possible so the joint will be even. It is best to trim the scion to fit the stock. Good clean cuts are preferable to much trimming. If the two can not be perfectly matched in size, be sure to join them perfectly at one side of the stem, so that the actively growing green cambium tissue, just beneath the bark of the two members, will abut evenly and form a union as they grow into one another.

After being joined, the scion and stock are tied in place with cotton twine. Experienced technicians develop their own methods of performing the various operations of cutting, fitting and tying. Some cut the twine into eight-inch lengths, while others use small balls. Beginning at the top of the cut, the twine may be wound around the stem, making sure to wind it over the upper end of the string and thereby hold it fast. Wind it around, about one-quarter of an inch apart, keeping the string firm but not so tight as to cut into the bark and injure it. When a point somewhat below the base of the cut is reached, the twine can be slipped beneath the final loop, drawn tight and cut off—not too short.

A somewhat simpler method and one that is probably preferred by most propagators of rhododendrons is the side graft. A long, slicing cut is first made in the stem of the stock plant. This is illustrated in figures 1 to 4 of the plate entitled "The Side Graft" (following page 206), which explains it better than it can be described in the text. This slicing cut is made about one and one-half inches long and downward on the understock, but leaving a flap which is attached at its base. Then the scion is cut wedge-shaped, on both sides, to exactly fit into the flap made by the first cut on the understock. When brought together the cut surfaces of the two members should match so that the cambium will join. The graft is then brought together and held there by winding with twine as in the veneer graft. Callus forms between the two cambiums and the two members grow together.

After the grafting operation is completed, the grafted plants, still in their pots, are put into the grafting-case; this should be done without delay, as each flat of plants is grafted. Each should be inspected to make sure that no disjoining or loosening has occurred and that the barks of stock and scion are in perfect contact. Then the plants are set into the case. It was formerly advised to set the pots into the peat moss within the case lying somewhat on their sides—at a 45 degree angle—but Wells * refutes this by saying that in his experiments the grafted plants do just as well when standing upright as when lying on a slope, and that an upright position is much more efficient. The peat should be moist and nearly cover the pots.

After the grafted plants are put in the case as described, the sash is closed and not opened except for a few minutes each day to allow the surplus condensed moisture to dry off the glass. The cases containing newly grafted plants should be shaded with cheesecloth, paper or muslin whenever the sun shines for the first few days. If the peat is wet at first, probably no additional watering whatever will be required for the first month. During this period the plants should never be subjected to draughts in event that the cases should happen to be open at any time.

The union will commence to form within four weeks or so and the plants may then have about one-third of the top cut away from the understock. At this period, the grower has an opportunity of moving the plants within the case. He should observe them carefully for possible disease, turning over the peat and wetting it if needed. After this, the grafting-case may be opened a little

* Wells, James S. *Plant Propagation Practices,* p. 271. 1955.

longer each day, increasing the period very gradually until, by eight weeks after grafting, the covers may be removed all day.

At the end of the two months the plants will mostly be able to leave the case. They may then be taken out and placed upright on the open bench of the propagating house or in some other house where the atmosphere is moist and close, without draughts. They should be closely watched and put back in the case if any show that the union has not been formed. The remaining portion of the understock, above the graft-union, should have another third cut off (eight weeks from grafting) and after four weeks in the open house (12 weeks from grafting) the remnant should be entirely removed, leaving nothing but the rootstock and scion with the graft-union joining them. In all these operations care should be taken not to strain the union as the plants are handled. Finally, the twine may be cut off carefully.

The grafting of azaleas will be considered in the next chapter when dealing with those raised for blooming under glass. It may be stated here, however, that for florists' sorts, such as the Rutherford hybrids, it is thought that they develop better in later life if grafted than when on their own roots. At Bobbink's nursery, the grafting of these hybrids is usually done between October first and June first, but it may be done at any time under favorable conditions. An Indian azalea clone called 'Concinna' (not *R. concinnum*) is recommended for understock. Cuttings of this are taken, beginning in April, and when rooted are potted in 2¼-inch pots. They are then grown about six weeks before the grafting operation. Grafting is done while the plants are in actively growing condition. A grafted azalea should attain a crown diameter of four to six inches in two years after grafting.

The grafting of deciduous azaleas as practiced in Europe involves the use of seedlings of the Pontic azalea (*R. luteum*) as understock for Ghent hybrids. The operation is done in winter and a whip-graft is used, making the point of union very low. Directions call for a cool temperature (40°F.), with the plants buried in moist sphagnum moss until the union is healed. They may be held cool for spring planting in frames, with sash and lath shades. Such plants are sometimes not too successfully grown on. It is commonly observed that a year or two is required for any azalea plants to adjust themselves to new conditions in America when coming from the peaty beds of the Netherlands. It therefore helps when imported plants, raised in peat abroad, can be carried on in peat beds after coming to America. Some grafted azaleas appear to suffer through inability to get enough water through the graft-union to support top growth during the critical growing period of June. The immediate result is a checking of growth and hardening of tissues in early summer, followed by increased susceptibility to winter injury the following autumn. While perhaps not killed outright, the plants tend to dwindle through winter injury in successive years and never attain health until new own-root shoots develop from the ground. American conditions of hot summers and cold winters are severe, so that the use of own-root deciduous azaleas is coming to be preferred instead of grafted plants. No doubt incompatibility of understock and scion is involved, and it would seem that better understock material than *R. luteum* might be found. Research is needed. Dr. Skinner has suggested that the American species *R. canescens* be tried as an understock, because it roots freely and also, in common with other azaleas native to the Lower South, does not need a winter rest-period; hence, it continues to grow if held indoors during the post-grafting season.

Other minor forms of vegetative propagation of rhododendrons or azaleas are possible, but seldom feasible. *Budding,* using a T-cut, has succeeded on *R. catawbiense.* The *cleft-graft* has been used in top-working old plants, and a commercial application of *tip-grafting* has been worked out. *Root-grafting* is still another method. All these are described in the literature.*

* See: Lem, Halfdan. Top-grafting rhododendrons out of doors. Am. Rhod. Soc. Yearbook 2:17-20, 1946; also, Yeates, J. S. Tip-grafting rhododendrons, azaleas and other plants. Roy. Hort. Soc. Rhod. Yearbook 7:83-88, 1953; also, Bowler, S. Root-grafting rhododendrons. Jour. Roy. Hort. Soc. 57:352. 1932.

CHAPTER XIV

CULTURE UNDER GLASS

RHODODENDRONS and azaleas may be grown as greenhouse subjects with relative ease. They are useful for commercial forcing or as conservatory plants. Their method of culture depends upon the kinds grown and the purpose for which they are intended.

Those most commonly grown under glass are the so-called Indian azaleas and their allies which have long been employed as florists' potted plants. Their natural season of bloom is early spring, with some varieties earlier than others, so that they can easily be brought into flower in midwinter and at Easter, making azaleas one of the most valuable commercial potted plants for that season of the year.

In this country at the present time the Indian azaleas, with their relatives the Kurumes and the intermediate or Sander types, are the only plants of the rhododendron group which are much cultivated under glass. There are other rhododendrons, however, which might well be employed also for commercial forcing or for conservatory use. Some of the wild species, both American and Chinese, are early blooming, force well and make good specimens when potted or tubbed. Some of these may be grown to blooming size rather quickly and a few others may be collected from the wild as mature plants, cut back and grown into acceptable commercial forcing plants with little expense. Others, of course, are primarily cool-house plants for the conservatory, some requiring a considerable time before reaching blooming size from seed. One class, those from the tropics, requires almost warm-house conditions. Thus there are already varied types of plants to suit different conditions, while a great many species still remain to be tested, some of which may prove of value under glass. The newer introductions, to a large extent, have been evaluated solely upon their merits as garden shrubs, and some which are useless in the garden may prove valuable in the greenhouse when the greenhouse men get around to test them. The Kurume azaleas furnish a good example of an introduced race which, failing to adapt themselves to outdoor culture in cold climates, have speedily become valuable additions to the commercial florist's list of potted plants for forcing. Out of this general source, also, have come some other hybrids, which bid fair to take a front-rank place as forcing azaleas because of their rich colors and general desirability. Myriads of possibilities exist in the scores of unworked-with species which may some day yield valuable new forms or hybrids. It is not too much to expect good new races of greenhouse azaleas and rhododendrons to arise at some future time.

Rhododendrons and azaleas will withstand living-room conditions in winter as well as the average potted plant and better than some. I have seen them growing, in a variety of species and forms, in a sunny kitchen window, where even seedlings were being raised.

An important use of azaleas and rhododendrons is in forcing them for exhibition at flower shows. Many sorts are forced annually for this purpose and they invariably make effective and beautiful displays. Winter forcing is also used by plant breeders in order to obtain out-of-season bloom for hybridization purposes. By the correct timing and temperatures, species which normally bloom at different times can be brought into bloom together. Experience alone will determine the correct time and temperature, unless the species is one commonly forced. (See also p. 133.)

Although certain species and clones may be made to bloom out of season by forcing them under glass, others are worthless for this purpose and cannot by any ordinary means be made to bloom out of their accustomed season. It is probably unsafe to draw conclusions in advance of actual knowledge, but it may be stated as a provisional rule that the early-blooming sorts will respond to forcing while the late-blooming ones are more difficult. It is improbable that any short-day forms exist in the genus. The species which naturally bloom early need little encouragement when given heat, light and water in winter. Among the common rhododendrons of America, for instance, *Rhododendron carolinianum* is an excellent forcer, requiring only six weeks in a coolhouse in February to make good flowers. The early azaleas, likewise, such as *Rhododendron dauricum, R. japonicum* and most of the members of the subseries Obtusum, are more or less ready forcers. *R. maximum,* on the other hand, although forced from January, failed to bloom before the latter part of June, only a week or so ahead of its natural schedule. In subsequent experiments, however, the combination of heat plus "long day" artificial light was successful in inducing *R. maximum* to bloom in early spring. Those which bloom in midseason may or may not respond to forcing, depending upon the particular variety, or even individual, involved. *R. roseum* can be forced with some degree of success, while *R. calendulaceum,* in our experiments covering two years, seemed unable to bloom indoors much ahead of its regular period. Several of the Chinese alpines appear to be successful forcers and precocious bloomers when raised from seed. Further experimentation is needed to determine which species hold desirable possibilities as subjects for commercial pot-plant culture, but the matter is one which merits attention. Day-length is important.

Another promising sidelight which may bring about important developments in the culture of rhododendrons under glass is furnished by the New Jersey sand-culture experiments, previously alluded to. The practical application of ·such methods is most feasible in a greenhouse where conditions are more controllable than outdoors. This work has demonstrated that some rhododendrons, at least, respond to culture in pure sand plus chemical nutrient solutions with such increased vigor and hastened maturity as to bring about a tremendous saving in time.

In former years quantities of azaleas, propagated in Holland and Belgium, were shipped to the United States, where they were promptly forced in greenhouses and sold by florists. Before the Plant Quarantine Act became effective, practically no azaleas or rhododendrons were propagated in America. The imported product was fairly cheap, while American climatic and labor conditions were relatively unfavorable. When the imported supply was cut off by the quarantine, however, it became necessary for American growers to produce their own stock. Several firms of specialists arose. Although it required some time for American production to get under way, it is now furnishing an increasing quantity of greenhouse azaleas to the domestic trade.

In view of the fact that several years are required in which to produce salable plants, it is probably more advantageous for the average florist to buy his plants from a wholesale azalea grower than to propagate them himself. The methods of propagation and culture are most efficiently worked out by commercial specialists who employ various methods, using those which best seem to suit their individual needs. Where climate and soil are especially good, where suitable labor is plentiful, production costs low and a good market available, a specialist can probably raise and sell plants of blooming size for less than an average person can grow them.

Some of the details of propagation have been covered in the last chapter. The Kurume azaleas and their allies—in other words, the small azaleas of the Obtusum subseries—are commonly raised from cuttings. These are made of the ripened wood of the current season's growth, young but not too soft. The cuttings are frequently one and one-half to two inches long and are placed straight down in the soil of a cutting bench or flat. This soil rooting medium is four to six inches deep and, in common practice, mild bottom heat is provided. Either sand or granulated peat furnishes a suitable rooting medium, but in tests at the Boyce Thompson Institute best results were obtained from a mixture of 50% sand and 50% acid peat. It was also found, in the same experiments, that cuttings from this type of azalea could be rooted in any month of the year.* Certain growers report that 75% sand and 25% German peat give excellent results as a rooting medium. Usually that time is chosen in which suitable wood is available on the stock plants. Frequently this is in late summer. In Germany, January is said to be the favorite month for rooting cuttings. Rooting requires about six weeks, after which the plants are potted and kept in a 55° greenhouse. Certain growers keep the young plants outdoors in shaded frames during the summer, while others allow them to remain indoors. Shading the glass and frequent syringing is practiced during the hot, dry weather to preserve cool, moist atmospheric conditions in the greenhouse or frame. Kurume azaleas have the advantage of blooming when fairly small, but the Indian azaleas require three to four years in which to reach salable size.

Since the larger Indian azaleas require more time to develop into good own-root plants from cuttings, it is generally considered that time is saved and other advantages gained by grafting them. Seedling stock is used by some growers, but most propagators prefer to use rooted cuttings as the stock for grafting. Any vigorous azalea of the Obtusum subseries may be used as stock and growers often employ certain favorite plants, sometimes mere nameless seedlings, as material for their stock-plant cuttings. *R. mucronatum* (commonly miscalled 'Azalea indica alba') is a vigorous and popular grafting stock. Since fairly large stock may be used, Indian azaleas may be brought to merchantable size about two years sooner by grafting than by propagation from own-root cuttings.

Some of the best American propagators do the grafting operation in January. Wood of the previous season's growth is used; for instance, wood grown in 1934 is employed for grafting in January 1935. The stock plant is usually at least two years old from cutting when used for grafting. Its age and size depend, however, upon the type of grafted plant desired. If a bushy plant is wanted, the graft is made at a low point on the stem. The prevailing custom is to graft most plants several inches up on the stem, producing a low-standard or short tree-like effect, with a small "trunk" six or eight inches long. For exhibition purposes regular "standard" specimen plants are produced, with the graft made two feet or more high on a long-stemmed stock plant. Such a result is attained by allowing the grafting stock to grow tall before the graft is made, keeping it pruned to one single main stem throughout this period. The grafting stock may be several years old before it is used and, when a large specimen standard is desired, several years more are required in which a large head is formed of the scion, so that the plant may be ten to fifteen years old before it is exhibited.

---

* Hitchcock, A. E. Effect of peat moss and sand on rooting response of cuttings. Bot. Gazette *86*:121–148. 1929.

The grafting operation is done on ripened new wood. This wood is smallish, the twigs upon which the scions are placed being not over one-half inch in diameter. The stock is potted. Several different types of graft are used, all of which are suitable, although the veneer graft or some of its modifications is often preferred. This is a side graft, similar to that described for rhododendrons, and may be made with or without a "heel." Splice and cleft grafts are also used. Ordinarily, the stock and scion should about match in size in the splice or cleft grafts.

The grafted area is wound with string, thread or some other suitable material and placed in a grafting case where the air is moist and the temperature even. After a union has formed, which should occur within two months, the plants should be removed from their case by gradually exposing them to more dry air until they can stand ordinary greenhouse conditions. As they start to grow and the stem expands, the thread or other material with which the graft was tied must be cut and removed to prevent strangulation of the stem. When summer comes the plants may be placed outdoors in shaded frames with their pots plunged in the soil or they may be allowed to remain within the greenhouse. In all climates where the winters are cold the plants should be brought indoors in the late autumn. They are shifted or repotted, of course, whenever necessary, to prevent their growth from becoming checked at any time. The soil should be a mixture of peat, sand and slightly acid loam or a similar mixture such as any light rhododendron soil. It should, of course, be acid.

It requires three years or more to grow a grafted Indian azalea into salable size under prevailing conditions. During this period the plant is regularly disbudded to prevent blooming, with the object of inducing a maximum of vegetative growth without loss of energy through flower production. It is customary, in many places, to keep the plants trimmed back to a flat top.

The forcing of most Indian and Kurume azaleas is simple. The plants are left outdoors in protected frames or else kept in a very cool greenhouse (about 40°F.) until December or January, when they are brought into a warmer place. During the entire forcing period they should be kept relatively moist, at 60°F. night temperature, or more, depending upon the time the flowers are wanted. The length and temperature of the forcing period will depend upon the time chosen for flowering, the amount of sunlight and the kind of varieties grown. In the daytime the temperatures in the greenhouse may be allowed to rise ten or fifteen degrees above the prescribed limits if the sun is shining. In general, the Indian azaleas of commerce are classed as either early or late blooming varieties. The earliest ones may be forced for Christmas and mid-winter, while the later sorts come for Easter and the first weeks of spring. Lists of azaleas suitable for forcing are given in Chapter XXIV.

It will be noted that more recently a number of additional hybrid races of azaleas have come into commercial use as florists' pot plants. These include the Pericat azaleas, the Belgian Indian azaleas, the Rutherford hybrids and others. Although almost any azaleas belonging to the Obtusum subseries may be forced, relatively few clones are presently being marketed for this purpose in America.

Mention will be made elsewhere of the Sander hybrid azaleas, some of which are included in a subsequent list. They are intermediate in size between the Indian and Kurume azaleas. Although 'Hexe,' an old hybrid clone dating from 1885, is well known and much used nowadays in the floral trade, the other clones are little known. Because of their rich colors and other advantages, I believe these hybrid azaleas offer good possibilities for the commercial florist. They seem to possess the floriferousness of the Kurume azaleas combined with a flower of larger size and stronger character. Although several of Sander's original varieties have been lost, those which remain are worthy of trial as greenhouse subjects.

The Mollis hybrids are not included in the list of forcing varieties (page 450). In some regions they are used extensively for forcing, but in America they seem to be little used under glass except as they are employed in the adornment of flower shows. They are not without advantages. Since there are no yellow or orange colors among the Indian azaleas or their allies, the Mollis and Japonicum groups provide this color in forms which have large flowers, force readily and make a bold display. They are, however, a bit more transitory than the others, since all the buds on a plant open almost at one time and when they are gone the blooming period is over. The flowers, I suspect, also lack something of the substance and keeping quality of the Indian sorts, while the plants are a bit coarser in structure and do not possess quite such an interesting branching habit. To remedy the situation resulting from a relatively short season of bloom, some growers and exhibitors prepare their Mollis plants for exhibition by dropping a bit of gum arabic into the center of each flower. It is claimed that this treatment will prevent the corolla of a flower from dropping off, so that while the corolla stays on it remains in good condition for a long time, thereby greatly prolonging the time that a plant will retain its good appearance. The gum arabic may be applied from the end of a straw or, with an eye-dropper or pipette. In passing, it may be mentioned that the grafting methods for the Mollis azaleas are similar to those used for the Indian types. Cuttings are rarely employed. *Rhododendron japonicum* forces well and should be an invaluable material for early spring flower shows. A Mollis hybrid known as 'Altaclarense' is also valuable.

R. carolinianum forces easily and makes a delightful plant when blooming in a pot or tub in mid-winter. Moreover, it loses most of its pinkish or magenta color when forced indoors, becoming a pearly white which is really attractive. Besides this, the perfectly white form, variety *album,* may also be forced and is often somewhat creamy in the bud. It is abundant in the wild and also comes true from seed. Some of the most beautiful large-sized potted plants I have ever seen have been specimens of *R. carolinianum* forced in a greenhouse for winter bloom. This species, however, has not been grown by commercial florists, doubtless because of their unfamiliarity with its advantages and also because its size is a trifle large for common usage. It is no larger, however, than the average potted hydrangea. And it needs to occupy greenhouse space for less than two months, which favors economy. Small collected and cut-back plants are relatively cheap. It may also be grown from seed without great difficulty, being one of the most rapid growers after it gets started. Being perfectly hardy, it need not be handled under glass from the time it is out of the seed-flat until it is ready to force. And it will bloom when small enough to make feasible the handling of it in eight-inch pots. Plants brought in from outdoors in January and carried at 60°F. will bloom in about eight weeks.

In Europe, hardy garden hybrid rhododendrons have long been used by florists to force as potted plants for spring sale. If the plants have been pinched back while growing in the nursery, so that they are bushy and well-budded, they may be brought into the greenhouse in February or March, potted up and sold to the public in from three to six weeks, depending upon the earliness of the clone. If hardy kinds are chosen, the buyer may remove the faded flowers and set out the plant in his garden in a permanent outdoor site as soon as the weather is suitable. While most of the azaleas forced in American greenhouses are too tender to grow outdoors in cold latitudes, some rhododendrons would serve this purpose admirably, provided they were not forced too strongly, and provided also that they are late enough so that they do not have to be kept indoors too long before being set in the garden. They make very handsome potted plants, however.

Rhododendrons are not all equally good for forcing in this way. In 1947 and 1948 the Growers Association of Boskoop, Holland, conducted some comprehensive trials in the winter-forcing of hybrid rhododendrons in their experimental greenhouses. Out of 125 clones tested, 45 were found to be satisfactory for this purpose. The Caucasicum hybrids were found to bloom very early. The results, both good and bad, have been reported by Grootendorst,* and those clones appearing most favorable are listed in Chapter XXIV, page 451. It should be noted that any kinds which do not have a good compact habit of growth,

---

* Grootendorst, Herman J. Rhododendrons en Azalea's. Vereniging voor Boskoop Culturen, pp. 69–71. Boskoop, 1954. See also (same author) Rhododendrons for Forcing. Am. Rhod. Soc. Yearbook for 1948, pp. 64–73. Portland, Oregon.

or do not set buds freely, or have loose flower trusses, or fade when forced or which cannot stand the heat of forcing should all be regarded as unsuitable. This rules out a number of the well-known clones.

Several of the large Chinese species, tender or only half-hardy outdoors, are suitable for the conservatory. Some of the highly colored species and hybrids, such as those which grow in Cornwall, England, will make excellent effects indoors, if species are selected which do not become too tall or which do not take too long to bloom from seed or grafts. Plants of many different series have been thus grown, but, at the moment, it is difficult to recommend any as outstanding. They are distinctly cool-house plants. Some of the excellent English hybrids are suitable for the American conservatory.

The species and hybrids of the Javanicum group belong in a class by themselves. They are rare in America, but some are interesting and beautiful. They are suitable only for the warm greenhouse, where the temperature never goes below 55° or 60°F., accompanied by plenty of moisture and by shade in summer. It is said that the Javanicums need to be planted in tubs or pots if flowers are desired, because, if planted in ground beds, they make such vigorous vegetative growth that they do not produce blossoms. Freely flowering plants are very fine, as they bloom almost continuously throughout the year, having shoots in various stages of development at all times. A striking demonstration of this was made in England many years ago by Mr. Veitch, who brought Javanicum flowers to the fortnightly meetings of the Royal Horticultural Society for an entire year. Javanicums require copious moisture at all times. They seldom exceed six feet in height and should be pinched back to retain a good shape. They are propagated from cuttings of half-ripened wood, rooted in a case. Some of the hybrid clones are listed in Chapter XXIII.

Besides the members of the Javanicum group, there are two other general classes of rhododendrons for the conservatory. The first of these are the species native to the Himalayan rain-forests, which are not winter-hardy at temperatures much below 30°F. These comprise such species as *R. Nuttallii* and *R. Griffithianum,* large plants which require much room and would be grown in a cool house (50° to 60°F.), while the Javanicums are warm house plants (70°F.).

The second group comprise the so-called Indian azaleas (*R. Simsii* hybrids) and also some medium-sized rhododendrons of Asiatic origin, such as *R. bullatum, R. burmanicum, R. ciliicalyx, R. Dalhousiae, R. Edgeworthii, R. formosum, R. Johnstoneanum, R. Lindleyi, R. Oldhamii* and a good assortment of hybrid clones, including 'Fragrantissimum.'

In growing the tropical or semi-tropical rhododendrons indoors, it should be remembered that several are more or less epiphytic and require a soil much higher in peat than the other species. This is especially true of the Javanese and Malayan species. While they require a very light soil (a mixture of peat, charcoal and sand is recommended, plus a mere dusting of loam), they bloom best if somewhat root-bound. So keep them in under-sized pots.

Along with other kinds of plants, azaleas are adaptable to the Japanese dwarfing treatment known as Bonsai. Forms of *R. indicum* appear in Oriental illustrations. We shall not here go into the particular treatments used to produce Bonsai plants. The interesting branching habit of azaleas, plus skillful pruning and restricted nourishment over long periods of years, can produce these picturesque results.

Large specimens of the Indian azaleas make excellent conservatory plants. They bloom every year during the late winter months and a succession of bloom over a period of considerable time may be secured by a proper selection of varieties. When not in bloom their foliage is handsome and their habit of growth attractive.

The standard greenhouse sprays and fumigants, so far as I know, are all suitable for rhododendrons and azaleas under glass. Systematic spraying or fumigation at regular intervals, whether the plants seem to need it or not, will prevent most of the commoner greenhouse pests which attack these plants if given a chance. Such frequent greenhouse visitors as mealy bugs, red spider and thrips may usually be controlled on these plants by following the general directions for the control of such pests in greenhouses. Most of the diseases are rusts or leaf spots. With proper management, none of these enemies will cause trouble.

As for soils and fertilizers, the directions given for outdoor soil mixtures and fertilizer dosages are applicable to greenhouse practice also. Soil mixtures should ordinarily contain some peat and should be kept carefully on the acid side, especially if manure-water is used as a fertilizer or if the water with which they are irrigated is "hard." In the latter case, measures must be taken to prevent alkalinity as a result of the accumulation of lime deposits or other precipitated mineral salts. Such preventive or remedial measures may consist of chemical treatment or merely the frequent repotting of the plants, using abundant quantities of acid peat in the soil mixture. Irrigation with stored rainwater, which is soft and free from lime, sometimes solves the problem where only a few plants are involved. As mentioned elsewhere, it is sometimes feasible to plunge the potted plants in peat, thus making it unnecessary to use so much water directly on the plants. Soil that is too acid will sometimes make azalea leaves turn yellowish and chlorotic.

CHAPTER XV

THE MECHANISM OF REPRODUCTION

THE plant world has always been an interesting field for biological research and not a few of the great fundamental discoveries concerning life processes, as, for instance, the original discovery of the cell, have been made by persons working with plant material. Again and again, areas in plant science have been opened up which have led to tremendous advances in human physiology and in medicine. In many of their vital phenomena, plants are similar to humans.

In the preceding chapters we have seen how some rhododendrons live and breathe, move their leaves, have illnesses, utilize food and undergo other life processes. In approaching the subjects of seedling production, inheritance and the origin of new varieties, we are again facing things that have an almost exact counterpart in the animal kingdom. To properly understand and take advantage of the very practical matters of making hybrids and raising new and improved strains of rhododendrons and azaleas, we must first know something of the vital processes which underlie these things. Accordingly, in the next three chapters, I propose to say a few words concerning what we know, thus far, of the phenomena of reproduction, inheritance and sterility as they occur in the genus *Rhododendron*. I shall also mention a few basic facts for the benefit of the layman, who might otherwise form misconceptions regarding some of the phenomena involved.

Every seed borne on a rhododendron is the result of a union between a male and female parent. We may assume, for the time being, that these two parents exist as separate plants, the mother or female parent being the plant upon which the seed is borne. Actually, this involvement of two separate plants as parents is the method most commonly found with rhododendrons in nature, although, as we shall see, one plant usually bears both male and female sex organs.

A perfect rhododendron flower is shown in the accompanying diagram. The single, slender, stalk-like structure which comes up out of the very center of the flower and has a little knob on its end is called the *pistil*. It derives its name from the fact that, as it rests in the cup-like enclosure formed by the petals, it resembles, in some flowers, a chemist's pestle resting in a mortar. This pistil consists of three parts: the little knob on the end is called the *stigma,* the larger part at the base is the *ovary* and the slender portion connecting these is called the *style.*

The pistil is the female reproductive organ. Each normal flower contains one, and only one, pistil. The pistil is surrounded by a number of slender but slightly different appearing structures. These are called *stamens* and are the

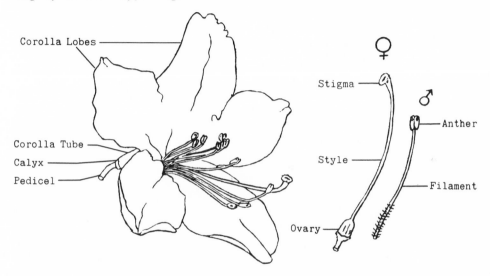

Corolla Lobes

Stigma

Anther

Corolla Tube

Calyx

Style

Pedicel

Filament

Ovary

THE PARTS OF A RHODODENDRON FLOWER

The structure marked (♀) is the pistil or seed-bearing organ, while the structure marked (♂) is a stamen or pollen-bearing organ. To effect a cross, pollen is placed upon the sticky surface of the stigma. Seeds are formed in the ovary. The two small holes at the tip of the anther are the pores through which pollen is shed. The "petals" of a rhododendron are properly known as corolla lobes, while the "throat" of the flower is the corolla tube.

male reproductive organs. There are only five stamens in each flower of the American azaleas, while the rhododendrons have ten and Asiatic species have various numbers, some having eight and others twenty or more. The number of stamens is often used in classifying species.

Each stamen consists of a long, slender stalk, called the *filament,* with a larger, double-barreled structure, called the *anther,* at its end. The anther has two similar pouch-like chambers, with a hole in the end of each. These chambers are called lobes or pollen sacs and contain masses of pollen grains which are shed from the holes. The holes are called aperatures or apical pores.*

* In shedding their pollen from apical pores, rhododendrons and other ericaceous plants differ from most flowering plants, in which the pollen is discharged by a longitudinal splitting of the anther.

The typical grain of pollen contains a cell which sooner or later divides to form the male cells which are involved in fertilization. Rhododendron pollen is unique in that each "grain" consists of four cells (microspores) instead of the common one-celled grain. In other words, four ordinary one-celled grains adhere together in a group to make up one rhododendron pollen "grain." Such a group of four is called a tetrad (see text figure), so, properly speaking, we should refer to them in rhododendrons as pollen tetrads and not pollen grains. This condition is characteristic of most members of the heath family.*

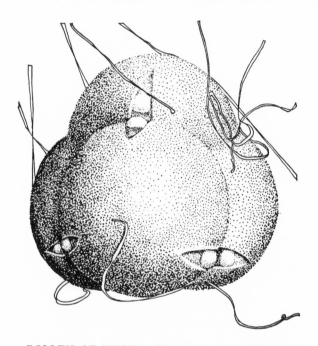

POLLEN OF RHODODENDRON CATAWBIENSE

A mature pollen "grain" (tetrad) with viscin strands adhering to its surface.

If you will notice rhododendron pollen as it occurs in a freshly opened flower, you will see that the pollen emerges from the anther sac as a long but irregular, stringy mass. All the pollen in one pollen sac comes out together in sort of a weft that appears like a spider's web. Upon close examination, it will be observed that this weft is composed of very fine strands of a cobweb-like sub-

* Bowers, C. G. The development of pollen and viscin strands in Rhododendron catawbiense. Bulletin of the Torrey Botanical Club 57:285–314. pl. 11–15 and figs. 25–27. 1931. The form and structure of the pollen-tetrad, as well as its development and the origin of its various features are quite fully discussed in this paper, so only brief reference need be made to it here. The four microspores are joined together firmly in a tetrahedral arrangement, as indicated in the text figure reproduced herewith.

stance in which the pollen tetrads are entangled. These are the so-called viscin strands.

Often one can see small bits of pollen, held by viscin strands, protruding out of the small apical pores of the anthers. If you touch this pollen, it will adhere to your finger and, if you pull, more pollen from within the anther will be drawn out until the entire contents of the pollen sac is removed. The viscin strands are attached to the pollen tetrads and thus function, in one of nature's ingenious devices, as a means of tying together the tetrads, so that when the upper ones are removed those in the lower part of the anther are also drawn out, thus emptying the pollen sac.

This, of course, is an adaptation for the purpose of pollination by insects. For reasons which I shall later point out, it is necessary for pollen to be transferred from one plant to another. Rhododendrons utilize the insects, particularly the bees, as messenger boys to carry this pollen from flower to flower. The bees do this work in the course of collecting nectar from the flowers they visit. Rhododendrons secrete this nectar as a sirup and it accumulates in droplets near the base of the pistil. In getting to the nectar a bee must brush against the anthers, where protruding bits of pollen, enmeshed in viscin strands, adhere to his body. Upon quitting a flower, the bee carries away a good load of pollen.*

When the bee goes to another flower, he has to pass over the protruding pistil, and, as he rubs against the sticky stigma, some of the pollen which he has collected from the first flower adheres to it. Thus, pollen from a male is transferred to the receptive organ of the female parent through the agency of the bee.

The stigma, when in a receptive condition, excretes a thin sirup. This gives it a sticky surface to which the pollen adheres. But the sirup furnishes nourishment for the pollen, which soon puts forth a slender, sprout-like process called a pollen tube.

The pistil has a sort of canal down its center, running from the stigma to the ovary. In rhododendrons this is not an open channel, but is, instead, an area where the cells are loosely built, leaving many inter-cellular spaces through which materials may pass easily. Now, when a pollen tetrad is placed upon a receptive stigma and comes in contact with the sugary sirup, the pollen germinates and a pollen tube starts to grow, heading down this stylar canal. The

---

* Viscin strands are not sticky or mucilaginous as formerly supposed, but are solid structures of great minuteness (1/2,000 millimeter in diameter), derived from the substance of the pollen mother-cell walls and firmly welded to the extine of the pollen tetrad. The strands one sees with the naked eye are not individual strands, but ropes of many. They are invisible in liquid microscopic mounts unless stained, and staining is hard to accomplish. Hence, for a century they were supposed to be composed of a mucilage which dissolves upon immersion in a liquid. This, however, I have shown to be false and have reported, in detail, concerning their origin and character. (Cf. citation in footnote, p. 138.)

pollen tube develops from a small, sprout-like process into a single long, slender, thread-like structure as it grows down the stylar canal toward the ovary. Near its lower end, the pollen tube carries the male cells and vegetative nucleus.*

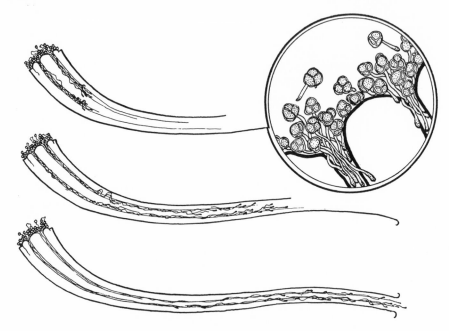

THE DEVELOPMENT OF THE POLLEN TUBE

following pollination in *Rhododendron maximum*. Microscopic drawings (diagrammatic) of the stigma and style, dissected at various hours after pollination, showing the progress of the pollen tubes as they grow toward the ovary. Enlarged view (in circle) shows pollen tetrads on the stigma four hours after pollination, with pollen tubes just germinating. The other views show the style with tubes (top) seven hours, (middle) seventeen hours and (bottom) twenty-four hours after pollination. In the lower view the most advanced pollen tubes have nearly reached the ovary.

At the lower end of the stylar canal is the ovary, where the female or egg cells are present. When the pollen tube finally enters the ovule, the male nucleus is discharged and fuses with the egg nucleus to form the beginnings of a new seed. The matter is actually somewhat more complicated, but this brief ex-

---

*By micro-dissection and staining methods, I have been able to observe the progress of pollen tubes down the style. In *Rhododendron maximum,* about 24 hours are required for the pollen tube to attain the complete length of the style at 68°F. Numbers up to several hundred pollen tubes may pass down a style at one time, and these need not be of the same variety or species. In my opinion, it is entirely possible for one rhododendron flower to be successfully pollinated by several different kinds of pollen at once, and this is probably what happens when bees are pollinating the flowers in a promiscuous collection of rhododendrons.

planation will suffice. The ovary of a rhododendron may contain as many as 300 or 400 ovules each of which, if fertilized with the nucleus of a pollen cell, eventually develops into a separate seed. A separate ovule and a separate pollen cell are required to produce each seed. Thus every seed is a separate individual, derived from the independent fusion of one definite male pollen nucleus and a definite female egg nucleus. The seed, then, is the offspring of two parents as a result of sexual reproduction, and, if the result of cross-fertilization, the two parents were separate individuals.

A *nucleus* is a definite structure included within a cell. When a male and female cell fuse, practically nothing enters the union but the nuclei of the respective cells. Whatever of hereditary characters are transferred from parent

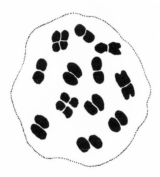

CHROMOSOMES

of Rhododendron catawbiense
at diakinesis.

to offspring, it is supposed, must necessarily be carried by the nuclei. Each nucleus is composed principally of chromatin, a substance which, during certain phases of cell development, segments into a number of smaller units called *chromosomes*. So much is heard about chromosomes, that a word should be said about them.

For various reasons, chromosomes have long been regarded as the bearers of inheritance. It has been thought that the transmission of characters from parent to offspring operates through their agency, so that the assumed factors of heredity, or genes, are supposed to reside in or on these chromosomes. The number of chromosomes in any given species remains relatively stable for that species ordinarily, but in some groups, the numbers vary widely with different species. This difference in chromosome number seems to affect the ability of species to cross with one another, although it is, by no means, the only reason for non-success in crossing. In some instances, chromosome number has a very significant bearing upon the character of the resulting hybrids.

No counting of chromosomes in the species of rhododendron was done until after 1928. All but two of the American species have a number (in the haploid condition) variously reported as 12 or 13, while two, *R. canadense* and *R. calendulaceum,* proved to be tetraploid with 26 chromosomes reported. In my examination of the chromosomes of *R. catawbiense, R. maximum* and *R. carolinianum,* I found no irregularities, even in the Catawba hybrids examined. The various phases in reductional division are substantially the same in rhododendrons as in other plants, so I will not take time to describe them here. They have been discussed more fully in technical papers.*

Let me remark that, as in all other organisms commonly observed, the number of chromosomes in the pollen cells and egg cells is only one-half that of the somatic or body cells. The fusion of the male and female nuclei, each with the reduced number, restores, therefore, the double or somatic number in the offspring. The tetraploid species are those regularly having twice as many chromosomes as the normal or diploid forms.

After the fusion of pollen and egg nuclei, the fertilized egg undergoes division until it develops into a seed. First it is simply an undifferentiated cluster of cells. Later, it develops into a definite embryo, plus stored food materials, which, upon germination, has the capacity of forming root, stem and leaves. Every seedling is thus a new individual, produced from two definite parents and having an equal share of inheritance from each.†

Recently and with the aid of new techniques, the chromosomes of rhododendrons have been carefully studied for number.‡ The somatic ($2n$) numbers of some 360 species, comprising at least one representative from each of the 44 series (excepting the Stamineum series), listed in the genus, including tropical (Javanese) species, have been set down in the paper cited here. The basic ($1n$) number for the genus is 13 chromosomes (the haploid or reduced number), or 26 ($2n$) for the somatic or diploid number found in the vegetative cells. It is only in the Luteum subseries of the Azalea se-

* Bowers, C. G. in Bull. Torrey Bot. Club *57*:285. 1931.

† Sax, Karl. Chromosome Stability in the Genus *Rhododendron.* Amer. Jour. Bot. *17*:247–251. 1930.—It was found, both in species and hybrids examined, that, although great morphological diversity exists among the rhododendrons, their chromosomal features are very uniform and constant, with no significant irregularities appearing during nuclear division. American and Asiatic species appeared to possess complete chromosome compatibility as shown in their hybrids, although probably separated by millions of years from any common ancestry. This is evidence that rhododendron chromosomes are exceedingly stable and are not easily changed. Sax reported that in an F_1 hybrid between diploid and tetraploid azaleas, about half the 26 chromosomes appear to be diploid and the rest tetraploid. My observations are preliminary to a further examination of somatic nuclei. I have noted that the secondary splitting, which functions in the homoeotypic division, occurs so nearly coincidental with diakinesis that the appearance of extra chromosomes is of more than common occurrence.

‡ E. K. Janaki-Ammal, et al. Chromosome Numbers in Species of Rhododendron and Polyploidy in the Genus Rhododendron. Roy. Hort. Soc. Rhod. Yearbook *5*:78–98. London, 1950.

Catawba Hybrid 'Lady Armstrong'

Rhododendron japonicum in its natural variations

Indian Hybrid Azalea 'President Comte Oswald de Kerckhove'

Rhododendron carolinianum var. album

Caucasicum Hybrid 'Boule de Neige'

Ghent Hybrid Azaleas

'Daviesii'   'Coccinea Speciosa'   'Pucella'

Rhododendron atlanticum in white and pink forms

Rhododendron roseum and R. nudiflorum

ries, and in nine other scattered series of the lepidote rhododendrons that any deviation from the usual diploid number (26) occurs. In other words, so far as studied nothing but diploids (2n) seem to exist in the entire elepidote (non-scaly) section of the genus. Thus most of our hardy cultivated sorts, excepting the two tetraploid American azaleas (R. calendulaceum and R. canadense), are apparently without polyploidy. Throughout the genus, not all species have been studied yet, but surprising stability has been found except in the lepidote groups. The two azaleas are tetraploids, having 52 chromosomes, the 4n number. Elsewhere, tetraploidy is the most common deviation. In the lepidote section, 78 polyploid species were found. Diploids (26) and tetraploids (52) occur in the Glaucophyllum, Lepidotum and Saluenense series; diploids (26), tetraploids (52) and hexaploids (78) in the Lapponicum and Triflorum series; these numbers, plus one dodecaploid (156), R. manipurense, in the Maddenii series; no diploids, but tetraploids (52), hexaploids (78) and one octoploid (104), R. pholidotum, in the Heliolepis series; and nothing but hexaploids (78) in the Cinnabarinum series. In a number of instances, differing numbers were found within the same species. Among the Triflorums and Lapponicums more polyploids than diploids occur. In one form of R. russatum (Rock's 59209) in the Lapponicum series, a triploid (39) was found. Polyploidy in the Asiatic species seems to be associated with high-altitude species. So far as I know, no chromosome numbers have been reported for the cultivated hybrids.

Recently chromosome counts of additional American azaleas have been made by Li.* He made repeated and careful studies in 15 species, involving 271 plants collected in 21 states by Dr. Henry T. Skinner. These included many natural hybrids. The only species typically tetraploid was R. calendulaceum, which is thought to have arisen from a more ancient diploid ancestor, possibly R. Bakeri. Wild hybrids of R. calendulaceum with diploid species are mostly tetraploid, but a few triploids have been found. Studies included R. Bakeri (cumberlandense), R. atlanticum, R. austrinum, R. speciosum, R. prunifolium, R. alabamense, R. canescens, R. serrulatum, R. viscosum, R. arborescens, R. nudiflorum and R. roseum, all of which were diploid. Contrary to expectations, many wild forms formerly thought to be hybrids of R. calendulaceum are diploid and appear, from cytological examination, to not actually involve that species at all. One aberrant plant of R. atlanticum proved to be a triploid.

* Li, H. L., in Amer. Jour. Botany 44:8–14. 1957.

CHAPTER XVI

STERILITIES AND THEIR SIGNIFICANCE

WE HAVE seen that, in order to bear seeds, a rhododendron must first bloom and that this blooming must be accompanied by pollination and fertilization. We have noted the chain of events which must occur from the time the ripe pollen leaves the anther of the flower until the eggs are fertilized and become embryos. *Pollination,* within our present meaning, is the act of transferring pollen to the stigma of a flower. *Fertilization* is the name given to the series of subsequent events which occur after the stigma is pollinated and which lead to the fusion of parental cells and the production of an embryo. These two terms are often loosely and inaccurately used by laymen, but should be very carefully distinguished, because their meanings are vastly different.*

Now, there are a number of points during the progress of fertilization at which the process may become interrupted. Both male and female elements must be functional and the several steps leading to their proper fusion must be complete or fruitfulness will not result. Any break in the chain of events which begins with pollination and culminates in the production of an embryo may be termed a cause of *sterility.* To those who merely wish to grow plants and who are not interested in propagating them from seed or in raising new varieties, this subject may not be of importance. But to all breeders of rhododendrons and raisers of seedlings, the sterilities found among these plants should be of considerable practical concern. I deem it necessary, therefore, to discuss this matter, as briefly as possible, pointing out some of the phenomena involved and noting their significance.

Strictly speaking, the following four different types of pollination are possible in rhododendrons: (1) *self-pollination,* in which pollen from a given flower is transferred to the stigma of the same flower; (2) *close-pollination,* in which pollen from a given flower on a given plant is transferred to the stigma of

---

* When we place pollen on the stigma of a flower we do not "fertilize" that flower; we "pollinate" it, and fertilization may or may not occur afterward.

other flowers on the same plant or within the same clone; (3) *cross-pollination,* in which pollen from another individual plant, outside the clone, is transferred to the stigmas of a given individual within the same species or race; and (4) *inter-specific pollination,* in which pollen is transferred from a flower of one species to a flower of another species. In other words, the scope of pollination and fertilization may embrace either one flower alone, two different flowers on the same individual plant or within the same clone, two flowers on different individuals within a species, or, lastly, flowers in separate species. We shall consider these types separately.

Let us begin with an individual flower and note what may occur with reference to sterilities. If a flower, pollinated by its own pollen (self-pollinated), becomes fertilized by the male cells from this pollen, it is said to be *self-compatible.* But if fertilization does not occur, we have the condition known as a sterility, of which there are several kinds.

First, we have those sterilities which are influenced by the environment. It is a matter of common knowledge among plant breeders that unfavorable moisture or atmospheric conditions will sometimes prevent successful fertilization. It has also been observed that fertilization occurs more readily (especially in difficult unions) when the plants are grown and pollinated under glass, as in a greenhouse. More will be said about this later when hybrids are being discussed, since it applies more to these than to self-pollinated plants. There are also such obvious environmental factors as weather conditions, frost, heat, dryness and so forth, which, if unfavorable, might prevent, delay or inhibit the process of fertilization. I have noted that the amount of seed setting from given pollinations varies appreciably from year to year, indicating that environmental factors are in operation. It is needless to go into further detail regarding the many unfavorable external factors which might conceivably operate to render a flower unfruitful.

Leaving the matter of environment and considering those other factors which might be concerned with sterilities in an individual flower, we shall first note the pollen itself. Abortive pollen is not uncommon, especially in plants of hybrid derivation and is, of course, entirely useless. Such pollen may or may not be produced and shed in abundance. Examined microscopically, it usually shows an abnormal appearance or it may merely refuse to germinate when placed in proper media. Pollen abortion is not always complete. I have frequently encountered pollen in which a few normal, functional grains are scattered among many abortive ones.

Then, the phenomenon of dichogamy frequently prevents self-pollination in Nature. This is an inherent difference in the ripening dates of the male and female parts in a flower. In rhododendrons and azaleas, the stamens frequently ripen earlier than the pistil, so that by the time the female parts are mature and in a receptive condition the pollen has been shed and is either all gone or ruined by age. In this form of dichogamy the flowers are said to be proterandrous. It is obvious that self-fertilization is usually impossible under such circumstances.

The impotence or complete absence of the organs of either or both sexes in a flower is another obvious condition of sterility. In double flowers, especially, the stamens may be absent, having been replaced by extra petals. This condition may be noted in the double Ghent azaleas shown in the color plate following page 366. Such flowers may be functional as females, but having no pollen they can neither act as males in crosses nor become self-pollinated. In the Yodagawa azalea, both the stamens and pistil are gone, so that the flower is completely impotent and utterly unable ever to set any seed in any circumstances. In other abnormal forms the sex organs, although nominally present, are completely non-functional.

In all the foregoing examples of inherent types of sterility, the causes are fairly obvious. Less obvious, harder to explain, but more frequent in occurrence are those sterilities which are due to incompatibility between the male and female parents. In cases of this kind, which I have found to exist in fully 25% of the Catawba hybrids tested, the pollen and eggs of an individual flower, although perfectly functional when used with certain other individuals, are utterly incompatible with respect to their mutual relations in attempted seed production. Despite the fact that the flowers are fully formed, the pollen entirely viable and the pollinations carefully made, such individuals fail to set seed when self-pollinated. For example, plant *A* may bear pollen that is normal in its capacity to germinate and produce living offspring when used to fertilize the eggs of plant *B*, but it is incapable of bringing about fertilization when applied to the stigmas of the flower upon which it is borne. Plant *A* is, therefore, said to be *self-incompatible*.

The most generally accepted explanation of this phenomenon is that the incompatibility rests upon certain hereditary factors present in the genetical make-up of the plant which, when combined in the union of pollen and egg, are mutually repellent, or, at least, refuse to work together harmoniously in the process of fertilization. The inhibiting element here seems to be the similarity of the factors present; as will be noted later, this is in contrast to the condition found in sterile hybrids where the limiting factor is not similarity, but extreme difference. The condition of incompatibility is thus restricted to the relations of plants within a species or within a race of hybrids where factors for incompatibility may be present and is not to be confused with the sterility of hybridity which concerns the affinities of species and not their incompatibilities.

Since the pollen and eggs of an incompatible plant are not actually sterile, but are functional in other combinations, the phenomenon should be spoken of as self-incompatibility rather than as self-sterility. They merely fail to work together harmoniously.*

In rhododendrons, incompatibility is present in varying degree. At one end of the scale we get complete self-incompatibility, while at the other end we find an individual flower that is entirely self-compatible and sets perfectly normal seed to its own pollen. Between these two limits, we find many plants which are not fully self-compatible. Such individuals are said to be *feebly* self-compatible and are characterized by abnormally small seed capsules, with or without functional seeds as the case may be. The size of the capsules and the viability of the seeds are probably a measure of the degree of compatibility.

Comber in 1925 † first reported self-incompatibility in rhododendrons, naming a few varieties. A year or two later I reported its occurrence in other species.‡ In controlled self-pollination tests of several well known hybrid clones, the following records were gathered. Except where otherwise noted, all are Catawba hybrids:

RESULTS OF SELF-POLLINATION

SELF-COMPATIBLE OR NEARLY SO

BOULE DE NEIGE ($\times$ *caucasicum*)	F. D. GODMAN
LADY ARMSTRONG	GENERAL GRANT
ATROSANGUINEUM	F. Y. SEIDEL (Azalea)
ALBUM GRANDIFLORUM	IGNEA NOVA (Azalea)

FEEBLY SELF-COMPATIBLE—CAPSULES LESS THAN ONE-HALF NORMAL SIZE

ABRAHAM LINCOLN	MRS. CHARLES THEROLD
CHARLES BAGLEY	PARSONS GLORIOSUM
KETTLEDRUM	PURPUREUM GRANDIFLORUM

* Investigating the possible causes of incompatibility in *Rhododendron maximum* and *R. catawbiense*, I dissected and stained the styles of incompatible flowers after pollination. I watched the progress of the pollen tubes during the successive stages of their growth down the styles. There seem to be no anatomical obstacles and no other features of the pollen, such as shortness of tube, slow rate of growth or bursting, that could be accounted a cause of unfruitfulness. The behavior of the pollen tubes in incompatible combinations appeared exactly as in normal matings. The progress of the pollen tubes down the style is shown in the micro-drawings on page 140. Conditions within the ovary were not studied. The styles of azaleas are similar.

† Comber, H. F. Self-sterility in the rhododendrons. Gard. Chron. III, 77:300–301. London, 1925.

‡ Bowers, C. G. Rhododendrons and azaleas for breeding purposes in America. Jour. N.Y. Bot. Gard. 28(328):81–86. New York, 1927. Bowers, C. G. Hybrid seedlings versus grafted plants. Florists Exchange 66(17):1445, 1454. 2 figs. New York, Dec. 24, 1927.

SELF-INCOMPATIBLE OR NEARLY SO

ALEXANDER DANCER	PARSONS GRANDIFLORUM
DELICATISSIMUM	GLORIA MUNDI (Azalea)
HENRIETTA SARGENT	BRONZE UNIQUE (Azalea)
H. W. SARGENT	*R. mucronatum* (Azalea)
MRS. CHARLES SARGENT	*R. mucronatum* f. *sekidera*
MRS. MILNER	clone DAMASK ROSE.

Tests on wild plants of *Rhododendron catawbiense* indicate that all three groups, as classified above, are to be found among the various individuals comprising the wild population of that species. Whether or not this phenomenon is universal within the genus is not known at present.

Leaving the individual flower and taking up the individual plant as a whole or extending it to include the clone, I have not yet found, within the genus *Rhododendron,* that close pollination differs in effect from self-pollination, except, of course, in such obvious matters as dichogamy where, with different flowers on a plant blooming at slightly different times, fresh pollen will be available for use on the later maturing stigmas, thus making close-pollination possible where self-pollination was prevented. The same factors as were cited for the sterilities of a self-pollinated flower, including the various incompatibilities, appear to be equally operative when the same plants are close-pollinated. Further investigation may later prove this conclusion to have been premature, but at present it appears that a self-incompatible rhododendron or azalea will be similarly incompatible in close-pollination relations and is incapable of close-fertilization.

Our next consideration involves the relations existing between two different individuals within the same species.* Here, of course, the usual environmental and morphological causes of sterility are likewise present. Here, also, inherent characteristics and abnormalities occasionally make themselves evident as causes of sterility, much as previously cited for the sterilities of an individual flower.

Although there is yet no evidence of its operation in crosses within a species of rhododendron, the occurrence of a cell condition called polyploidy may, in rare instances, become a factor in sterility. This condition is characterized by a multiplication of the number of chromosomes (which will be referred to later) and it sometimes results in an unbalanced and unworkable nuclear condition, causing failure of the pollen to be properly formed or failure of the fertilized egg to function.

* In the genus *Rhododendron* we might extend this class to include a few members of very closely related species, where no conspicuous differences in character exist, and which, to all intents and purposes, are little farther separated than geographical forms of one species. Since the genus abounds in such close affinities, it is difficult to apply strict rules such as those cited to distinguish intra-specific and inter-specific crosses.

Incompatibilities are present, also, in crosses between individuals as well as in self- or close-pollinated plants. In crosses within the limits of a species, such incompatibilities do not seemingly differ to any extent from self-incompatibility. Apparently, the basic mechanism is the same: similar hereditary factors occurring, which, when present together, refuse to work in harmony, the underlying cause of the failure being the exact similarity of the two sets of factors. No exact genetical proof of this has yet been secured in rhododendrons, but observation indicates that it is a valid hypothesis. We need not go into its details or its theoretical aspects. All we need to say is that a condition, called cross-incompatibility, exists between given individual plants and that its effects are similar to those of self-incompatibility. Like the latter, cross-incompatibility gives results similar to those of self-incompatibility in producing intermediate degrees of feeble compatibility. Such intermediate forms occur uniformly among the seedlings of certain crosses—appearing as abortive seed capsules, or sparse seed or similar weaknesses—or they may appear as a few good seeds contained in the same capsule with many others that are worthless. Such results are probably an evidence of the segregation and recombination of genetic factors, some of which combine successfully, while others combine in a futile manner. Almost all rhododendron breeders must be familiar with these symptoms, as well as with the condition in which two plants, so closely related that they *ought* to cross successfully, nevertheless refuse to set seed when brought into combination.

Heretofore, we have been considering only those sterilities which operate within a species. Now, going a step farther, we come to the relations which exist between two plants belonging to different species. First, we may pass over, without comment, those obvious properties which render plants sterile in any event—such matters as impotence, pollen abortion, doubleness, anatomical misfits, the absence of essential properties, and so forth. These factors naturally apply here as well as in the other classes previously cited. We may also pass by, without comment, the inter-relations of species which are so closely allied that in their mutual hybrid relations they behave no differently from plants belonging to the same species. We shall take time to note that environmental conditions, as pointed out before, may considerably affect the success of hybridizing experiments, for plants which are difficult to cross are more apt to combine successfully if the hybridizing operation is performed under the favorable environment of a greenhouse. I have noted that this is especially true of wide, interspecific crosses.

But what we are chiefly concerned with here is the *sterility of hybridity*. When plants in widely separated species refuse to cross successfully, their condition is not one of incompatibility within the meaning of the term as we have been using it. The incompatibilities we have been discussing were based upon the failure of similar genetic elements to work successfully in combination— a supposed mutual antagonism between similarities. In the sterility of hybridity the basis of the failure of the cross to function rests upon opposite grounds— the wide differences existing between the species, and not their similarities. While crosses within species are often rendered more workable by physical differences existing between individuals, plants in interspecific combinations are less and less likely to cross successfully and produce desirable offspring when their physical relationships are farther and farther apart. Crossing the mice with the elephants, of course, is usually done in vain. And there are other similar physical inconsistencies. But the crux of the matter rests in such abstruse considerations as harmonious chromosome complements and cytoplasmic properties, these things being internal cellular qualities which can not be seen and diagnosed by outward manifestations. Often a hybridist will be surprised to find that two species very unlike in appearance (such as the parents of azaleodendrons) will produce living offspring when crossed, while two other species, which look like close relatives, will absolutely refuse to mate successfully. The rule generally holds, however, that the most unlike forms are the least apt to cross. Best results may be expected from combinations which prove by trial to be entirely harmonious in their physiological and genetical make-up. Because such qualities as these are subject to wide variation and because they produce innumerable interactions when combined in hybrid relations, we can seldom determine *a priori* the outcome of an untried cross. It is a good rule, therefore, to experiment in many directions, for surprising things do occasionally result.

Hybridity often induces pollen sterility or similar abnormalities, and it is not uncommon for widely crossed plants, such as azaleodendrons, to be without functional pollen or eggs. Lacking complete evidence, the exact cause of such sterility in rhododendrons is not yet fully apparent, but it seems likely that unbalanced polyploidy may, in some instances at least, be a factor. Sometimes such hybrids will grow and bloom successfully, the two sets of chromosomes derived from their respective parents functioning in all the vegetative parts, only to break down when pollen or egg formation is reached. Again, it is often only the individual that counts and not so much the species which it represents, for a cross between two given species may sometimes be successful between two definite individuals representing those species, while the substitution of other individuals belonging to the two respective species might result in failure. This has occurred repeatedly in some of my wide crosses.

After fertilization has been effected and a young embryo starts to develop, further interruptions in the progress toward successful fruition may result.

Embryo abortion is a form of sterility that arises from the failure of the young embryo to adjust itself to life. Abortive seeds are the results. Similar abnormalities and maladjustments may occur during the later phases of growth and development, so that death from inherent causes might occur at various subsequent times. These are not unlike the sterilities which we have been considering and may result from similar genetical causes. Sometimes an embryo will live and seed will be produced, but trouble will come when the seedling puts out its first leaves and finds itself unequipped for life. Still, again, a living plant may be produced, but it may be so lacking in vigor as to never attain blooming proportions. Or a plant may even develop to nearly normal proportions and just fail to become entirely normal in its vigor or physical functions. Weakness, vigor, ability or inability to live and function are all characters which may be transmitted by genetical factors in the germ-plasm and, as such, are probably not essentially different from several forms of sterility which we have noted. Very little work has actually been completed in the investigation of such matters among rhododendrons, so the theoretical conclusions here drawn are largely conjectures based upon somewhat parallel cases in other genera. But the observed results among rhododendrons and azaleas are exactly as here recorded.

Whatever its causes, the practical effects of sterility are significant. Self-incompatibility has an important bearing upon the collection and use of rhododendron seeds. Where self-incompatibility is the rule, it is obligatory for a plant to be pollinated by some other plant before seed can be produced. This necessitates crossing and implies that the subsequent seedling, as a result of the cross, will seldom come true to the type of its seed-parent unless the pollen parent also happens to be of similar genetical make-up. Hence, unprotected seed taken from a rhododendron plant, especially if it comes from a garden where many kinds are in bloom at the same time, is very apt to be variable in character as a result of mixed parentage. Seed from wild plants, collected in their native habitats, are much less liable to be crossed outside their own race or species. Of course, such seedlings will vary in minor characters, but the gross features of the race will mostly be perpetuated.

Self-pollination often results in reduced vigor. This is usually a disadvantage, but in some situations is desirable. For instance, it may be a first-class method of producing dwarf forms and, hence, is not without value to the plant breeder. Such forms, however, are often intolerably slow of growth. The extent and nature of the reaction, of course, depends upon the species used as parents, of which there is an endless variation.

Definite sterilities often place restrictions upon the breeder or propagator. A desirable hybrid may be absolutely impotent. Or the plants may be of one sex only, preventing reciprocal crosses. Sometimes, as noted, environmental factors may be so adjusted as to assist in the production of difficult crosses. The methods and technique are discussed elsewhere. In many cases, the study of a problem will reveal some feasible means of overcoming it.

As a sort of corollary of incompatibility, it should be mentioned that certain combinations of individuals or species mate together especially well and produce superior seedlings. Even in the hybrid relations between species, it is not always so much a matter of species as of individuals concerned in the union. Plant breeding experience, the making of carefully protected crosses and the keeping of accurate records are the methods by which such combinations may be discovered.

Because of self-incompatibility, an isolated plant will often set no seed. It is possible to obtain seed from such a plant by having suitable pollen shipped by mail or otherwise transported to the place where it may be used on the stigmas of the self-incompatible flowers.

CHAPTER XVII

INHERITANCE

A QUESTION whose outward manifestations and inward workings we know less about in rhododendrons than in some other plants is the matter of heredity. Characters of certain kinds are surely inherited in the genus *Rhododendron,* else we would never have the many beautiful hybrids we now possess. But controlled work has seldom been done, few accurate records kept and little reliable knowledge recorded concerning, in rhododendrons, the features which now make up the science of genetics. We cannot safely draw conclusions by analogy from what obtains in other plants, for there are many and diverse possibilities of error in such procedure. Yet, we do know the sum-total of results that have been obtained through the years and can consequently speak, in a broad way, of these accomplishments, although we may not know exactly how all of them occurred. One comforting fact is that a few definite genetical experiments are now under way and, whether or not they prove of practical value, will at least provide accurate data concerning some of the more important factors involved. The five years or more required for each generation of these plants makes genetical work with rhododendrons particularly tedious and slow of accomplishment. It will be many years before much actual knowledge is available.

Japanese workers are about the only ones who have published reports, to date, upon genetical work in the genus *Rhododendron.* This work has been done upon azaleas of the subseries Obtusum, which have the advantage of blooming rather soon from seed and, hence, are better adapted for quick results than some other species.

In 1922, Miyazawa * reported that in the Kirishima azalea (*R. obtusum*) upright stems appeared to be dominant over horizontal growth, solid colors (self-color) were dominant over variegated color forms, short stamens were dominant over long stamens, single flowers were dominant over double flowers, while leaf-breadth and size of flower were intermediate between those of the

* Miyazawa, B. Rhododendron indicum Sweet var. obtusum Max. Idengaku Zassi. Japanese Jour. Genetics *1*:153-157. 1922. Abstract in Botanical Abstracts *14*:512. 1925.

parents. Ikeno * later reported upon the manner of inheritance of three abnormal flower forms: hose-in-hose, apetalous and sympetalous flowers.†

The results of a series of crosses between the various Japanese species of
azaleas has been reported by Noguchi.‡ He made certain crosses between the
members of 16 species of native Japanese rhododendrons, representing five different sections of the genus and including some of the true rhododendrons
(section Eurhododendron). The species belonging to the subseries Obtusum
(section Tsutsutsi) could be crossed *inter se* with great ease, but crosses between these and species in other sections, series or subseries were difficult of
accomplishment and seldom successful.§ Chlorophyll defects, such as white,
yellow or variegated leaves, were frequently encountered in seedlings involving
the subseries Obtusum and were much more pronounced in the intersectional
crosses than in those within the subseries, especially with respect to hybrids
between the Obtusum group and *Rhododendron japonicum.*

Considerably more data will appear from time to time in the future as scientific researches now under way are reported upon and new projects are investigated. At the present time we are working in the dark, for the most part, so
far as definite, genetical knowledge of rhododendrons is concerned. There are,
however, certain general principles which we can assume to be true and which
may well be kept in mind by all who are endeavoring to raise seedlings or do
breeding work. Without becoming too deeply involved in the complications of
genetics, I might mention a few basic facts.

The first of these is the fact that hybrids seldom breed true and that our
common garden forms of rhododendrons and azaleas have been crossed and
re-crossed for several generations, until such simple heritable characters as a

---

* Ikeno, S. Some crossing experiments with Rhododendron species (in German). Studia
Mendeliana P. 104–111. 1 pl. 1 fig. Typos: Brünn, Czechoslovakia, 1923. Abstract in Botanical
Abstracts *14:*510. 1925.

† Ikeno considered the hose-in-hose type heterozygous, *Aa,* and the normal type recessive,
aa, giving a 1:1 ratio when crossed together. By the reduction of petals to extra stamens, an
apetalous race was apparently produced, with 3 general types in the F_1 generation, *viz.:*
apetalous = *PpRr;* normal = *pprr;* and intermediate = *Pprr* and *ppRr.* A polypetalous race,
characterized by complete separation of the corolla lobes, was postulated as heterozygous for
one factor.

‡ Noguchi, Yakichi. Studies on the species crosses of Japanese Rhododendron, 1. On the
crossability between various species and the cotyledon color of F_1 seedlings. Japanese Journal
of Botany *6*(1):103–124. pl. 1–2. Tokyo, March 1932.

§ Noguchi succeeded in producing hybrid F_1 seedlings from the following intersectional
crosses: *Rhododendron Degronianum* (Series Ponticum) ♀ × *R. japonicum* (Azalea, subseries Luteum) ♂, a hybrid of the Azaleodendron group, having characters intermediate between the evergreen and deciduous parents. *R. Schlippenbachii* ♀ × *R. japonicum* ♂, producing
weak seedlings, all of which soon died; *R. poukhanense* ♀ × *R. mucronulatum* ♂, character
of seedlings not reported; and various clones within the subseries Obtusum ♀ × *R. japonicum* ♂,
of which the seedlings were mostly abnormal and soon died. In all intersectional crosses but
the last, reciprocal combinations failed completely.

wild species might originally possess are shuffled together in an unrecognizable hodge-podge of mixed and inter-reacting genetical factors. To draw conclusions and base judgments of such matters as flower color, for instance, upon the behavior of these hybrids of heterogeneous internal constitution (genetically heterozygous) is, more often than not, an unreliable practice and one that frequently induces more confusion than clarity. Still, it is out of such hybrids that many of our best new forms emerge. So it behooves us to keep accurate records of what we do and see, in hope that, even among these complex hybrids, a few general principles may come to light which will aid us in determining which lines to follow for best results in future breeding work. It is necessary, however, to understand that like does not always beget like and that the only sure method of attaining given results, even by the trained geneticist when he is working with unknown factors as in rhododendrons, is by the old and infallible system of trial and error.

When any new species is being introduced into a hybrid strain, as, for example, the crossing of a Chinese species with some of the old Catawba hybrids, certain definite effects of the newcomer can very often be recognized immediately. Such effects should be carefully noted.

But many of the effects of the new species may not appear in the first generation. Indeed, certain prominent characters of the new parent may be utterly submerged in the first generation (F_1) progeny, as, for example, the disappearance of the woolly, tomentose foliage of *Rhododendron Smirnowii* when crossed with the smooth-leaved type. In cases where the desired combination does not immediately appear, therefore, the F_1 progeny should not be cast aside, but should be carried on for one or more subsequent generations, by brother × sister matings between seedlings, as the probability is good for its reappearance in F_2 or F_3 * if a large enough population is raised. A large F_1 population is not necessary, as the plants, if from ancestry breeding true to the character concerned, are frequently quite uniform, but, especially when characters of a quantitative nature are sought, it may be necessary to grow relatively enormous numbers of the F_2 generation, in order to recover the desired recombination of characters. Where many factors are involved, plants of the desired type are sometimes very rare.

The fact that characters are often carried over in a latent or unexpressed

---

* In genetical parlance, the generation of which the original plants are a part is known as the parental or P_1 generation. The first progeny of a cross, that is, the children of the P_1 plants, is known as the first filial or F_1 generation. When the members of the F_1 generation are self-fertilized or crossed *inter se,* the resulting progeny is known as the second filial or F_2 generation. Thus, the F_2 plants are grandchildren of the original P_1 stock. Subsequent generations are similarly labelled F_3, F_4 and so forth. Female parents are designated by the symbol ♀ and males by ♂.

condition to reappear in the second or subsequent generations is attributed to the effect of Mendelism, a principle with which many readers are doubtless already familiar. A large portion of our present science of genetics is built around the Mendelian doctrine. We have learned, however, that the simple, independent, monohybrid condition, familiarly used as the stock example of Mendelism in popular literature and elementary texts of biology, appears in only occasional characters. More often the situation is tremendously more complicated and difficult of interpretation, so that a highly complex system has to be employed in order to work out the genetical formulae of the average heritable character. Some forms of inheritance are quite different from the simple Mendelian ratios of ordinary "dominance" and "recessiveness." All definite knowledge of inheritance in rhododendrons, however, will come only from careful work, done under controlled conditions by persons who are familiar with genetical research. Of what practical importance this will be is a matter of conjecture. Probably the old methods of breeding will continue to result in new and improved varieties far into the future. But no real knowledge of heredity in rhododendrons can come from the common "shot-gun" methods of breeding, where guesswork, the law of chance and the kindly interference of a few friendly bees are all involved. Many of our records of the past are nearly worthless, because of such inaccuracies.

The most progress in attaining new and better rhododendrons will probably come, not from research in pure genetics, but from a combination of genetical knowledge with accurate plant breeding technique. Plant breeders, both trained and amateur, working for new "breaks" or accidentally discovering them, will be the ones most likely to usher in new races and better things for the garden. In this the amateur, as of old, will have a share, but a lesser share, because modern technical aids have put the trained man several jumps ahead of him. Modern plant breeding and genetics are fast embracing the related sciences of cytology and physiology, from which they are securing valuable technical assistance. The main motto for all is to work carefully, know what you are doing, keep accurate records and leave behind a trail that can always be followed by your successor. The practical breeder will go on producing valuable new forms, many of which, as in the past, will be genetically undeterminable. With any slow-growing group of plants, progress is naturally slow, so rhododendron breeders should remember that great accomplishments exceed, in the making, the lifetime of one man, and that an accurate record of one's work for the benefit of posterity is a real obligation.

The admonition is often quoted that a breeder should have a definite ideal in mind toward which he should work. This is true where selection is concerned, but is of very limited application in the matter of hybridization. Where well-recognized qualities exist among closely related forms or species, and these qualities are suspected of being heritable, one may select individuals which tend toward the desired type and breed from them with every prospect of success. This is especially true where such qualities as size or hardiness are concerned. Such qualities frequently are not controlled by one single heritable factor, but increase or pile up in a cumulative manner as a result of the combined influence of many factors. If two varieties are not too unlike in type and ancestry, it may readily be conceived that the best individuals of each would tend to produce good progeny, and, conversely, that poor examples would produce poor offspring. In other words, that "like begets like." This is, indeed, a practicable breeding practice where closely related forms are involved. It is, however, fundamentally a method of selection rather than one of hybridization. Sudden, new "breaks" seldom occur under such a system of breeding.*

The theory of hybridization is based upon quite another premise. The principle here is not that "like begets like" but that the bringing together of two unlike species results in increased variability, often bringing about a third form, unlike either of its parents and constituting, in effect, an entirely new production. Strange characters are injected into existing strains by means of crossing in hope that, in subsequent generations, a valuable combination of characters may be segregated. This is how most of our distinct hybrid races get their start. It is a method more easily followed by the trained hybridist, however, than by the lay worker, who usually finds it more satisfactory to follow the selective method of breeding for the best existing type rather than to endeavor to initiate new types. A hybridist seldom knows in advance what he is going to get, unless a similar cross has been made before. Hence, it is better for him to work on as broad a scale as possible, rather than to narrow his efforts toward a preconceived ideal. After a "break" has been secured, he may then set up an "ideal" and work toward it by selective breeding, but in making initial crosses an ideal is of little use and is frequently a detriment.

Although, strictly speaking, the analogy is inaccurate, I like to explain the hybrid relations of plants on the basis of chemical reactions. For the purpose of illustration, picture two species as separate chemicals and their progeny as

---

* In several of my hybrid pedigrees, seedlings of great vigor have resulted from crosses where one or more parents have been notoriously slow-growing sorts. This phenomenon occurs repeatedly in plants. Do not avoid the use of a plant that is not vigorous, therefore, because it may produce offspring as good or better than those from fine parentage. This should be especially remembered where weak F_1 plants result from crosses between especially desirable parents. Many breeders throw away these poor F_1s, when, if they would cross them together and raise another generation, all the vigor of the original parents, plus the desired combination of characters, might be recovered in the F_2 seedlings. Many persons deride wide crosses because of the reduced vigor of the F_1 seedlings, but, if such crosses were continued into the F_2 generation, results of surprising significance might, in certain instances, appear

the salt which has resulted from a reaction between those chemicals. As the chemicals are unlike each other and the salt is unlike either of the substances which have combined to form it, so a hybrid may sometimes display certain traits utterly unlike those of either parent. Again, as a salt may react in further combinations to form still other compounds of different kinds, so an F_1 hybrid may later be modified and recombined in all sorts of ways to produce new and distinct variations. Now, two species which have never been crossed together are, in a measure, like two chemicals which have never been combined. One does not know, until he learns by actual experiment, what the outcome of a union between them will be.

These statements would apply, of course, only to crosses of species that are quite different in at least one character. Closely related species, or those which belong to groups commonly crossed, can be counted upon to some extent to follow predictions in the character of their progeny, but I believe we can seldom predict by analogy the outcome of any wide cross that is distinctly different from anything already tried. It is on this basis that the so-called "hit or miss" system of breeding has a legitimate place in scientific practice. It is pure experimentation. To bring unusual things together in crosses without preconceived ideals, but merely for the purpose of initiating new combinations and observing results is, in my opinion, both scientifically correct and of great practical usefulness. The entire value of such practice, the measure of whether or not it is scientific, rests in the care and accuracy of the work done, the completeness of the observations and the reliability of the conclusions drawn. Such factors, and these alone, determine whether "hit or miss" breeding is an experimental process or merely a bungling attempt to do something without rhyme or reason. It may be either, depending upon the man who does the work.

I shall not go into the genetical argument for hybridization, but will simply state that the idea of bringing together species in new combinations has behind it the full force of genetical theory as a means of "breaking the type" and inducing variability. It is the initial step in a legitimate application of the experimental method of research. It is, in its way, the essence of that quality known as pure science, for it is here that we are exploring the unknown.

As a method of procedure with rhododendrons, the system of making wide crosses to obtain sudden variations is perhaps not quite so effective as in some other groups of plants. In studying the hybridization work of the past, I have not noted sudden "breaks" among rhododendrons, but rather have gained the feeling that the results of crossing have, in most cases, been a merging of the parental qualities in a hybrid of intermediate type. A blending of characters, rather than a violent reaction, has appeared to be the rule, but no definite statement regarding this is possible until actual experiments are completed. It seems evident, too, that better results are secured by crossing within rather narrow limits, than by using too widely divergent series.

A popular fallacy that has been given currency in America by recent horticultural writers is the doctrine that we should use only hardy species in our breeding work in order to secure hardy progeny. Now this statement is perfectly true, if only the first-generation progeny is considered. It fails to recognize the fact that certain important characters, such as flower color, are sometimes separable from the qualities of tenderness if several generations of breeding follow the original cross. That a new color, derived from a very tender parent, may, in time, be carried over to the hardy strain by subsequent intelligent breeding is well demonstrated by the history of the Catawba hybrids. These have derived their red coloration from the tender *Rhododendron arboreum*. Originally, the F_1 hybrids were very tender, but in later generations a large share of the brilliant coloration segregated out in combination with hardiness, so that we now have several fine red varieties in the "ironclad" class. Many are not so highly colored, to be sure, as *R. arboreum,* but if the color had not been, to some degree, separable, this result could never have been secured. Other characters are doubtless heritable in this way also.

A phenomenon known as linkage exists in many plants and will doubtless be discovered in rhododendrons, although definite evidence of its occurrence will necessarily await genetical research. Briefly explained, linkage consists in the tendency of certain characters to travel together. Such characters need not of necessity have any other relationship in common beyond this quality of appearing together a large proportion of the time. Where one occurs, the other may often be found also. Such characters are said to be "linked," and a cytological explanation, based upon the position of two or more genes on the same chromosome, is given to account for the phenomenon.

Although most of the foregoing statements regarding inheritance were written a quarter-century ago, it still must be said that little practical knowledge has been added by way of genetical research or breeding within the genus since that time. It is true that we now know much about chromosome numbers, we have developed a few useful techniques and we have acquired a vast repository of pedigree data which are recorded in the Rhododendron Stud Book.* But the leading new hybrids are still mainly those produced by practical gardeners working with plants, either hybrid or not, which they have found by experience to be successful parents. Occasionally someone makes a wide cross which turns out well and starts work on a new tangent. But actual genetical work has

* Incorporated in Part Two of The Rhododendron Handbook, published by the Royal Horticultural Society, London, 1956, and revised periodically.

been almost nil, because fraught with the following difficulties: (1) The difficulty of obtaining a genetically "pure" line, since almost all plants, either wild or cultivated, are nearly as heterozygous as hybrids; (2) self-incompatibility, which often reduces inbred sorts to practical impotence and prevents the securing of homozygous forms by continued inbreeding; (3) the slow growth of progeny, which makes sustained breeding programs expensive and discouraging; (4) the fact that most characters desired in horticultural varieties, such as hardiness, color, size and vigor, are not qualities which, even if genetically explored, could be simply and easily bred into a race, because of their multiple-factor nature; (5) the unknown ancestral basis upon which most of the best hybrid cultivars have been built originally; and (6) the raising, for experiment only, of vast numbers of slow, expensive and commercially worthless plants necessary for genetical research.*

It has become increasingly apparent that the mixing of genotypes has been almost as prevalent in the wild as among the cultivated rhododendrons, with many wild forms as variable as hybrids although usually in lesser degree. Hybridization is possible across extremely wide limits, yet crossing between certain seemingly close relatives is sometimes quite impossible. Inducements toward mutation, such as treatment with radiation and colchicine, have been tried and the results thus far have been unimpressive. In general, no startling new breaks have appeared suddenly. Complete dominance is rare, yet practical experience indicates that gene reactions are present. In my experience, *yellow × yellow* in azaleas results in total yellow progeny. Also *red × red* in rhododendrons, while producing variable seedlings, tends to give a preponderance of red offspring. The wild or lilac color of *R. catawbiense* is hard to get rid of; a near-white flower crossed with another near-white plant will frequently yield all-lilac progeny. Frilling of the corolla margins, as in the hybrid 'Everestianum,' is definitely heritable in my experiments. Susceptibility to fungus disease, such as *Exobasidium vaccinii,* is heritable and appears clear-cut in certain pedigrees, totally absent in others. Genetical inhibitors appear to be present, too.†

Hardiness is an elusive quality. Since hardiness ratings are subject to different kinds of influences, the quality of a "tender" species may sometimes be cancelled out in hybridization, resulting in progeny more hardy than the parent. Such results cannot be predicted *a priori,* but result from the interaction of

---

*Bowers, C. G. Possibilities for improving hardy rhododendrons and azaleas. Proceedings Am. Hort. Cong. 1950. pp. 60–63.

†Lee, Frederic P. The Azalea Book. Am. Hort. Soc. Washington, D.C., 1958. It is noted on p. 97 that in azaleas size of flower and time of bloom are usually intermediate in F_1 plants as compared with parents. White is usually recessive. Sterility occurs in some double and hose-in-hose clones, but not in all.

complex factors. It is worthy of note that many of the "best" hybrid clones of today are the result of many generations of intercrossing and selection, incorporating a highly complex ancestry of unknown genetic origin. With wild species that are variable to start with, such is the material we have to build upon.

CHAPTER XVIII

THE TECHNIQUE OF CROSSING

THE technique of making artificial crosses is simple with rhododendrons. The pollen is merely transferred from the anther of one parent to the stigma of the other parent. The flower must be protected or bees will bring in pollen from other flowers, thus contaminating the cross. I shall describe the process in detail.

In most rhododendrons, the pollen ripens before the stigma is in a receptive state, usually, in fact, before the flowers open. After a flower is opened, the pollen is soon lost under outdoor conditions.

The first step in crossing is to emasculate the flowers of the prospective female or seed parent. Since some rhododendrons will set seed to their own pollen and such pollen is not always gone when the pistils mature, it is generally advisable to emasculate all flowers to be crossed. Emasculation, in this case, is simply the removal of the anthers with their pollen before the flower opens. A small pair of forceps, or even the fingers, will suffice for removing these organs, which should be simply picked off and thrown away. A day or two before the buds open, when they are showing color prominently, is a good time to emasculate the flowers.

After emasculating, the flowers should be covered with glassine * bags to prevent contamination (see plate "The Technique of Hand Pollination" following page 206). Usually, at this time, the pistils are not yet mature and the flowers must be held under the protection of these bags until ready to pollinate. In a majority of species, the flowers occur in groups or trusses of from 5 to 25. In crossing, I generally pollinate 10 or more flowers of a kind with one sort of pollen. I ordinarily select a truss having several flowers, pick off some of them if there are too many, emasculate the ones to be crossed and then place a glassine bag over the entire truss. The type of bag which has bellows-like folds on its sides is the most desirable.

There are various methods of fastening on the bag. Personally, I like to fold the bag together around the stem, as shown in the illustration, and hold it in

* Glassine is a translucent paper, not cellophane. It endures moisture.

162

place with a wire paper clip of the "gem" type. Another method is to tie on the bag by means of a wire to which a label is attached.

Soon after the buds open, which may be two or three days after emasculation, the pistils become mature. When the pistils are mature and the flower is ready to pollinate, a sticky sirup appears on the surface of the stigma. When the stigma (which is the little knob at the end of the pistil) becomes somewhat sticky, therefore, the flower is in a receptive condition to be pollinated. Protected by a bag, a flower will sometimes remain in a receptive condition for a week or longer.

When the time for pollination arrives, the bag should be removed and fresh pollen applied to the sticky surface of the stigma of each flower. Then a label, preferably a wooden tree label, should be written, identifying the cross, and attached to the stem just beneath the flower cluster. The bag should then be replaced immediately. If the bag is not replaced, the bees will visit the flowers and bring in foreign pollen of all sorts. As previously mentioned, it is perfectly possible for one flower to become fertilized by a dozen or more different kinds of pollen. For this reason, the use of bags or some other protective measure should never be omitted. No one who has ever looked at the pollinated stigma of a rhododendron through a microscope would consider employing the old-fashioned methods of open-pollination without testing his material first, although such methods are still widely used by amateurs.*

In applying the pollen, simply take a small quantity on the end of a pair of finely pointed forceps and apply it lightly to the sticky surface of the stigma, to which it will readily adhere. Cover the surface well with pollen. A toothpick or a pine needle may be used instead of forceps if desired. Or, better yet, a whole anther, from which pollen protrudes, may be touched against the stigmatic surface and the pollen will all adhere. This method is quick, economical of pollen and free from any danger of contamination. Do not use a camel's hair brush or other elaborate instruments, for they are unnecessary, wasteful of pollen and difficult to clean, hence, time-consuming and unsanitary. I have successfully pollinated thousands of flowers using nothing but my fingers and the whole anthers of rhododendrons. My favorite instrument, however, is the small pair of forceps with a fine, rounded point.

---

*In place of the bagging method, some hybridists simply remove all the petals from the flowers which are crossed, leaving nothing on but the pistils. They claim, with probable truth, that the bees do not approach the flowers after all the brightly colored parts are removed. In the use of this method, however, it would first be well to test your conditions by thus preparing a number of flowers and then leaving them unpollinated. If, under these conditions, they set seed, you may be sure that they have become contaminated. Under greenhouse conditions, when flowers usually bloom too early in the season for insect interference, no special protection seems to be necessary. If, however, you wish to be absolutely certain of controlled conditions, always use bags.

The bags may be removed in from two weeks to a month after pollination. Sometimes it is desirable to let the bags remain in order to better mark the crossed flowers for seed collection. If allowed to remain, the bags should be broken open within a fortnight after pollination to allow for development and leaf growth.

Generally the ovaries will begin to swell within a month after pollination if the plant is going to set seed. The seeds will not be ripe, however, until autumn. Some species, as noted in Chapter XII, ripen their seeds earlier than the rest. Small seed capsules do not necessarily indicate feeble compatibility. They frequently result when only a few seeds are set, owing to old pollen, poor pollination or some other preventive of complete fertilization. Such seeds may be perfectly good, but few in number.

The seed capsules may be collected and stored under ordinary living-room conditions. After drying, some of the seed will shell out of its own accord. A good method for removing the seed is to crush the dry seed capsules lightly under a rolling-pin as indicated in Chapter XII. Seed envelopes should be properly labelled.

One who attempts hybridization among rhododendrons must face numerous practical difficulties rather than the mere making of crosses and the keeping of records. One of the greatest handicaps is the difficulty of obtaining plants of various species suitable for use as parents and, when obtained, of accomplishing the hybridization of two sorts that ordinarily bloom at different seasons. We in America are faced with greater disadvantages in this respect than are our friends in England where many species have been introduced and the climate is kind to the Asiatic sorts. We also have to contend with stringent plant quarantine regulations, which make importation a hazardous undertaking. Besides this, the time required to bring young plants to blooming age renders every possible short-cut a real saving.

A method of circumventing some of these difficulties, which has proved successful in my own experience, is the preservation and shipment of pollen.* While we cannot import the plants themselves, except under rigid restrictions, we are not forbidden to receive pollen from abroad. The method is useful, also, in keeping the pollen of early varieties for use on later blooming flowers. I have worked out a method for rhododendrons, based upon the results of previous experiments by others.† It has been necessary to experiment with many different sets of conditions before determining what is best for rhododendron pollen preservation and it has also been necessary to devise special artificial

---

* Bowers, C. G. Preservation, storage and artificial germination of rhododendron pollen. Proceedings of the Sixth International Congress of Genetics 2:10. Ithaca, 1932.

† Kellerman, Maud. Successful long distance shipment of citrus pollen. Science, n.s. 42:375–376. 1915. Also later work by Dr. A. C. Fraser and certain rose breeders.

media for germinating rhododendron pollen before these tests could be carried out. The method which has proved best is one in which the pollen is placed in gelatin capsules and stored at room temperature in a sealed chamber in the presence of calcium chloride. I use empty gelatin capsules of the size known as Number I. I pick off the whole anthers, with their enclosed pollen, from flower-buds which are just about to open and place these anthers in the capsules, never filling a capsule more than one-third full. I then put the capsules containing anthers and pollen into a glass test tube or pill vial which has been previously prepared. In the bottom of the tube or vial is a small quantity of granular, anhydrous calcium chloride, and above the calcium chloride is a bit of cotton to keep it in place. The capsules are placed on this cotton, then, after several capsules are put into the tube, another bit of cotton is added, the tube is corked and finally sealed by dipping the corked end into melted paraffin. For shipment, the tube is placed in a special mailing box and sent by post to its destination.

Rhododendron pollen will sometimes keep for several days if merely placed in a dry, paper envelope and stored in a dry place. As early as 1877, Burbidge * reported the storage and shipment of rhododendron pollen by a variation of this method. I have found, however, that such practice is not dependable and that a more precise technique will pay for itself. The envelope method is useful, however, for shipment of pollen by air mail.

Refrigeration of stored rhododendron pollen does not help it, but rather makes matters worse if the calcium chloride is used.† The function of the calcium chloride is to produce a completely dry atmosphere inside the sealed chamber. It absorbs atmospheric moisture as a sponge absorbs water. After the pollen is collected and the vials are sealed, the calcium chloride will dry out everything within the vial, including the anthers if they are wet when placed in the capsules, for the drying influence of the chemical will penetrate through the capsule walls. I have found that tubes or vials are preferable to a glass desiccator, because they may be easily transported and because their small size and cheapness make it possible to use many of them, thus making it necessary to

---

* Burbidge, F. W. Cultivated plants, their propagation and improvement, p. 292. Edinburgh and London, 1877.

† Bowers, C. G. 1932. l.c. p. 156. The pollen of *Rhododendron catawbiense* was tested under 17 different sets of temperature and humidity conditions. Best vigor and greatest length of life was attained when storage was in complete dryness at about 68°F. After five weeks of storage, 75% of the pollen germinated vigorously, while very slight germination persisted for 131 days and fertile crosses resulted from pollen 71 days old. When two weeks old, 95% of the pollen germinated, but viability dropped quickly after that time. Rhododendron pollen requires an acid medium for germination. For artificial germination to test pollen viability, 1% agar plus 5% cane sugar and enough malic acid to bring the H-ion concentration to pH 4.5 is generally best. Germination takes place in less than 24 hours in a moist chamber, and the pollen is stained with aceto-carmine for microscopical examination.

open only one at a time, whereas, if a desiccator is used, the entire store of pollen capsules will be immediately exposed to moist air the moment the cover of the desiccator is lifted.

The use of capsules is advantageous. If collected and stored in large masses, the pollen does not dry so quickly as when stored in capsules. Moreover, a fresh capsule may be used for each pollination, thus insuring the use of pollen which has not been injured by previous exposure to the air. Pollen is very sensitive to moist air and when the cover of a receptacle is lifted, if the pollen is not protected by capsules, moist air rushing in will injure the entire stock. The contents of one capsule should not be used beyond the day that the capsule is opened.

Storage of pollen at room temperatures in the presence of calcium chloride as described is generally adequate for most purposes and I have used pollen successfully after two months of such storage. Also, it is entirely successful to ship fresh pollen in an envelope across the ocean by air mail and then storage it in capsules upon arrival four days later. Do not ship it in plastic or air-tight containers when fresh, as it will mold.

While it is possible to use stored pollen in making crosses of an early-blooming sort on to a later-blooming one, the reciprocal cross, in which the pollen of a late sort is used on an early-blooming flower, is much more difficult. In a large laboratory where elaborate apparatus is available to control temperature and moisture conditions for an indefinite period, Dr. John L. Creech of the United States Department of Agriculture has recently been able to storage the pollen from a late summer-blooming azalea and use it successfully on an early-blooming azalea the following spring. A more available method is to force early bloom on a normally late-blooming plant by means of higher temperature combined with artificially lengthened days. By giving the plant a July day by means of heat and electric light in March or April, flowering can be forced to occur in May or June. There is some danger here, however, that the resulting pollen or ovary may be abortive unless both temperature and illumination are in balance. This has been noted in Michigan by Davidson.*

Retarding the blooming date by storage at 40°F. is an entirely practicable method of securing late bloom on a normally early rhododendron or azalea. If the plants are potted and placed in cold storage just before growth starts in the spring, they may be held for some weeks before removal. Even if somewhat further advanced when placed in storage, their growth may be checked for a number of days, although the best practice is to hold them in storage only in the dormant condition.

* Davidson, Harold. Effect of photoperiod on Rhododendron. Proc. Amer. Hort. Cong. 1956. p. 21.

Whenever crosses are made, the hybridist should be careful to see that a properly marked label is placed on the truss which has been pollinated. Since the labels must often remain on the plants from May to October, only durable labels should be used for this work. Pasteboard tags usually become defaced and the writing is obliterated in this time. Wooden tree labels have proved very satisfactory for this work. One who makes many crosses will devise code numbers to designate the parents used in the work, in order to avoid the writing of long names. As noted elsewhere, it is customary to place the name or code number of the female (seed) parent ahead of the male (pollen) parent's designation.

In raising hybrid seedlings, it is again necessary to use care in keeping them properly labelled and in preventing seedlings of different crosses from becoming mixed. Most breeders find it desirable to give a pedigree number to each separate cross. Pedigree numbers must remain with the plants until they bloom or are disposed of. This frequently requires five or ten years, during which time a wooden label becomes completely defaced. Small pieces of thin copper sheeting, written upon with a stylus or merely with a nail which impresses an indented or embossed letter on the metal, make the best cheap label that I know about, for they will not rust nor fade and will last for years if attached to the plant with a loose piece of copper wire. Be sure to have the wire loose or it may strangle the branch to which it is attached. Labels similar to these, having an eyelet and rounded corners, are on the market as a commercial product, but the home-made sort, with a nail-hole for the wire, are cheaper where large quantities of plants are to be labelled. A more expensive label is the kind which is made by embossing the letters on an aluminum ribbon by the use of a regular embossing machine.

CHAPTER XIX

WHERE THE HYBRIDS CAME FROM

WE HAVE previously noted that when two different rhododendrons or azaleas are crossed, a new sort results which may be unlike either parent. Continued hybridization brings into existence new cultivars and races, some of which may be utterly different from any known wild species. Often great improvements are wrought. Sometimes not.

Rhododendron hybrids are not only interesting, but beautiful. Many of the most gorgeous of all rhododendrons are to be found in the choice garden forms which cannot be classified as belonging to any one species, but which may possess several divergent lines of ancestry. A glance at the historical development of these races would seem warranted, in order to better understand the existing hybrids as well as to evaluate the possibilities for future development along the lines of modern plant breeding.

In the genus *Rhododendron,* species hybridization is possible over a wide range. Naturally, plant breeders have experimented with these plants since the early days of their cultivation. Much hybridization has occurred without records being kept of definite crosses, so that the immediate parentage of some of our best cultivars is unknown. Many good things have resulted from chance seedlings or accidental pollinations, for which no plant breeder or introducer deserves credit except for the raising of the plants from seed, but they are interesting and furnish clues for further development. The methods used in the old days, too, were subject to gross error. Therefore, with the element of guesswork so apparent, it is safer to be general rather than specific in approaching the historical records of the old-time hybrids.

We can learn much, however, from the historical records. At first only a few species were in cultivation and it is easy to see in retrospect the influences of hybridization at work among these first introductions. Later, the original hybrids were further influenced by the admixture of new "blood." We can perceive the benefits of crossing, as well as some of its dangers.

Mr. Lionel de Rothschild, after much experience and observation, has noted a point concerning the hybridization of rhododendrons which has been fully confirmed by my own results and which, I believe, is further evidenced by the historical records. It is, in brief, that crosses between widely separated *series* are not so successful or desirable as those between more closely related groups. Or, conversely, that the nearer the series are related, the better the result will be.* While it may be desirable, for definite reasons, to bring in new "blood" from distant sources through wide crossing, we can seldom expect good off-spring immediately from such unions, although we may subsequently obtain valuable results from them after further breeding between species within the same or closely related series. Several generations may be needed to develop the new type.

Rothschild divides the genus by certain natural boundaries which he feels represent barriers to profitable hybridization. He mentions the lepidote or scaly-leaved sorts, comprising many series and scores of species, which, he feels, are not practicable to cross with the non-scaly-leaved species. There may be exceptions to this rule, but the indications are strongly in favor of keeping the lepidote species by themselves, which, however, still provides opportunities, since there is an infinite amount of variation within this one huge group.

Within the non-scaly-leaved, or elepidote rhododendrons, there are further lines of demarcation. The big-leaved sorts, such as those in the Falconeri series, could not be expected to give successful results when crossed with the vast majority of other rhododendrons, and so are probably best kept to themselves. Then, of course, there are the tiny alpine and arctic sorts, and, lastly, the azaleas. Although we have such wide combinations as Azaleodendrons, these are exceptional and, if sterile, are of little use as stepping-stones to further ends. In a scientific way, of course, we may derive a great deal of knowledge and an occasional "lucky break" from exceptionally wide crosses, so that we may always approach new and untried cross-combinations with the open mind of an explorer and should never hesitate to experiment with odd or "crazy" crosses if we have the time to make them. But we cannot really bank upon practical results unless we are working with relatively reasonable combinations. Hybrids can be made within one series, or even between species in different series, and still have parents of widely divergent character while retaining an ability to set good seed and produce vigorous seedlings. We should always remember that all "series," and species, too, are man-made categories and may not actually represent the true biological relationships prevailing in nature.

Since our modern hybrids are complex mixtures of several species instead of simple, first-generation hybrid clones, they may best be considered in rather

* de Rothschild, L. Notes on Hybrid Rhododendrons. Yearbook of the Rhododendron Assn., 112. 1934.

broad groups. Hybrids, although of slightly different ancestry, may appear so similar (phenotypically) as to belong in the same general classification. In most cases, therefore, I can see no advantage in drawing the lines of separation too closely between related groups. At the same time, it is misleading and inaccurate to place all hybrids upon an equal footing under the single title "hybrids."

Accordingly, in the following treatment, and in Chapter XXII and elsewhere, I have endeavored to segregate as many as possible of the hybrids into definite racial groups. In almost all cases, the individuals comprising these races are clonal varieties, with obvious genetical differences existing between one another. Although some have been gathered into groups * and designated as artificial species, these aggregations of hybrids are not to be regarded in the same light as natural species. They are exceedingly variable and can not be expected to breed true from seed. There are almost no clear-cut distinctions between the hybrid groups; frequently the border of one will overlap that of another. Like the series, the hybrid races are merely aggregations of variant individuals clustering about a central type. In the case of hybrids, however, the basis of classification is ancestry. This is, I believe, the only feasible basis upon which they may be separated. The group lines, therefore, cannot be regarded as hard and fast in hybrid races, while they are fairly definite in the wild sorts. Horticultural notes and an enumeration of clones will be found in Chapter XXII. The data given here are historical only. No attempt has been made to unravel the secondary hybrids of the various Asiatic series, the primary hybrids alone being recorded under their respective headings.

Much as we might like to keep the different racial groups of rhododendrons separate and distinct from one another, this is becoming increasingly difficult as intercrossing between the large groups is erasing all boundary lines. For practical purposes in horticulture we can retain such broad divisions as those between the lepidote and non-lepidote sorts, and, to some degree, continue to classify such groups as tree rhododendrons, conservatory sorts, dwarf alpine and arctic sorts and perhaps others. But the intermingling of extremes, as might be illustrated by the hybrids between the very dwarf *R. Forrestii* var. *repens* and large standard sorts, as well as the complex, multi-specific ancestry of many others, defies all attempts at systematic treatment. In many cases, a new group of primary hybrids is known only by the name of its originator, as the Dexter hybrids, or by an early type-form, such as the Loderi group. But such collective names usually disappear as they are eventually lost in further intercrosses. Outside the stud book records, therefore, most hybrid clones of true

---

* As in the Ghent hybrids, where the various members of the race have been grouped together as an artificial species under the name of *Rhododendron gandavense*.

rhododendrons are now listed under the general title of "hybrids," although azaleas still retain a semblance of individuality in such groupings as Ghent hybrids, Mollis hybrids and the like. These, however, are rapidly disintegrating as the new improved deciduous azaleas arise and, in the Obtusum subseries, inclusive hybrid groups, such as the Glenn Dale azaleas, cut across former boundaries.

For the purposes of this chapter, however, the historical development of the various races is dealt with more or less chronologically and in as much individual detail as seems warranted for a clear presentation.

The Catawba Hybrid Rhododendrons

Although this race is founded primarily upon American species, its early beginning and much subsequent improvement occurred in England. The first evergreen rhododendron to be formally introduced there was *Rhododendron maximum,* native of North America.* This is said to have been introduced in 1736 and first bloomed in London in 1756. *R. ponticum* was introduced from Gibraltar in 1763. *R. caucasicum* was introduced in 1803, and it was not until 1809 that *R. catawbiense,* destined to play a major role in hybridization, was brought into cultivation.

Up to this time, nothing seems to have been recorded of hybrids between any of these four species. About 1820, a cross of *Rhododendron catawbiense* ♀ $\times$ *ponticum* ♂ (= 'Morelianum') was made, but seems not to have attracted much attention, although the hybrid was said to have a finer inflorescence than either parent. Another cross of the early days was *R. maximum* ♀ $\times$ *ponticum* ♂ (= 'Intermedium'). This originated before 1826 and Dean Herbert, one of the most illustrious hybridists of the time, stated that the resulting beautiful white-flowered hybrid was entirely seed-constant.† Another primary hybrid, *R. catawbiense* ♀ $\times$ *maximum* ♂ (= 'Wellesleyanum') was made many years later and cultivated in 1880. All these hybrids lacked good, clear color.

The magnificent *Rhododendron arboreum* from the Himalayas was introduced into England in 1811 and began to bloom in the year 1825. It was tender, however, in all but the most protected districts. Its red flowers were highly desirable and almost immediately an effort was made to combine this species with the winter-hardy kinds. It was hoped, by such crossing, to develop new

* The small-flowered species from the Alps, *R. hirsutum,* had been introduced into cultivation in 1656, according to Aiton's *Hortus Kewensis,* but was apparently little known.

† It would seem that *album* varieties of the parental species must have been used if white flowers resulted in F_1, or else that the records are inaccurate, for one would expect white progeny from neither type species.

sorts which would be capable of resisting the English winters but still retain the desirable color of *R. arboreum*.

Lord Carnarvon of Highclere caused his eminent gardener, J. R. Gowen, an experienced hybridist, to undertake experiments of this kind. In 1826, Gowen pollinated the flowers of three hardy rhododendrons with pollen of *R. arboreum*. From these crosses, capsules resulted, out of which about 1800 seedlings came. Lord Carnarvon retained only a part, while the most were divided among numerous English and Scottish horticulturists. The first of these hybrids to be accurately described and pictured was *R. (catawbiense* ♀ × *ponticum* ♂) ♀ × *arboreum* ♂. This was named 'Altaclerense,' a Latinized rendering of the name Highclere. About the same time a number of similar hybrids were produced by English commercial nurserymen. The hybridists were now busy.

The admixture of *Rhododendron arboreum* in crosses with hardier species initiated an era of active hybridization.* Hardiness was not achieved immediately, however, and the first-generation hybrids were very tender indeed. Although 'Altaclerense' was the first really important hybrid, it was hardy only in fairly warm gardens in England and not hardy at all in the climate of New England. As a whole, the first hybrids from *R. arboreum* were disappointing. Said a writer in the *Gardeners' Chronicle* of 1855: "They never bloom till they are twenty years old and then very sparingly. . . . In very severe weather . . . the plants themselves are killed or damaged." The flowers were of a very rich color, but were frequently damaged by early spring frosts and the plants had to be bundled up in any except warm gardens.

Nevertheless, hybridization continued. Arboreum hybrids were backcrossed to their hardy parents or crossed with other hardy species. Until about 1850 there were no more species in use in crosses than the five I have enumerated. How well the hybridists succeeded in transferring the rich coloration of *Rhododendron arboreum* to the hardy sorts is testified to by the Catawba rhododen-

---

* A number of other crosses with *R. arboreum* are on record. *R. ponticum* ♀ × *arboreum* ♂ was first produced by Smith of Coombe Wood and called 'Smithii.' It had red flowers flaked with purple. Here belongs also 'Cunninghamii.'

R. catawbiense ♀ × *arboreum* ♂ was, according to Focke, first produced by Russell in Battersea and described as 'Russellianum.' Dean Herbert raised the same cross under the name 'Haylocki.' According to Herbert, this hybrid is distinguished by its striking leaves which, Rehder says, are tomentose beneath. It is the most beautiful rhododendron hybrid that Herbert saw (see Herbert, W., Amaryllidaceae, p. 362, 1837). The hybrids of *R. arboreum* with *R. catawbiense* are said to have been the hardiest of all Arboreum hybrids. In this category also belong the hybrids 'John Waterer' and 'Neige et Cerise.'

R. maximum ♀ × *arboreum* ♂ was among others crossed by Herbert. Gowen produced numerous specimens of *R. maximum* var. *purpureum altissimum* ♀ × *arboreum* ♂. A hybrid known as 'Alstroemeriaefolium,' of uncertain origin, but thought by Focke to be a French garden hybrid, was used as a seed parent in crosses with *R. arboreum* in Cannstatt, Germany. The resulting series of hybrids were sold as Wilhelma rhododendrons.

drons of today. Most of those on the "ironclad" list (see Chapter XXIV) were produced more than 75 years ago and probably contain little but the "blood" of the hardy sorts. Yet the color of the red cultivars must have come, to a large degree, from *R. arboreum,* although some rather clear rose forms can be found among the wild *R. catawbiense,* which might have become intensified a bit by selective breeding. It was, in my opinion, a real achievement in plant breeding when some of the pigmentation of *R. arboreum* was successfully transferred, in part at least, to the hardy strains of garden hybrids without bringing in tenderness or the disadvantage of tardiness in reaching blooming age. This should give heart to future plant breeders who seek to do similar work with the genus.

Focke * records an observation which is difficult to accept as positively or universally true, but which is interesting and perhaps significant in certain species combinations. He states that in reciprocal crosses (crosses in both directions) between *Rhododendron arboreum* and *maximum, ponticum* or *catawbiense,* made by Smith of Norbiton, the F_1 hybrids with *arboreum* as the seed-parent were inferior in beauty of bloom and much more sensitive to the cold than the hybrids of the reverse direction, where *arboreum* was the pollen parent. The use of *R. arboreum* as a seed-parent was therefore given up. While it is a common genetical observation that reciprocal crosses are often unequal, there is no evidence to indicate that a general rule may be made with regard to *hardy* × *tender* crosses. If, however, Focke's statement should prove uniformly true, then it would become an important consideration in rhododendron breeding, especially where hardiness is a factor, to employ the hardy species as seed-parents only. This is highly improbable, however.

Other species, besides the five here mentioned, have since been bred with the Catawba hybrids, some admixture of these, no doubt, becoming incorporated into the race which we today speak of as the Catawba hybrid rhododendrons. In this group, however, there can be no doubt as to the predominating influence of *Rhododendron catawbiense,* although some, such as *R. ponticum,* have had too large a share.

The late Anthony Waterer was a notable English rhododendron breeder who did much to expand the Catawba race. The Parsons family of Flushing, N.Y., were the best-known American breeders. Others in Holland, France and Germany have participated in the development of this race.

* Focke, W. O. Die Pflanzen-Mischlinge, p. 237. Berlin, 1881.

The Maximum Hybrids

Several early crosses in which *Rhododendron maximum* was used are noted in the preceding paragraphs. There have doubtless been others, many, perhaps, included in the general lists of Catawba hybrids. There are a few clones, of probable ancestry similar to that of the Catawba hybrids, in which the influence of *R. maximum* is obviously predominant. These I have classified as Maximum hybrids. Unfortunately, there are but few of these and little is known about their ancestry. They are hardy and of late blooming nature. Certain clones, listed by European growers as 'Maximum Album' and 'Maximum Roseum' are unquestionably of hybrid origin, as they differ markedly from the wild botanical varieties known respectively as *R. maximum* var. *album* and var. *purpureum,* which are merely color variants of the typical species. The clone 'Maximum Album' has much larger flowers than the wild *album,* is more tender and blooms earlier. It shows evidence of hybridity with *R. ponticum* as it fails to undergo leaf movements in winter. The clone should be renamed to avoid confusion with the wild form which is not a clone and which is rather abundant in the American trade. This may be a synonym of the clone 'Mum.'

In 1850, George Cunningham introduced a hybrid of *R. maximum* × *R. cinnamomeum,* correctly called clone 'Cunninghamii.' This clone is probably now extinct, but its parentage has been confused with that of 'Cunningham's White,' which is a cross between *R. caucasicum* and *R. ponticum* var. *album,* produced 20 years earlier, in 1830, by another man, James Cunningham of Edinburgh. By error, the Caucasicum hybrid, 'Cunningham's White,' has been described as a Maximum hybrid in much of the literature.

I believe it might pay to make fuller use of *Rhododendron maximum,* in superior individuals of the wild type, for hybridization in America where hardiness is essential. By its use, the blooming period of the Catawba hybrids could probably be extended to meet that of the Maximum hybrids, thus providing continuity of bloom in the group. Nearly a century ago, Dean Herbert urged the use of *R. maximum,* and since then other botanists, including E. H. Wilson, have likewise done so, but most breeders have preferred not to work with it. From experience I do not believe it so easy to cross as some of the other sorts, nor does it always produce such vigorous seedlings. And it is inclined to grow slowly. But it is hardy, late blooming and free from magenta color. Its chief disadvantage is that the flower trusses, blooming after the new foliage is formed, are often hidden by the leaves, so that the plant is not so showy or well-formed as the Catawba rhododendron. Where it has been possible to use *R. maximum* as the pollen parent the results seem better.

The Caucasicum Hybrids

Another component of the Catawba hybrid amalgamation was *Rhododendron caucasicum* from Russia. This is noted for hardiness and early bloom, and a number of the Catawba hybrids doubtless owe their early blooming characteristics to this ancestor. High-altitude forms only are hardy.

The Caucasicum hybrids, as here identified, are those which show the early bloom and underleaf rust color of *R. caucasicum*. There is question about the authenticity of most cultivated plants under this specific name, and perhaps the light yellow clone, 'Cunningham's Sulphur,' comes near to being the typical species. Perhaps the previously mentioned hybrid clone, 'Cunningham's White,' grown extensively, may be the parent of several Caucasicum hybrids. Some early-blooming popular garden hybrids, such as 'Boule de Neige,' certainly exhibit characters of *R. caucasicum*. Not least important is the capacity of some to strike root easily from cuttings. Other hybrid clones, presumed to have *R. caucasicum* as an ancestor, include some of our best old hardy garden hybrids.

There are several good relatives of *R. caucasicum* which are hardy and worthy of more extended use in hybridization. From Japan, *R. brachycarpum*, *R. Degronianum* and *R. Metternichii* are compact shrubs with pink or blush flowers, while *R. Fauriei* is pinkish with occasionally a yellow tinge. The slow-growing, compact *R. yakusimanum* with white flowers, bright rose in the bud, is a choice species. *R. Smirnowii* is well known and more vigorous. Some of these are of proven value to impart hardiness in hybrids. *R. chrysanthum* is small, weak and disappointing.

Some early crosses of *Rhododendron caucasicum* are on record. Hybrids with *R. arboreum* were, of course, not hardy. A varied progeny has come from *R. caucasicum* ♀ × *arboreum* ♂. One of the earliest was a rose red F_1 seedling raised by W. Smith of Kingston, England, in 1829 and called 'Venustum.' One other is a scarlet form called 'Nobleanum,' which was raised by Waterer of Knap Hill. These are said to be much dwarfer than *R. arboreum*. The reciprocal cross, *R. arboreum* ♀ × *caucasicum* ♂, was described in 1832 as 'Pulcherrimum.' *R. caucasicum* ♀ × *arboreum album* ♂ produced a white form known as 'Nobleanum Album.' The same species have been reported as parents of a clone called 'Sulphereum' (not *R. sulfureum*). Backcrosses of some of these to *R. caucasicum* have produced further forms.

An attractive clone called 'Dr. Stocker' was produced by Abbey, gardener to Col. North in England, from a cross of *R. caucasicum* clone 'Cunningham's sulphur,' ♀ × *R. Griffithianum* ♂. Some complex hybrids have been made, such as (*R. caucasicum* ♀ × *campanulatum* ♂) ♀ × (*R. caucasicum* ♀ × *arboreum* ♂) ♂ . *R. caucasicum* has been crossed also with *R. campylocarpum*, *R. Fortunei* and *R. Smirnowii*.

The Griffithianum Hybrids

The success attending the early hybridization of rhododendrons induced breeders to experiment with more of the Himalayan species as, from time to time, they were introduced into cultivation by Sir Joseph Hooker and others. Anthony Waterer of Knap Hill, Surrey, was one of these hybridists. Many of our best hardy clones were originated by him. Since hardiness and compact flower trusses were in vogue in the early days, it was some time before *Rhododendron Griffithianum*, a quite tender species with loose inflorescence, was worked with at all. This is one of the largest flowered Himalayan species.

H. J. Mangles of Hazlemere, England, began work about 1860 and devoted much attention to crossing *Rhododendron Griffithianum* with some of the Catawba hybrids, producing some notable seedlings. A certain cross of *R. Griffithianum* with a white, hardy hybrid, possibly 'Album Elegans,' produced, out of one seed-pod, five celebrated clonal varieties: 'Anthony Waterer's Aucklandii Hybrid,' 'Gauntletti,' 'George Hardy,' 'Manglesii' and 'White Pearl.' Other hybrids were 'Beauty of Littleworth,' 'Daphne Daffarn,' 'Dulcie Daffarn,' 'Dawn,' 'Isabella Mangles' and 'Loder's White,' besides additional sorts.

Another early breeder, Captain John Tremaine of Heligan, crossed *R. arboreum* (blood-red form) with *R. Griffithianum,* a combination that was later used by Richard Gill of Penrym, Cornwall, when, about 1893, he began producing a whole series of hybrids from these two species. The hybrids were of remarkable variation, some being crimson-scarlet, others white and pink. As might be expected, all these hybrids proved tender except in the warm gardens of Southern England.

Anthony Waterer, prior to 1880, attempted crosses of *Rhododendron Griffithianum* with certain garden hybrids, but, finding the F$_1$ plants tender, he discontinued the use of *R. Griffithianum* for the time being. Many years later John Waterer crossed F$_1$ and F$_2$ Griffithianum hybrids with hardier sorts and, out of these secondary crosses, came several excellent hybrids, among them the well known 'Pink Pearl.' *

In 1888 a plant from the cross of *R. Griffithianum* × *Fortunei* first bloomed at Kew and was named 'Kewense.' Much later Sir Edmund Loder of Leon-

---

* For a list of notable hybrids see Frederick Street's Hardy Rhododendrons, pp. 52–62, London, 1954.

ardslee, England, duplicated this cross, but used highly selected individuals of both species as parents. The result was a very superior series of clones under the cultivar group name of 'Loderi,' of which perhaps the clone 'King George' is best. The individual flowers of some of these attain as much as seven inches across and come in clusters up to ten or more. This is one of the finest hybrids extant and greatly outclasses its parents. It is interesting to note that, instead of employing any two plants that happened to be available of the parental species, Loder used the very best individuals he could select and the results justified his care.

Several hybridists have crossed *Rhododendron Griffithianum* with *R. campylocarpum*. From this combination, using Hooker's dwarf form of *R. campylocarpum,* Mangles produced the cream-colored 'Mrs. Randall Davidson.' S. Smith of Penjerrick later repeated the cross, using the taller form of *campylocarpum* and originated a series of pink, yellow and ivory clones known as the Penjerrick hybrids. A cross with *R. Thomsonii* was called 'Cornish Cross.' I have already mentioned an old-time cross between *R. caucasicum* 'Cunningham's Sulphur' and *Griffithianum,* an ivory-colored hybrid called 'Dr. Stocker.' This clone was later crossed with *R. campylocarpum* and resulted in a fine yellow hybrid. 'Dr. Stocker' was also crossed with *R. Thomsonii.*

T. H. Lowinsky of England made a series of crosses, using a fine clone of *R. Griffithianum* called 'Roseum Superbum,' with many other sorts, among them being 'Doncaster,' 'White Pearl' and 'Corona.' Some of his productions were called 'The Don,' 'Donna Theresa,' 'Mrs. Tom Lowinsky' and 'Tittenhurst Belle.' Messrs. J. C. and P. D. Williams of Cornwall, Mr. R. Veitch of Exeter and Captain Johnstone of Trewithen are other English hybridists who have achieved notable results in crosses of *R. Griffithianum* with various other species. A cross with *R. discolor* made at Sheffield Park has produced flowers as fine as 'Loderi,' but flowering later which is an advantage. Although the possibilities of F_1 crosses of *R. Griffithianum* with the established races, such as the Catawbiense, Caucasicum, Fortunei, Thomsonii, Barbatum and Arboreum groups, have been quite thoroughly explored by the hybridists mentioned, other work is being done with the newer Chinese species which offer still further opportunities, and it is probable that many interesting new things will arise in Griffithianum hybrid races. The clone 'Pink Pearl' has been the ancestor of many fine hybrids.

The possibilities of good hybrid cultivars arising in the F_2 and succeeding generations have not yet been exhausted. It is not improbable that we will get, from some of these, the fine floral characters combined with greater hardiness which will put this hitherto tender race into cultivars which may be grown widely. Several breeders, especially nurserymen, have been getting out secondary hybrids for a good many years. Besides the English breeders mentioned, Van Nes and Koster in Holland have been doing this kind of work. Few Griffithianum hybrids of any sort have proved hardy anywhere in the northeastern United States, but most of them are grown on the West Coast.

The Fortunei Hybrids

While the hybrids of *Rhododendron Fortunei* do not compare in attractiveness with those of *R. Griffithianum*, they have the advantage of being considerably hardier and, hence, are of greater potential usefulness for America and other regions where winter-resistant races are required. *R. Fortunei,* although not so hardy as the common American species, is one of the hardiest of the Chinese rhododendrons and has decidedly larger flowers than most of the American sorts, with the added advantage of fragrance and clear color. Most of the plants which have been tested in America have proved unreliable north of Philadelphia, although most of them can be grown in sheltered places on Long Island and Cape Cod. Recently, however, a number of seedlings have been found able to withstand the climate in the vicinity of Boston, if given some protection, and a few of them survived the terrific cold of the winter of 1933–34 at Boston. On Cape Cod,. those having the greatest amount of fragrance seemed to be the more tender. Where *R. Fortunei,* in its natural forms, appears to survive under protection in the north, it probably needs to be hybridized with some of the "ironclads" before it can ever become usefully adaptable in the cold regions of America. This has not been done to any extent as yet, so the species as it stands today cannot be regarded as the equal in hardiness to the native *R. maximum, R. catawbiense* and *R. carolinianum,* although a much finer flower where it can be grown.

The first extensive hybridization of this species was begun about 1870 by Mr. Luscombe of Coombe Royal, Devon, who crossed it with existing garden hybrids and with *Rhododendron Thomsonii,* obtaining such clones as 'Luscombei' and 'Luscombe's Scarlet' from the latter. Mr. George Paul crossed *R. Fortunei* with certain Catawba hybrids in England and produced a series of sweet smelling hybrids, mostly pink or rose in color. A late red clone, called 'Essex Scarlet,' is another of Mr. Paul's Fortunei hybrids. Crosses have also been made with *R. Griffithianum* (as noted) and *R. campylocarpum,* the latter producing an intermediate hybrid with ivory flowers. A late flowering form has produced good July flowering progeny when crossed with red Catawba hybrids.

Among the existing Fortunei hybrids, the majority are no hardier than the type *Rhododendron Fortunei,* being mostly crosses with other species from the Orient. The Kewense group, referred to as Griffithianum hybrids, are of considerable importance. Another group, known as the Naomi hybrids, was produced in England from the cross of ('Kewense' ♀ × *R. Thomsonii* ♂ (= 'Aurora')) ♀ × *R. Fortunei* ♂.

Other Hybrids of the Fortunei Series

More recently *Rhododendron discolor, R. decorum, R. sutchuenense* and a few other members of the Fortunei series have been used in crosses. While the Discolor crosses produce good progeny, it takes eight or ten years for them to begin flowering. The stud book lists 35 primary crosses. Because it does not flower too early in the year and because of its fine character, *R. discolor* makes a good parent, but it often gives its offspring a bluish tinge. For making crosses with earlier blooming species, *R. discolor* is capable of being forced to bloom under glass. Many crosses have been made between *R. discolor* and fine Chinese species, such as *R. Griffithianum, R. arboreum, R. Thomsonii* and *R. campylocarpum*. Crosses with the tall form of the latter resulted in a race similar to the Penjerrick hybrids and (from the dwarf *campylocarpum*) a series of constant pale ivory-yellow seedlings. Crosses have also been made with *R. Fortunei, R. Griersonianum, R. eriogynum* and *R. auriculatum,* as well as with the hybrids 'Loderi' and 'Gill's Triumph.'

Other hybrids of the Fortunei series include *R. decorum* × *Griffithianum, R. diaprepes* × *auriculatum, R. sutchuenense* × *calophytum* and white *arboreum,* all of those mentioned being notable for one feature or another.

Crosses between members of the Fortunei series and Catawba hybrids have been made extensively in the past, mostly by English and Dutch hybridists, but, from the British standpoint at least, the results have not been encouraging and most of the seedlings have been discarded. De Rothschild states that, in his experience with crosses made between the old Waterer Catawba hybrids and members of the Fortunei series, only the dominant wild color, mauve or lilac, came out in the F_1 progeny.* In this series also belongs the new and important American race of rhododendrons called the Dexter hybrids. These are of recent origin and will be discussed under a subsequent heading.

The Dexter Hybrids

About 1922, the late Charles O. Dexter of Sandwich, Massachusetts, who lived in a spot on Cape Cod where the climate is mild, began testing new species and raising seedlings. His basic stocks were a few unique plants belonging to the Fortunei series acquired from the neighboring Farquhar Cape Cod

* de Rothschild, L. Yearbook of the Rhododendron Assn. London, 1933. p. 71.

nursery, coming originally from Veitch in England, it was said. Though labelled 'Fortunei,' these miscellaneous plants varied considerably, some showing characters of *R. decorum,* and one or two showing yellowish tinges suggesting the influence of *R. campylocarpum.* Whether they were mixed seedlings or selected clones of named cultivars has not yet been decided, but the evidence favors seedlings, because no clones have been identified which possess exactly the same combination of characters.

The present author saw the original collection as early as 1928. By that time Mr. Dexter had acquired plants and seedlings of other species and garden hybrids amounting to scores, which he got from New England collections or from imported seed. E. H. Wilson in America and J. C. Williams in England were among those who sent him seed of exotic species and fine hybrids. His landscape architect, Paul Frost, did much to build up his collection. In the congenial climate of Cape Cod, Mr. Dexter raised thousands upon thousands of seedlings that would not survive elsewhere in New England, making many crosses between the best sorts and trying new things. Out of these came a race of Fortunei series hybrids that closely resembled the original plants from Farquhar's—so closely that, except for certain subsequent crosses which carried stronger colors, from *R. haematodes* and other species, I should regard these Farquhar originals as the main stem of Dexter's race. Surprisingly, these plants, quite free from the old Catawba influence, have proved somewhat winter-hardy along the American East Coast north of Boston, as well as in sheltered sites inland. One doubts that the present stock will be reliable in places of sustained sub-zero temperatures in winter, but further selective breeding may some day make them competitors with the old "ironclads."

Dexter's hybrid rhododendrons are quite the equal of most British garden hybrids of Fortunei derivation, save for such exceptional sorts as 'Pink Pearl' and the giant Loderis. But for hardiness, they seem to excel all others within that series. They are good wherever boxwood will survive. In size of flower they reach four inches across; in color they are mostly pink, showing a scarcity of whites. A few of Dexter's last crosses developed stronger color, but quite free from purplish tinge, except in some. There have been few dark shades. Those having a yellowish or apricot effect are noticeably weaker and more tender. Some have a nutmeg-like fragrance. Their trusses tend toward looseness, but some are round and full. They grow faster, with a more open habit and are not so tall as the old Catawbas, and their leaves are pale. They bloom about two weeks earlier than the Catawba hybrids.

The Thomsonii Hybrids

This is a group of brilliantly colored hybrids, only half-hardy in Britain but frequently spoken of. The deep blood-red species, *R. Thomsonii,* crossed with a garden hybrid (Catawba?) by Mr. Standish in the early days, produced the clone 'Ascot Brilliant,' a bright red hybrid. *R. Thomsonii* × *barbatum* (= 'Shilsoni') was produced by Gill, and later *R. arboreum* × *Shilsoni* (= 'Cornubia') by Smith of Penjerrick. This latter clone is said to continue blooming for as long as two and one-half months at a time and is apt to kill itself by over-flowering. Other crosses between *Thomsonii, barbatum* and *arboreum* are on record.

Methven of Edinburgh raised crosses between *R. Thomsonii* and the hardy species *R. catawbiense* and *R. caucasicum,* the latter being the best, it is said. More recently Sir Edmund Loder made crosses between *Thomsonii* and a large number of other species, while Smith of Penjerrick produced a strain of brilliantly colored hybrids. John Waterer has used an infusion of *Thomsonii* "blood" in some of his more hardy hybrids known as 'J. G. Millais,' 'Brilliant,' 'Bagshot Ruby' and 'Corona.' 'Orange Queen' and 'Harrisi' are the clonal names of other Thomsonii hybrids. A long list of crosses, including 'Cornish Cross' and other notable clones, has been subsequently reported. Seventy primary crosses are on record.

The Hybrids of R. Williamsianum and R. Forrestii

One of the more unique and attractive dwarf, compact rhododendrons is *R. Williamsianum,* usually under three feet tall, with heart-shaped leaves and pink bell-like flowers. As a foliage plant for the foreground, it is superb. Unfortunately it is tender (B) and blooms too early. However, it has proved crossable, and the hybrid 'Temple Belle' came from Kew in 1916. Rothschild, Aberconway and other British hybridists used it and about a dozen more primary hybrids followed. About 1936 Dietrich Hobbie of Oldenburg, Germany, in a somewhat colder climate, began crossing *R. Williamsianum* with garden hybrids. Raising vast numbers of seedlings, he found the hybrids hardier and blooming later than the species. A promising race has developed.

Another exotic species, the dwarf creeper formerly known as *R. repens* and now called *R. Forrestii* var. *repens,* has proved surprisingly good as a parent of dwarf hybrids. This little species, with brilliant blood-red flowers, is difficult to grow, but when crossed with larger and hardier sorts it has produced some strikingly brilliant dwarfish hybrids, notably the Griersonianum cross 'Elizabeth.' Lord Aberconway has done much of this work. About 1938, Dietrich Hobbie crossed var. *repens* with the red clone 'Britannia' and other garden hybrids. Forms resulted which are said to be as hardy as the clones, 'Dr. V. H. Rutgers' and 'Catherine van Tol' and having dwarf growth combined with brilliant color.

Miscellaneous Rhododendron Hybrids

The German hybridist, T. J. R. Seidel, working in a cold climate near Dresden for many years produced hybrids with *R. Smirnowii, R. caucasicum* and *R. Metternichii* and garden hybrids. Koster in Holland carried on work with these species also. These have enriched our list of very hardy rhododendrons. In the United States the work of Joseph B. Gable of Pennsylvania has covered a wide area of exploratory crossing and has resulted in many fine clones of diverse character, difficult to place in any one category. In Britain, the late Lionel de Rothschild, the late Lord Aberconway and the late P. D. Williams, plus a host of others less prominent, have certainly laid foundations for several new races, although much of their work has been for fanciers only. Meanwhile the British and Dutch nurserymen have been busy producing popular sorts that merit wide distribution.

An interesting story of hybridization concerns some reciprocal crosses of *R. Griffithianum* on hardy hybrids, made in 1892 at the Royal Porcelain Works in Berlin. J. H. Van Nes took 230 seedlings to Holland where most died in winter. Crossing a few survivors, 'Queen Wilhelmina' and 'Stanley Davis' resulted. Crossing these two then produced 'Britannia,' 'Earl of Athlone,' 'Unknown Warrior,' 'C. B. Van Nes' and 'Jean Mary Montague'—all superb!

Recently American hybridists on the West Coast have been producing some superior new hybrid clones, notably in the Fortunei series. These have included Endre Ostbo and Halfdan Lem of Washington and Rudolph Henny of Oregon.

Hybrids of the Lepidote Rhododendrons

Although hybrids of the more spectacular large rhododendrons have occupied the spotlight, a few very good lepidote hybrids have appeared from time to time, and stud book records show a few crosses with almost every one of the leading lepidote species. Of the older ones, those with the Alpine Rose and a few with the Carolinianum series represent modest but useful productions. Most striking, perhaps, are those of the Cinnabarinum series, such as the clone 'Lady Chamberlain,' while some of the blue hybrids of *R. Augustinii,* such as

'Blue Tit,' are quite extraordinary. Although a great many dwarf or small-flowered kinds exist among the lepidote species, much of the progress to date, with notable exceptions, has been along the line of discovering and selecting good color forms and superior strains among the species themselves. Since polyploidy exists among this group, although relatively uncommon elsewhere in the genus, there are possibilities for interesting genetical developments. The Maddenii series, with a number of hybrids including some crosses with the Cinnabarinum series, belongs in this lepidote section, too. Also, in a place by themselves, are those tropical species clustering around *R. javanicum,* constituting a hybrid group noted below. Despite the large number of small or "table-top" species in this section, probably more important work has been accomplished in breeding dwarf rhododendrons from those belonging to the elepidote section.

The Javanese and Malayan Hybrids

This group of hybrid rhododendrons is quite unrelated to those we have been discussing except for the fact that they, too, belong among the evergreen or true rhododendrons in the so-called Lepidorrhodium subgenus. They are warm-house plants, coming from the tropics and suitable only for conservatory use. Some, however, are very beautiful things.

Rhododendron javanicum was introduced into cultivation from Java in 1847. It has deep orange flowers, pink in the throat. It was at once crossed with other species from Malaya by Taylor of Kew and the Messrs. Veitch. It was found to produce hybrids of great beauty. It has been crossed and re-crossed for several generations, entirely with related species from the tropics, among which have been *R. jasminiflorum, R. Teysmanni, R. Lobbii, R. Brookeanum, R. multicolor, R. malayanum* and perhaps others. Millais (1917) stated that nearly 200 varieties are known and that their colors range from deep crimson to golden yellow and pure white. In form, they range from jasmine shape to large bell-shaped flowers. A double form, called 'Balsaminaeflorum' (not to be confused with the azalea, *R. indicum* clone 'Balsaminaeflorum'), was obtained by self-pollinating a flower which had one or two petaloid stamens. A race of double-flowered forms has arisen from further crosses with 'Balsaminaeflorum.' The Javanicum hybrids are valuable greenhouse plants, some variety being in bloom at any season of the year, and are probably better adapted for conservatory use than for the commercial florist. Some of the species are epiphytic in nature.

The Azaleodendrons

Curiously, the first rhododendron hybrid on record was a wide, difficult and unusual one. It was a cross between an evergreen rhododendron with thick leathery leaves and a deciduous American azalea. Probably no hybridist of the time would have dreamed of attempting so wide a cross if this first azaleodendron mating had not occurred accidentally. This cross took place before any of the other rhododendron hybrids were recorded.

This first hybrid came to light in 1800 at the Thompson nursery at Mile-End, near London. It was said to have come from seeds of *Rhododendron ponticum* which had been fertilized by pollen from some American azalea. The pollen parent could hardly have been other than *R. nudiflorum*. The hybrid was described as having rather large green leaves and pale purple flowers, not spotted, with wavy lobes. It is reported by some to have been sterile, while others state that a hybrid of this type produced viable seeds. If fertile, such a plant would be unusual, to say the least, for the statement has been reliably made that azaleodendrons are almost invariably sterile "mules." The original hybrid was first called *R. ponticum* var. *deciduum,* but the name was soon changed to *R. Azaleoides.*

A similar hybrid, but in the reverse direction, was raised by J. R. Gowen before 1828. This was called 'Gowenianum' and was the F_1 result of *"R. nudiflora* or *viscosa* fertilized with the pollen of a hybrid rhododendron between *R. ponticum* and *R. catawbiense."* It was evergreen with pale rose colored flowers. In 1825 Gowen raised 97 plants from a cross of *R. nudiflorum* ♀ × *catawbiense* ♂. They varied somewhat in size of truss and flower color, but were mostly purple. Their leaves were evergreen. The hybrid was called 'Cartonianum.'

Dean William Herbert of Spofforth, England, raised *R. viscosum* ♀ × *maximum* ♂ which was called 'Hybridum.' It had evergreen leaves and rather small whitish flowers with a pinkish border and yellow spots on the upper lobe. Dean Herbert also raised *R. viscosum* ♀ × *ponticum* ♂, with very fragrant white flowers. A Catawba hybrid ♀ × *viscosum* ♂ was produced accidentally at Vauxhall, England, by Chandler and Sons. It was compact in habit and quite evergreen, but possessed the azalea fragrance. Other similar crosses are on record. Besides these, additional hybrids of uncertain parentage are considered by Rehder * to be probable crosses between the Ghent hybrids or *calendula-*

* Wilson, E. H. and A. Rehder. A Monograph of Azaleas, p. 191. 1921. Complete records and synonymy of many azaleodendrons are included.

ceum with *R. catawbiense*. Most of these have pink flowers with an orange blotch on the upper lobe.

Some further productions of Dean Herbert were four evergreen seedlings from a cross of *R. luteum* ♀ × *ponticum* ♂. This hybrid was called 'Laetitiae.' Two of the seedlings bore fragrant yellow flowers, while another was of lemon yellow and the last a chestnut brown. Instead of taking on an extreme mixed hue, these hybrids discarded much color and often showed variegation. Hybrids of similar origin were raised by Bretschneider in Germany and offered for sale in 1850. Also, Rollisson of England is said to have bred some before 1863. A number of other early azaleodendron crosses are recorded in the literature.*

R. (maximum × ponticum) ♀ × *molle* ♂ was raised by Smith about 1830 and called 'Norbitonense.' A number of different forms were evidently raised from this same parental combination, since fifteen or more clones of 'Norbitonense' were listed. They must have been considered sterile, as they were called "yellow and coppery mules." The seed parent was a fine white hybrid. This is significant, since the absence of purple (anthocyanin) pigmentation in either parent may account for the fact that the resulting azaleodendron seedlings had yellow flowers instead of pink ones, as occurred when yellow azaleas were crossed with purple rhododendrons. These yellow flowered hybrids attracted much attention at the time and two of them, 'Smithii Aureum' and 'Broughtonii Aureum,' are still listed in the trade catalogues today, while most other azaleodendrons have passed out of sight.

Others, similar to the Norbiton hybrids, were raised later by Standish and Noble, Anthony Waterer, White of Sunningdale and Williams of Holloway, all in England. A series of azaleodendron hybrids was raised by G. Vander Meulen from crosses between *R. japonicum* and certain of the Catawba hybrids, including 'Prince Camille de Rohan' and 'Leopard.' These hybrids were exhibited at Ghent in 1892. Their colors ranged from white to rose or lilac, with spotted lobes. A yellow azaleodendron was obtained by Croux et fils before 1908 as a result of a cross between *R. molle* and an unknown true rhododendron. Croux also reported a semi-double form.

---

* A cross recorded as *R. (maximum* ♀ × *ponticum* ♂) ♀ × *calendulaceum* var. *chrysolectrum* ♂ and another cross of *R. maximum* ♀ with the same pollen parent were made by Gowen, but the seedlings perished when young. Focke records a cross of *R. caucasicum* ♀ × *luteum* var. *albiflorum* (?) ♂ which produced a white flowered hybrid very much like an azalea. Herbert produced the cross *R. canadense* ♀ × *luteum* ♂, and reported the seedlings tender and sickly. This, however, is not an azaleodendron, but a very wide cross within the Series Azalea instead. William Smith of Norbiton Common, near Kingston, England, raised a number of interesting azaleodendron hybrids. He produced *R. speciosum* ♀ × *arboreum* ♂ in 1829. This hybrid had thin, evergreen leaves and crimson flowers with dark purple dots. *R. arboreum* ♀ × *molle* ♂ had the habit of a later hybrid, 'Smithii Aureum,' but its flowers were pink.

A hybrid clone called 'Lone Eagle' was produced in 1928 by Mr. John Baardse, propagator for Messrs. Bobbink and Atkins of Rutherford, N.J., from a cross between the Griffithianum hybrid clone 'Pink Pearl' and a Kurume azalea. The plant was of intermediate height in many respects, although the leaves closely resembled an azalea. The flower was a clear blush pink, about one and one-half inches across. It may be an apomict rather than a true hybrid.

Other azaleodendrons have been produced from time to time and seedlings under blooming size are now being grown by more than one hybridist. Azaleodendron breeding is not, by any means, a new idea. Perhaps the best commentary is that few are listed in the catalogues and fewer yet are spoken of with praise. During 100 years few have been good enough to persist in commerce. Whether any could ever be fertile and what would result if F_2 seedlings were produced is interesting to speculate upon, but this seems not to be within the realm of possibility unless some new technique is developed. The best of those now sold in England are not hardy in the northern United States.

In 1837 Dean Herbert wrote the following statement: "I have raised many weak plants from the seed of Rhododendron by yellow and orange azaleas, but I have found extreme difficulty in rearing them and have lost them at an early age . . . It is remarkable that the difference of constitution between the rhododendrons and the American azaleas seems to render the mules more impatient of wet than either of the parents, which is manifested by a sickly variegation of the leaf, rendering it difficult to rear them and indicating the want of a more sandy and drier soil."

From my own experience, I can say that Dean Herbert's description is a very accurate picture of conditions in the few pedigrees from which I have derived any seedlings at all. In over fifty hybrid combinations, only 4% produced seedlings which were capable of living more than a few weeks. Most of the crosses set no seed whatever. Mortality has been very high in the remainder. Growth has been slow and languid. While I have noted some young azaleodendrons that appear promising, I am inclined to think that the odds are greatly against the breeder of azaleodendrons. He might expect, however, to obtain a valuable seedling in a rare instance.

Herbert and others noted extreme variation among sister seedlings of azaleodendrons. In my material, pollinated under controlled conditions, several seedlings appeared, alongside obvious azaleodendrons, which looked exactly like the seed-parent—true evergreen rhododendrons. My best explanation is that this is an instance of induced apogamy. It seems logical to conclude, also, that similar apomictical seedlings may have resulted from azalea × rhododendron crosses elsewhere, falsely assumed to be azaleodendrons.

The Ghent Hybrid Azaleas

Historically, the basis of the Ghent hybrids is the cross of *Rhododendron* (*calendulaceum* × *nudiflorum*) × *luteum* (and partly *viscosum* or *arborescens*). The American azaleas, *R. calendulaceum* (yellow), *R. viscosum* (white, fragrant, late) and *R. nudiflorum* (pink), were introduced into England in the year 1738. Fifty-five years later, in 1793, the large yellow Pontic azalea, *R. luteum*, from the Black Sea region, made its first appearance in western Europe. Early in the nineteenth century crosses between *R. luteum* and the American species were made at Hammersmith, England. About 1831, J. R. Gowen of Highclere and Dean William Herbert raised similar hybrids. Two additional species, *R. roseum* and *R. speciosum*, were probably used also under the name *R. nudiflorum*, since we know, from colored illustrations, that these species were in England under that name in the early days.

It was in Belgium, however, that the more important work of developing this group of azaleas took place, and the city of Ghent became the center for the breeding and propagation of this race. Hence, the name Ghent hybrids and the artificial specific name which has been applied to the collective group of cultivars as a whole: × *Rhododendron gandavense*.

In 1825 a master baker of Ghent, named P. Mortier, raised the first of his hybrids, made by crossing *R. luteum* with early and late American azaleas. According to Focke, *R. luteum* and the three or more American species mentioned will all cross with one another without any marked loss of fertility. The methods used by Mortier in his breeding work were kept secret, but it is regarded as evident that *R. calendulaceum, nudiflorum, viscosum* and *luteum* were employed and that the best hybrids were then used for further crossing.

Louis Verschaffelt of Ghent acquired some of Mortier's choicest varieties and continued the work of breeding, which was later engaged in also by Cassell, Vuylsteke and Van Houtte. In recent years, Koster and others have further developed the industry by introducing other species into the racial mixture, as we shall see in considering the next hybrid group.

One of Mortier's first hybrids was *R. calendulaceum* × *nudiflorum* (and partly × *speciosum*), which was called × *R. Mortieri*. It appeared in two color forms, one a bright copper and the other orange with a flesh-pink center. This and other American species crossed with *R. luteum* furnished the basis for the × *R. gandavense* type. In later years, *R. occidentale* has evidently entered into the mixture in certain strains. As early as 1836, Loddiges enumerated 107 clones of the Ghent hybrids. The cultivars have been extensively crossed *inter se* since that time.

The Ghent hybrid race, sometimes called the Pontic-American azaleas, partakes, in general, of the colors of the parental species. Few races of plants in any genus can compare with the Ghent hybrid azaleas in the extent of their coloration which covers a wide range and includes practically all possible intermediate hues and combinations of the parental species. They comprise light and dark shades, from flowers of flaming brilliancy to the most delicate of pastel hues and many of the so-called "art" types. Fixed color patterns occasionally occur. A frequent characteristic is for the upper lobe of the corolla to be more highly colored than the remaining segments. Although this race has not been explored genetically, a possible explanation of its extreme variability in color rests in the fact that it represents a combination of both the anthocyanin and yellow pigments in its floral parts and that *R. calendulaceum,* being tetraploid, has a double number of chromosomes.

A double form occurs and is called × *R. gandavense* var. *plenum.* This seems to have originated as a spontaneous variant among seedlings, which has transmitted its double-flowered character to its offspring. One of the earliest double forms was raised from seed and figured by Van Houtte in 1858. It was semi-double and pink, with three or four upper lobes orange. A common form of doubleness is for the stamens to turn into petals. There are many double clones today.

The Mollis Hybrid Azaleas

The history of this race has been fully discussed by Wilson.* He regarded it as fundamentally a cross between the Japanese and Chinese species, *R. japonicum* and *R. molle,* respectively. It seems evident, however, that some of the more recent varieties are of considerably more complex parentage, the influence of the Ghent hybrids possibly entering. The Mollis hybrids are regarded as a collective group and have been given the artificial specific name of × *R. Kosterianum.*

According to Wilson, the first crosses of this race were made by William Tillery in 1872 when he started crossing several varieties of *R. japonicum* with *R. molle.* Anthony Koster and Sons of Boskoop, Holland, and Anthony Waterer of Knap Hill, England, followed very shortly afterward. Both parent species had been intercrossed earlier but were lost for some time and subsequently reintroduced. The pure species were in cultivation in several seminal strains and had also probably become intermixed with other species of azalea through chance pollination and by artificial hybridization, so that numerous varieties of each parental species were in existence before the advent of the

* Wilson, E. H. and A. Rehder. A Monograph of Azaleas, p. 97. Cambridge, 1921.

Mollis hybrid race. It was from stock of this sort that the European Kos-terianums arose.

In 1913 the late Mr. T. D. Hatfield of Wellesley, Mass., raised a hybrid be-tween the pure species, *R. japonicum* $\times$ *R. molle,* which appears very much like the Koster hybrids, but is somewhat hardier. In size and color it is en-tirely equal to the more complex hybrids. Mr. Hatfield's original hybrid was called 'Miss Louisa Hunnewell.' Seedlings from this have been quite widely disseminated under the name of 'Miss Louisa Hunnewell,' but since the cultivar is not entirely seed-constant the seedlings are often merely *japonicum* and *molle* variants and are seldom as good as the best F_1 example of the original cross. The latter, therefore, should be treated as a clone, propagated vegetatively and sold under the name 'Miss Louisa Hunnewell,' while the use of this name for seedlings should be immediately discontinued.

A double-flowered group of Mollis hybrids (once known as *Azalea rustica fl. pl.*) are now recognized under the name of $\times$ *R. mixtum.* It is considered that these plants have derived their doubleness from an infusion of the "blood" of the double-flowered Ghent hybrids and are therefore regarded as hybrids between the Ghent and Mollis races.

The Knap Hill Azaleas (Improved Ghent Hybrids)

In more recent times the Ghent and Mollis azaleas have become considerably interbred, and along with this has come a small infusion of *R. occidentale.* The result has been several strains of hybrids, much like Ghent azaleas but with larger flowers. These have been developed mainly in England, first by Anthony Waterer of the Knap Hill Nursery, who is reputed to have used *R. occidentale* $\times$ *R. molle* to get 'Albicans.' Waterer's hybrids, begun in the 1870s, became the Knap Hill group of Ghent azaleas. Later the Slococks carried on further breeding and developed the Goldsworth group. Meanwhile, the late Lionel de Rothschild of Exbury, acquiring some of the Knap Hill material, developed the Exbury group. Also using the Knap Hill strain, the late Edgar Stead of Australia developed a race known as the Ilam group.

The present writer has not made direct comparisons of all these sub-groups, but is prepared to say that among them are probably some of the finest deciduous azaleas in existence. On the basis of what I have seen, I do not believe that vast differences exist between the best plants of these different strains. They appear very lovely in England, some having single flowers up to about three inches across. At the same time there are inter-grades, some being no larger than the old Ghent hybrids. One might suppose they would do well in the colder parts of the United States and this seems to be indicated from trials.

Hybrid Azaleas of the Orient

When one considers the azaleas of Japan, he is dealing with highly developed material from obscure origins. Native species, taken into cultivation by a flower-loving people centuries ago and subjected to the vagaries of selection and accidental cross-pollination, have so beclouded their identity that even specialists lose their bearings when trying to place the different forms into systematic order. Wilson and Rehder, along with others, have endeavored to find their wild progenitors, but often only after some mutant, monster or abnormal garden variety has been previously discovered and made to do duty as the "type" species. In this situation, one may speak of species and hybrids in only a very loose way, for who knows? The "species" itself may turn out to be a hybrid. The only things that we can really depend upon are clones. There are probably hundreds of these, originating in Japan. Whether they are actually hybrids or merely selected individuals from among chance seedlings within a species does not particularly matter to a gardener. Some of them are beautiful and a good many are listed under Japanese names. The United States government has imported a great many clones from time to time. Some of them are listed in Chapter XXIII as merely miscellaneous azalea clones. Others are broadly grouped into races.

The Mucronatum Azaleas

These are not interspecific hybrids, to any extent, but are all probably members of the Japanese species, *R. mucronatum* or closely allied thereto. Some may be hybrids with *R. indicum,* but the group should be strictly distinguished from the Indian azaleas of the greenhouse which, although including *R. mucronatum* as an ancestor, represent development along a totally different line.

When or how early the various forms originated is not known. They come from Japan, where many forms have been known in gardens for years. More recently, clonal varieties have been bred elsewhere from seedling stock. They are hardy enough to grow at New York City and, with protection, may be successfully handled farther north.

The common form of *R. mucronatum* is grown as a clone and is often labelled 'Indica Alba' or 'Ledifolia Alba.' This is relatively seed-constant. Pink or lilac forms occasionally occur. A form known as 'Sekidera' exists and a clone called 'Damask Rose' is sometimes cultivated. This has rose-colored spots. A double form with purple flowers, known as 'Fujimanyo,' should be regarded as a clone only, because it has no essential organs and must be propagated vegetatively only. Another form, called 'Amethystinum,' has white flowers which are delicately flushed with pale lilac and bear a few faint rose spots. A form with double white flowers is known as 'Narcissiflorum' and should not be confused with a Ghent double-flowered clone of the same name. There are many other forms.

It may be appropriate to mention here a few other Japanese azaleas which have played a part in the development of hybrids. These include the Ryukyu azaleas: *R. macrosepalum, R. ripense, R. scabrum* and var. *phoeniceum,* the latter possibly being of garden origin. These come from southern Japan and are generally plants for the south or for greenhouses. They are further described elsewhere under specific categories. The Luchu azalea, *R. scabrum,* also from southern Japan, has large flowers ranging from orange-red to rosy purple.

The Indian Azaleas

These are the familiar large-flowered greenhouse azaleas of today, sometimes grown outdoors in the Lower South, which actually contain very little of the true *Rhododendron indicum* ancestry, but are mainly hybrids of the related species *R. Simsii,* plus an admixture of *R. pulchrum, R. mucronatum* and their various forms. *R. Simsii* is a Chinese species.

In the 1830's a number of color forms of *Rhododendron indicum,* of which there were many clones in Japan, were brought to England and America from China. The species appears also to have been previously taken to Holland, by way of China and Java, and later lost. With forms of *R. pulchrum* var. *phoeniceum* and *R. mucronatum,* they came to be known collectively as Indian azaleas, although they were not Indian at all. Some varieties of *R. Simsii,* with which the name of *R. indicum* was hopelessly confused in the early days, came into the hybrid mixture at some time during the first years of their cultivation. Many of the plants now grown at Magnolia-on-the-Ashley, S.C., doubtless represent the early forms and hybrids of *R. pulchrum* var. *phoeniceum, R. mucronatum* and *R. indicum.* The introduction of further cultivars of *R. Simsii* by Robert Fortune about 1850, notably several striped clones such as 'Vittatum' and 'Bealii,' resulted in a further admixture of *R. Simsii* into the hybrid group. All these forms belong in the subseries Obtusum.

Wilson, who studied the matter carefully, concluded that neither *Rhododendron pulchrum, R. mucronatum* nor *R. indicum* have had much part in the development of the present race of greenhouse Indian azaleas. *R. indicum,* especially, is regarded as having no influence in the modern hybrids, since it is a late blooming species and is definitely not amenable to forcing into bloom out of its regular season. The time-honored name of Indian azaleas is, however, being continued as a title for the group. They are sometimes called "Chinese."

A large list of named clones was introduced during the nineteenth century, but very little information is available as to their immediate ancestry. A number of double-flowered clones are listed, some of which might originally have come from the double-flowered forms of *R. indicum,* of which there were several. A total of some 800 clones have been listed altogether.

Most of the breeding work was evidently done in Europe. The Belgian breeders included Joseph Vervaene of Ghent and the Messrs. Eeckhaute, Haerens, Van Houtte, Van Geert, Verschaffelt, J. de Kneep and Van der Cruyssen. Other breeders were Ivery, Rollisson, Knight and Perry of England; Lesebe, Truffaut, H. de May and Mabire of France; and Schulz, E. Liebig, Seidel and Rose of Germany.

The Belgian Hybrids and Their Allies

These constitute a further development of the so-called Indian azaleas especially bred for forcing as florists' pot plants under glass in later winter and early spring. Thus, they possess almost no trace of *R. indicum,* a late-blooming species, and include several hundreds of named clones. Some of the flowers are very distinctive and a few are familiar florists' plants, such as 'Vervaeneana' and 'Madame Petrick.'

Some subgroups have developed within this section. Two American developments are the Pericat and Rutherford hybrids. Alphonse Pericat of Pennsylvania introduced the first of his azaleas in 1931, and many more were named and introduced by florists to whom he sold unnamed plants. Although intended for forcing under glass, they are hardy outdoors at Washington, D.C. Their parentage is not recorded, but they are of medium height, compact and variable as to being single, semi-double or with petaloid sepals. Some have a rosebud effect. The flowers range up to two and three-quarter inches across. They are of clear colors, and the best are unexcelled in attractiveness as greenhouse azaleas. There are about forty clones.

The Rutherford hybrids (sometimes called 'Rutherfordiana' gr.) were developed by Bobbink and Atkins of Rutherford, New Jersey, from repeated crossings among *R. mucronatum,* 'Omurasaki' (a clone allied to *R. phoeniceum*), *R. indicum, R. scabrum* semi-double, various Belgian hybrids and the Kurume azaleas. The claim that several true rhododendrons are included in this hybrid complex is hardly possible, since no evidence appears in their progeny; instead, apogamy is probable. These hybrids were introduced in the 1930's for forcing in greenhouses. They are tender at subfreezing temperatures, but do well outdoors at San Francisco. Ordinarily rather low and spreading, they make good florists' pot plants, covering the color range from reds, through pinks and whites to purple. The flowers are single or double, two to three inches across, and there are forty clones or more.

The Satsuki Azaleas

In this category are placed certain forms and hybrids of the low, late-blooming Japanese species, *R. indicum* (syn. *Azalea macrantha*). There are a good many clones of this species and its variety *eriocarpum* which may or may not be of hybrid origin. Some of these are very old, for as early in 1692 as many as 168 garden forms were on record in Japan. 'Gumpo' clones belong here.

The Chugai hybrids are of more recent Japanese production and are derived from *R. indicum* and the Belgian hybrids or *R. Simsii*. They are low, spreading and dense in habit, and are distinguished by blooming very late. They are filled with variegations (chimeras), their striped or flaked markings continually mutating, so that color patterns are inconstant and subject to change even on the same plant. However, they are very beautiful, with large single flowers, some attaining four inches across, sometimes frilled. They are about as hardy as *R. indicum*. About fifty named clones were imported by the United States government from the Chugai Nursery, Kobe, Japan, in 1938 and 1939.

The Wada hybrids, also from Japan, are from various crosses of *R. indicum* with the Kurume, Belgian and Kaempferi azaleas. Several are described as resembling Kurumes, but with larger flowers.

The Sander Hybrids

This is a very promising greenhouse race combining the Indian azaleas with forms of *R. obtusum*. One of the earliest members was a clone known as 'Hexe' or 'Firefly.' This was raised about 1885 from the cross *R. obtusum* clone 'Amoenum' × *R. Simsii* clone 'Duc de Nassau,' by Otto Forster, Lebenhof, Lower Austria.

The most extensive and important work to date was done by Charles Sander, gardener to the late Professor C. S. Sargent at the Holm Lea estate, near Brookline, Mass. Beginning with a carmine red Indian azalea of dwarf compact habit (named 'Garnet,' a seedling of 'Decora'), and crossing this with a red-flowered form of *R. obtusum*, Sander obtained a race of red-flowered, compact hybrids. These, in turn, were crossed with a white-flowered form of *obtusum*, and progeny having rose-pink flowers was obtained. More recently, 'Hinodegiri' and other Kurume azaleas have been used in the breeding work.

The net result of some forty years' effort has been the production of a race of compact, twiggy azaleas with good flowers up to one and one-half or two inches in diameter. The richness of the fiery red and crimson flowered varieties is a notable feature of the race, no other strain of azaleas, so far as I know, possessing such deep, rich colors. There are also a number of fine clones in rose and salmon. Certain clones have flowers which are over two inches across.

This race is amenable to forcing and offers interesting possibilities as a florists' pot-plant material as well as a subject for conservatory adornment. There is a likelihood of Sander azaleas proving useful also in warmer regions where they may be grown outdoors. Mr. Sander's original collection has been broken up and some of the clones have apparently passed out of existence, but the remainder are being intensively propagated for commercial introduction.

The Kurume Azaleas

The probable origin of this beautiful and interesting race of azaleas has been a subject of discussion among American and Japanese botanists. It seems to have arisen from the amalgamation of two or three wild Japanese species growing on or near Mt. Kirishima near the city of Kurume in Japan. *R. Kaempferi,* a species widespread in Japan, and the Kyushu azalea (*R. kiusianum*) are two of these. The third is the Kirishima azalea (*R. obtusum*), a small dense plant with long-tubed flowers, rose, red or purple. Presumably, natural hybrids between these wild species furnished the basic material which was later cultivated and intercrossed by gardeners, notably Mr. Motozo Sakamoto of Kurume, early in the nineteenth century. A magenta-crimson clone of the Kirishima azalea, known as 'Hatsu-giri,' (now called 'Amoena' and also clone 'Album,' a white form, were introduced into England as early as 1843. Later, but before the general introduction of Kurume azaleas, the red azalea known as 'Hinodegiri' was also brought in. Aside from these and one or two others, the Kurume race remained isolated until 1906 when dwarfed, old specimens were offered by the Yokohama Nursery Company. None appeared in America, however, until 1915 when thirty clones were exhibited and took prizes at the Panama-Pacific Exposition in San Francisco. These had come from Mr. K. Akishi of Kurume, who had been working for forty years to improve Sakamoto's original collection. A California nursery firm, Domoto Brothers, purchased some of these and imported others, and a few found their way to eastern nurserymen. Subsequently Dr. E. H. Wilson found their source in Japan and sent fifty selected clones to the Arnold Arboretum in Boston in 1919. This was later augmented by further collections for the United States government by Mr. R. K. Beattie. An admirable historical account of this development in azaleas has been compiled and presented by Mr. Frederic P. Lee,* with full lists of clones under Japanese and English names. There have been later importations.

The azaleas of Mt. Kirishima were studied on the site by Wilson in 1919 and by Dr. John L. Creech in 1955, as well as by several Japanese botanists. Present opinion favors their origin as from the three species here described, and also regards *R. Kaempferi* as a separate species (integrating into others at points of contact as do certain American wild species), and not as a form of *R. obtusum* as Wilson had maintained. During recent years there has been great activity in raising and introducing seedlings and new hybrids of the Kurume azaleas, and too many clones are now listed. No effort will be made to include all of them in this book.

Although originally described as dwarf and compact, which may have been correct for the original introductions, some subsequent seedlings have proved rather tall—up to eight feet—which indicates that the dwarfness may have been a selected character and that the race as a whole is variable in height, perhaps because of the effects of *R. Kaempferi* and other non-dwarf species which have been bred into it. The plants are almost always dense, however. They bloom early or at midseason, so are suitable to force as florists' pot plants. The flowers are generally one to one and one-half inches across, but may vary down to one-half inch or up to two inches. They come in the usual color range for the Obtusum series. Further hybridized, the Kurume race has been able to add form and dwarfness to certain other subsequent combinations.

Several groups of clones have resulted from recent work with the Kurumes and their allies. The Coolidge group (Pasadena, California) are single or hose-in-hose Kurumes crossed with *R. Kaempferi*. The Chisholm-Merritt group (Maryland) are selected tall Kurume seedlings. The Sherwood group (Portland, Oregon) are hybrids of 'Hinodegiri' with other Kurumes. The Deerfield group (Deerfield Street P.O., New Jersey) represent crosses mainly between Kurume clones. The de Wild group (Shiloh, New Jersey) are crosses between a Sander hybrid seedling and the Kurume clone 'Hinomayo.' The Mayo group (Augusta, Georgia) are later-blooming Kurume hybrids with Kaempferi or Indian azalea crosses. The Yerkes group have been developed by the late G. E. Yerkes and R. L. Pryor of the United States Plant Industry station at Beltsville, Maryland. They are being developed for florists' greenhouse propagation, but are as hardy as ordinary Kurume azaleas. They are characterized by single hose-in-hose flowers up to two inches across, pinks and whites, either upright or spreading.

* Lee, Frederic P. The Azalea Book, 136–144. 1958.

The Kaempferi Hybrids and Their Allies

This class is here established to accommodate a small but increasing number of hybrids in which *Rhododendron Kaempferi* plays a leading role. They may be expected to assume greater importance as time goes on. The group now comprises mostly miscellaneous hybrids, although one or two racial lines of importance have developed. Further work is being done by hybridists and there is every prospect that additional interesting and important strains may be opened up for development. The comparative hardiness of *R. Kaempferi,* its great variability, its ease of crossing with other members of the subseries Obtusum, plus its desirable and unique color, are all in its favor as a parent.

The most important (to date) is a strain of Kaempferi hybrids known as the Malvatica hybrids. These comprise crosses of *R. Kaempferi* with hybrids of *R. obtusum* clone 'Hinodegiri' and a Japanese clone of uncertain origin called 'Malvatica,' thus: *R. Kaempferi* × ('Hinodegiri' × 'Malvatica') = Malvatica hybrids. The plants are of less than medium stature, with flowers larger than those of the Kurume group and having desirable colors of the red-rose-white range. They are reported as being considerably more hardy than the Kurume azaleas. The clone 'Malvatica' itself is reported to be a plant only 2½ feet tall, with single mauve flowers. It, of course, belongs somewhere in the Obtusum subseries.

Since the above two paragraphs were written in 1934, their prophecy has been amply fulfilled, and now there are a large number of additional groups in which *R. Kaempferi* plays a leading part.

The Gable hybrids constitute a group of some seventy clones, originating from a cross of *R. Kaempferi* × *R. poukhanense,* the hardiness of which was used as a base for further crosses with *R. mucronatum,* the hardier Kurumes and others. A few clones have been introduced by other persons without the consent of the originator, Joseph B. Gable of Pennsylvania, and these may not live up to the standard of hardiness demanded by Mr. Gable. The flowers are single or semi-double, sometimes frilled, and are of good size, up to 2¾ inches across. Their colors range from white and orange-red (Delft rose) to reddish violet (rhodamine purple). They are probably no more hardy than *R. Kaempferi* itself, and some might be less hardy.

The Arnold hybrids (*R.* × *Arnoldianum*) were developed by the late Jackson Dawson of the Arnold Arboretum from an 'Amoena' × *R. Kaempferi* cross about 1910. The plants are tall, with inch-wide single flowers in midseason which are mostly all crimson-rose or purplish, not very attractive in color. They are no hardier than *R. Kaempferi.*

The Dawson hybrids represent crosses between *R. Kaempferi* × *R. mucronatum* made about 1923 by H. S. Dawson of Eastern Nurseries, Massachusetts. They are tall, upright and large-flowered (to 3¼ inches), with some of the hardiness of their *Kaempferi* parent. Two clones are listed, with fine flowers in cyclamen purple and lilac purple.

Vuyk hybrids (*R. × Vuykianum*) are the progeny of Malvatica clones × *R. Kaempferi* and other azaleas, such as *R. mucronatum* and *R. phoeniceum* cl. 'Maxwellii.' Although it is claimed that one original male parent was a Mollis hybrid clone, there are no substantiating evidences in the offspring to indicate that this was a fertile cross and not apomixis. Substantially, these are hybrids of the Kaempferi group. They originated in Holland before 1926 and have good-sized flowers in the usual range of this subseries. They bloom rather late and are tallish plants of medium hardiness. The clones are named for musical composers.

The hybrids of *R. Kaempferi* × *R. Oldhamii,* a Formosan species, by the late Lionel de Rothschild of Exbury, England, are here called the Rothschild azaleas. Elsewhere they have been termed Exbury hybrids, which is confusing, since this group is quite distinct from the better-known deciduous Ghent hybrid group of azaleas generally called the Exbury azalea group. There are six or seven clones, with flowers up to three inches across and colors from bright orange-red to pale pink. Several are quite tall. I have no data on their hardiness.

The Glenn Dale Hybrids

This is perhaps the most important array of hybrid azaleas yet originated and possesses the most comprehensive ancestry. In scope, it amalgamates the good qualities of many species, extending across the full range of the Obtusum subseries. It is the result of more than twenty years of hybridizing, preceded by more than ten years of assembling and testing material from many parts of the world. This work was done by Benjamin Y. Morrison, former head of the Division of Plant Exploration and Introduction of the United States Department of Agriculture. It takes its name from the Plant Introduction Station at Glenn Dale, Maryland, where much of the work was done. To date, this group comprises over 400 named clones.

Breeding was begun before 1935, and the parentage embraces mostly selected clones from four main races, although others are included over a broad span, and an effort was made to restrict the stock to plants that could be grown outdoors along the middle Atlantic coast of America. The main lines of ancestry come from these four groups: *R. Kaempferi, R. mucronatum, R. indicum* (in forms such as the Macrantha hybrids) and the Kurume azaleas. In some, there are also traces of *R. Simsii* (through the Indian azaleas of the South) and, on the other extreme, a few carry the "blood" of *R. poukhanense,* the hardiest Obtusum.

In size, color, habit of growth, time of bloom, and probably in hardiness, too, these azaleas cover a tremendous range, and hence, are susceptible of subdivision into categories on these bases. Since they were bred and tested first in the neighborhood of Washington, D.C., and have not been immediately observed at all places in their possible range, one cannot certainly know the extent of their adaptability. It would seem a fair conjecture to say that clones best for Washington might differ from those ultimately best in New York, San Francisco, the South or other places where ecological conditions differ. With so many clones available for trial, time only will determine which are the superior ones for any given place.

The general objective of this far-flung breeding project has been to produce garden azaleas of reasonable hardiness which will carry flowers as large and variable as those seen in the greenhouse azaleas. This result has been very nearly attained. The flowers are medium to very large—up to 4½ inches in some—and their habit of growth varies from upright to spreading, and from low and medium to tall. There are singles, semi-doubles and doubles, and their colors and patterns embrace most of those to be found anywhere in the Obtusum subseries. Some are striped, flecked or otherwise variegated. A practically continuous succession of bloom throughout the azalea season has been attained, from very early sorts to very late ones.

It is difficult to appraise the ultimate usefulness of these azaleas until reports of their behavior in distant places are received. But it can be said at once that, wherever they thrive, they will hold their own against or supersede the best Obtusum azaleas that can be grown in any such place. There is every prospect that many Glenn Dale azaleas will prove to be much hardier than originally supposed, since all azaleas are tender when small and many of the plants tested in cold places were too young when planted outdoors to evaluate fairly on their first trials. On the West Coast, they have proved hardier than most other Obtusums. Although their blooming season is a very long one, the main bulk of Glenn Dale azaleas are later than most Kurumes. Some very good new sorts are still in the offing.

Chapter XX

ENEMIES OF THE RHODODENDRONS

No ATTEMPT has been made here to cover all the diseases or pests that have ever been found on rhododendrons or azaleas.* The report of a new pest does not mean that it is dangerous. Neither does the discovery of a new insecticide or fungicide mean that older remedies should be abandoned. In fact, it is advised to try old standard treatments first before using most of the newer high-powered poisons which sometimes unbalance the natural controls. Bordeaux mixture, nicotine sulphate and certain of the other old materials, when properly used, are still sufficiently effective for many purposes and introduce less hazards. Yet certain new chemicals, notably malathion and chlordane, when used with discretion, are valuable for specific purposes.

It is well for everyone to recognize the difference between injuries caused by chewing and sucking insects respectively and those due to plant disease infections. While there are certain combination sprays, one should always remember that fungicides are for plant diseases, not insects, and insecticides are for insects, not diseases, excepting in cases where insects transmit disease or where one is secondary to another.

It is not often necessary for a grower to accurately identify an insect or disease organism in order to know what to do about it. Dr. Breakey writes that malathion will probably kill more kinds of insect pests than any other material that has come to light in recent years. It even kills spider mites. While dangerous, it is safer than many others. "When treating ornamentals like the evergreen rhododendrons, I prefer to use the emulsion concentrate, since it will leave no visible residue," he says. A concentrate containing 25% actual malathion should be used at the rate of 1/400, or approximately one level table-

* For technical discussions, see various papers in the literature of plant pathology. Good résumés have been published by Drs. R. P. White (in Jour. Econ. Entomology 26(3):631-640, 1933), Cynthia Westcott (Brooklyn Botanic Garden Record 5(1):60-63, 1949), E. P. Breakey (in "Rhododendrons," Amer. Rhodo. Soc. 40-58, 1956), and Gould, C. J. & M. Eglitis (in "Rhododendrons," 59-70, 1956). A tabular list of symptoms and control methods is presented on pages 214-216 herewith.

spoonful per gallon. In a 50% malathion emulsion concentrate, use only half as much per gallon of spray.

Regarding fungicides, Bordeaux mixture and others containing sulphur are safer if used only on cloudy or coolish days, as hot sun activates the sulphur too much and may cause burning. It is recommended that Bordeaux mixture be applied on rhododendrons in more dilute solution than is commonly recommended for other plants. It should be used no stronger than 2:2:50; this means two pounds of copper sulphate, 2 pounds of hydrated lime and 50 gallons of water. Directions for smaller quantities are usually on the package. Experienced growers say that with these precautions, plants will not be injured. Some favor a 2:1:50 mixture for acid-loving plants. It should be remembered that fungicides are preventives, not cures.

Chlordane has proved effective for pests in the soil such as weevils, grubs, borers, ants and moles, but should be used with precautions against injury to persons and domestic animals.

FUNGOUS DISEASES
FLOWER BLIGHT

AZALEA FLOWER SPOT OR PETAL BLIGHT (*Ovulinia azaleae*). A devastating enemy from the Orient which infests the petals of evergreen azaleas in southern gardens, extending from the Atlantic westward to Texas and California. Dr. Cynthia Westcott describes its symptoms on Kurume and Indian azaleas in the Charleston area as a fast-working fungus which may infect perfect flowers on one day, appearing next day as "a bit rain-spotted," but by the third day "all the millions of blossoms on thousands of bushes in a whole town will have collapsed simultaneously to a slimy mush." Decayed flowers adhere to the plants for weeks thereafter. Sclerotia (black resting bodies) form on the flowers, which, upon dropping to the ground, provide over-wintering quarters for the disease. Spores arising from these in spring infect the new crop of flowers, spreading with speed, especially in wet weather. A vigilant spraying program (three times a week) protects the opening flowers. Dithane D-14, prepared in a packet form by Rohm & Haas, with directions, is recommended. Or the spray may be mixed as follows: 1⅛ quarts of liquid Dithane D-14, 1 pound of 25% flake zinc sulphate, ½ pound of hydrated lime, one ounce of Dreft or other spreader, plus 100 gallons of water.

LEAF SPOTS

CERCOSPORA LEAF SPOT (*Cercospora rhododendri*). More active on the lower foliage of young stock. Forms angular dark brown spots with a grayish down (consisting of spores) in the center of the spots on the upper leaf surface of *Rhododendron ponticum*. On Catawba hybrids, however, the center of the spots may become silvery white, due to the falling away of leaf epidermis. It is not a serious or important disease. Bordeaux mixture at 2:2:50, sprayed at 10- to 14-day intervals during the growing season is recommended for control.

YELLOW LEAF SPOT (*Exobasidium burtii*). This, in my observation, seldom causes serious injury to anything but one-year-old seedlings of *Rhododendron ponticum* and similarly young plants of one or two other species or strains which appear susceptible, notably *R. macrophyllum*. The injury occurs mainly in the summer, but may be carried over until October and November. In the typical form the spots are bright yellow at first, later becoming brown in the center with margins scalloped and reddened. Mealy white spores may appear on the under surface of the spots. The spots are very small at first, eventually enlarging to one-fourth inch in diameter. In severe cases, adjacent spots will coalesce, causing defoliation and death of the young plants. While typically a summer disease, this fungus, or some other species of *Exobasidium,* sometimes makes headway in greenhouses in the very early autumn, before the artificial heat is turned on. In my experience this is usually checked automatically when the houses become warm and the air less humid. Otherwise, Bordeaux mixture, applied regularly after midsummer, is an effective preventive. As in the previous leaf-spot disease, there is a marked varietal or racial susceptibility among the host plants, suggesting that immunity and susceptibility are heritable characters and that the disease may be controlled by the breeding of resistant strains. I find certain pedigrees among my hybrid seedlings in which nearly all the members are susceptible to summer leaf spot troubles, while the majority of other pedigrees are unaffected, although growing in the same plot.

GALL (*Exobasidium vaccinii*). Large white protuberances are formed on the young leaves and the petals of opening blooms and seed pods by this gall-forming fungus, giving rise to the popular fallacy (current in the mountains of the South and elsewhere) that these structures are some sort of "fruit" of the rhododendrons and azaleas upon which they occur. The galls are said to be edible and are used by southern cooks for the making of pickles. They are called "honeysuckles" locally and are esteemed as a culinary delicacy. This no doubt explains the origin of the common name "honeysuckle bush" which is applied to the wild azalea in certain localities. Galls occur very commonly upon such azaleas as *Rhododendron nudiflorum* and its allies, as well as upon the evergreen species *R. maximum* and *R. catawbiense* in their native homes. Sometimes galls appear upon the greenhouse azaleas. Leaf spots as well as galls may be formed by this fungus. It is seldom important, but, where control measures are needed, hand-picking the young galls or spraying with Bordeaux mixture is recommended.

PHYLLOSTICTA LEAF SPOTS (*Phyllosticta* species). These may affect the leaves of larger plants, not being confined to young seedlings. The fungus causes brown circular spots, sometimes having concentric rings or zones of development, often near the margins or tips of the leaves. It also invades, as a secondary factor, leaf tissue which has been previously injured or winter-killed. The spots become large and often cover half the leaf. Their upper surfaces may be slightly rough, due to spore sacs which are scarcely visible as minute black dots. Several species are found, of which *P. saccardoi* seems to be the most active parasite. Bordeaux mixture is recommended as a control measure, but where the plants are of salable size and discoloration of the foliage by spray residue must be avoided some other fungicide, such as the more recent copper compounds, may probably be substituted. Two applications, ten days apart, should be made immediately after blooming. This disease is not listed as of major importance.

LOPHODERMIUM LEAF SPOT (*Lophodermium rhododendri*). The spots caused by this fungus are rather large (up to one inch across) and quite distinctive. The upper surfaces are silvery white with reddish raised margins, having very prominent black oval raised fruiting bodies scattered irregularly over them. The lower surfaces of the spots are light chocolate brown. Apparently this disease is very unimportant and has been found only upon wild or collected plants of *Rhododendron maximum, R. catawbiense* and *R. californicum*. Even in the wild it is of small significance and control measures are not indicated. Another species, *L. vagulum,* is reported.

AZALEA LEAF SCORCH (*Septoria azaleae*). This occurs most severely upon Indian azaleas and related forms (subseries Obtusum) under greenhouse conditions in fall and winter. 'Hinodegiri' and 'Madame Petrick' are especially susceptible varieties. It has also been reported upon Ghent and Mollis hybrids. The tissues become brown in spots, surrounded by a deep reddish border, and the leaves fall prematurely. In most cases the first symptom is the appearance of diffuse yellowish areas, becoming brown in the center and developing bright red margins on some varieties. Primary yellow spots, however, do not always occur. Bordeaux mixture or some other copper fungicide, sprayed on every ten to 14 days, from July 15th until the plants are housed, is the treatment recommended. This is one of the more important diseases. As sporulation is abundant on fallen leaves, rigid sanitation should be practiced and all old leaves should be disposed of by burning as soon as they fall.

Rusts

RHODODENDRON RUST (*Pucciniastrum minima*). This occurs on young seedlings of *Rhododendron ponticum* and appears as a red spotting of the foliage, with orange-red pustules, eventually becoming powdery, on the under surface. This or a similar rust also occurs upon young seedlings of *R. japonicum* and other azaleas in the greenhouse. Very small seedlings may be killed; otherwise, only the lower leaves die. On *R. ponticum* this infection is often followed by Pestalotia Leaf Spot (*P. macrotricha*), the latter causing brown spots and giving the impression that these dead areas were caused by the Rust disease. Dusting the plants with sulphur dust every two weeks during July and August will effectively prevent injury from rust. This should be a regular practice with *R. ponticum* seedlings. The rust itself is unimportant, but the Pestalotia which follows it is apt to be more serious on young grafting stock.

WESTERN RUST (*Melampsoropsis piperiana*). This occurs at present only upon *Rhododendron macrophyllum* on the Pacific coast. Small reddish pustules appear beneath the leaves. Dusting with sulphur is the probable control method. Three species of *Chrysomyxa* are also listed as rusts. Control methods are the same.

Leaf and Stem Diseases

PHYTOPHTHORA BLIGHT (*Phytophthora cactorum*). This is often called rhododendron blight and is sometimes confused with rhododendron wilt (*Phytophthora cinnamomi*) which, however, is more exclusively a disease of very young plants and is confined to the soil, roots and stem. Phytophthora blight, on the other hand, is primarily confined to the young growth and leaves at the top of the plant, the stems and roots being only last attacked. This fungus is parasitic upon many hosts besides the rhododendron and may go to rhododendrons from neighboring old lilac bushes which were previously infected. The fungus works primarily under conditions of dense shade and high humidity, such as occur in midsummer. On leaves, infections first appear as water-soaked areas increasing in size during wet weather and later becoming brown zonate (with concentric rings) and silvery white above, with light chocolate brown below. These spots may enlarge to infect the whole leaf. On new buds and tender growth a general die-back is produced, characterized by dark brown sunken cankers. The infection gradually works its way down the stem, producing girdling cankers, and an entire plant may be killed, although the disease works less rapidly in older wood. Dr. White states that practically all infected plants observed have been growing under rather heavy shade. The removal of the shade and high humidity accompanying it is indicated as the first step in control. The removal of all badly infected plants and the pruning out of all infected twigs and branches of others, well below the visible infected area, is the next step. Lastly, the protection of foliage and young growth by spraying every two weeks with Bordeaux mixture, 2:2:50, is recommended. Spraying should commence in June or immediately after blooming. All diseased wood should be taken away and burned. With more sun and better aeration the disease will subside. In nursery beds and frames it is advisable to shade lightly if at all and to depend more upon mulches and less upon overhead irrigation for the water supply where the plants are large enough to endure such treatment. The lace bug, of course, will make greater inroads when shade is removed, since it thrives in the sun, but this insect is easier to control than is the blight. Moreover, a light shade, accompanied by adequate aeration and not too much overhead watering, will effect a compromise in which neither the blight nor the lace bug will be troublesome. This fungus has, upon occasions, assumed the role of a major disease of young seedlings, especially in midsummer.

Phytophthora is a common cause of leaf spots and dying of branches on older plants, especially in shade. It is often present along leaf margins where water accumulates. When irrigating, water the soil but do not wet the foliage. Lilac mildew also may occur on rhododendrons in the shade. Die-back of old unthrifty branches is sometimes caused by winter cold, not necessarily the result of any disease.

PESTALOTIA LEAF AND STEM SPOTS (*Pestalotia macrotricha* and *P. rhododendri*). These are not serious diseases, as once believed, but are weak parasites, working slowly and usually entering the plant through weak or injured places, such as sunburnt areas, winter-injured leaves, or the mechanical injuries caused by insects or handling. They cause silver-gray spots on the upper side of the foliage, thickly dotted with black fruit-bodies and having concentric rings. The lower surfaces are light brown. They sometimes occur upon azaleas. Control is largely effected by preventing injuries through which the disease may gain entrance. Mulch well, provide windbreaks and control insects.

PHOMOPSIS LEAF SPOT AND CANKER (*Phomopsis* species). This fungus makes rather large spots (one-half inch or so across) on the foliage of certain *Rhododendron maximum* hybrids. These spots are silvery white in the center, with fruiting structures concentrically arranged on the upper surface, and having a broad reddish brown border. On older stems indefinite cankers are produced causing death of infected branches. Control is by means of cutting out and burning diseased branches. This is not regarded as a major trouble.

BOTRYTIS BLIGHT (*Botrytis* species). A common gray mold which becomes serious only on young seedlings or in grafting chambers where plants do not dry out readily after watering. The infected foliage becomes light green and looks watersoaked in places, later being covered with a grayish-brown powdery felt composed of spores and conidiophores. When infected leaves fall to the ground small black sclerotia are formed which are capable of over-wintering in the soil. This disease is a cause of losses in the grafting case of both scions and understocks. It may be controlled by rotation of seedling frames and by careful attention to ventilation in grafting cases. Bordeaux mixture 4:5:50 in seven to ten day applications as a spray during moist weather is effective in the frames. In grafting cases, copper-lime dust is indicated. Captan may likewise be used.

ROOT AND STEM DISEASES

RHODODENDRON WILT (*Phytophthora cinnamomi*). This disease occurs mainly on young plants, being partial to seedlings of *Rhododendron ponticum* which are just under the grafting size. It rarely appears on any plants older than three years. It differs sharply from Phytophthora Blight in that this organism lives in the soil and causes a root rot. The first symptom is a wilting of the young leaves and a yellowing of the foliage. Infection takes place through the young rootlets, working its way upward to the base of the stem. It also enters the plant at the surface of the ground through cracks in the stem which come at the time of bark formation. Pestalotia sometimes follows it as a secondary infection. Decayed tissue can be found where the disease has been working. The disease is most active in warm weather and under moist conditions. The fungus is harbored in the soil, so control measures must include changing the soil or rotating the frames from year to year. The fungus is also unable to endure as much acidity as rhododendrons, so that if the soil acidity is adjusted to pH 4.0 or pH 4.5 the disease will be held back. Light soils with good drainage and care to prevent excessive watering also constitute effective control measures. Resistant strains or species of rhododendrons offer possibilities for a permanent solution of the control problem.

DAMPING-OFF AND BASAL CANKER (*Rhizoctonia solani*). A common fungus which affects seedlings and also bothers graft-unions. It sometimes causes a basal canker at the soil level on young plants of *Rhododendron ponticum*. Occasionally it kills branches on older plants. It is sometimes called Stem Rot. Its external evidences on *ponticum* seedlings are not unlike those of Rhododendron Wilt, but the roots are still healthy, since *Rhizoctonia* attacks at the soil level, where it rots the stem. This disease appears with crowding of young plants, poor drainage, over-watering or lack of ventilation. The correction of these matters will generally control the disease. Some light mist sprays of organic mercury fungicides have proved effective when used on flats of seedlings. Sterilization of the seed by shaking it up in a solution of copper carbonate before planting is effective for the control of one type of damping-off.

Root Rot (*Armillaria mellea*). The roots are attacked by black strands of fungus tissue, producing a wet decay which has a strong mushroom odor. White fans of mycelium are also present under the bark above the soil level. The control advised is to increase the vigor of the rhododendron by fertilization and to expose the crown of the plant to the air for a year. This disease occurs on both rhododendrons and azaleas, but is not regarded as a serious pest.

BUD DISEASES

Bud Blast (*Sporocybe azaleae*). This causes a browning and death, before opening, of the buds of rhododendrons and azaleas. It occurs on wild plants in the Carolina mountains, where it is especially severe on *Rhododendron maximum*. It is prevalent also in England. Remove infected parts, spray in fall with Bordeaux and control leaf hoppers. Another cause of the death of flower buds is not a disease, but freezing at low winter temperatures.

DISEASES DUE TO OTHER CAUSES

Mosaic. A disease of the plant and leaves caused, presumably, by a virus. The leaves are often malformed, being crinkled or rugose, and pale green or yellowish (chlorotic) areas appear. There is still some doubt concerning the true nature of the disease. It is reported as a mosaic upon *Rhododendron ponticum* and certain hybrids. Graft-union troubles of deciduous azaleas in June can simulate mosaic symptoms.

Dodder (*Cuscuta gronovii*). One of the flowering weeds. It climbs on to rhododendrons and azalea plants, clinging to them as a parasite and deriving all its moisture and nourishment from the host plant. It causes reddening of the foliage and sometimes defoliation. Control is effected by picking out the runners—they are bright orange-yellow—and by not letting the plant go to seed.

Slime Mold (*Physarum cinereum*). This organism is not a true parasite, as are the real diseases, but by attaching itself to the lower leaves of seedlings it may, under conditions of high humidity, overrun the seedlings and cause their death by suffocation. It has been noted upon the seedlings of *Rhododen-

The Catawba Rhododendron at Home in the Appalachian Mountains

Catawba Hybrids in a Naturalistic Setting

Old Indian Azaleas at Magnolia-on-the-Ashley, South Carolina

Veneer Grafting and Layering

The Side Graft

The Technique of Hand Pollination

A Japanese Azalea Garden

Rhododendrons and Their Kin on a Residential Property

dron Schlippenbachii. It first covers the leaves with slime and later with a dark purplish gray powdery spore mass.

WINTER INJURY. While scarcely a disease, winter injury nevertheless plays a double role similar to that of a disease: (1) it is the direct cause of impairment or death of the plant or portions of it; and (2) it causes physical injuries which open channels for secondary infection by invading disease organisms. The whole subject has been discussed in Chapter IX, under the head of hardiness. The symptoms of winter injury upon the foliage of the evergreen rhododendrons are usually a water-soaked condition of the leaf-margins after freezing, followed soon by browning of the margins which, in severe cases, may involve the whole leaf. The part of a rhododendron plant most easily injured by winter conditions is the flower bud. The flower buds fail to open in spring and, if cut across with a sharp knife, will reveal the blackened flower corollas in a dead condition, although the external bracts of the bud-cluster may show no signs of injury. Injury to the stems and branches results in the killing of tissue and the death of the portions above the lowest injured point. If, by chance, a branch is injured on only one side or is impaired after winter exposure, it is usually so damaged that it will never function perfectly thereafter and should be removed, allowing healthy new growth to replace it. In severe cases, plants may be killed outright, or the portions above ground may die and new growth subsequently start from the roots. The root is generally the last part of the plant to die. Although there are no leaves to be injured, deciduous species, like the azaleas, will lose their buds and branches by direct killing during the winter. Use resistant varieties and provide shelter.

SUN SCALD. This appears as discoloration and sometimes killing of leaf tips, margins and other portions of the foliage due to the desiccating effect of hot sunlight during summer days. The injuries produced from this cause are sometimes mistaken for fungous disease symptoms, which fact furnishes the only reason for mentioning the trouble here. Sun scald seldom does much damage and is, of course, easily overcome by placing light shade over the plants or by moving them to a less exposed situation. Copious irrigation of the soil also helps to prevent the trouble.

YELLOW LEAF OF AZALEAS. This is apparently a physiological trouble connected with the plant's failure to obtain or to utilize iron. It may possibly be a mosaic disease, but failure to transfer the trouble from sick to healthy plants indicates that it is hardly of such a nature. The symptoms are a general unhealthy appearance, the leaves gradually losing their rich green color and becoming pale, yellowish and chlorotic. Root action stops and the plant eventually

dies. Although these symptoms are almost identical with those of chlorosis due
to alkaline soil, the Yellow Leaf disease may occur on plants growing in soil
that is favorably acid. While the causes of all cases may not be identical, it is
known that in some instances Yellow Leaf of azaleas has occurred as a result
of a deficiency of available iron in the soil. Spraying the foliage with a ½ of
1% solution of ferrous sulphate will rapidly restore the green coloration in
typical cases. Applying ferrous sulphate to the soil at the rate of 500 pounds per
acre is probably of more permanent benefit. Application of chelated iron to soil
or foliage is also recommended. It should be noted that similar symptoms occur
on grafted deciduous azaleas, probably because of failure of the graft union to
transmit solutions upward adequately. Along with a mottled appearance, the
leaves are distorted as if by a virus.

Plants held in pots for some time will gradually lose the soluble iron from
their soil through leaching and become chlorotic. A change of soil, of course, is
indicated in such cases. Another condition of pale or yellowish leaves on azaleas
exists which apparently is quite a different matter from the one just described.
I have observed a plant of *Rhododendron calendulaceum* which consistently
bears yellowish green leaves every year. The plant grows well and appears
not to be suffering from any unfavorable ecological conditions. The soil is sufficiently acid and other plants, growing beside it for five years, have been unaffected. It is impossible to make the foliage greener by spraying with ferrous
sulphate. I can only conclude that this condition is of the nature of an inherent
abnormality affecting the chloroplasts and inhibiting the normal green development. It is thus similar to some of the many *aurea* forms of ornamental plants
in general.

It is also to be noted that rhododendrons and especially azaleas will develop
yellowish leaves when the soil becomes too acid. This appears similar to chlorosis
caused by lime, but is of an opposite nature. In this case, test the soil and if it
appears to be more acid than pH 4.0 to 4.5, apply a small amount of lime or
manure to adjust the pH upward.

CHLOROSIS DUE TO ALKALINITY. This is the common unthrifty appearance
encountered when rhododendrons are grown in soil which is insufficiently acid.
The most noticeable symptom is the pallor and yellowing of all the leaves
and the failure of the plant to grow as it should. A slow, lingering illness and
death is the usual course. The subject has been covered in Chapter VI, which
deals with soils. The trouble is controllable by adjusting the soil acidity to
pH 4.5 or pH 5.0. As noted elsewhere, the underlying cause is probably the
plant's failure to obtain and metabolize iron under alkaline conditions. The use
of iron chelate is recommended.

SUCKING INSECTS AND THEIR KIN

Lace Bugs (*Stephanitis pyrioides* on azaleas and *S. rhododendri* on ever-green types). One of the most common insects on rhododendrons and azaleas growing in sunny places, but seldom serious in the shade. These insects are commonly miscalled "lace-wing flies" and derive their name from the delicate lacy appearance of their wings. They are about one-fourth of an inch long. They cause small spots which give a grayish mottled or finely speckled appear-ance to the upper surfaces of the leaves. Dark spots of excrement, cast nymphal skins and brownish egg shields appear on the under surfaces of the leaves. They overwinter in the leaf tissues as eggs, emerging about June 1st. Most American species are affected and certain clones are especially susceptible, nota-bly 'Boule de Neige,' which is one of the finest hardy varieties in the shade, but should not be planted in the full sun because of lace bugs. Dr. R. P. White reports that Campylocarpum and Auriculatum hybrids are likewise susceptible. The use of nicotine and soap sprays is recommended, or some of the newer spray compounds for sucking insects may be successfully employed. Or safe summer oil sprays,* applied every ten days during June and somewhat there-after, are advised. Moving the plants to a partially shaded spot will reduce this pest materially. Malathion is now recommended as a control.

Thrips (*Thripidae*). These are not true sucking insects, because they rasp the plant tissues and then suck out the sap, instead of inserting a sucking organ. In greenhouses and frames these may occur on almost any kind of rho-dodendron or azalea, but are not particularly troublesome elsewhere. A diffuse grayish-white mottling on the surface of the leaves and many minute spots of dark excrement beneath are evidences of thrips. A "silvered" appearance sometimes occurs beneath the leaves. If severe, they will ruin the leaves and even kill the plants. They should be exterminated by spray or fumigation as soon as discovered, as they are capable of doing damage quickly if not con-trolled. Spraying with nicotine or similar contact insecticides is usually effec-tive. Under glass, fumigating with tobacco preparations, such as Nicofume or the use of stronger fumigants such as Cyanogas, is sufficient. Repeat the control treatment soon to kill succeeding generations as they hatch out.

Scale (*Aspidiotus hederae*). This may occur on the leaves and twigs of rhododendrons, particularly in the greenhouse. It is not uncommon on ivy and

---

* Kerosene diluted 1 to 75 and properly emulsified, plus 1 pint of 50% free nicotine solu-tion per 100 gallons, makes a safe summer spray. Nicotine sprays of ½% soap plus free nicotine of 1–2400 to 1–3000 are recommended by Dr. White.

oleander. It causes a yellow spotting of the foliage and weakens the plant. In the greenhouse it may be controlled with the same fumigants and sprays that are effective against mealy bug. Dormant oil sprays are recommended by some writers for outdoor use in the spring while the plants are still dormant, about two weeks before new growth starts. Good spray pressure is necessary. The Azalea Scale (*Eriococcus azaleae*) is another minor pest occurring on the bark of rhododendrons and azaleas.

There are other scale insects, such as the peony scale (*Pseudaonidia paeoniae*), which is reported in the southern U.S., as is also *Pulvinaria ericicola*. Malathion is used to control all scale insects and mealy bugs. Try to spray in the young crawler stage and repeat at frequent intervals. Scale insects often produce a sugary exudate on stems and bark. A nonparasitic fungus, in turn, may establish itself on this exudate and produce thick masses of black material on stems and twigs.

MEALY BUGS (*Pseudococcus* sp.). These can become serious greenhouse pests, but are not often a factor in outdoor cultivation. The insects appear as little white oval flattish creatures, in various stages of growth ranging from one-sixteenth to one-fourth inch long, often covered with a waxy secretion and sometimes a mass of waxy threads, giving them a "mealy" appearance. They persistently get into the leaf axils and the young buds of rhododendron plants, where they suck out the juices and cause girdling and death of everything above the point of injury. Heavy infestations may occur in a short time. They develop nest-like areas in leaf axils and buds where they are fairly protected against sprays. The male is an insignificant white fly, very small in size, which seems to do no damage. This pest is a common greenhouse insect and one of the worst, feeding upon all sorts of plants. One of the standard control measures is the use of a strong fumigant, such as Cyanogas. Nicotine fumigation or nicotine sprays, or contact insecticides of pyrethrum or rotenone are not generally very effective. When there is danger of foliage injury from the spray, a syringing of plain water about one hour after spraying will reduce such injury but not prevent the mealy bugs from being killed. At Cornell Dr. Blauvelt has controlled mealy bugs by the use of the following spray, which has been used also by Dr. White as an effective remedy for thrips on rhododendrons: Nursery Volck oil, five level tablespoonfuls; Black Leaf 40 (nicotine sulphate), one to 200; 40% soap, two tablespoonfuls; water, one gallon. Repeated sprayings are necessary. Malathion is now generally used.

MIDGE (undetermined). This causes a spotting of the leaves, rolled margins and malformed growth on the common evergreen rhododendrons both in the nursery and on wild plants. The white larvae, about one-quarter inch long at maturity, may be found under the rolled leaf margins in August. Contact insecticidal sprays, such as nicotine and soap, will control them outdoors and indoors.

SPIDER MITES (*Tetranychus telarius*). The "red spider" of the greenhouse is not a serious factor under field conditions with the evergreen sorts, but may occur abundantly on azaleas outdoors. In the greenhouse they may infest the evergreen rhododendrons and are often troublesome on the Indian azaleas, especially Madame Petrick. Fumigation or the use of recommended proprietary spray compounds or a safe summer oil plus one pint of free nicotine solution (50%) to 100 gallons of spray have all given good control. Frequent applications are necessary. (See new control treatments on chart.)

RHODODENDRON WHITE FLY (*Dialeurodes chittendeni*). This is a new pest coming presumably from the Himalayan region and is identified by the yellow mottling it produces on the upper leaves, pupa cases underneath the lower leaves and sooty molds appearing on the upper surface of the lower leaves. There is also a white fly (*Aleyrodes azaleae*) which attacks azaleas of the Obtusum subseries. Both of these pests have established themselves in America. Treatment with malathion is the approved control.

CHEWING INSECTS

JAPANESE AND ASIATIC BEETLES (*Popillia japonica, Phyllopertha orientalis* and *Autoserica castanea*). The Japanese beetle produces injury to the foliage, severe in spots in the field, which skeletonizes the leaves. This is controlled by keeping the foliage covered with arsenate of lead (dust or spray) while the beetles are flying. This and the other beetles produce grubs which may do damage by feeding on the roots, girdling the stems and causing the tops of the plants to suddenly wilt and die. Applying arsenate of lead by working it into the upper four inches of soil at the rate of 1500 pounds per acre is the control method advised by those who are in the beetle district. Treatment of the soil with chlordane to kill the grubs is indicated.

PITTED AMBROSIA BEETLES (*Corthylus punctatissimus*). The symptoms are sudden wilting and death of the plant. These are small black beetles about ⅛ of an inch long, infesting the stems near the surface of the ground and making a series of blackened, closely set, nearly horizontal galleries and brood chambers there. Control is by removing and burning the infested plants, which may include other species in the neighborhood besides rhododendrons or azaleas. There is a long list of woody plants which these insects may infest. They are ordinarily of local importance only upon rhododendrons.

STEM BORER (*Oberea myops*). This insect may infest either rhododendrons or azaleas, causing the death of branches or whole plants. Eggs are laid in June or July at the tips of the branches and when the young larvae hatch out they bore down the center of the stem for a distance of 12 or 15 inches, where they stop and pass their first winter. The following season they continue downward in the stem, making frequent holes to the outside through which they push coarse borings. These grubs are about one inch long and yellowish when fully grown. They reach the base of the plant by autumn of their second year and usually girdle the stem before entering the roots. The girdled plants die and are easily blown over by fall winds. Extermination by removing and burning all the infested parts is the method recommended. The adult is a moth.

CLEAR WING (*Sesia rhododendri*). The larvae of a moth which appear as grubs, white with a brown head and about one-half to three-quarter inch long. The eggs are laid in June and the injury appears in early fall as a wilting and death of the stems and branches. The eggs are laid in the bark and the grubs burrow just beneath the bark, pushing out borings as fine sawdust near the soil level or a foot or so above ground. Control is effected by pruning out and burning the infested branches in the fall or winter.

CRANBERRY ROOT WORM (*Rhabdopterus picipes*). These are night feeders working during June and July and eating holes out of the young leaves of rhododendrons. The holes are characteristically crescent-shaped or in the form of a sharp angle. The insects spend the day in the mulch at the base of the plants. They may be killed by a stomach poison in the form of arsenate of lead, with which the foliage should be kept covered between June 15th and August 1st in localities where these worms are prevalent.

WEEVILS (*Brachyrhinus sulcatus*). These weevils chew the leaves of rhododendrons from July to fall, and their larvae feed upon the roots during autumn and spring. The weevils work during the night and stay under the mulch beneath the plants during the daytime. They make small holes on the edges of the leaves, but do not eat the midribs. While there are several kinds of root weevils, the black vine weevil is most important. Plants may be girdled at the base and killed, or the roots may be eaten by grubs and growth of the plant stunted. The chief damage is done by grubs in the soil. The adults are small beetles, black or brown, about one-quarter inch long. The use of lead arsenate has not proved entirely effective for controlling the black vine weevil. The use of poisoned bran or apple bait, such as "Go-West," is much to be preferred.

Applying 5% chlordane dust at the rate of one pound per 200 square feet of area and working it deeply into the soil during the spring is an accepted control method today.

LEAF SKELETONIZER (*Gracilaria azaleella*); also called AZALEA LEAF MINER. Emerging from eggs laid near the midrib, these worms turn under a tip or margin of a leaf and fasten it down while they feed underneath its protection. They are able to kill leaves. When not numerous they may easily be hand picked from the plants. Otherwise they may be controlled by fumigating with cyanide or spraying with arsenate of lead. Malathion is worth trying.

RHODODENDRON BUD MOTH (*Eucordylea huntella*). A native to the West Coast; the larvae of a small moth girdle and enter flower buds. Detect and remove injured buds in winter, and burn them.

OTHER PESTS

RABBITS. In some localities rabbits become serious pests. The damage is usually done in winter when other food is scarce. The animals will chew the young buds and tender stems from dormant azaleas and sometimes nibble the leaves and stems of evergreen rhododendrons. I have used successfully a chicken-wire fence around my rhododendron plantation, keeping the wire close to the ground by pegging it down where necessary. Since the rabbits do not desire to enter the rhododendron plot except in the winter months when the ground is frozen hard, the wire fence gives adequate protection, because the animals cannot burrow beneath the fence at that season. Permitting hunters and trappers to kill rabbits in the immediate locality has also effectively decimated their numbers.

MOLES. Mice and moles may eat the roots of plants, especially when under a heavy mulch, causing sudden death of all or part of the top. Cats, traps, poison gas, chlordane and even miniature windmills have been tried with varying success in eradicating these rodents. Be careful not to poison domestic animals.

SOME COMMON PESTS AND THEIR CONTROL

SYMPTOMS	CAUSE	CONTROL
Finely speckled or gray mottled appearance on surface of evergreen leaves. Dark spots of excrement on under side of leaves. Small flies with lacy wings on underside of leaves, especially in the sun. Appears also on azaleas.	LACE BUG (*Stephanitis pyrioides* and *S. rhododendri*). A sucking insect which appears in June.	Spray, repeating in 10 days, with nicotine sulphate (Black Leaf 40). Be sure to treat underside of leaves. Be ready for them every year. DDT may cause mite troubles. Remove susceptible plants from sunny location and give some shade.
Death of branches or of whole plants. Often accompanied by presence of borings and holes in the lower stem.	STEM BORER, a chewing insect. Eggs laid in June or July at tips of branches. Young grubs work their way downward. Girdle the stem.	Remove and burn all parts infested or suspected. If you don't find an insect, look for a wire label or anything else, such as animal injury, that may have girdled the stem.
Injury to roots and/or lower stem, resulting in death.	ROOT BORER, a chewing insect.	Treat the soil with Chlordane 5%. Dust according to directions on package or 2 lbs. per 1,000 square feet. Observe precautions in use of dust.
Holes chewed in leaves or along leaf margins. Defoliation results.	"INCH WORM" and beetles of several kinds, often working at night. Look for the insects after dark. Chewing insects.	Use a stomach poison, such as Lead Arsenate dust or spray. Watch your azaleas closely for sudden attack in late spring or early summer when leaves are young. Try malathion.
Small white mealy insects in leaf axils or around young buds.	MEALY BUGS, sucking insects.	15% parathion wettable powder, 2 lbs. per 100 gallons. Use strict precautions, very poisonous. Try malathion.
Soft scales on leaves and twigs.	SOFT SCALE insects and small crawlers; sucking insects.	By careful timing, after crawlers hatch but before being protected by scale, Nicotine Sulphate may be effective. Otherwise 15% parathion, as above. DDT not effective on rhododendrons.
Mostly on azaleas, as a fine leaf discoloration of small light dots.	SPIDER MITE ("Red Spider").	Do not use DDT. Sulphur dust is all right but poor in cool weather. Rotenone, aramite and TEPP all require second treatment in 7–10 days.
Young stems neatly cut off, as with a penknife.	RABBITS.	Kill rabbits if possible, or protect plants in winter by cylinder of "little" chicken wire.

SOME COMMON PESTS AND THEIR CONTROL—*Continued*

SYMPTOMS	CAUSE	CONTROL
Root injury causing sudden death of all or part of top. Sometimes mole-burrows in soil.	MOLES, in peat beds and under leafy mulch.	A good cat will sometimes catch moles with great success. Mole traps not very effective. Cyanogas is recommended. It is said that a miniature windmill placed in the location will scare moles (see Bull. Amer. Rho. Soc., July 1951 and Jan. 1953).
Leaf spots of various sizes and twig blight.	FUNGUS DISEASES of several types, notably *Exobasidium* and *Phytophthora.*	Remove diseased leaves and spray with Bordeaux Mixture 4:4:100, or other copper sprays to protect healthy leaves. Do not wet the foliage, if irrigating plant. Repeat protective spray every few days, if weather is rainy. Plants in total shade are most affected. Certain clones are especially susceptible. Move plant if shade is dense and disease occurs repeatedly.
Dieback of twigs or of young plants at time of first bark formation. Wilt.	*Phytophthora* species. Also due to winter injury.	Reduce shade and water. Apply Bordeaux as above every 10 or 12 days.
Affects flowers mainly of Obtusum Subseries, and mainly in South. Starts with small spot on corolla, very quick spreading and reducing flowers to soggy mass, especially if moist. Dead mass dries on the twig. Attacks only the flowers, but very destructive to them.	*Ovulinia azaleae,* a fungus disease, transmitted by spores. Carried by insects up to one mile, and by wind and rain to adjacent flowers.	Dithane D-14 (Rohm & Haas) in prepared packet with accompanying directions. Apply soon enough and often enough to cover all flowers as soon as they open; at least 2 to 3 applications per week during bloom. Re-covering beds with new mulch just before flowers bloom also deters disease.
Failure of flower buds of evergreen sorts to open in spring.	WINTER INJURY, due to sub-zero temperature. Will freeze at −20°F.	Protect plant if possible by covering.
Water-soaked leaf margins, followed by death of marginal tissue or involving whole leaf. Dieback of branches or whole plant.	WINTER INJURY, due to low temperature or drying-out, or combination of both. Wind injury and sun scald also produce similar symptoms. Often occurs in autumn.	Windbreaks, screens and shading from winter sun will help. Valuable plants may be framed around and covered with burlap. A wire mesh cylinder covered with burlap for individual plant.
Yellowing of leaves not due to normal leaf-fall.	CHLOROSIS due to too much acidity or too much alkalinity.	Test soil and correct to pH 4.5–5.0 with proper soil amendments. Or move plant.
Red spotting of leaves and red pustules.	RUSTS of rhododendron and azalea.	Use sulphur dust as a preventive.

SOME COMMON PESTS AND THEIR CONTROL—*Continued*

SYMPTOMS	CAUSE	CONTROL
Gray mold on young seedlings or grafts.	BOTRYTIS BLIGHT.	Prevent by good ventilation and Bordeaux mixture.
Silvery white spots on leaves.	LEAF SPOT (*Pestalotia* and *Phomopsis*).	Remove diseased parts.
Damping-off of seedlings, basal canker or stem rot.	DAMPING-OFF *fungi* (*Rhizoctonia solani*).	Correct over-crowding; give proper drainage; use sphagnum as medium (see Mist Culture); give heat and light.
Browning and death of flower buds without opening, on both rhododendrons and azaleas.	BUD BLAST (*Sporocybe azaleae*) in southern U.S. and southern England.	Bordeaux mixture as a preventive spray; DDT to control leaf hoppers. Spray in autumn with fungicide.
Bronzing of leaves around margins or near midvein.	Summer DROUGHT and excessive sun heat.	Prevent drought by heavy summer mulch; shade against sun.
Dying or dwarfed growth as result of roots eaten by grubs in soil or plants girdled at base and killed.	BLACK VINE WEEVIL and other weevils; small (¼ inch) black or brown beetles, and other beetles.	Treat soil with Chlordane 5% dust, 1 lb. per 200 sq. ft. deeply raked into the soil.
Chewing injury to leaves or roots.	JAPANESE BEETLE.	Spray with malathion, and treat soil with chlordane to kill grubs.
Yellow mottling on upper leaves; sooty molds on lower leaves.	WHITE FLY (*Dialeurodes chittendeni* or *Aleyrodes azaleae*).	Use malathion.
Grubs entering and girdling flower buds of rhododendron.	BUD MOTH (*Eucordylea huntella*).	Detect and remove injured buds in winter and burn them.

Chapter XXI

NAMES AND DESCRIPTIVE TERMS

From the viewpoint of a horticulturist or a plant breeder, the most amazing feature of rhododendrons, outside of their beauty, is their variability. Unlike some other groups of plants wherein species are fairly stable, the rhododendrons and azaleas appear to be in active evolution. Indeed, the whole genus seems to be in a gigantic state of flux. New species, introduced by the score in recent years, possess such a seemingly endless capacity for variation as to make one wonder if they are not natural hybrids. Intergrades from one species into another are not uncommon in both Asiatic rhododendrons and American azaleas. In cultivation this ability to intercross and to produce widely variant types of progeny has made them doubly interesting. But by the same token, the wild forms are difficult to classify with any degree of finality, while the cultivated kinds give rise to many sorts of anomalous and puzzling situations. The same features which are attractive to a plant breeder pose problems for a taxonomist. Obviously, in the genus *Rhododendron* we are dealing with a group of plants which can be made to fit into the man-made rules of systematic botany only with some difficulty.

Since this is primarily a horticultural treatise, the terminology of systematic botany will be kept in the background as much as possible. No effort will be made to incorporate technical details which more properly belong in a taxonomic book. It is essential, however, to understand the meaning of some of the more important descriptive terms commonly used, as well as some of the rules of nomenclature.

Natural (wild) rhododendrons are named at three main levels: genus, species and variety. On the species and varietal levels certain special rules governing cultivated plants are now in force.

The FAMILY into which rhododendrons fall naturally is *Ericaceae,* known popularly as the heath family. It is composed of about 70 other genera, besides the genus *Rhododendron,* all of which bear certain natural characteristics in common. They are woody plants, mostly shrubs, having nearly regular corollas with the petals more or less united, and possessing certain. finer similarities. *Ledum, Menziesia, Loiseleuria, Kalmai, Andromeda, Enkianthus, Pieris, Oxydendron, Leucothoë, Epigaea, Calluna, Erica, Gaultheria, Pernettya, Arbutus, Arctostaphylos, Zenobia, Gaylussacia* and *Vaccinium* are all members of the family, as well as many other less familiar genera. To use a few common. names, we may say that rhododendrons are related to the mountain-laurel, the huckleberry, the cranberry, the wintergreen, the bearberry, the various heathers, the Japanese bellflower, the trailing-arbutus and Labrador tea.

The GENUS has been variously subdivided. *Azalea* was not included in the genus *Rhododendron,* but stood by itself as a separate genus when Linnaeus, the father of modern botany, made his original classification. This was very simple and wholly desirable at that time, when none but American species and their close kin were known to science. When plants began coming in from the Orient, however, intermediate forms began to appear, so that no strict line of demarcation between azaleas and rhododendrons could longer be maintained. Accordingly, in 1834, the species were all placed in a single genus. Certain border line species, such as *R. dauricum,* still appear in horticultural catalogues listed as either rhododendrons or azaleas. The use of the single broad term *Rhododendron,* to cover all the species, has gradually come into almost universal use and because of this widespread acceptance among rhododendron societies and in the horticultural literature, I have chosen to employ it in this book. It follows the International Code of Botanical Nomenclature.

Mention should be made of the American Code of Nomenclature, in which the group was divided into five genera, namely, *Rhododendron, Azalea, Rhodora, Biltia* and *Azaleastrum.* This system applied only to the American species and was never extended to the Asiatic sorts. It would probably have been necessary to set up numerous new genera besides these if it were. While the American Code had certain advantages, it was never accepted by the trade, beyond the use of the term *Azalea.* It is now considered obsolete.

In many botanical works the genus *Rhododendron* is divided into SUB-GENERA for purposes of classification, and these sub-genera are in turn subdivided into SECTIONS. In the present usage, following a scheme employed by rhododendron specialists abroad, the sub-genera and sections are temporarily omitted and, for the sake of convenience, the genus is subdivided directly into series, each series consisting of a group of closely related species. A few large series have been subdivided into subseries.

The SERIES, within the present meaning, is a group of rhododendron species which resemble one another and are supposed to be closely related. It is conceived as a temporary device by which new species are "pigeonholed" until such time as a permanent determination of their inter-relationships can be made.

"Certain of the better known species have been chosen as centers and in many cases give their names to the respective series. Under the wing of each representative species are placed all the species deemed to be of kinship with it." * This arrangement greatly facilitates a grasp of the immense numbers of new species recently introduced from Asia and will doubtless endure for some time to come pending a systematic rearrangement of the genus.

The SPECIES itself constitutes a category of classification lower than a genus or subgenus and higher than a subspecies or variety, comprising a group of individuals which may interbreed and still reproduce the distinguishing characters of the species in their offspring. The species is the most important group in the wild and to it the typical binomial term is applied. In cultivation, lower subdivisions, as varieties or clones, often assume greater importance than the species. There is often a considerable variation within a species. The form which represents the prevailing wild type, or sometimes merely that form which was first described in botanical literature, is known as the TYPE or type species. In a few cases, species are divided into SUBSPECIES. It should be noted that a species is a collective term, representing a group or population rather than an individual.

A natural or botanical VARIETY, as used in this work, denotes a group of individuals, within a species, which may and commonly does reproduce the distinguishing varietal characteristics in its progeny when propagated by seed. Coming from seed, it is sometimes called a seminal variety. It is a natural group, similar to a species in nature, but on a smaller scale, usually being a geographical form or a variant in color, form or some other simple character by which it is distinguished from the prevailing species type. Thus it may constitute a race or strain within the species. Natural varieties are ordinarily propagated from seed, thus differing from non-true-breeding forms and hybrids. To be kept pure, any race, strain or variety of rhododendron should be protected from intercrossing with other forms outside its own varietal or racial limits. Certain types of variants occur quite commonly in nature and frequently breed true if isolated from other types, but soon revert to the typical form of the prevailing wild species if crossed outside the limits of their own race. White-flowered forms, color variants, dwarf strains and types with special foliage are relatively common as natural varieties. Certain horticultural varieties have been so "fixed" that they will similarly breed true to type from seed. They are essentially no different from wild or botanical varieties, except that the strain may have been consciously selected and developed by a plant breeder. All rhododendron varieties grown from seed, rather than by vegetative propagation, are alike in that each plant is a separate individual and the members

*Species of Rhododendron, iv (1930).

comprising the race are not exact duplicates of one another, but are merely similar enough to bear in common the identifying marks of the race.

The CLONE or clonal variety, on the other hand, differs sharply from the seedling-propagated, botanical or seminal variety. A clone is a group of plants composed of individuals which have been propagated vegetatively from one single original seedling or stock. The members of a clone, therefore, are thus virtually all pieces of the same original plant and not, as in a seminal (seedling) variety, all separate individuals. While there is much variation between the members of a seminal group or variety of rhododendrons, the members of a clone are practically identical with one another. Variation is so marked among rhododendrons that aberrant individuals often arise which will not "come true" and must be propagated by grafting, cutting or layering. Thus a clone originates. It happens that many of the choicest forms, not only of hybrids but among natural species as well, are obtainable only as clones. Heretofore, there has been little distinction made between clones (which almost never reproduce their exact likeness from seed) and true-breeding varieties. The broad term "variety" or "horticulture variety" or "named variety" has covered them all, so that only the initiated knew whether they were clones or not. Indeed, people have raised seedlings from clonal forms expecting them to "come true," only to discover, when they bloomed, that the plants were inferior or diluted specimens. In this work, therefore, I propose to list the clonal varieties separately, so far as possible, in order to distinguish them from the seminal or seed-propagated sorts. A clone may be either hybrid or non-hybrid. While hybrids are commonly clones, all of them are not necessarily such. Plants of any botanical status may become clones when propagated vegetatively. Any individual plant, no matter if it is a type species or merely an odd variant or hybrid, whether it bear a Latin name or an English name, may be a clone. Impotent individuals, which are incapable of producing seeds, exist necessarily as clones. Somatic mutations or "bud-sports" occurring in some varieties are ordinarily reproduced as clones. Owing to the unusual natural variability among seedlings in the genus *Rhododendron,* the clone assumes greater importance here than in some other plants. In studying the genus as a whole, one cannot fail to be impressed by the occurrence of good and poor colors, found repeatedly side by side in sister plants of the same species. The matter of securing the best forms and avoiding the inferior ones is of far greater importance in practical horticulture than the mere consideration of the average or typical botanical specimen. As good forms are discovered and selected, they should be given special names as clonal varieties and disseminated as such in the trade. While many good forms reproduce readily from seed, making it useless to bother about clones, other rare qualities can often only be transmitted by vegetative reproduction.

Hence, the emphasis which I have placed upon the distinction between clonal and non-clonal varieties.

The terms so far discussed (genus, species, botanical variety and clone) are those set up by the International Code of Botanical Nomenclature and apply to all plants. Among cultivated plants, however, where hybrids, special forms and common names are involved, the situation is much more complicated. Accordingly, a supplemental code of nomenclature governing cultivated plants has been devised to cover these additional features. Presented in 1952 and later revised, the International Code of Nomenclature for Cultivated Plants has been ratified by the International Botanical and Horticultural Congresses and adopted by the International Union of Biological Sciences to become effective in 1959. All provisions of the older Botanical Code still govern the use of scientific (Latin) names for both cultivated and wild plants, but, in addition, more precise terminology expressly designed for horticultural plants is now in effect, too.

Recognizing the differences which exist between a botanical variety (Latin *varietas*) as above described and a horticultural or garden name, such as a clone, a new term, CULTIVAR (cultivated variety) has been adopted. This new term denotes an assemblage of cultivated individuals which are distinguished by any characters significant for the purposes of horticulture and which when reproduced (sexually or vegetatively) retain their distinguishing features. Thus, a cultivar may be any one of the following kinds of units: (a) A *clone*, consisting of uniform material . . . propagated entirely by vegetative means, as by cuttings, grafts, divisions, etc.; (b) a *line*, consisting of a sexually reproducing population of uniform appearance, propagated by seeds; (c) an assemblage of individuals showing genetical differences, but having one or more characters by which it can be differentiated from other cultivars; or (d) a uniform group of first-generation (F_1) hybrids, reconstituted on each occasion by crossing standard parents.

The first category (a) is that usually obtaining among cultivated rhododendrons and azaleas, where the cultivar is merely a clone. The second (b) applies only rarely, while (c) and (d) are almost never encountered in this genus. If we use the word "clone" it is self-explanatory and we need have little employment of "cultivar" or any other term.

For convenience, related clones or cultivars are sometimes gathered into groups and given collective (group) names. A collective name may be either a word of Latin form (in which case it is preceded by the multiplication sign " × "), or a phrase in modern language. Such a phrase must contain a word such as "hybrids," "crosses," "group" or "grex" (abbreviated "g." in international parlance), indicating the collective nature of the unit. For example, we may write $\times$ *R. gandavense* (using italics) or, instead, Ghent Hybrids. In most collective groups the Latin form is not used, because it is usually unnecessary, and to be legal it must be accompanied by a Latin diagnosis (description) under Botanical Code rules when first introduced. Another approved way of insuring clarity is by accompanying the cultivar name with the abbreviation "cl." when the plant is a clone, "cv." when it is some other kind of a cultivar and "g." when the name represents a group or grex. Whenever a non-Latin name stands alone, it is generally assumed to be a clone.

Common or "fancy" names in a modern language are used to distinguish cultivars, including clones. The rules require that they be distinguished typographically from the Latin genus or species names to which they may be attached. Usually the Latin name is printed in italics. The cultivar (or clonal) name is then printed in ordinary roman type with capital initials and enclosed within single quotation marks, or else placed with the abbreviation "cv." or "cl." placed before it, in which case quotation marks are omitted. Thus, the correct form for writing the name of a clone could be either *Rhododendron* 'Purple Splendour' or *R.* cl. Purple Splendour. In a list where its status is understood by implication, quotation marks or symbols are, of course, unnecessary.

Where a collective (group) name is used, it should generally be placed in parentheses after the generic name, for example *Rhododendron* (Jalisco grex) 'Eclipse,' or *R.* (Jalisco Hybrids) 'Eclipse.'

A FORMULA consists of the scientific or cultivar name of the parents connected by a multiplication sign. It was long the custom to place the name of the female (seed) parent first, followed by the name of the male (pollen) parent, and this may still be followed where the parentage is known. For better precision, the genetical symbols ♀ (female) and ♂ (male) are used after the respective names. If it is not known which are male and female, the names of the parents are placed in alphabetical order.

An APOMICT is an individual derived from seed, coming from cells within the embryo and identical with the mother tissue, apparently arising without actual fertilization and showing no influence of the male parent. In effect, it amounts to a form of asexual (vegetative) reproduction. In rhododendrons there are occasional instances of induced apogamy, where pollination seems to stimulate the production of apomictic seed without, however, reaching the point of gametic fusion. I observed an instance where both hybrid and apomictic seedlings were simultaneously produced from one female parent. Apomixis is sometimes observed in cases of wide crosses.

Under the Code there are rules for the naming of new cultivars. The name should be non-Latin and should consist of one or two words only, never more

than three. An abbreviation or symbol is counted as a word and is never recommended. Words with accessories like "The," "Mrs.", "Rev.", and excessively long or difficult words, are to be avoided. Also words that exaggerate or
are vague, or which are confusing or repetitive in the same genus, such as
'Altaclerense' (rhododendron) and 'Altaclerensis' (azalea). Names combining
parts of the parental Latin epithets, such as 'Augfast' (= R. Augustinii × R.
fastigiatum), are inadmissible if used on the cultivar level. The provisions of
the Code are not retroactive, however, so that names established before 1959
are retained.

Under the new rules, a registration authority has been set up for each
of several plant genera. By agreement with the Royal Horticultural Society,
that organization, with a technical staff at London and Wisley, will act as
international registrars for rhododendrons and azaleas. National plant societies,
such as the American Rhododendron Society and the American Horticultural
Society, will probably act as agents for the registrar in North America, while
similar groups elsewhere, such as the Deutsche Rhododendron Gesellschaft
in Germany, will probably function in a similar way. Persons wishing to
register new rhododendron or azalea clones and give them official names
should communicate with the secretary of one of these organizations. Descriptions will be asked for and, where possible, pedigrees will be sought. A book
containing a list of all the known rhododendron and azalea cultivars is now
available from the Royal Horticultural Society, Vincent Square, London,
S.W.1. Current copies of the International Code of Nomenclature for Cultivated Plants are available from the same source or from the American
Horticultural Council, Arnold Arboretum, Jamaica Plain, Mass.

At this point a few more explanatory words should be added with reference
to the manner in which this author has handled the subjects of height, flowers,
color, hardiness and merit ratings in the descriptive parts of this book which
are to follow.

HEIGHT is given in approximate feet or inches when the plant is mature.
This is not always an index of what it will do in cultivation, and, with the
larger species at least, must be discounted liberally, because it would take many
years for a specimen to attain its maximum stature. Probably few large species
will develop their maximum height in cultivation.

INFLORESCENCE and habit of growth are given in approximate terms by
comparison with the diagrammatic drawings cited under index letters. These
examples should not be taken too literally, for several reasons. First, because a
great deal of variation exists within species and the type illustrated may not be
typical of the species as a whole or of certain extremes within the species. Sec-
ondly, because the comparison is merely an approximation—an effort to fit a

species to an illustration conforming to its general appearance and without regard to details. Also, the looseness or compactness of a truss, for instance, may vary considerably with the location or nutrition of the plant or its water relations. This method of presentation is followed, however, because it leads to a more graphic comprehension of the horticultural character of a plant by the amateur than a written description and also because it avoids the use of cumbersome technical terms. An effort has been made, however, to make it reasonably, even if loosely, accurate. Habit of growth is suggested by such terms as upright, spreading, loose, compact, dwarf, etc.

FLOWER FORM is similarly suggested by means of outline diagrams. These also are approximations, but, in most cases, will help to give the reader a better mental impression of the species than he can obtain from descriptive terminology such as "tubular campanulate," of which there are many degrees. The author believes that anything which will convey the general effect of the plant referred to, even if at the expense of nice exactitude, is justifiable as an aid in practical garden use, especially where such a complexity of species exists as in the genus *Rhododendron*. The diagrams are presented, therefore, for the convenience of the gardener rather than as an accurate botanical record.

FLOWER SIZE is given in inches, usually the length of corolla. Where possible, the size is given as diameter of the flower, since this is usually the character that makes for showiness. But, unfortunately, the width across a flower is seldom measurable on a dried herbarium specimen, and dried specimens, you should know, have been the basis for most of the botanical descriptions of species published to date. So flower length, and not width, is the common measurement given. Knowing its length, some idea of its width can be obtained from the diagrams, where these are available.

COLOR is generally given in accordance with the most reliable description at hand. It is unfortunate that a standard set of color terms could not be applied under the present circumstances, but with living specimens of only a relatively few species available this was practically impossible. Many designations of color are deceptive rather than descriptive, because broad terms, as "magenta" for instance, are subject to wide differences of interpretation. It is not only impossible to put hundreds of species under one standard color code at present, but slight variations in color of individuals, especially among seedlings, render such nice accuracy unattainable in any event. Colors may be somewhat lighter or darker according to the season or the site in which grown. Greenhouse grown flowers are apt to be considerably lighter in color than those grown in full sunlight outdoors. The colors referred to in this treatment are intended to be as accurate as possible under present circumstances.

MARKINGS occur most commonly on the upper lobe of the flower, although they may occur anywhere on the plant. The upper lobe is frequently more highly colored than the other parts of the corolla and it often carries a definite color pattern of dots or blotches of red, purple, black, brown, yellow or green. Where the markings produce a distinctive color pattern or where they are essential for identification, they are cited in the description.

HARDINESS is a relative matter, subject to the interaction of many factors. It is not a fixed quality that can be assigned to a species or clone and made to do duty throughout the world. For instance, hardiness ratings assigned in Britain are of little direct value elsewhere, but are of some use as a basis of comparison between species, because the British experience represents long-time observations on a large plant population, grown in a relatively compact area where conditions are comparable. Hence, the British ratings are used in this work, with the warning, however, that they are far from absolute, since each biotic province needs its own set of hardiness values. "Hardiness" as defined in Britain may mean merely a plant's ability to withstand late spring frosts, while in America it may refer to minimal winter temperatures, or the residual effects of hot summer weather or perhaps to drought resistance.

MERIT RATINGS, inserted at the paragraph ends in Chapter XXII, are adapted from the current British scale, but differ in that only the important ratings are recognized. If a species or clone bears four asterisks in the new British handbook, or if it has received three asterisks plus an Award of Merit or an Award of Excellence, it is given only one merit symbol. In case it has received both four asterisks and an Award, it is given two symbols in this list. Lesser merit marks are not regarded as broadly significant outside of the British Isles and are therefore omitted. The British merit ratings followed in this book should, in fact, be regarded elsewhere as comparative only. Because of climatic and other dissimilarities, the actual garden behavior of these plants may be vastly different from that in Britain. For instance, in New England the leading rhododendron clones are the old-fashioned "ironclad" sorts that are regarded as obsolete and not worthy of being grown in good British gardens. But the fact that the British growers have many, many sorts for comparison and that they have been growing them for a long time favors the use of their judgment as to comparative values of plants with the higher merit ratings. The hardiness and merit ratings applied here are adapted from the 1956 edition of the Royal Horticultural Society's Rhododendron Handbook.

PART II

DESCRIPTIVE NOTES AND COMPILATIONS

CHAPTER XXII

NOTES ON THE SERIES AND NATURAL SPECIES

THIS is a horticultural work rather than a taxonomic one. Accordingly, the material is arranged for gardening convenience and technical descriptions are avoided. Those seeking taxonomic data are referred to the works cited in the Bibliography.

In the following enumeration, the natural species are all listed under series groups in order that the natural relationships among the species may be better comprehended. The various series, however, are presented in alphabetical order and the species themselves are placed within the series groupings in alphabetical order. An alphabetical index to all the species and cultivars is provided in the back of the book. Hybrids and recognized cultivar groups are listed in Chapter XXIII.

In describing each species the following order is used:

1. *Name of species,* followed by author's name.
2. *English meaning* of Latin name (in parentheses).
3. *Synonyms,* if any.
4. *Common* or *fancy name.*
5. *Comparative hardiness ratings,* according to British measurements of 1956, indicated by letters from *A* to *F* in italic type, *A* indicating the hardiest sorts, *F* the greenhouse subjects (see table, p. 230).
6. *Height* in feet, when mature.
7. *Inflorescence,* referring to diagrams a to z (in back of book).
8. *Flower shape,* referring to diagrams 1 to 76.
9. *Flower size, color* and *markings,* given in that order.
10. *Illustrations* cited.
11. *Habitat* of species in its wild state.
12. *Remarks,* usually with reference to horticultural usage.
13. *Varieties* and natural forms.
14. *Clones* or cultivar groups.

229

15. *Merit ratings* (**X**) and (**XX**) follow the R.H.S. (British) ratings of 1956, but in this book only the two higher ratings are recognized. To avoid confusion with other systems, boldface **X**'s are used. One **X** is equal to four British stars or three British stars plus an Award of Merit (A.M.). Two **X**'s are equal to four British stars plus an Award of Merit. Where these symbols occur, they refer essentially to the species itself, rather than to the variety or clone name which may immediately precede them.

EQUIVALENT HARDINESS RATINGS

Minimum Temperature Zones	British Ratings Royal Hort. Soc.	American Ratings Amer. Rhod. Soc.
−20° to −30°F.	—	H − 1
−15° to −20°F.	—	H − 1
−10° to −15°F.	A	H − 2
−5° to −10°F.	A	H − 2
0° to −5°F.	A or B	H − 3
5° to 0°F.	B or C	H − 4
10° to 5°F.	C	H − 4
15° to 10°F.	D	H − 5
25° to 15°F.	D	H − 5
32° to 25°F.	E	H − 6
Above 32°F.	F	H − 7

It should be noted that other factors beside temperature alone are involved in the winter hardiness of rhododendrons (see Chapter IX). The British ratings are to be regarded as reliable in America only where temperatures do not descend below −10°F. In many instances the B and C ratings are interchangeable in America. In regions of subzero temperatures it will be wise to consult the lists of recommended species and cultivars for particular geographical areas presented in Part III, rather than to rely solely upon the rated hardiness. Hardiness ratings, however, do provide a useful measure of the relative hardiness of the different sorts. British figures are used because they cover a large number of kinds within a limited range and over a long period of observation.

ALBIFLORUM SERIES

This contains but one species, a rather distinct form, native to the Rocky Mts., from Oregon to British Columbia and eastward to Colorado. Cultivation in the East has not been successful. It is a six foot, deciduous shrub, with small white flowers which occur along the branches, ten stamens and a large calyx.

R. ALBIFLORUM

Millais speaks of the almost impenetrable thickets of *Rhododendron albiflorum* which grow in some parts of the Rocky Mountains in British Columbia. I am unable to say just how far north this species extends, but it has been reported from beyond the frontier in northern British Columbia, in the same geographical region where *R. lapponicum* occurs. Mary G. Henry found it in bloom beyond the Peace River on July 27th, at an altitude of about 5,000 feet. There is a form in Colorado sometimes called *Rhododendron Warrenii* (A. Nels.) MacBride, but which is said not to be very distinct from the species *R. albiflorum*. Rehder regards *R. albiflorum* as allied to the members of the Ovatum series. *Rhododendron albiflorum* seems never to have been the parent of any hybrids and I have never heard of attempts to cross it with other species.

This is the only species of rhododendron to occur in the Rocky Mountains, except in the immediate area of the Pacific coast. The fact that it occurs alone in this territory, and the further fact that it appears difficult to cultivate under conditions presumably favorable for ordinary rhododendrons, and the still further fact that it is morphologically distinct from other species, are significant observations when considered together. Very often such aberrant species possess unexpected usefulness, because of their tolerance for conditions which other species abhor. Is it possible that this rhododendron possesses any such unrevealed virtues?

Rhododendron albiflorum Hooker (white flowers), syn: Azalea **albiflorum** Kuntze and Azaleastrum albiflorum Rydberg. *C.* Up to 6 ft. Inflor. (**w**). Flowers (22), 4/5 in. across, white, with yellow spots sometimes. Intro. before 1837. Bot. Mag. t. 3670. Rocky Mts., N. Amer. 4,000–10,000 ft.—A rather unattractive species, forming thickets above the timberline. It is hardy, but difficult to cultivate. Very distinct. Var. *plenum* Rehder is said to be a handsome double form, not in cultivation.

ANTHOPOGON SERIES

R. ANTHOPOGON

This and the former Cephalanthum Series have recently been merged and all are now referred to under the collective name of Anthopogon Series. In the valuable study made by Cowan and Davidian * other changes in the status of these species were made, including the reduction to varietal rank or to synonymy of nearly 20 former species. It is noted that as collections were received from abroad, new forms of slightly different appearance were given specific rank, which now after further study are found to be synonymous with or mere variants of former established species. This means that a number of names have been abandoned, while others have been changed. This will upset some persons who have learned to call certain plants by their original names, as for example the former R. ledoides, which now becomes *R. trichostomum* variety *ledoides*. Fortunately, many of the species whose names have undergone this change are not commonly grown in gardens and hence horticultural usage will not be seriously affected.

These are alpine shrubs with small evergreen leaves, often aromatic. Flowers are small, borne in compact trusses. With few exceptions they are short-lived and difficult in cultivation. While they possess a certain attractiveness, they are strictly for the fancier in an appropriate climate.

Former species in the Anthopogon Series which have now become varieties or synonyms are:

R. acraium = *R. primulaeflorum*
R. Adamsii = *R. primulaeflorum*
R. cephalanthoides =*R. primulaeflorum* var. *cephalanthoides*
R. cephalanthum var. platyphyllum = *R. platyphyllum*
R. chamaetortum = *R. cephalanthum*
R. clivicola = *R. primulaeflorum*
R. crebreflorum = *R. cephalanthum* var. *crebreflorum*
R. cremnophilum = *R. primulaeflorum*
R. daphniflorum = *R. rufescens*
R. fragrans = *R. primulaeflorum*

* Cowan, J. M. and H. H. Davidian. The Anthopogon Alliance. Roy. Hort. Soc. Rhod. Year Book 2:55–86. London, 1947.

R. gymnomiscum = *R. primulaeflorum*
R. haemonium = *R. anthopogon* var. *haemonium*
R. hedyosmum = *R. trichostomum* var. *hedyosmum*
R. ledoides = *R. trichostomum* var. *ledoides*
R. nmaiense = *R. cephalanthum* var. *nmaiense*
R. praeclarum = *R. primulaeflorum*
R. radinum = *R. trichostomum* var. *radinum*
R. sphaeranthum = *R. trichostomum*
R. temoense = *R. laudandum* var. *temoense*
R. tsarongense = *R. primulaeflorum*

Rhododendron anthopogon D. Don (bearded flower). *C.* 2 ft. Inflor. (d). Flowers (7) ¾ in. long, pink. E. Himalaya and S. Tibet (Nepal and Sikkim) 11,000–16,000 ft.—Variable. Not very showy. Var. *haemonium,* flowers yellow.

Rhododendron anthopogonoides Maximowicz (resembling *R. anthopogon*). Small shrub. Inflor. (e?). Flowers (8?), ½ in. long, white. Kansu.

Rhododendron cephalanthum Franchet (flowers in head). *B.* A low shrub. Inflor. (e?). Flowers (8?), ⅔ in. long, white. Yunnan and Szechuan, 9,000–10,000 ft. Var. *crebreflorum* Cowan is dwarf with pink flowers. Var. *nmaiense* Cowan has yellow flowers. The flower heads remind one of *Viburnum Carlesii.*

Rhododendron Collettianum Aitchison & Hemsley (after Gen. Collett, discoverer in 1879). *C.* 8–10 ft. tall. Inflor. (e?). Flowers 1 in. long, white, tinged rose. Jour. Hort. ser. *3* (36) : 331. Afghanistan and Indian frontier, 10,000–13,000 ft.

Rhododendron hypenanthum Balfour (bearded flowers). *C.* 1–3 ft. Inflor. (d). Flowers (7) similar to *R. anthopogon,* golden yellow. Bot. Mag. t. 3947. W. Himalaya, 11,000–15,000 ft.

Rhododendron kongboense Hutch. (from Kongbo, E. Tibet). *A.* 2 ft. Inflor. (e?). Flowers (8), ¼–⅜ in. long, bright rose. Tibet-Bhutan border.—A very dwarf twiggy shrub, blooming early.

Rhododendron laudandum Cowan (praiseworthy). *A.* Small shrub up to 3 ft. Inflor. (e?). Flowers very pale pink, covered outside by long whitish hairs. Var. *temoense* Ward has white flowers, not densely hairy. Tibetan-Bhutan border, 12,000–15,000 ft.

Rhododendron platyphyllum Balfour f. & W. W. Smith (broad leaved). *B.* Short, twiggy branchlets. Inflor. (e?). Flowers ¾ in. long, white. Yunnan, 11,000–12,000 ft.

Rhododendron pogonophyllum Cowan & Davidian (bearded leaves). Prostrate shrub. Inflor. (f?). Flowers (8?), ¾ in. long, white to pink. Central Bhutan, 14,000–15,000 ft.—A little, bristly leaved plant, that creeps over rocks.

Rhododendron primulaeflorum Bureau & Franchet (primrose flowered). *A.* Shrublet to 5 ft. Inflor. (e?) of funnel-shaped flowers, 2/3 in. long, white with yellow or orange tint at base; sometimes yellow or rose. Southern Tibet, between Lhassa and Batang, and in variant form in Yunnan, Szechuan and Kansu, 11,000–15,000 ft.—Described as highly aromatic. Var. *cephalanthoides* has corolla tube densely puberulous outside, and var. *lepidanthum* has corolla tube densely scaly outside. A number of variants, formerly regarded as other species, are so closely allied to *R. primulaeflorum* that they are now regarded as synonymous names. See list above.

Rhododendron radendum Fang (bristly, needing a shave). Small shrub up to 3 ft. Inflor. (f?), 8–10 flowers, small, tubular, purplish-white, less than ½ in. long. Sikang, China, 10,000 ft.

Rhododendron rufescens Franchet (becoming reddish). *C.* 1–2 ft. Inflor. (e?). Flowers narrowly tubular, ¾ in. long, white to bluish. Szechuan, 11,000–13,000 ft.

Rhododendron Sargentianum Rehder & Wilson (after Prof. C. S. Sargent of the Arnold Arboretum). *C.* 2 ft. tall. Inflor. (q.). Flowers (57), ½ to 2/3 in. long, lemon yellow. Bot. Mag. t. 8871. W. Szechuan, 9,000–11,000 ft.

VAR. LEDOIDES

Rhododendron trichostomum Franchet (hairy mouthed). *D.* A twiggy shrub up to 3 ft. or more, intricately branched. Inflor. (e). Flowers (8), ⅓ to ¾ in. long, rose or white. Narrow leaves. Yunnan and Szechuan, 8,000 ft.—A variable species, under which are now placed as varieties several forms previously listed as species. The plants are dwarfish, usually under 2 ft. in the garden, with round trusses of flowers which sometimes remind one of the flower clusters of *Viburnum Carlesii*. The forms are inconstant and distinguishing marks sometimes break down. Var. *hedyosmum* Balfour has the longest corolla. Var. *ledoides* has a glabrous corolla and var. *radinum* has corolla densely scaly. Other names formerly applied are now regarded as synonyms.

ARBOREUM SERIES

A group of large, handsome species, mainly from the rain forests of the Himalayas and, hence, of relatively tender constitution. Its nearest affinities are with the series Barbatum and Irroratum. The larger members have a tree-like habit and all are slow in coming into bloom, for 20 years may elapse before a good display of flowers takes place. It is only in the south of England, or in very warm gardens, that *Rhododendron arboreum* may be found in cultivation. Where it thrives, it is an exceedingly handsome object. As noted elsewhere, *R. arboreum* is a parent of the Catawba hybrids and is the source from which they probably derived much of their red colora-

R. ARBOREUM

tion. There is a good deal of variation in most of that species. All may be said to be woodland plants and need the protection of a wooded area for best results in cultivation.

Subseries Arboreum

These generally are tree-like in habit and are relatively tender. They have a wide geographical range, extending from Tibet to Ceylon. The colors range from white to pink, lilac, crimson and crimson-scarlet.

Rhododendron arboreum Smith (tree-like). C. 20–40 ft. tall. Inflor. (a). Flowers (65), 1½–2 in. across, deep scarlet with deeper dots. Intro. 1814. Bot. Reg. t. 890. Temperate Himalaya; Kashmir to Bhutan; Ceylon. 5,000–10,000 ft.—An exceedingly variable species, blood-red in the type, notable as the first red rhododendron introduced. An ancestor of the hardy garden hybrids. Tender except in the most protected parts of England. Slow to bloom from seed. Forma *album* Wallich, has white flowers with purple spots, while forma *roseum* Sweet, from Nepal, has rich pink flowers; both these forms are somewhat hardier than the type. Certain geographical forms have been described as sub-species, the most important being: *R. Campbelliae* Hooker f., with purplish rose flowers and rusty, tomentose leaves; *R. cinnamomeum* Wallich, with cinnamon-colored tomentose leaves and white or rose flowers, spotted; *R. Kingianum* Watt, with broader leaves and compact, deep scarlet flower trusses, but slow growing and small; *R. nilagiricum* Zenker, with rugose leaves, rusty tomentose beneath, and large trusses of crimson or rose flowers;

R. *Windsorii* Nuttall, from Bhutan, with elongated calyx-lobes, leaves white beneath, and flowers crimson-scarlet; and R. *zeylanicum* Hort., from Ceylon, with rich pink flowers. Also the following additional variations are mentioned in the literature: var. *Andersonii*, rosy red; var. *carneum*, blush pink; var. *crispum*, pink with fimbriated edges; var. *fimbriatum*, fimbriated; var. *giganteum*, having large trusses of rose flowers; var. *Kermesinum*, fine crimson, leaves white beneath; var. *limbatum*, pale rose-purple with darker margin; var. *nepalense*, red; var. *nigrescens*, dark maroon; var. *ochraceum*, pink, with ochre tomentum; var. *Paxtonii*, with very large, blood-red flowers; var. *puniceum*, purplish red; var. *Wearii*, rose-pink; and var. *Wardsonii*, with small, deep crimson flowers. Numerous clonal varieties have arisen as seedlings, among them being 'Blushing Beauty,' 'Maxima,' 'Lady Falmouth,' 'Rosamond Millais,' 'Henry Shilson' and 'Mrs. Henry Shilson,' all pink; 'Sir Charles Lemon,' white; 'Mesell's Arboreum,' pink suffused with carmine. **X**

Rhododendron Delavayi Franchet (after Abbé Delavay, early collector), syn: R. pilovittatum Balf. & Sm. *E*. 20–40 ft. tall. Inflor. (a). Flowers (65), 1½–2 in. long, bright cherry-crimson to deep crimson, fleshy. Bot. Mag. t. 8137. W. Yunnan and Burma, 8,000–10,000 ft.—This is a Chinese affinity of R. *arboreum*. In England it has not developed its described height, and is but a shrub. Probably, like R. *arboreum*, it has many forms; forms with white and pink flowers, say the authorities, should be avoided, but the blood-red type is fine. All are tender and suitable only for warm gardens. Plants have proved tender in the United States. **X**

Rhododendron niveum Hooker f. (snow-like). *B*. 12–15 ft. tall. Inflor. (a). Flowers (65) 1½ in. long, magenta or purplish lilac with deep purple nectar pouches at base of tube. Bot. Mag. t. 4730. Sikkim Himalaya, 10,000–12,000 ft.— A small tree, with handsome leaves, but flowers of a color that should not be used except in the woodland, as it clashes with scarlet forms. Blooms early May in England. Var. *fulvum*, Bot. Mag. t. 6827, has a buff tomentum on the under surface of the leaves. **X**

Rhododendron peramoenum Balfour f. & Forrest (very pleasing). *E*. Shrub 6–12 ft. tall. Flowers 2 in. long, cherry scarlet to rose crimson. W. Yunnan, margins of forests 9,000–10,000 ft.—Very close affinity of R. *Delavayi*.

Rhododendron silvaticum Cowan (woodland). *B*. Small tree to 20 ft. Flowers dark magenta to reddish purple. Notes Bot. Gard. Edinburgh *19*:185 (1936). Tibet.— The flower buds have an interesting rust-color indumentum on the outside. Clone 'Silvia' won Award of Merit in 1954. **X**

Rhododendron Wattii Cowan (after Sir George Watt). A 20 ft. tree found in Manipur by the late Sir George Watt. Flowers pink with purple spots. Notes Bot. Gard. Edinburgh.

SUBSERIES ARGYROPHYLLUM

These are more bushy than the true Arboreums, less showy and with less compact trusses. A thin plastered indumentum is quite characteristic; when present it is white, buff or tawny. They extend over a wide area of southern China, going as far as the maritime provinces and Formosa. While clearly a Chinese extension of the Himalayan Arboreums, they also show certain points of affinity with the northern Ponticum series, particularly the Subseries Caucasicum. Their colors range from white to pink, lilac and rose.

Rhododendron argyrophyllum Franchet (silver leaf). *A.* 6–20 ft. Inflor. a loose racemose umbel of 6–10 fls. Flowers 1–1½ in. long, white or white flushed rose, deep pink or rose spots on the upper part. Wilson, 1904, from Mupin, W. Szechuan, 6,000–8,000 ft.—A shrub with pretty, slender leaves, white beneath, but said to be slow growing. Var. *cupulare* Rehder & Wilson has smooth branchlets. Var. *omeiense* Rehder & Wilson has smaller leaves, a dun-colored tomentum and a broader corolla than the type. Var. *leiandrum* Hutchinson has glabrous filaments. **X**

Rhododendron Chienianum Fang (after Prof. Chien). *A.* 30 ft. tree with pinkish-purple flowers. Ic.Pl. Omeiensium, *1* : t. 3. (1942). China.

Rhododendron Coryanum Tagg & Forrest (after R. R. Cory). 10–20 ft. tall. Flowers 1 inch long, creamy white, marked within by brownish crimson spots. S.E. Tibet, 12,000–14,000 ft.—An outlier of the subseries from the Tibetan borders, having more flowers on its truss than its allies.

Rhododendron denudatum Léveillé (naked), syn: R. xanthoneuron Lévl. 12 ft. tall. Inflor. corymbose umbel with 9–12 flowers. Flowers 1–1½ in. long, rose, blotched and spotted deep crimson. E. Yunnan, 9,000–10,000 ft.—A little known species.

Rhododendron farinosum Léveillé (mealy). *C.* 4–6 ft. tall. Inflor. umbel of about 6 fls. Flowers 1–1½ in. long, white, campanulate. Yunnan, 9,000–10,000 ft.

Rhododendron floribundum Franchet (free flowering). *B.* 9–15 ft. tall. Inflor. (b) racemose umbel of 8–12 fls. Flowers 1½ in. long, magenta rose, blotched and spotted dark crimson.—The color disappointing. W. Szechuan, 4,000–8,000 ft.

Rhododendron fokienense Franchet (from Fokien), imperfectly known. 4–5 funnel-campanulate flowers in a racemose umbel. Flowers 1½ in. long, color not described. From Fokien Province in eastern China.

Rhododendron formosanum Hemsley (from Formosa). 6–18 ft. tall. Inflor. a rounded corymb of 10–20 fls. Flowers white or pink with purple-brown dots. 1½ in. across. Formosa, 4,000–6,000 ft.—Little known.

Rhododendron Hunnewellianum Rehder & Wilson (after the Hunnewell family of New England, patrons of horticulture), syn: R. leucolasium Diels. *B.* 6–16 ft. Inflor. racemose umbel of about 7 fls. Flowers 1½–2 in. long, white, tinted pink, with pink spots on the upper lobe. W. Szechuan, 6,000–10,000 ft.—A fairly slow grower.

Rhododendron hypoglaucum Hemsley (blue beneath), syn: R. gracilipes Franchet; R. chionophyllum Diels. *B.* Shrub or small tree up to 20 ft. Inflor. (b). Flowers (65) 1½ in. long, white, flushed rose, with deep rose spots. Bot. Mag. t. 8649. Hupeh, 5,000–7,000 ft.—Exceedingly common in western Hupeh, and therefore might be some hardier than the species from western China. The under side of the leaf is white and the plant is attractive.

Rhododendron insigne Hemsley & Wilson (remarkable). *B.* Inflor. a short lax corymb of about 8 fls. Flowers 1½ in. long, pinky white, with crimson spots inside. Szechuan, 7,000–10,000 ft.—A slow grower with good flowers. Leaves very distinctive with a shiny coppery indumentum. **X**

Rhododendron longipes Rehder & Wilson (with long foot stalk). *C.* 3–8 ft. tall. Inflor. a rounded umbel of 10–15 fls. Flowers 1¼ in. long, 1½ in. across, pale rose spotted with a deeper tint. W. Szechuan, 6,000–7,000 ft.

Rhododendron Pingianum Fang (after Prof. Ping). A 20 ft. shrub with purple flowers. Contrib. Biol. Lab. Sc. Soc. China, Bot. Ser. *12*:20 (1939). Szechuan.

Rhododendron Ririei Hemsley & Wilson (after Rev. B. Ririe, China Inland Mission, friend and helper of Wilson). *B.* Up to 18 ft. tall. Infl. a corymbose raceme of about 10 fls. Flowers 1½–2 in. long, dull purple, with 5 black-purple nectar pouches. From Mt. Omei in Szechuan.—Suitable for southern England. Blooms early. Attractive.

Rhododendron Rockii Wilson (after Dr. J. F. Rock, plant collector in China). *C.* 12–18 ft. tall. Inflor. a racemose umbel of 6–12 fls. Flowers 1½ in. long and 1½–2 in. across, pale rose, spotted. S. Kansu, 6,000–7,000 ft.—A shrub or small tree.

Rhododendron simiarum Hance (of the monkeys), syn: R. Fordii Hemsley. *C.* 6–8 ft. tall. Inflor. (b). Flowers (71) 1½ in. long, pale pink, with rose dots. From Kwangtung Province in S.E. China.

Rhododendron Thayerianum Rehder & Wilson (after a New England family, patrons of horticulture). *B.* 9–13 ft. tall. Inflor. (g) a compact racemose corymb of 10–20 fls. Flowers (73) 1–1¼ in. long, white, flushed pink, without dots or spots. Mupin, W. Szechuan, in woodlands at 9,000 ft.—A good species, flowering late, with long, narrow dark leaves and small trusses of white flowers. Blooms late June and early July in England.

Rhododendron Youngae Fang (after Mrs. Young Fang). To 12 ft. Flowers rose with purple spots. Contrib. Biol. Lab. Sc. Soc. China, Bot. Ser. *12*:20 (1939).

A Forty-year-old Catawba Hybrid

Rhododendrons in the Heart of a Great City

AURICULATUM SERIES

A small series of only two species, having a distinctive flower form, a somewhat lanceolate or oblanceolate leaf, a long pointed leaf-bud and woolly tomentum on the foliage. Both species are rather valuable garden acquisitions, *Rhododendron auriculatum* especially for its late blooming habit and *R. Griersonianum* for its distinctive flower color, said to be unlike that of any other rhododendron. They may be crossed with some of the old-fashioned hardy sorts. The two species occupy quite different areas in western China, *R. auriculatum* coming from the more northern district, at a lower level, and evidently the hardier. Both appear relatively hardy in England, but are evidently injured unless grown in very special places in America.

R. GRIERSONIANUM

The color of *R. Griersonianum,* reported as bright geranium scarlet, is better described as "geranium lake," a well-known paint term. Transmissible in crosses, the color has made this species famous as a parent of red hybrids notably better than itself. Both *R. Griersonianum* and *R. auriculatum* are hardy at San Francisco, but the former is a bit tender at Seattle, while the latter is growable in sheltered places in the East, and more generally in the West.

Rhododendron auriculatum Hemsley (ear shaped). B. 6–15 ft. tall. Inflor. (b) a large, loose umbellate raceme of 7–15 fls. Flowers (72), 2½–4 in. across, with 7 lobes, white or rose-pink, splashed greenish at the base of the tube inside. Bot. Mag. t. 8786. Intro. by Wilson in 1901 from Hupeh, where it grows in woods at 5,000–7,000 ft.—A rather remarkable species in that it blooms as late as August. It is a large shrub, but has the disadvantage of not blooming well until it reaches a big size. The flowers have a sweet, lily-like scent. It is hardy in England, except in the coldest districts, where it makes its growth too late in the fall. It needs moisture in dry seasons and grows in the shade of the woods in its native home. Its habitat in Hupeh gives evidence of hardiness, but it has not, thus far, shown signs of adapting itself to the American East. Mr. C. O. Dexter propagated it on Cape Cod, but it is not quite happy there. It grafts easily, but is said to be difficult to layer. It is being used quite extensively by certain English hybridists who wish to induce later bloom in hybrid races. It possibly does not ripen off early enough in the fall to be useful in the north. The size, color and fragrance of the flowers, as well as its lateness of bloom, commend it. X

Rhododendron Griersonianum Balfour & Forrest (after R. C. Grierson, friend and helper of George Forrest). *C.* 5–10 ft. tall. Inflor. (b) or (c) an open racemose corymb of 5–12 fls. Flowers (72) 2½–3 in. long, 3–4 in. across, bright geranium-scarlet, dappled with darker spots inside, sprinkled outside with mealy hairs. Spec. Rhodo. p. 40; Revue Hort. (1928) Jan. (1), p. 16; Millais, J. G. Rhododendrons (1924) ser. 2:150. Introd. 1917. W. Yunnan, 7,000–9,000 ft. One of the most notable of introduced species. This will probably have a profound effect upon future hybrids. Its color is unique. **XX**

AZALEA SERIES

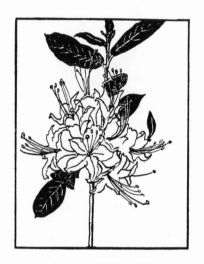

R. CALENDULACEUM

Horticulturists have long regarded azaleas as a group of plants distinct from others and, for all practical purposes, a separate genus, related to, but not a part of, the rhododendrons. When only the American species are considered, this distinctiveness is indeed prominent.

In the time of Linnaeus and for many years thereafter, only the distinctive azalea and rhododendron species were known and the two groups came to be classed as two separate genera, distinguished from each other by the well-known characters of the American species, such as deciduous versus evergreen foliage, five versus ten stamens, and so forth. With the introduction of the Asiatic species, there came a time when this method of differentiation was no longer workable. Certain azaleas with evergreen leaves appeared, as well as borderline forms, such as *Rhododendron dauricum* which looked like an azalea, was usually deciduous but sometimes evergreen, had ten stamens and would cross with either azaleas or true rhododendrons.

Here, indeed, was a problem for the botanists. Some of the investigators finally solved it by placing the entire list under the one comprehensive generic name *Rhododendron,* which, in turn, they subdivided into sections embracing the various sub-groups. Thus, the extreme and intermediate forms were all classified under the one genus *Rhododendron.* Other botanists continued to apply the name *Azalea* to the ordinary five-stamened group of American azaleas, setting up the additional genera *Biltia, Rhodora* and *Azaleastrum* to take care of the other American species that did not fit into the first two groups. They did not work with the Asiatic species, or, if they did, their nomenclature has never become current among horticulturists. If followed, it would perhaps mean twenty new genera.

The present classification according to series places all the azaleas into the one series Azalea, which, in turn, is subdivided into six subseries. These embrace the four "sections" *Tsutsutsi, Sciadorhodion, Rhodora* and *Pentanthera,* plus two new sections, *Tashiroi* and *Viscidula,* which have been established to accommodate two recently discovered divergent species.

Regardless of what we may call these plants, no garden lover will have difficulty in appreciating the value and beauty of the azaleas. They have long been popular, and deservedly so. There are forms to fit nearly every climatic requirement and many of them, once the tenderness of early youth is passed, are easier to cultivate than the true rhododendrons. Although the general directions for planting and growing azaleas are similar to those for other rhododendrons, certain of the deciduous sorts, particularly those native to the northeastern United States, can be successfully used in places where the exposure is too great to permit of growing evergreen species. Enough has been said in previous chapters to describe the use and culture of azaleas without further repetition here. Suffice it to say, that within the series Azalea may be found flowers of nearly every color, size and constitution known in the genus at large and suited to an infinitude of uses.

Among the subseries, the most important horticulturally are the subseries Obtusum and Luteum, the former sections *Tsutsutsi* and *Pentanthera* respectively. The first group is exclusively Asiatic, with large representations in Japan, and the latter is North American, except for the addition of two Asiatic and one European species. The Obtusum group runs exclusively in the color range of white, pink, red and purple—the anthocyanin colors—and nowhere does yellow pigmentation appear on the flowers. The members of the Luteum group, on the other hand, carry both the anthocyanin and yellow types of pigment, so, as a class, the Luteum group has a much wider color range than that of the subseries Obtusum. Certain species are restricted to one or the other type of pigmentation, but in *Rhododendron calendulaceum* and *R. japonicum* both the anthocyanin and yellow pigments are combined. The same condition has been brought about artificially in a number of other species by hybridization.

Species in the Obtusum and Luteum subseries are generally quite able to cross with one another within the limits of a given subseries, but crosses between different subseries are attended with great difficulty. From the evidence at hand, it seems that the same general statement will probably hold true throughout the Azalea series, with certain definite exceptions. It is true, however, that certain azaleas will cross with other rhododendrons, some in quite different series, where the element of physiological affinity appears to be quite independent of morphological similarity. Hence, too specific lines must not be drawn in attempting to define the limits of hybrid affinity.

The Trichocladum and Semibarbatum series approach the series Azalea, while the transition toward the azalea group is also seen in the series Triflorum. Rehder states that the most nearly related series are Stamineum, Ovatum and Albiflorum, which, all having their flowers in the axils instead of in terminal buds, are easily distinguishable from the azaleas. Besides these, the only other series in which deciduous-leaved sorts may be found are Dauricum and Triflorum, and these possess leaf-scales, which azaleas do not have.

Subseries Canadense
(Section *Rhodora*, G. Don)

This subseries and the subseries Schlippenbachii are somewhat similar, but the flowers and leafy branchlets do not spring from the same bud in the subseries Canadense, while this occurs in the subseries Schlippenbachii.

These species are all of considerable ornamental value, especially *Rhododendron pentaphyllum* and *R. Vaseyi*. All are comparatively hardy, some very hardy, and all except *R. Albrechtii* bloom very early in the season. The colors run to rose and purple, although an excellent pure white form of *R. Vaseyi* occurs. *Rhododendron canadense* is perhaps rather unattractive in flower color, but has an interesting habit of growth. All are deciduous.

Rhododendron Albrechtii Maximowicz (after Dr. M. Albrecht, Russian naval surgeon, who discovered it in 1860) ALBRECHT'S AZALEA. *B.* 3–5 ft. tall. Flowers 2 in. across, red purple with short, wide tube (47?). Nakai, Trees and Shrubs of Japan, ed. 2, p. 67 (1927). Central and northern Japan, on margins of forests and in thickets.—A handsome shrub, not unlike *R. Vaseyi,* but less showy, blooming in June or July. In England it is considered hardy, but fastidious as to situation. It grew for several years in the Arnold Arboretum, Boston, Mass., but never really flourished. The flowers are bright magenta. The leaves which are borne in whorls of five, turn yellow in autumn. It differs from *R. pentaphyllum* in color of flowers, time of bloom, height, shape of leaves and other characters. *R. pentaphyllum* is probably handsomer. **XX**

Rhododendron canadense Torrey (from Canada), syn: Rhodora canadensis Linnaeus. RHODORA. *A.* 1–3 ft. tall. Inflor. (1). Flowers (16) ¾ in. long, 2-lipped, magenta-rose or lilac to nearly white. Bot. Mag. t. 474. N.E. America, from Labrador and Newfoundland to S.W. Quebec, New England, N.Y., Penn., and N.J. Along river banks, in moist woods and swamps.—Although its color is not attractive in many situations, this species blooms well and is interesting in the woodland or naturalistic setting. It is rather low, with a fairly good branching habit and is so hardy in the North that it is valuable for this feature. It is well liked by some persons and inspired Emerson's well known poem. It blooms in May, about as early as *Rhododendron Vaseyi*. Forma *albiflorum* Rehder has white flowers. Forma *viridifolium* Fernald has green leaves instead of the glaucous (covered with bloom) leaves of the typical form.

Rhododendron pentaphyllum Maximowicz (five leaved) ; syn: R. nikoense Nakai. FIVELEAF AZALEA. A shrub or small tree of 10 ft. or more, sometimes with sympodial branching. Inflor. 1–2 fls. Flowers (14) 1¾–2 in. across, very bright clear, rose-pink, sometimes with an inconspicuous faint yellow coloration deep down toward the base of the upper lobe. 10 stamens. Leaves deciduous and in whorls of 5. Nakai, Trees and Shrubs of Japan, ed. 2; *1*:85–86 (1927). Central and southern Japan, Nikko, in woodlands.—This beautiful species is rare in America, but is particularly handsome where large-sized specimens are growing. Its value is not alone in the fact that it has flowers, 2 in. across, bright rose-pink without a trace of purple, but that it blooms when no other azalea is in flower. It comes soon after *Rhododendron dauricum* and *R. mucronulatum,* but before *R. Vaseyi,* and makes a gorgeous sight with its large flowers borne on leafless branches. Although Wilson found young plants tender and difficult to manage at the Arnold Arboretum, other growers have succeeded in growing it in the vicinity of Boston. It is a woodland species and probably needs shade and shelter. Specimen plants 10 ft. tall or higher are growing on Long Island, where they make an impressive appearance about the last of April. The species is said to be capable of reaching a height of 25 feet. It has a branching habit not unlike that of *Cornus florida.* In England it is considered fastidious and is given a rating of *C,* but in America it deserves a hardier classification. Doubtless the English rating is due to its blooming before late spring frosts, but it behaves satisfactorily over here. Due to its foliage in whorls of 5 leaves, it has been confused with *Rhododendron quinquefolium,* being sometimes sold as "Azalea quinquefolia pink," but it is easily distinguishable from *R. quinquefolium* by its pink flowers and the fact that it blooms before the leaves unfold. It may be difficult when very young, but larger plants are certainly very satisfactory on Long Island and the species is well worth attempting in sheltered situations in the colder regions. I feel that it deserves rating as one of the most promising sorts for America. **XX**

Rhododendron Vaseyi Gray (after G. S. Vasey, discoverer, in 1878), syn: Biltia Vaseyi Small. PINKSHELL AZALEA. *A.* Perfectly hardy in N. America. Height 5 to 15 ft., irregularly branched. Inflor. (see colored illustration following page 366), 5–8 fls. Flowers (49) 1¼ in. long, 2-lipped, light clear rose, deeper toward outside, 1½–2 in. across, sometimes inconspicuously dotted. Bot. Mag. t. 8081. Blue Ridge Mts., N. Carolina.—One of the very best hardy American sorts, blooming in early May at New York. It is very attractive, is among the very hardiest and is listed as one of the finest for both England and America. Its color is clear and sprightly. It tends toward an upright habit of growth. Forma *album* has white flowers, and there are other variants intermediate between the white and pink forms. **XX**

Subseries Luteum
(Section *Pentanthera*, G. Don)

R. ROSEUM

Perhaps this is the most important group of azaleas, so far as cultivation in America is concerned. It also has about as wide a range of color as can be found in any group within the genus *Rhododendron*. The colors range from white, through lemon and spectrum yellow to orange and vermilion, with salmon and apricot intergrades, then through varying shades of pink to clear rose and, finally, to purplish rose. Crimson forms are found in the hybrids and in one species. Flower color and form are variable, especially in species like *Rhododendron calendulaceum* and *R. japonicum*, and several species normally white have purplish rose forms as natural variants.

The species in this group are mostly good sized shrubs, usually attaining a height of from ten to 15 feet. *Rhododendron atlanticum* is distinctly dwarfish, and *R. roseum* seldom exceeds six or eight feet. Many have yellow blotches on the upper lobes of the flowers. Two Asiatic species, *R. japonicum* and *R. molle*, have considerably larger flowers than the species of the eastern United States, while *R. occidentale*, of California, bears flowers of somewhat intermediate size. The Asiatic species also have flowers with a more open, funnelform shape than those of the eastern American species, which tend to have more cylindrical funnels. These differences in shape, which also characterize the Ghent and Mollis hybrid races, can best be understood by reference to the illustrative diagrams.

In the northeastern United States, the most useful species for gardens and ornamental plantings are *Rhododendron calendulaceum, R. roseum, R. japonicum, R. arborescens* and *R. viscosum*. The typical *Rhododendron nudiflorum* is very inferior, both in color and fragrance, to *R. roseum*, its close relative, regarded by some as merely a geographical variety. *Rhododendron atlanticum* is a species new to the trade, but of promise, especially where dwarfness is required, and is almost as hardy as the others mentioned above. *Rhododendron canescens*, in its true form, is scarcely better than *R. nudiflorum* in form or flower color and is distinctly tender in the North, being native only in Georgia and southward to Florida. It is frequently confused with *Rhododendron roseum* in the trade, but has little resemblance to it. *Rhododendron austrinum* is not, in my opinion, equal in beauty to the vermilion and scarlet forms of *R. calendulaceum* and is tender in the North, while the latter are hardy. *Rhododendron speciosum* is not hardy in Boston, but survives outdoors in Maryland, although the merits of its flowers over those of *R. calendulaceum* are doubtful. *Rhododendron serrulatum* is a useful species for the far South, but should be replaced by *R. arborescens* and *R. viscosum* in the North, the two latter species being perhaps equally beautiful and much more hardy. *Rhododendron alabamense* is a little-known form, related to *R. canescens* and *R. nudiflorum,* but said to be superior to *R. canescens,* because of its somewhat larger, snow white flowers and for its fragrance. *Rhododendron oblongifolium,* which ranges in Arkansas, Oklahoma and Texas, is related to *R. viscosum* and is probably not hardy in the North. *Rhododendron prunifolium* is a species by itself, little known, but interesting because of its flower color which is orange and its habit of blooming in July. The best dark red is said to be found in *R. speciosum* in Georgia lowlands along the Savannah River. *R. Bakeri* has bright red color, but turns orange when grown at low altitudes. *Rhododendron occidentale* is one of the most beautiful American azaleas, but its half-hardy character makes it unsuited for cultivation in cold climates. It has, however, contributed somewhat to hybrid races.

Although very similar to each other in appearance, the species *Rhododendron japonicum* and *R. molle* behave quite differently in hardiness when grown in New England and New York. *Rhododendron japonicum* is far superior in its ability to adapt itself to these conditions and readily makes itself at home in the climate and soil of New York State. In both its typical and its yellow forms, it grows from seed with rapidity, has a wide variation in color and seems to endure the warm summers and cold winters of the region excellently well. *Rhododendron molle* and its hybrids, on the other hand, tend to become thriftless and "dwindle" when grown in this region. This Chinese species comes from a climate of rainy summers and this, perhaps, accounts for its failure in the relatively dry, warm summer weather of America. Another species which does not do well in America is *Rhododendron luteum,* the Pontic azalea, which is greatly inferior to *R. calendulaceum* in this country.

Several species within the subseries Luteum merge into one another, transitional forms often being found in the wild, so that it is difficult to correctly place these borderline individuals. This is true of *Rhododendron nudiflorum* and *R. roseum,* and also obtains among such species as *R. arborescens, R. viscosum* and *R. atlanticum,* with possibly a great many more examples to be found among the southern species if investigated. All that can be done is to take the typical form of any species, as described in the literature, and regard it as a center around which these variants and natural hybrids seem to revolve.

The same condition is doubtless true of *Rhododendron japonicum* and *R. molle,* and probably occurs also between such species as *R. obtusum* and *R. Kaempferi* in another subseries. It is probably repeated many times throughout the whole genus, outside of the Azalea series.

The hybrids in the subseries Luteum are numerous and important. They are described elsewhere in this treatment, but should not be overlooked by the horticulturist. The opportunities for further improvement in fitting these hybrid races to American conditions are very great.

Rhododendron alabamense Rehder (from Alabama), syn: Azalea alabamensis Ashe. ALABAMA AZALEA. *E.* Low stoloniferous shrub, up to 3 ft. tall, good in its "best" forms. Inflor. 6–10 fls. Flowers tubular-funnel-shaped (41?), 1½ in. across, white, lemon-scented. There is a pink form. Dry woods, coastal plain and adjacent regions. Alabama. Blooms mid-May in Ala.

Rhododendron arborescens Torrey (tree-like), syn: Azalea arborescens Pursh; A. verticillata Loddiges. SMOOTH AZALEA. *A.* Height 8–20 ft. Inflor. (k). Flowers (42) 1½–2 in. across, after leaves, white, fragrant with odor like heliotrope. Bot. Cabinet t. 1632. E. United States, from Pennsylvania to Georgia and eastern Tennessee, woods in mountains and uplands.—One of the very good American species, perhaps the best native white azalea that is hardy in the North. It is distinctly an upland species, and grows chiefly on the banks of mountain streams in the Appalachian mountain regions. In cultivation it blooms at about the same time as *Rhododendron calendulaceum* or sometimes a little later. It is extremely variable and has many forms, some becoming confused with forms of *R. viscosum.* In order to emphasize the distinctions between the typical forms of *Rhododendron arborescens* and *R. viscosum,* the following table of contrasting characters, developed with the able collaboration of Mr. E. J. Alexander, is here presented. It should be borne in mind that the distinctions are made between *typical* forms of the species and does not necessarily include their variants. **X**

R. arborescens	*R. viscosum*
Habitat woods, uplands	Habitat swamps
Height 8–20 ft.	Height 1–8 ft.
Manifestly petioled	Very short petioles
Young branchlets glabrous, usually with slight bloom	Young branchlets often with appressed hairs
Leaves usually glaucous beneath	Leaves glabrous on both sides
Filaments purplish red, very long	Filaments white
Fresh flowers have scent resembling heliotrope	Fresh flowers have scent of cloves
Blooms, June, or 2–3 weeks earlier than *R. viscosum.*	Blooms July, sometimes into August.

Several forms and varieties are recognized. Two color forms are f. *rubescens* Rehder, in which the flowers, not necessarily smaller, are rose or purple with a little yellow on the upper lobe, and f. *flavescens* Rehder, which has pale yellow flowers with darker yellow blotches on the upper lobe. Variety *Richardsonii* Rehder is a smaller form with low, widely branched stems, which comes from the higher mountains. Some named forms may be natural hybrids.

Rhododendron arborescens has flowers with somewhat wider tubes than *R. viscosum* and is, in my opinion, a somewhat more showy species. Its delightful fragrance is not the least of its charms. Following *R. atlanticum* and preceding *R. viscosum* in time of bloom, it forms the backbone of the native white-flowered azaleas, and has long been appreciated by rhododendron growers in England.

Rhododendron atlanticum Rehder (from the Atlantic seaboard), syn: Azalea atlantica Ashe. COAST AZALEA. *A.* Height 18 in., stoloniferous and spreading. Inflor. (see color plate following page 142), 4–10 fls., appearing just before or with the leaves. Flowers (42), 1¼ to 1½ in. across and about as long, rarely larger, pure white, light pink or, in one form, purplish pink, with short, gland-tipped hairs on the back of the corolla. From southern Penn., southward to S. Carolina, restricted to the Coastal Plain. Most abundant in Virginia and N. Carolina, low altitudes, margins of woods.—In its best forms, this is a little gem among American azaleas, occupying a place in the subseries Luteum not unlike the position occupied by the varieties of *Rhododendron obtusum* in the Obtusum subseries. It is seldom over 18 in. tall, is often quite twiggy, is inclined to have a running root-stalk and often occurs in colonies of considerable size. In its native habitat it is quite floriferous and its flowers, delicately scented with a rose-like fragrance, are nearly as large as those of *R. roseum* and *R. calendulaceum,* and fully as big as those of *R. viscosum.* Blooming about the same time as *R. nudiflorum,* its flowers are conspicuous, because they are not hidden by leaves. White and pink forms are almost equally abundant, with transitional forms between. My personal preference is for the white form, which is most distinctive and effective. It is sometimes confused with *Rhododendron viscosum* in a low, stoloniferous form, but should be easily distinguished from this by its much earlier blooming date, its rose-like instead of clove-like fragrance and by several other features. I have found forms which I believe to be natural hybrids with *R. nudiflorum.*

Rhododendron atlanticum in cultivation is probably as hardy as *R. Kaempferi.* Plants from Virginia and North Carolina have endured the very severe winters of central New York in my experimental garden, but apparently do not want to bloom unless protected in winter, although they bloom satisfactorily at the Arnold Arboretum in Boston. Plants of the pink form from southern Pennsylvania, however, bloom well for me; hence, I believe plants from the northern limits of the range will prove best for extremely cold climates. Plants from the Carolinas, nevertheless, should be entirely satisfactory for all but the most severe climates. Not being a mountain species, *Rhododendron atlanticum* is not subjected to the cold of high altitudes, such as is found within the range of *Rhododendrons viscosum, calendulaceum, roseum, arborescens* and others, but, since it comes from a region of relatively hot summers, with occasional dry spells, it should be fairly resistant to exposure of this sort.

Rhododendron atlanticum is suggested as an excellent plant for open or shaded spots in the foreground or around the base of larger azaleas or rhododendrons. It is useful wherever dwarfness is needed. It is said to root readily from cuttings or layers and, I suspect, may also be multiplied by division. Seeds of the white form, collected in the wild, will probably produce a fair proportion of pink seedlings. To perpetuate the white forms, therefore, seed plants should be hand pollinated to other white forms to produce true-breeding seeds. I suspect that it may be propagated most easily by layering.

Several wild forms of *Rhododendron atlanticum* are recognized. A color form with pinkish purple flowers is f. *neglectum* Rehder. Variety *luteo-album* Rehder has bluish green leaves and white flowers which are yellowish in the bud. Several other variations have been noted. A form with pure white, smaller flowers, with narrower corolla lobes and a delicate appearance, is sometimes called 'Sylva.' Certain others are distinguished by pale green or pink coloration at the base of the corolla tube. Superior forms should be isolated and propagated as clones. **X**

Rhododendron austrinum Rehder (southern), syn: Azalea austrina Small. FLORIDA FLAME AZALEA. *C.* Up to 10 ft. tall. Inflor. (k). Flowers (41), about 1½ in. across, varying from light cream to yellow, orange and orange-red, with a purplish tube or sometimes with 5 purplish stripes. Blooms in early spring with expanding leaves. Scented. River banks, northern Florida and adjacent parts of Ga. and Ala. An attractive species with smallish flowers in round trusses of a dozen or more. The yellow form with orange-red base is typical. Hardy in Philadelphia.

Rhododendron Bakeri Lemmon and McKay (after Dr. W. F. Baker). Syn: R. cumberlandense Braun; A. Bakeri. CUMBERLAND AZALEA. *A.* A deciduous, late blooming hardy azalea, from 3 to 9 ft., occasionally in dwarfer forms, blooming from early June to August in various parts of its range, about June 20th in cultivation at New York. Flowers tubular funnel-shaped, in clusters of 4–7, but often borne in aggregations of 25–30 in a good-sized round rhododendron-like truss. Color mostly red or orange-red, but also pure yellow and intermediate shades. Cumberland Plateau in Kentucky and its southern extensions above 3,000 ft. through Kentucky, Tennessee, North Carolina and Georgia. Bartonia *19*:16–17 (1937).—This is a spectacular azalea in its native habitat, and is valuable horticulturally because of its round rhododendron-like trusses, its late bloom and its hardiness. It comes 2 to 3 weeks later than *R. calendulaceum,* and its flowers are a bit smaller and slimmer, suggesting that it may be a diploid, and this has been confirmed. Plants from Black Mountain, Kentucky (4,000 ft.), a selection sometimes called 'Camp's Red Azalea,' have proved hardy enough to withstand winter temperatures of −30°F. in upper New York State, but do not retain the same blood-red brilliancy of color in this low altitude which the same individuals displayed on their native mountain-top where the light was intensely bright and the air cool. The flowers became orange-red when grown at Ithaca, New York, at Boston, Massachusetts, and at Edinburgh, Scotland. For some time this species was believed to be a form of *R. calendulaceum,* but is found to be quite distinct from the latter. **X**

Rhododendron calendulaceum Torrey (like marigold), syn: Azalea calendulacea Michaux; lutea L., in part; A. flammea Bartram, nom., nud., A. aurantiaca Dietrich.

FLAME AZALEA. *A.* See color plate, following page 366. 4–10 rarely to 15 ft. tall. Inflor. (k) and (1). Flowers (42), typically orange, but varying to yellow and scarlet, orange blotch on upper lobe; about 2 in. across; sometimes with wavy margins, sometimes plain; variable in form, size and color. Discovered in N.Y. State in 1749, but ordinarily confined to the mountains from Pa., southward to Ga. Cumberland Mts., Appalachian provinces.—The most showy and one of the most notable American azaleas; a parent of the Ghent hybrid race. Although some of the best of the Ghent hybrid clones have flowers somewhat larger than those of *Rhododendron calendulaceum,* the best of these wild flame azaleas are as good as the average of the hybrids and nearly equal to the best. At the same time, the native sorts are much better adapted to the American climate. The color range is so great that individuals may be found in practically any intermediate shade between light yellow and scarlet red, while various blends and color patterns are not uncommon. There is also considerable variation in the shape of the flower, the frilling of its edges and the way it is borne, either in round, compact, rhododendron-like trusses or in loose, scattered clusters. Intermediate colors may be lemon to dark yellows, tawny, apricot, salmon, deep flesh color, pinkish, and the brilliant shades of orange, vermilion and scarlet. Occasionally the flowers will have dark stripes down the midrib of the petals. The upper lobe is generally most highly colored. The yellow form has been called var. *croceum* Sweet and the vermilion form var. *auranticum* Rehder.

With all these variations, it is apparent that many very beautiful and interesting forms may be found among the wild plants of *Rhododendron calendulaceum.* At present, very few have been preserved, named and propagated as clonal varieties, but there is no reason why forms that are notable should not be perpetuated and multiplied by grafting or cuttings, to be sold in the trade after the manner of hybrids. In my opinion, such varieties should be developed to replace the Ghent hybrids for use in the eastern United States, where few of the Ghent varieties are able to thrive. I believe that fully half the Ghent colors and forms can be found in the native *Rhododendron calendulaceum,* and that, by hybridization and the use of such other species as *R. roseum, R. arborescens* and *R. viscosum,* other improvements can be made which will lengthen the blooming season and add new colors, to the ultimate end of producing nearly all the Ghent effects in these American strains which are better adapted to our climate.

In its present state, *Rhododendron calendulaceum* is an exceedingly useful plant. It follows *R. roseum* in succession of bloom and usually precedes *R. arborescens* and *R. viscosum.* It grows abundantly in the mountains of North Carolina where whole mountain sides are said to be covered with it, making a spectacular sight when in bloom. It grows well, is hardy and is relatively cheap. It should be more generally used. **X**

Rhododendron canescens Sweet (hoary), syn: Azalea canescens Michaux; A. bicolor Pursh. FLORIDA PINXTER. *C.* Slender shrub to 12–15 ft. Inflor. (k). Flowers (41) 1½ in. across, pinkish, nearly white, with pink tube, glandular on outside. Stamens prominent and very long. On the Coastal Plain, South Carolina to Florida and westward. Not in the Blue Ridge or Piedmont regions. Low altitudes, stream banks.—This species has been confused with a bright pink azalea, presumably a form of *Rhododendron roseum,* which grows in the Piedmont region of Virginia, sometimes called the Piedmont Azalea. *Rhododendron canescens* is neither so hardy nor so beautiful as the former. Its flowers are smaller and are of a light washy pink or impure white, much like some forms of *R. nudiflorum*. It may prove useful in the lower south, but should be avoided for planting in the north. The name PIEDMONT AZALEA, applied to *R. canescens,* is a misnomer and should be dropped. Its glandular corolla tube is one distinguishing mark from *Rhododendron nudiflorum*. Variety *candidum* Rehder (A. candida Small) has white flowers and leaves that are glaucous beneath. Some forms are excellent.

Rhododendron japonicum Suringer (from Japan), syn: Azalea japonica Gray. JAPANESE AZALEA. *A.* A stoutly branched shrub to 6 ft. Inflor. (j), with 6–12 fls. Flowers (24) large, 2–3 in. across, 2 in. long, orange, with variations from light yellow to brick-red, sometimes salmon-rose. Central and northern Japan, in open country.—This is a large-flowered, showy azalea of remarkable hardiness and of great potential usefulness. It is one of the few foreign azaleas which can accommodate itself to the cold and somewhat alkaline conditions of central New York and appear as happy as the native *Rhododendron roseum*. Moreover, it is a species of great variability in color, with showy flowers which, without hybridization, produce seedlings encompassing most of the color range of the Mollis hybrids. It grows to 6 ft. and seems to stand open situations very well. Because of its hardiness and adaptability to American conditions, it is infinitely better suited than its close relative, *Rhododendron molle,* for growing in the United States. It grows well in the Arnold Arboretum at Boston, in the Rochester, N.Y. park system and at Cornell University, where the climatic conditions are severe. It grows equally well in the vicinity of New York City and Philadelphia.

Like the flame azalea, *Rhododendron japonicum* combines the anthocyanin and yellow pigments in its flowers and has a tremendous color range. The form known as var. *aureum* Wilson is a beautiful spectrum yellow. A wealth of other color variations may be found among seedlings, the colors embracing all the intermediate shades from yellow, through light and dark orange, salmon, apricot, and many delicate "art" shades, to vermilion. Occasionally forms are found which have a definite rosy cast, the lighter forms being quite rose-colored with a touch of salmon in certain areas and the darker forms being a fiery rosy red, similar to the color of *Rhododendron Kaempferi*. Occasionally a dull brick-red or tawny scarlet is produced. Variation also exists in the markings and the size and width of the corolla lobes. Its typical color is rosy orange.

Rhododendron japonicum is a rather rapid grower from seed. Superior forms should be named, grafted and disseminated as clonal varieties. It should be generally used in America to replace *Rhododendron molle,* with which it has until recently been confused. The morphological differences between the two species seem to be negligible, but there is a great difference in hardiness under New England conditions. Presumably there is little of *R. molle* remaining in the so-called Mollis hybrids now growing in America, the main influence being that of *R. japonicum*.

Rhododendron japonicum blooms before the leaves expand, usually May 20–30 in New York and Boston, at the same time as *R. roseum*. **X**

Rhododendron luteum Sweet (yellow), syn: R. flavum G. Don; Azalea pontica L. PONTIC AZALEA. *A.* 2–12 ft. tall, densely branched. Inflor. (k) or (l) with 7–12 fls. Flowers (42) bright yellow 1½–2 in. across. Bot. Mag. t. 433. Eastern Europe to the Caucasus.—This European species, introduced in the early days, has had much to do in the development of the Ghent hybrids. It is not sufficiently hardy to withstand American conditions north of Philadelphia, but is a good plant where it can be grown. For many years it has been used as a grafting stock for the Ghent hybrids. For American conditions, it does not equal *Rhododendron calendulaceum,* but may be considered superior elsewhere. One form, var. *macranthum* Wilson, is said to have flowers nearly 2½ in. across. The species is somewhat fragrant. **X**

Rhododendron molle G. Don (soft), syn: R. sinense Sweet; Azalea mollis Blume; A. sinensis Loddiges. CHINESE AZALEA. *A.* 1–4 ft. tall. Inflor. (j). Flowers (24) yellow, with a large greenish blotch, separated into dots, 2–2½ in. across. Brit. Flow. Gard. ser. *3*: t. 290 (1829). Eastern China, on open hillsides, among coarse grasses and shrubs and in thin pine woods.—This species, very much like *Rhododendron japonicum* in floral characters, is, however, considerably less hardy in America. It has a smaller and less bristly calyx, longer stamens and the winter buds are pubescent while those of *R. japonicum* are smooth. The leaves differ in that those of the Chinese species are larger and have a soft, nearly white, pubescence on their under sides, while those of *R. japonicum* are smaller and smooth underneath when mature. It comes from a climate of rainy summers and winters that are less severe than those of the northeastern United States. Its flowers are commonly yellow, while those of *R. japonicum* are rarely so. Wilson says that it lacks stamina as a garden plant. It makes an excellent pot plant and forces well. It is, with *R. japonicum,* a parent of the Mollis hybrid azaleas, but this race would probably be benefited, for American conditions, if it could be totally freed of the influence of *R. molle.* The true species was introduced into western gardens in the early days and has had a complicated history. Some of its hybrid strains have been given artificial names as cultivar groups: *Rhododendron Kosterianum* Schneider, *R. albicans* Waterer, *R. mixtum* Wilson, and certain Azaleodendrons. For many years, *R. molle* was known by its synonym, R. sinense. **X**

Rhododendron nudiflorum Torrey (naked flowers), syn: Azalea nudiflora L. PINXTERBLOOM. *A.* Much branched shrub 3–6, rarely 10 ft. tall. Inflor. (1). Flowers (41 or 42) 1½ in. across, light pink or impure whitish, with narrow tube dark purplish red at base. Fragrance very sweet, but insipid, almost oppressive, not spicy. Blooms late May in North. Bot. Reg. *2*: 120 (1816). Introd. 1725. Mass. to N.C. from the coast to the mountains, west to Ky. and Tenn. Dry, open woods. —Perhaps the most common azalea of the northeastern United States, of which *Rhododendron roseum* is thought by some to be a variety. (See color plate facing page 143). Transitional forms of nearly all degrees between the two species can be found. Typical *Rhododendron nudiflorum,* however, is greatly inferior to *R. roseum* in color, fragrance and probably in habit of growth and the flowers of *R. roseum* are sometimes slightly larger. *Rhododendron nudiflorum* is not recommended as a garden plant when *R. roseum* can be obtained. The two species cover practically the same range and are similar in hardiness and time of bloom. The most noticeable difference between the two species is in color, fragrance and pubescence. All these characters break down, however, in dealing with intermediate types and should be considered as effective only when plainly typical forms are compared. The color of the flowers of *R. nudiflorum* is usually a pale pink, often with a suggestion of purple and in the lighter forms it becomes washy in which it is neither a blush pink nor a white. The tube of the flower is marked at the base by a rather dark, dull red or plum color, giving a considerable contrast to the lighter upper portion. The stamens are very long. *Rhododendron roseum* is more evenly colored, usually with a brighter rose pink, free from purplish tinge, and the tube is not so dark at the base, being simply a darker shade of the rose color of the petals. The fragrance of *R. nudiflorum* is oppressively sweet without any of the spicy, clovelike odor which is characteristically a feature of *R. roseum*. A few contrasting features of the two species are set down as follows:

R. nudiflorum	*R. roseum*
Flowers light purplish pink or whitish	Color clear rose pink
Petals (corolla lobes) slightly narrower than in *R. roseum*	Petals (corolla lobes) slightly wider than in *R. nudiflorum*
Corolla-tube purplish red at base; rather narrow	Corolla-tube deep rose at base; wider than in *R. nudiflorum*
Outside of tube not glandular	Corolla-tube glandular outside
Fragrance sickly sweet	Fragrance spicy, clovelike
Leaves and winter buds only slightly pubescent.	Leaves densely grayish-villous beneath; winter buds pubescent.

A variety known as var. *glandiferum* Rehder, with glandular corolla-tube and pedicels, is recorded. Other variations have been mentioned, including a double-flower form. Forma *album* Sweet has white flowers.

Rhododendron oblongifolium Millais (oblong leaves), syn: Azalea oblongifolia Small. *C.* Up to 6 ft. tall. Inflor. (1?). Flowers (41?) 1¼ in. across, white. S.E. Texas, Arkansas to Oklahoma, in moist sandy woods or along streams.—This species belongs to the eastern group of American species, and is its most western representative, ranging west of the Mississippi River. It is closely related to *Rhododendron viscosum* and *R. serrulatum*, but blooms earlier.

Rhododendron occidentale A. Gray (western), syn: Azalea occidentalis Torrey & Gray. *A.* 8 ft. tall. Inflor. (j), 6–12 fls. Flowers (74) 1½–2½ in. across, white with a yellow blotch on the upper lobe; blooms when the leaves are expanding. Bot. Mag. t. 5005. Introd. 1850. From southern Oregon to southern California, in mountains by brooks, up to 5,800 ft.—A beautiful species from the West Coast, with good sized flowers. This is the only azalea west of the Rocky Mountains in America, where it extends over a long north and south range and exhibits great latitude in time of bloom. Good specimens appear near the ocean on the southern Oregon coast where they bloom about May 15. This is a very handsome azalea, too little known outside its native habitat. The wild American species bears little resemblance to the form (clone?) under this name that was formerly produced in Holland. This, I suspect, was an old hybrid. The species most closely related to it is *Rhododendron calendulaceum*. It exhibits much variation. Its flowers are slightly larger than those of the other American species. It is usually white, with yellow blotch, but sometimes pink forms appear. It has been found to be tender in the

Northeast, but is rated as hardy in England and has been used in the development of the Ghent hybrid race. Were it not for its comparative tenderness, it would be one of the finest of the American azaleas. Its autumn foliage is highly colored. Used on the west coast. Var. *sonomense* Rehder is smaller, with rose colored flowers and narrow leaves. **X**

Rhododendron prunifolium Millais (plum leaved), syn: Azalea prunifolia Small. PLUM-LEAVED AZALEA. *B.* Slender shrub to 8 ft. tall. Inflor. (1?) 4–5 fls. Flowers (42?) 1½–2 in. across, orange, blooming in July. S.W. Georgia and E. Alabama, moist woods in shady ravines and on the banks of streams.—This summer-blooming azalea is not crimson as formerly described, but more often apricot or orange-red. Its flowers are borne in clusters of 4–5. It is mainly valuable for its late flowering. Although a specimen is reported as surviving at the Arnold Arboretum in Boston, this species has not yet been accepted as reliably hardy.

Rhododendron roseum Rehder (rosy), syn: R. nudiflorum var. roseum Wiegand; Azalea prinophylla Small. ROSESHELL AZALEA. (syn: MAYFLOWER AZALEA; PIEDMONT AZALEA). *A.* Much-branched shrub. Inflor. (1), 2–8 ft. tall, rarely up to 15 ft., often as broad as tall. Flowers (42) about 1½ in. across, usually bright pink, sometimes pale, with pink tube darker at base but not purplish; corolla-tube glandular outside, rather wide and short. Very fragrant, with clove-like scent. Blooms late May in North, before or just as leaves unfold. New Hampshire, Vermont, New York and Quebec, western New England, Pennsylvania to southern Virginia; westward to Ohio, southern Illinois, western Tennessee. Centers in Virginia. Dry woods and edges of swamps, in acid soil sometimes underlain with limestone. See color plate, page 143.—This azalea, long regarded as *Rhododendron nudiflorum* and also confused with *R. canescens,* is widely distributed in the northern United States. From the horticultural standpoint, it is far superior to either of the relatives mentioned. It is exceedingly hardy and also displays more than ordinary tolerance toward conditions of greater alkalinity than are commonly relished by the other azaleas. Its flowers are more showy than those of *R. nudiflorum* or *R. canescens,* being relatively wide of limb and short of tube, with a sprightly rose color, free from any bluish or "dirty" appearance. Its delightful fragrance increases its value as a garden subject. It endures exposure to sun and wind better than some other azaleas. Transitional forms between *Rhododendron roseum* and *R. nudiflorum* exhibit intermediate characters of almost every degree. The contrasting characters of the typical forms of each species are set down under my discussion of *R. nudiflorum* (see page 252). The differences between *R. roseum* and *R. canescens* are very distinct, but, because these species are confused in commerce, I shall briefly set down their contrasting points in a few outstanding features, as follows: **X**

R. roseum	*R. canescens*
Flowers type (42)	Flowers type (41)
Color bright rose pink	Color pale pink or whitish
Stamens 2 × length of tube	Stamens 3 × length of tube
Hardy in the North	Very tender in the North
Habitat Northeast and Va., not on Coastal Plain.	Habitat Carolinas to Fla., exclusively Coastal Plain.

Rhododendron serrulatum Millais (with small teeth), syn: Azalea serrulata Small. SOUTHERN SWAMP AZALEA. *B*. Shrub to 20 ft. tall or less. Inflor. (k). Flowers (41) slender, 1¼ in. long, white, very sweet scented, sticky on the outside. Florida, wet hammocks and swampy places, extending to central Georgia and westward to eastern Louisiana, along the Coastal Plain.—This is valuable for the South as it blooms from June to August, but it has little usefulness for the North, because it is not hardy. In many respects this species resembles *Rhododendron viscosum,* from which it may be distinguished by its serrulate (toothed) leaves and red-brown twigs. A form with densely soft pubescence beneath the leaves is called f. *molliculum* Rehder, while a variety with silky pubescent winter buds is var. *georgianum* Rehder.

Rhododendron speciosum Sweet (showy), syn: Azalea speciosa Willdenow; A. fulva Michaux, nom. nud.; R. flammeum Michaux. OCONEE AZALEA. *B*. 1–6 ft. tall. Inflor. (k), 6–15 fls. Flowers (41) 1½–2 in. across, scarlet or bright red, with a large orange blotch on the upper lobe; blossoms appearing with the leaves. Central Georgia, in open dry woods and on sand hills, blooming about May 1 in its native habitat.—This species was in cultivation in Europe more than a century ago under the name *Azalea nudiflora* var. *coccinea* and may have had a part in the early development of the Ghent hybrids. It has long been confused with red forms of *Rhododendron calendulaceum,* from which it differs in certain of its corolla-tube and leaf characters, as well as in geographical situation and hardiness. The flowers are said to be always scarlet or bright red to orange-apricot. Plants have proved tender at the Arnold Arboretum, but have survived in southern Pennsylvania, although they refuse to bloom in that locality. It is obviously a plant for the South and cannot be expected to succeed at Philadelphia or northward. It would probably prove valuable as an ornamental plant for a wide area in the South if grown from seed by nurserymen. In the North the red forms of *R. calendulaceum* should be substituted for similar effects. Skinner says that the darkest red forms occur in the Georgia lowlands along the Savannah River.

Rhododendron viscosum Torrey (sticky), syn: Azalea viscosa Linnaeus. SWAMP AZALEA; SWAMP HONEYSUCKLE. *A*. See color plate, following page 78. Height up to 8 ft. Inflor. (l), 4–9 fls. appearing after the leaves are fully developed. Flowers (41) slender, white, rarely pink, about 1 in. across, sticky to the touch, very fragrant with a clove-like scent. Widely distributed in the eastern United States, from S.W. Maine to South Carolina and west to Ohio and Tennessee; in swamps, both along Coastal Plain and on mountains.—This species blooms the latest of any of the American azaleas and frequently has flowers in the North until the middle of August. Its usual flowering time is July when it appears after the other azaleas have gone and furnishes an interesting and delightful feature for the azalea garden. Its value is greatly enhanced by its rather strong spicy fragrance, not unpleasant, which scents the air around it. It has served a useful purpose in transmitting to hybrid races some of its fragrance and late blooming qualities, thereby lengthening the blooming season of the Ghent hybrids and others. While its slender, white flowers are not showy, especially since they are borne after the foliage is big enough to hide many of them, they are, nevertheless, of considerable ornamental value, being well formed, delicate in appearance and of an unobtrusive color. The foliage and branchlets are usually smooth and covered with a whitish bloom which gives the vegetative parts of the plant a bluish appearance, a not unattractive feature when properly placed in the landscape design, but yet not blue enough to appear prominent or exotic.

The species is extremely variable and, covering a wide geographical range, numerous forms and varieties are to be found. Sometimes it assumes a low, stoloniferous habit, like that of *Rhododendron atlanticum,* from which it may be distinguished by its later blooming date and other features. This form might be very valuable for foreground planting. A form with pink or purplish flowers appears not infrequently and is called f. *rhodanthum* Rehder. In some instances this form is a bright pink, while in others it is more purple than any other American azalea I have seen, except *R. canadense.* Some of the pink forms are rather different from the ordinary pink azaleas of other species and are attractive; others are unattractive. A variety with green leaves, not covered with bloom as in the type, is var. *glaucum* Torrey, BLUELEAF AZALEA. Variety *nitidum* A. Gray has a dwarfish habit and often pinkish flowers and brighter leaves. Var. *tomentosum* Rehder has leaves pubescent beneath. Var. *hispidum* Voss has hispid pedicels and branchlets. Var. *montanum* Rehder has pubescent winter buds. A form of *montanum* with bluish green leaves and more or less pink flowers, carmine in bud, is called f. *coerulescens* Rehder and is said to be one of the handsomest forms of *R. viscosum* as an ornamental shrub. Another form with carmine buds is f. *rubescens* Rehder.

In discussing *Rhododendron arborescens,* I presented a series of contrasting characters distinguishing this species and *R. viscosum* (see p. 246). X

It is difficult to estimate the extent to which *Rhododendron viscosum* has played a part in the Ghent hybrid race of azaleas. It was introduced into cultivation in 1738, along with *R. calendulaceum* and *R. nudiflorum,* and the records show one or two early crosses. Its part in the Ghent race is apparent in certain late-blooming, fragrant or viscid varieties. In 1842 Anthony Waterer crossed *R. molle* ♀ × *R. viscosum* ♂. The progeny of this combination has been given the artificial specific name of *R. viscosepalum,* two of its best clones being 'Daviesii' and 'Altaclarensis.' I have crossed *R. japonicum* ♀ × *R. viscosum* ♂ with excellent results.

SUBSERIES NIPPONICUM
(Section *Viscidula* Matsumura and Nakai)

This subseries contains only one species, a little known plant from the mountains of central Japan. It has very distinctive small white tubular flowers and large leaves not unlike those of *Rhododendron Schlippenbachii.*

Rhododendron nipponicum Matsumura (from Japan). *B.* Bushy shrub 3–6 ft. tall. Inflor. (w), 6–15 fls., expanding with or after the leaves; viscid. Flowers (3) tubular or tubular-campanulate with shorter style and stamens included, ¾ in. long, white; nodding. Species Rhodo. p. 74. Central Japan, in the mountains.—A little known species with flowers unique for the Azalea series.

Subseries Obtusum
(Section *Tsutsutsi* G. Don)

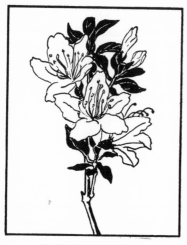

R. MUCRONATUM

This subseries contains 43 species, many of which are rather twiggy, much branched shrubs. They are mostly said to be rather low in habit of growth, but certain of them will, in time and under favorable conditions, attain a considerable size, as witness the famous plants at the Magnolia Gardens, South Carolina.

In the group there are perhaps no members quite so hardy as certain of the most northern members of the Luteum subseries, but several are, nevertheless, of sufficient hardiness to grow very satisfactorily at Boston, Mass., and Rochester, N.Y. Certain others are comparatively tender, such as the members of the so-called "Indian azalea" race, much grown for forcing under glass, all of which belong within this subseries.

The azaleas of Japan are, to a very large extent, members of this subseries. Many of them have been in cultivation for a long time and variant forms, perpetuated as clonal varieties, are relatively common. These clones are not always hybrids, but may be merely special color forms or floral variations.

In horticultural importance the leading species of this subseries are *Rhododendron Kaempferi, R. indicum, R. obtusum, R. mucronatum* and the hybrid race known as the "Indian azaleas."

In the North, the most valuable species for outdoor culture is *Rhododendron Kaempferi* which, because of its relative hardiness, fine color and prolific bloom, should be regarded as one of the most valuable and beautiful hardy azaleas in existence. In certain severe places, it may not be quite hardy enough to bloom abundantly. The type species *R. indicum, R. mucronatum* and the hardier forms of *R. obtusum* are generally useful as far north as New York City, but need protection in exposed places at that latitude. *Rhododendron poukhanense, R. pulchrum* clone 'Maxwellii' and possibly *R. Tschonoskii* may be considered as within the possibility of satisfactory outdoor culture at Boston or its equivalent. Certain lesser known clones of Japanese azaleas, of which there are many, may prove upon trial to be hardy in cold regions. The other species of this subseries, so far as they have been tested, have proved either half-hardy or tender. Several are not yet known to cultivation in this country.

It should be emphasized that variation within the species is pronounced within this subseries. One can not always judge, from the nature of a type specimen, what the characters of the other members of the species may be. Races or clones, differing considerably from the average in hardiness, color or other character, appear repeatedly. Hardy variants occur in the species *Rhododendron indicum, R. pulchrum* and *R. obtusum*. Color variations are numerous. Double forms are not infrequent. Variegation occurs sometimes. Emphasis, therefore, must be placed upon the individual rather than upon the race or species. Fortunately, the members of this subseries are rather easy to propagate from cuttings, so that when superior individuals appear they may easily be perpetuated as clonal varieties. This doubtless accounts for the fact that so many horticultural forms have been perpetuated since time immemorial, chiefly in Japan and China.

Yellow flower color does not occur in this subseries. The flowers are characterized by typical anthocyanin pigmentation, running through the delicate pinks to rose, crimson and lilac colors. White forms are relatively abundant. Markings in the form of spots or blotches are common. Chimeras occur as flakes and segments in the Indian azaleas and related forms.

Two kinds of leaves (dimorphism) occur on the plants of this subseries. These are the so-called "winter" or evergreen leaves, which are usually small and narrow, and the broader "summer" leaves which do not persist after cold weather begins.* These dimorphic leaves represent an interesting transition stage between the deciduous and the truly evergreen members of the genus. Some of the hardy species, deciduous in the North, will retain all their leaves if grown in the greenhouse or in a warm climate. This character is so subject to environmental conditions that it is a poor feature to use for classification. *Rhododendron Kaempferi* also becomes genetically variable in its foliage, some individuals occurring which are inherently predisposed toward evergreen-ness and *vice versa*.

The members of the subseries Obtusum hybridize readily if crossed to species within the subseries, but are not so amenable when combined with other species outside the group. There are, however, a number of wide combinations on record. Perhaps the direction of greatest promise in future breeding lies in the selection and development of forms within the subseries which will be better adapted to American and European conditions of culture. Selective breeding of this sort offers greater possibilities than the production of hybrids from wide crosses and the natural variation existing in the group furnishes unusual advantages for this work. Varieties like the "Indian azaleas," if more hardy, would become useful over a wide area. Also, the improvement of the existing

* These two forms of leaves are shown on the color plates of *R. Kaempferi* and *R. obtusum*.

hardy forms by the addition of better colors or improvements in size or form are projects entirely within the possibility of realization. There is no reason why important advances may not be made and several have recently occurred.

The Western world has scarcely noted the full range of uses to which the various Japanese azaleas may be put. Many of the hardy sorts are of a low, twiggy, compact habit, extremely useful where ground-cover shrubs of one and one-half to two feet are desired. As foreground plantings or dwarf specimens they may be clipped, a custom not uncommon in Japan.* Upon occasion, certain of the larger species have been utilized as hedge plants. For naturalistic plantings they have a wide diversity of usage. Several would be useful in rock gardens. E. H. Wilson tells of seeing whole hillsides red with *Rhododendron Simsii* along the Yangtze River in China; it seems not improbable that regions could be found in this country where this species would be useful in a limited way. Millions of plants of *R. Kaempferi* occur along the margins of woods in Japan. Despite the fact that the American azaleas are unexcelled for certain purposes, there is yet room for the azaleas of the Far East.

Rhododendron annamense Rehder (from Annam), *F.* Flowers 1½ in. long, rose-purple. Annam.—The southernmost azalea. Related to *R. hainanense,* but with smaller flowers and leaves.

Rhododendron atrovirens Franchet (dark green). Large shrub or small tree. Inflor. 2–4 fls. Flowers 1–1½ in. across, 1¼ in. long, red with darker spots. Yunnan.—An imperfectly known species.

Rhododendron boninense Nakai (from Bonin). Spreading shrub to 6 ft. Flowers 1¾–2 in. long and same across, white. Bonin Islands.—A presumably tender species with large white flowers and pubescent shoots.

Rhododendron breviperulatum Hayata (with short buds). Much branched shrub. Flowers funnelform, about ¾ in. long, color not recorded. Formosa.—An imperfectly known species, probably tender.

Rhododendron chrysocalyx Léveillé & Vaniot in Fedde Repert., *2*:113 (1906).—Wilson in Jour. Arnold Arb. *6*: 200 (1925).—It belongs near *R. Mariae.*

Rhododendron Chunii Fang (after Prof. W. Y. Chun). A shrub presently unintroduced; up to 6 feet tall; flowers lilac with dark purple spots on upper lobe. Jour. Bot. Soc. China *2*:615 (1935); also Sunyatsenia *7*:1 (1948). From Kwangtung, China.

Rhododendron hainanense Merrill (from Hainan). Shrub with many erect twiggy branches, height not given. Flowers funnelform 1–1½ in. long and broad, red.

* See halftone plate illustrating this usage.

Eastern China.—A distinct species, related to *R. Nakaharai* and *R. Kanehirai,* but not in cultivation. Probably not hardy.

Rhododendron indicum Sweet (Indian), numerous synonyms: Azalea indica L.; A. macrantha Bunge. MACRANTHA AZALEA. Not of the Indian azalea race, which is more tender and usually grown in greenhouses, see p. 191. *C.* Up to 6 ft. tall, but usually much lower and sometimes prostrate, often densely branched. Inflor. (0), 1–2 fls. Flowers (45) 2–2½ in. across, deep rose-red or scarlet. Bot. Reg. *20*: t. 1700 (1834). Southern Japan, in open country or banks of rocky streams.—This Japanese species which was accidentally misnamed the INDIAN AZALEA is quite different from the INDIAN AZALEA of the florists or that of southern gardens. It is also distinct from the so-called 'Indica Alba' (*R. mucronatum*). It is a low, late-blooming species, which cannot be forced in the greenhouse, but in some forms considerably hardier than the *R. Simsii* hybrids (the INDIAN AZALEAS of the trade) and a very attractive garden plant. It is, according to Wilson, very like the clone in the American trade named 'J. T. Lovett,' and is as hardy as *R. obtusum* clone 'Amoenum.' It blooms in late June or early July. It is a good foreground plant for moist, mild regions. Several forms are recognized. A white-flowered form is f. *hakatashiro* Millais, and one with salmon-red flowers, whitish at the base is f. *tanimanoyuki* Millais. Perhaps the best-known form is the clonal variety 'Balsaminaeflorum' Nichols, the BALSAM AZALEA, which is a little plant with double red flowers, about the color of *R. Kaempferi,* and which will survive, if protected, north of New York City and sometimes in the vicinity of Boston. It is a handsome little plant, of slow growth, suitable for foregrounds and for rockeries. In Japan it is known as Komanyo-satsuki. A similar form, but less double, is f. *kinnozai* Millais. An old form with red and white striped flowers is f. *variegatum* De Candolle. It blooms irregularly the year around and was a prolific parent of early hybrids prior to 1850. Two abnormal forms in Japan are f. *polypetalum* Wilson, with a petaloid calyx and no corolla ('Kin-no-zai') and f. *laciniatum* Wilson ('Shide-satsuki') with a laciniate corolla. A form with thicker leaves and flowers with very wavy margins is var. *crispiflorum* Schneider. A number of other forms have been recognized. Var. *eriocarpum* Wilson belongs here. **X**

Rhododendron Kaempferi Planchon (after E. Kaempfer, Dutch merchant-adventurer, who in 1690 introduced various Japanese plants), syn: R. obtusum var. Kaempferi Wilson; R. scabrum var. Kaempferi Nakai; Azalea Kaempferi André. TORCH AZALEA. *A.* A loosely branched shrub to 8 ft., averaging 3–5 ft. tall. Inflor. (n), 1–3 fls. Flowers (46), 1½–2 in. across, bright red, usually with a salmon tinge, 5 stamens. Dimorphic leaves, all becoming deciduous in cold climates. Central and northern Japan, thickets and edges of forests.—This azalea, which has been known under the botanical name of *Rhododendron obtusum* var. *Kaempferi* Wilson, but which has persisted in the trade as *Azalea Kaempferi,* I am relisting by its former name, *Rhododendron Kaempferi*. Although, according to Wilson and Rehder (1921), the typical form is quite distinct from *Rhododendron obtusum,* intermediate forms exist which link the two. This, it seems to me, is the same situation existing between the two American azaleas *Rhododendron nudiflorum* and *R. roseum,* with possible parallels elsewhere. Where Wilson and Rehder place *R. Kaempferi* in the same species with *R. obtusum,* they make two separate species of the American sorts, *R. nudiflorum* and *R. roseum.* To be consistent, one should treat both situations alike. Bailey, in *Hortus,* has done this by classifying each pair as a single species and variety. I feel that the natural relationship, as well as the one most useful in practical horticulture, is the classification of these as separate species. Intermediate forms must have existed in the past between many other species. The fact that these have persisted while others have disappeared should not, in my opinion, bar the main central groupings from specific rank.

Rhododendron Kaempferi is one of the most beautiful and useful of hardy azaleas. It was first introduced to western gardens by Professor C. S. Sargent who brought seeds from Japan to the Arnold Arboretum in 1892 and it is undoubtedly one of the most valuable foreign plants ever cultivated in New England. Its color is absolutely distinct from the red forms of any other hardy species, although some of the red forms of *R. japonicum* approach it. The flowers of *R. Kaempferi* might be described as carmine-pink or scarlet-pink, but not rose-pink. It is not an intense color, but it is a vivid color, with no trace of crimson or no bluish hue about it. It fades easily, but in fading it does not become purplish, as other flowers frequently do, but becomes whitish or yellowish instead. The color might perhaps be described as having a salmon tinge. It is a very clear color and considered highly attractive.

In the North *Rhododendron Kaempferi* is entirely deciduous, but on Long Island and southward certain individuals appear occasionally which are almost or quite evergreen. I am not certain as to the' hardiness of these semi-evergreen individuals. Plants of the ordinary type are entirely hardy at Boston and Rochester but they do not withstand the winter climate at Ithaca or in my garden where conditions are somewhat more severe. They should be regarded as tender in places where the winter temperature descends to $-10°$ or $-15°$F. It is to be hoped that a hardier strain, coming from a colder part of Japan, may be introduced. Elsewhere, they grow vigorously and bloom abundantly, making a great show of color when in full bloom about May 30th. There is an unusual amount of variation among seedlings in the time of bloom, with the result that, in a collection of mixed seedlings, it is possible to find some plants in bloom over a period of nearly a month—an exceptionally long time for one species to show flowers—by reason of the succession of early and late-blooming individuals. This fact leads one to believe that an even greater season of bloom might be obtainable by selective breeding to produce extra early and late blooming plants. If a series of early, mid-season and late varieties of fine quality were selected, named and propagated as clonal varieties, such a combination would be valuable for use in a group planting where continuous bloom over a long season was desired. Where mixed seedlings are used, one expects to find some variation but he can not rely upon obtaining a complete series of early, mid-season and late forms. With clones, however, this could be assured.

Rhododendron Kaempferi makes a plant about the size of *R. roseum,* but slightly broader and not quite so tall. Good plants in cultivation average around 4 or 5 ft. high. Compared with the American species, its flowers are shallow, with a somewhat wider petal, but not so very much broader across than good specimens of *R. roseum* or *R. calendulaceum.* They tend to be borne singly or in twos or threes, rather than in clusters of greater size, but are quite evenly distributed over the plant and are very numerous. In fact, a plant of *R. Kaempferi* in full bloom is fairly covered with flowers.

Owing to its tendency to fade quickly under the sunlight, *Rhododendron Kaempferi* should be planted in a position where it does not get the full sun all day. In other words, a condition of semi-shade furnishes probably the best situation. Wilson recommends conifers and other evergreen plants as furnishing the ideal setting for *R. Kaempferi,* in which I heartily concur, as this dark background makes the brilliant color of the azaleas show off to best advantage.

Several forms are recognized. A white-flowered form, unknown in this country, is f. *album* Nakai. A strain which departs from the type in color and produces seedlings of variable hue, ranging from pale pink or mauve to purple and magenta, is known as var. *multicolor* Bowers, n. comb. A form which is double, with petaloid stamens and pistil, presumably sterile, is var. *plenum* Nakai, of which there is more than one clone. Another form has hose-in-hose flowers and a petaloid calyx and is called var. *Komatsui* Nakai. A queer form with monstrous flowers is f. *monstrosum* Bowers, n. comb., which has white, hose-in-hose flowers, a petaloid calyx, abortive stamens and an abnormal pistil. It is probably sterile and a clone. A curiosity, without garden value, is f. *cryptopetalum* Bowers, n. comb., which has practically no corolla, and is known in Japan as 'Kinshibe-tsutsuji.' A form with purple flowers and more stamens, up to 10, is var. *mikawanum* Makino and is an occasional variant from the type. In Japan it is called the MURASAKI YAMA-TSUTSUJI (purple hill azalea). X

Rhododendron Kanehirai Wilson (after R. Kanehira, Japanese botanist). Probably tender. Low shrub, sometimes attaining 6 ft. Inflor. (o?). Flowers (45?), ¾–1 in. across, carmine-red to scarlet; 10 stamens. Formosa, in mountains.— Closely related to *R. indicum,* of which it may be a Formosan variety with 10 stamens instead of 5.

Rhododendron kiusianum Makino (from Kyushu Mountains, Japan). Syn.: R. ob-tusum f. japonicum Wilson. KIRISHIMA AZALEA. *A.* A low twiggy shrub up to 3 ft. with dimorphic leaves, semi-evergreen. Inflor. (p), 2–5. Flowers (46), purple to deep rose and scarlet, rarely white; about 1 in. across. Bot. Mag. Tokyo *28*:174 (1914). Mt. Kirishima, Japan.—This is thought to be one of the wild species from which the Kurume azaleas have descended, probably through hybridization with other wild forms of *R. Kaempferi* and *R. obtusum.* These all hybridize freely with one another and intergradient forms are found in nature. A Japanese botanist, Hara, states concerning the Kurume azaleas that some forms are derived from *R. Kaempferi,* some from *R. kiusianum,* and a few from *R. obtusum,* along with other complicated hybrids between these species.

Rhododendron kwangtungense Merr. & Chun. (from Kwangtung). Flowers white.

Rhododendron lasiostylum Hayata (woolly style). Probably tender. 3 ft. tall. Flowers 1 in. across, pink. Leaves dimorphic. Formosa.—A pretty pink flowered species not in cultivation and probably tender.

Rhododendron linearifolium Siebold & Zuccarini (linear shaped leaves), syn: R. macrosepalum var. linearifolium Makino. SPIDER AZALEA. *B* or *C*. Height to 3 ft. Flowers (75) pink, cut into very narrow corolla lobes. Leaves narrow and strap-shaped. Bot. Mag. t. 5769. A Japanese garden plant, unknown in the wild.—This apparently abnormal garden plant is rather generally conceded to be merely a monstrous individual, perpetuated as a horticultural variety and not a true natural species. In all probability it is entitled to no more distinction than that of a clone, but its true status in this respect remains to be proved. It survives at the New York Botanical Garden, but is injured during the winter and seems to be at its northern limit there. The plant is mainly useful as a curiosity and, in my opinion, is not worthy of cultivation considering its doubtful hardiness and unattractive appearance.

Variety *macrosepalum* Makino (with large sepals), syn: Rhododendron macrosepalum Maximowicz; Azalea macrosepala Koch. *B*. Usually 1–3 ft. tall, sometimes up to 8 ft. Inflor. (i). Flowers (46?) 1½–2 in. across, lilac-pink to rose-purple, with dark purple dots on upper lobes; fragrant. Gartenflora *19*: t. 662. Central and southern Japan.—This is presumed to be the phylogenetic form of the species and is known in Japan by the common name of 'Mochitsutsuji' (glandular azalea). It grows there on gravelly soil in dry pine woods and thickets. Plants raised at the Arnold Arboretum did not prove hardy there. Several forms are classified under this variety. Forma *dianthiflorum* Wilson is a wild azalea with double flowers. Another form, which differs from the type in having 10 stamens instead of 5, is f. *decandrum* Wilson. Several anomalous forms are known. One of these, probably a clone, is f. *rhodoroides* Makino with a short, deeply cleft corolla and distinctive stamens; in Japan it is called 'Kocho-zoroi' or 'Seikan-tsutsuji.' Another form, with rose-purple corolla and shorter stamens, is f. *hanaguruma* Makino. This is known in Japan as 'Oyeyama-tsutsuji' or 'Hanaguruma.' Other azaleas of this species are grown in Japan under the names of 'Usuyo,' 'Amaga-shita' and 'Suruga-momyo.'

Rhododendron longiperulatum Hayata (with long bud scales). Probably tender. Flowers 1½ in. long and broad; red. Formosa.—Apparently not in cultivation here.

Rhododendron macrogemmum Nakai (large bud); syn: R. Kaempferi var. macro-gemmum Nakai. Hardiness not rated. Height 3–10 ft. Flowers purple.

Rhododendron Mariae Hance. *C?* 3–10 ft. tall. Inflor. 7–12 fls. Flowers ¾ in. across, lilac, fragrant. Eastern China.—Not in cultivation here.

Rhododendron microphyton Franchet (small plant). *D*. 1–6 ft. tall. Inflor. 3–6 fls., several together at the end of branchlets, appearing as a many flowered cluster. Flowers ½–¾ in. across (17), white, flushed pink, with red dots on 3 upper lobes. Spec. Rhodo. p. 90. Yunnan, 6,000–10,000 ft.—A distinct form, very floriferous, and not unlike some of the Triflorum series, but differing in not having scales beneath the leaves. The westernmost and most alpine Chinese azalea.

Rhododendron minutiflorum Hu (tiny flowers). An upright shrub up to 7 ft. having small white flowers. China.

Rhododendron Miyazawae Nakai & Hara (after B. Miyazawa, a collector). Up to 6 ft. with densely setose branchlets. 1–3 mauve flowers to a truss, purple spotted. Jour. Jap. Bot. *11*:823 (1935). Japan.

Rhododendron mucronatum G. Don (pointed), syn: Azalea indica alba Lindley, A. ledifolia Hooker; R. leucanthum Bunge; R. ledifolium G. Don; R. rosmarinifolium Dippel. SNOW AZALEA. *C.* Up to 6, or rarely 10 ft. tall, but usually about 4 ft.; broad and spreading; dimorphic leaves, semi-evergreen. Inflor. (o), 1–3 fls. Flowers (45), about 2 in. across, pure white or greenish white, rarely rosy pink or flaked with bits of rose; 10 stamens. Flowers viscid outside, fragrant. Bot. Mag. t. 2901 (1829). Japan.—A handsome and widely cultivated species, half-hardy if carefully protected in the North and perfectly hardy on Long Island and southward. Wilson regarded it as a white form of a rose-purple wild azalea of Japan, described below as var. *ripense.* It is able to reproduce itself with fair constancy from seed, however, although it frequently produces pink forms and chimeras in which purplish rose has a part. It roots readily from cuttings and is a favorite in Japan where it is known as the 'Shiro-yodogawa' or "white Yodogawa." In the American nurseries it is very commonly known as Azalea indica alba, although it is not a form of *R. indicum.* It is grown in China and Java as well as in Japan, and found its way to England in 1819. It probably had a part in the early hybrids that preceded the development of the hybrid Indian azaleas of the greenhouse, and is probably also in the collection at Magnolia, S.C. It is not reliably hardy at Boston, but may be grown there and even in more severe climates if given the protection of a lath house or otherwise sheltered from exposure. Because of its rather compact, low habit, its semi-evergreen foliage and its delightful white flowers, it is a very desirable plant to grow in foregrounds and is not out of place where more or less formal effects are desired. It grows in a rather solid mound, with a broad, flat top, and is well "feathered out" at the base. Where it can be grown, it is one of the most valuable garden azaleas. Variety *Noordtianum* Wilson has slightly larger flowers than the type, and a similar form, with a yellowish blotch on the upper lobe and with ruffled edges is a clone known as 'Mattapan' or, sometimes, 'America.' The form with double white flowers is called f. *narcissiflorum* Wilson. A form with very large flowers, spotted and splashed with rose, is f. *sekidera* Wilson, known also under the various clonal names of 'Sekidera,' 'Damask Rose,' and also as Azalea magnifica and Azalea indica rosea. It is an attractive plant and is grown quite extensively on Long Island, but deserves wider cultivation. There may be some difference in the clones. The original wild form from which all the others are presumably descended is var. *ripense* Wilson (R. ripense Makino), which grows along the river banks in southern Japan and differs from the typical white form only in having rose-purple flowers. A double flowered form of this purple type, which seems to have perfectly sterile flowers, is f. *plenum* Wilson, known to me only as clonal variety called 'Fujimanyo,' but known in Japan also under the name Murasaki-Botan-tsutsuji (purple peony-azalea). It has been in cultivation for over a century, but is not very attractive, in my opinion, and by no means the equal of

R. poukhanense Cl. 'Yodogawa' (R. yedoense). A form intermediate in color between the white type and var. *ripense* is var. *amethystinum,* clone 'Amethyst,' n. comb., sometimes sold under an incorrect and misleading synonym: Azalea japonica alba. It is an attractive plant, however, with flowers white, delicately flushed with pale lilac and faintly spotted with rose-pink. It is no doubt a clonal variety. **XX**

Rhododendron naamkwanense (from Naam Kwan Shan). Hardiness not rated. Up to 3 ft. tall, with rose flowers. From Kwangtung, southeastern China, and hence probably not better than *C* in hardiness.

Rhododendron Nakaharai Hayata (after G. Nakahara, Japanese collector), syn: R. serpyllifolium Hayata not Miquel. Low growing, twiggy shrub (height not given). Flowers less than 1 in. long, dark red, with 10 stamens. Formosa.—A little known species, probably tender, related to R. serpyllifolium Miquel, but with larger flowers and 10, instead of 5, stamens.

Rhododendron obtusum Planchon (blunt), syn: R. Thunbergii Planchon; Azalea obtusa Lindley. KURUME AZALEA; (KIRISHIMA AZALEA). *A.* Low, twiggy shrub, sometimes nearly prostrate, generally under 3 ft. tall. Dimorphic leaves, semi-ever-green or evergreen. Inflor. (p), 1–3 fls., but covered with flowers when in bloom. Flowers (shape 46, but smaller), about 1 in. across, but variable, salmon or salmon-red, pink, rosy mauve, magenta to scarlet and crimson; white in one form; 5 stamens. Bot. Reg. *32*: t. 37 (1846). Central and southern Japan.—*R. obtusum* is reputedly a wild species in Japan which has crossed extensively with two other species, *R. kiusianum* and *R. Kaempferi,* and intergradient forms, plus these species, are presumed to be the basis for the garden race known collectively as Kurume azaleas. The form called by Wilson f. *japonicum* is now regarded as *R. kiusianum* Makino (see Chap. XIX). Some of these intermediate forms grow abundantly on and around Mt. Kirishima, an active volcano in Japan, above the tree line in coarse grasses and low shrubbery. It varies greatly in color, the commonest variations being shades of rosy mauve and magenta, although salmon is plentiful and pink, scarlet, crimson and white sometimes occur among these wild plants. The plants are generally low, but occasionally, in sheltered places, strong shoots will develop and the plants become relatively tall and sparsely branched. Forms intermediate with *Rhododendron Kaempferi* are found, which led Wilson to classify *R. Kaempferi* as a variety of *R. obtusum.* The form *Rhododendron obtusum* × *R. kiusianum* hybrid is known in Japan as the KIRISHIMA AZALEA and has been cultivated in gardens there for centuries. It has small, scarlet, slightly scented flowers and, like all the rest, blooms early and is very floriferous. When in bloom the entire plant appears blood-red, and in the fall it becomes red again with autumn leaves. The leaves which are formed in the spring are shed in the fall, but the so-called "summer leaves" which appear later are smaller and persist all winter. Thus there are two kinds of leaves (dimorphism), which is relatively common in the entire Obtusum subseries. Three other forms are recognized under Latin names, f. *album* Schneider, f. *macrostemon* Wilson and f. *amoenum* Wilson. I do not feel that these are much different from or deserving of greater distinction than any of the other selected variants of the species, which are known collectively as the Kurume azaleas, since Wilson, after studying the matter says * they are all selected cultivated forms of the wild species which grows on Mt. Kirishima. Accordingly, I am classifying them as clonal varieties along with the other named clones of the Kurume race. These are listed among the clonal varieties in the succeeding chapter.

The Kurume azaleas are probably not species hybrids, but are superior garden forms developed during a century of selection and crossing within the species in the city of Kurume, Japan, where two or three fanciers took up the breeding of improved forms many years ago. I discussed their origin in Chapter XIX. Over 200 clones are extant.

Rhododendron obtusum and its varieties in general are not considered hardy in the northeastern United States, although some are hardier than others. 'Amoenum' is perhaps the hardiest clone, as well as the oldest in cultivation here, but cannot be regarded as reliable north of New York City. 'Hinodegiri' is another that is hardier than the rest, but not quite so dependable as 'Amoenum.' A number of the genuine Kurume varieties, of Wilson's introduction, will succeed in sheltered spots on Long Island, and several will succeed even in central New York State if given the protection of a lath house. In an effort to isolate some hardy individuals from a large population of seedlings, offspring of the best Japanese Kurume varieties, Mr. Richard Wyman of Framingham, Mass., grew some 44,000 seedlings and finally isolated only two individuals out of the entire population which appeared hardy enough to withstand the climate of Boston. This experiment indicates that little can be expected of *Rhododendron obtusum* and its varieties in a cold climate.

Where they can be grown, the various forms of *Rhododendron obtusum* offer splendid opportunities for ornamental use. Their low, compact character makes them desirable in formal situations and for foreground planting, while their floriferousness is extremely useful where color is desired. They come in nearly the full range of anthocyanin colors (the rose-red-purple series), but contain no yellow coloration. In mild climates their semi-evergreen character makes them additionally useful, while in greenhouse culture they retain their full leaf character and will bloom in winter. Since they may be readily propagated by cuttings and bloom at an early age, they are decidedly valuable as potted plants, especially where small plants are desired. If they could be made more hardy, their usefulness would be greatly extended. **XX**

Rhododendron Oldhamii Maximowicz (after Richard Oldham, early collector for Kew). OLDHAM'S AZALEA. *D*. A bushy shrub up to 10 ft. tall, twiggy; evergreen. Flowers on the ends of the shoots and, at low altitudes, appear every month in the year; red, funnel-shaped, 1¼–2 in. across. Formosa.—Wilson thought this azalea worth cultivating as a greenhouse shrub. It was first introduced in 1878, and in 1918 reintroduced through the Arnold Arboretum. There are long, red-brown hairs on the branchlets and the leaves are hairy.

Rhododendron ovatosepalum Yamam. (ovate sepals). From Formosa, probably tender.

* Wilson and Rehder. A monograph of azaleas, p. 31. Cambridge, 1921.

Rhododendron poukhanense Léveillé (from Mt. Poukhan, Korea), syn: R. yedoense var. poukhanense Nakai; R. coreanum Rehder; Azalea poukhanensis Hort. KOREAN AZALEA. *A*. To 3 ft. tall, forming a broad mat on exposed locations; in shaded places more loosely branched, sometimes to 6 ft. Leaves dimorphic, all deciduous in cold climates, orange or red in autumn. Inflor. (o), 2–3 fls. Flowers between (45) and (46), 1½ to 2 in. across, pale lilac-purple, fragrant; 10 stamens. Korea, from Seoul southward, open country, on grassy mountain slopes and in thin pine woods. Nakai, Fl. Sylv. Kor. *8*:t. 18.—This is the common wild azalea of southern Korea, hardy and desirable in every way except that it possesses an unpopular color. Although Wilson describes the color as "rose to rosy purple," I suspect that the rose form is rare, since I have never seen any and gardeners are constantly complaining of the "bluish" or "magenta" hue of the species. I doubt if a *clear* rose exists. The common lilac-purple color, however, can be excellent and effective in a garden if placed among plenty of green foliage and not in proximity to other bright-colored flowers. It seems to be reliably hardy and this, plus its tendency to form a low compact bush, is an extremely valuable quality. There is no reason why a proper use can not be found for this species in many gardens. It blooms early enough to be fairly free from clashing with other azaleas, most of which bloom later. Its flowers are of fairly good size, varying from that of *Rhododendron Kaempferi* to nearly that of *R. mucronatum,* usually about halfway between these two. It has a mildly pleasant fragrance. Japanese botanists accredit 14 garden forms to this species.

A horticultural clone with double flowers, having no essential organs and, hence, sterile, is var. *yodogawa* Rehder (syn: Rhododendron yedoense Rehder), the YODOGAWA AZALEA. This is obviously a monstrous form, unknown outside gardens, totally incapable of setting seed and propagated only by vegetative means. It is, however, a very attractive garden plant. Its good-sized flowers are very double and are of a rather bright lilac color. Owing to their doubleness, the flowers do not drop off so quickly as in the single forms, so the apparent blooming period is longer. The plant is compact, usually about 3 or 4 ft. tall and is abundantly floriferous, this condition, no doubt, being aided by the fact that seeds are never produced. When out of bloom the foliage is good and tends to be semi-evergreen. In Japan the plant is known as Botan-tsutsuji (PEONY AZALEA). It is, in my opinion, much superior to another double Japanese clone called 'Fujimanyo' (*R. mucronatum* var. *plenum* Wilson) which it resembles slightly. The Yodogawa azalea is hardy in the Arnold Aboretum, Boston, Mass. It perhaps needs shelter in other places of comparable climate. Owing to its color, it appears to best advantage if planted alone or, at least, where other azaleas will not be blooming near it at the same time, although it harmonizes well with white forms, such as *Rhododendron mucronatum.* J. B. Gable has produced a good race of *poukhanense* hybrids.

Rhododendron pulchrum Sweet (beautiful), syn: R. indicum var. Smithii Sweet; R. phoeniceum f. Smithii Wilson. *B*. Low shrub, sometimes up to 6 ft. or more, but often dwarfish. Inflor. (o). Flowers (45), 2½ in. across, rosy purple, spotted dark purple. In some varieties rose-red or carmine. 10 stamens. China and Japan, unknown in the wild.—This species may possibly be a hybrid between *Rhododendron scabrum* and *R. mucronatum.* It is variable. The clone known as var. *Maxwellii*

n. comb., is worthy of special note as a garden form. It grows beautifully at some places on Long Island, where it makes a plant about 2 ft. tall having bright rose-red flowers of large size, blooming about the last of May. The flowers are much larger than those of *R. indicum* clone 'J. T. Lovett,' which it resembles somewhat in garden character. With slight protection, *Maxwellii* appears to endure the winters in the neighborhood of Boston, so can be considered a possibility for sheltered places in cold regions. Var. *phoeniceum* Rehder (R. phoeniceum G. Don; R. puniceum Planchon not Roxburgh; Azalea Rawsonii Paxton) is an old form still growing in the collection at Magnolia. It is a magenta flowered form, illustrated in Bot. Mag. t. 2667. Variety *calycinum* Rehder has rose-purple flowers with crimson spots and is illustrated in Paxton's Flow. Gard. *2*: t. 70. As a clone it is known as 'Omurasaki' (large purple azalea) and is much grown in Japanese gardens. It is superior to the type and its large magenta-red flowers are said to be handsome. It is vigorous, free-flowing and of compact habit. Introduced by Robert Fortune before 1851. A variety with double flowers is known as var. *tebotan* Rehder. This is very double, with small green leaves coming up out of the center. Wilson states that it is now rare and nurserymen substitute the inferior clone 'Fujimanyo' (*R. mucronatum plenum*) for it. It is remarkable for its color, which is similar to that of *Bougainvillea glabra*. It is illustrated in Nakai's Trees and Shrubs of Japan, 2nd ed., *1* : 152.

Rhododendron rivulare Handel-Mazzetti (growing by streams). More than 3 ft. tall. Inflor. many-flowered. Flowers funnelform, with 5 stamens. Kweichow, southwestern China.—An incompletely known species.

Rhododendron rubropilosum Hayata (red-haired), syn: R. caryophyllum Hayata; R. randaiense Hayata. *D*. Up to 10 ft. tall. Flowers ½ to 1 in. across, pink, spotted with rose. Formosa.—A tender shrub with small pink flowers and very small light green leaves.

Rhododendron rufo-hirtum Handel-Mazzetti (red-haired). *E*. Height not given. Flowers funnelform-campanulate, about ¾ in. long, deep rose. Yunnan.—An incompletely described species, related to *Rhododendron Oldhamii* and *R. rivulare*.

Rhododendron saisiuense Nakai (from Saishu, formerly Quelpart, Island off Korea). A 1-foot azalea with pink flowers. Bot. Mag. Tokyo *44*:587 (1935).

Rhododendron Sasakii Wilson (after Sasaki), syn: R. breviperulatum Wilson. Probably tender. Up to 6 ft. tall. Flowers red, 1¼ to 1½ in. long and wide. 5 stamens. Formosa.—Related to *R. Simsii,* but distinguished by 5 stamens.

Rhododendron scabrum G. Don (rough), syn: R. sublanceolatum Miquel; R. sublateritium Komatsu; R. liukiuense Komatsu. LUCHU AZALEA. *E*. 3 to 6 ft. tall. Inflor. (0). Flowers (45), about 2½ in. long and across, rose-red to bright scarlet, with dark dots. 10 short stamens. Bot. Mag. t. 8478 (1913). Liukiu Islands.— This laxly branched shrub from the Liukiu Islands is cultivated in the warm parts of Japan, but is a greenhouse species only here. The flowers are normally intense scarlet, but vary to rose-red. Wilson said it has the largest flowers of all azaleas and is strikingly conspicuous in the wild or in gardens, but, except for *Rhododendron Oldhamii,* and perhaps other Formosan species, it is the least hardy of all the red-flowered species from eastern Asia. In Massachusetts it blossoms but sparsely under greenhouse conditions. The type species, although most uncommon, is the deep rose form, while the common wild form with scarlet flowers is distinguished as f. *coccineum* Wilson (syn.: sublanceolatum). There are hybrid clones.

Rhododendron Seniavinnii Maximowicz. Up to 6 ft. tall. Inflor. (m?). Flowers (17?), ¾ in. across, white, tinged with rose in the tube, spotted with purple above. Fukien and Hunan in eastern China.—A little known species, related to *R. microphytom.*

Rhododendron serpyllifolium Miquel (leaves like thyme), syn: Azalea serpyllifolia A. Gray. WILDTHYME AZALEA. *B.* Up to 4 ft. tall. Inflor. (q). Flowers (46), about ½ in. across, rosy pink. Central and southern Japan.—Characterized by small flowers and very small leaves. Forma *albiflorum* Makino has white flowers.

Rhododendron Simsii Planchon (after John Sims, Editor Botanical Magazine), syn: R. indicum var. ignescens Sweet; R. Calleryi Planchon; R. indicum Hemsley, in part; Azalea indica Aiton, in part. *D.* Evergreen up to 5 ft. tall, rarely 8 ft. Inflor. (o). Flowers (45), 1½–2 in. across rose-red, through bright to dark red, spotted. Bot. Mag. t. 1480 (1812). Temperate parts of China and in Formosa, varieties elsewhere.—This is the common red azalea of eastern China, abundant in the Yangtze valley and elsewhere, painting the hills red when in bloom. For years it has usurped the name *indicum* and has become hopelessly entangled with the hybrid race of Indian azaleas of the greenhouse, of which it is, perhaps, the chief parent. At low altitudes the leaves are large, becoming smaller at higher levels. *Rhododendron Simsii* has 10 stamens, or sometimes but 8 or 9, while *R. indicum* is described as having only 5. A form with white flowers is known on Tin Hill, West Lake, Hangchow. In var. *vittatum* Wilson, the flowers are white, striped with lilac-purple (see illustration in Flore des Serres, *9*: t. 886, 888). This is a sectorial chimera and is variable and irregular, sometimes producing entire white or purple flowers and occasional flecks and blotches. A form of var. *vittatum* in which the stripes are red is forma *Bealii* Wilson. These have been useful in the development of the present race of Indian azaleas. Var. *mesembrinum* Rehder comes from Yunnan and has smaller, white, purple-dotted flowers. **X**

Rhododendron subsessile Rendle (nearly destitute of stalk). Tender. Height not given. Flowers ¾ in. long and 1 in. across, lilac to violet purple. Highlands of northern Luzon, Philippine Islands.—This small species, related to *Rhododendron rubropilosum,* slightly resembles *R. mucronatum* in pubescence and foliage, but is very much smaller throughout, the flowers not being one-third the size of the Japanese species.

Rhododendron Tamurai Masamume (after Tamura, Japanese horticulturist). A close ally of *R. indicum.*

Rhododendron tosaense Makino (from Tosa), syn: R. Komiyamae Makino. *E.* Up to 5 or 7 ft. tall. Flowers funnelform, about 1¼ in. across, lilac-purple, 5–10 stamens. Tosa, southern Japan.—The color is not attractive and the plants have not proved hardy in the United States, where seeds were distributed by Wilson in 1915. Somewhat similar to *R. Kanehirai.*

Rhododendron Tschonoskii Maximowicz (after a collector who sent seeds from Japan), syn: R. trinerve Franchet. *A.* 1–5 or rarely 8 ft. tall, sometimes forming a low, broad mat. Inflor. terminal clusters of 4–6 fls. Flowers (7b) ⅝ in. across, ⅜ in. long, white, without fragrance. Alpine or sub-alpine situations from central Japan north to Sapporo; also southern Korea.—A hardy alpine species from Japan, with insignificant flowers and foliage that turns red in autumn. "As a garden plant," said Wilson, "it has little to recommend it." Its Japanese name is 'Shirobana-no kome-tsutsuji.' A form with 4-merous flowers is f. *tetramerum* Makino, and one with 3-nerved leaves is called var. *trinerve* Makino.

Rhododendron tsoi Merrill. A rather newly reported species. Described as 3 ft. tall, with pink flowers, smaller than those of *R. microphyton,* to which it is closely allied.

Rhododendron yakuinsulare (Yaku Island). Newly described Formosan azalea, from the island of Yakusima.

Rhododendron yedoense Maximowicz (see *R. poukhanense* clone 'Yodogawa').

SUBSERIES SCHLIPPENBACHII
(Section *Sciadorhodion,* Rehder & Wilson)

The species in this section all come from eastern Asia and, as a group, are fairly distinct. *Rhododendron Schlippenbachii* is the best known of these species in cultivation at the present time and, as such, has been chosen to represent the group as a whole despite its cumbersome name. A distinguishing characteristic of the subseries is its whorled, deciduous leaves. It also has leafy shoots coming out of the same terminal buds as the flowers. The flowers most resemble those of the subseries Canadense which, I suspect from crossing experiments, is the most closely related group.

An important feature of this subseries is that half the species are fairly hardy in the northeastern United States. These comprise *Rhododendron Schlippen-bachii, R. quinquefolium* and *R. reticulatum.*

In color the flowers range from white through pink and rose to reddish and rose-purple. No yellow is present in the subseries. The height varies from low to medium sized shrubs. The leaves of *R. Schlippenbachii* are very distinctive in size and shape, while those of *R. reticulatum* are equally, but not identically, characteristic.

Evidently the species of this group are sensitive to ecological conditions such as climate, temperature and moisture. All of them prove refractory at times in the United States, but the hardier sorts are regarded as almost in the "iron-clad" class so far as ability to withstand northern winters is concerned. In England, however, *Rhododendron Schlippenbachii,* the hardiest one in America, is classed as *C* in hardiness. Growers here at times find this species eccentric, as it sometimes tends to suddenly stop growing when young, the reasons for this behavior being obscure. Wilson reported *R. Weyrichii* as tender at the Arnold Arboretum, but said that it survived in Massachusetts when protected by a cold-frame. The unique color of its flowers, described as being almost brick-red, is an interesting feature and might make it valuable where it can be grown.

Rhododendron amagianum Makino (from Mt. Amagi, Japan). *A.* A deciduous shrub, up to 12 ft. Blooms late. Leaves large and lustrous, in threes at ends of twigs. Flowers orange-rose with deeper blotch, in a loose truss. Middle and late July in northern Japan. Enum. Spermat. Japan, Pt. 1 :27 (1948).

Rhododendron Farrerae Tate in Sweet (after Mrs. Farrer, wife of Capt. Farrer, East India Co., 1829), syn: Azalea squamata Lindley. *F.* Flowers 1½–2 in. across, pale to deep rose with red-purple spots. Bot. Reg. *33*: t. 3 (1847). Hong Kong and vicinity, China.—A low shrub, not cultivated in America and hardy only in southern England.

Rhododendron Mariesii Hemsley & Wilson (after Charles Maries, a Veitchian collector), syn. R. shojoense Hayata; R. gnaphalocarpum Hayata. *C.* 3–10 ft. tall, Inflor. (o). Flowers (48) 1½–2 in. across, rose-purple, spotted with red-purple. Bot. Mag. t. 8206. Southeastern and central China; Formosa.—A tender species related to *R. Farrerae,* but distinguished by its larger leaves and other characters.

Rhododendron quinquefolium Bisset & Moore (leaves in fives), syn: Azalea quinquefolia. CORK AZALEA. *B.* Shrub or small tree, 4–25 ft. tall, Inflor. 1–3 flowered. Flowers 1¾ in. across, pure white with green spots at base. Icon. Pl. Koisikav. *1*: 59, t. 30 (1912). Central Japan; shady, rocky ravines in the Nikko region.— Grows slowly, but proves hardy in the Arnold Arboretum and elsewhere in America; it is regarded as distinctly difficult in England. Semi-shade and shelter from cold winds is advised. It is deciduous and is attractive when in leaf and flower. In its 5-leafed character it resembles *Rhododendron pentaphyllum,* but is easily distinguished by its white, instead of bright pink, flowers and in leaf-bud characters. It blooms early at Rochester. X

Rhododendron reticulatum D. Don in G. Don (netlike), syn: R. dilitatum Miquel, R. rhombicum Miquel, R. decandrum Makino, R. wadanum Makino, R. lagopus Nakai, R. nudipes Nakai, Azalea reticulata K. Koch, etc. RHOMBIC-LEAF AZALEA. *A.*

The Use of Clipped Azaleas in Japan

An Azalea Garden in New England

3 to 25 ft. tall. Inflor. similar to *R. Schlippenbachii,* flowers expanding before the leaves. Flowers (48) 1½–2 in. across, rose-purple to magenta, usually unspotted; 2-lipped appearance; 10 stamens. Bot. Mag. t. 6972. Japan, widely distributed.— This hardy species, variable in color and other features, is characterized by leaves which tend toward a rhombic shape. It has grown slowly in America, but appears to be hardy in the North. It is a deciduous species, blooming early in the season before the leaves have expanded and having flowers which range from rose or red-purple to rich magenta-purple. The richest colors, in the wild, occur on plants grow-ing in the open, for the color becomes quite pale and the branches more sparse in dense shade. Wilson, who has seen this plant blooming in Japan, states that, although the color is not a popular one in the West, this species is impressive when blooming in masses and separated from other colors save for varying shades of green. Owing to its variability, the different forms have, from time to time, acquired names as separate species, most of which have since been dropped, few existing even as varieties. The white flowered form is var. *albiflorum* Wilson. An-other form has 5 stamens, instead of 8 or 10, but it is questionable if this character is constant. The pentamerous form is known as f. *pentandrum* Wilson, formerly known as *Rhododendron dilitatum* Maximowicz, illustrated in Bot. Mag. t. 7681. **X**

Rhododendron sanctum Nakai (holy). Hardiness not given. Up to 15 ft. Flowers rose. "Growing in the sacred area of the Great Shrine of Ise." A little known species.

Rhododendron Schlippenbachii Maximowicz (after Baron von Schlippenbach, naval officer and traveler), syn: Azalea Schlippenbachii Kuntze. ROYAL AZALEA. (See color plate, p. 303.) Flowers (47) 2¼ to 3 in. wide, pale to rose pink, with wide-spreading lobes, the upper ones spotted lightly with red-brown. Discovered in 1854, but not introduced in the West until 1893. Bot. Mag. t. 7373. Korea and north-eastern Manchuria, on the lower slopes of the Diamond Mts. Also sparingly in central Japan. In thin woods.—One of the finest azaleas, but a little sensitive to ecological conditions, although perfectly hardy in the North. It has fine, large flowers, slightly fragrant and usually of a clear but pale pink color, with no trace of magenta. The flowers open just as the leaves are expanding, which is generally the last week in May in the latitude of central New York. The leaves are very distinctive, being large and broad, obovate, deciduous and changing to shades of yellow, orange and crimson in autumn. They are borne in whorls of 5. The flowers occur in umbellate clusters of from 3 to 6. Given good growing conditions, the plants become quite upright. They have been very satisfactory plants, when raised from seed, in Boston, Rochester, New York City and other places. In England this species is considered fastidious and is given a rating of *B* by the English Rhodo-dendron Association. It behaves eccentrically in this country, at times refusing to thrive for reasons which, at present, remain obscure. Propagators, raising young seedlings, have noted that sometimes half-grown plants will become checked and unthrifty. For some reason this species has done better as soil acidity has declined. Possibly it needs more calcium than other species. It does well, however, in many situations in this country and is one of the finest of the Asiatic azaleas. It is not closely related to species in other series, with which it will, in most cases, refuse to hybridize. **XX**

I have made controlled cross-pollinations in reciprocal directions between *Rhododendron Schlippenbachii* and the members of other subseries within the Azalea group, such as the Indian azaleas, the Ghent and Mollis hybrids, *Rhododendron Kaempferi* and *R. Vaseyi*. With the exception of the last species named, which appeared none too successful, the results of these attempted interspecific combinations were utterly fruitless. *Rhododendron Vaseyi,* of course, belongs to the Canadense subseries. These results, therefore, might lend color to the belief that the subseries Canadense is more closely affiliated with the subseries Schlippenbachii than are the members of the other subgroups.

Rhododendron Weyrichii Maximowicz (after Dr. Weyrich, Russian naval surgeon, who discovered this species in 1853), syn: R. shikokianum Makino; Azalea Weyrichii Kuntze. Inflor. 2–4 flowered, expanding before or with the leaves. Flowers (47?), almost brick-red, 1½–2½ in. across. Nakai, Fl. Sylv. Kor. *8*: t. 16 (1919). Introduced by Wilson in 1914. Southern Japan and on the Korean island of Quelpaert, in thickets and open woods, from near sea-level to 3,000 ft. On old lava flows.—A vigorous shrub, sometimes tree-like in its native habitat, with deciduous leaves and blooming rather early in the spring. This species is distinct from all others in the color of its flowers which are almost brick-red. Apparently it is somewhat fastidious, although, like *Rhododendron Schlippenbachii,* it is not too tender to be useful in the North under protection. Plants raised at the Arnold Arboretum proved tender, but, protected in a cold frame, they flowered in another Massachusetts garden.

SUBSERIES TASHIROI

This subseries has been set up in *The Species of Rhododendron* to accommodate a single species ·which does not fit into the other existing groups. This species is supposed to be related to members of the subseries Obtusum and Schlippenbachii, being in a position between them in character of pubescence and the manner in which the leaves are borne. This subseries resembles the Obtusum group in pubescence and the Schlippenbachii group in leaf habit. It possesses, however, persistent leaves and on that basis was classed with the true rhododendrons for some time. It seems, nevertheless, to be an azalea. The one species included herein has not yet been introduced into cultivation. Judging from its description, it is not of special ornamental value and would probably not prove hardy if introduced into the United States.

Rhododendron Tashiroi Maximowicz (after Tashiro, a Japanese collector). Probably tender. 5–15 ft. tall. Inflor. see (*R. Schlippenbachii*). Flowers (38) 1–1½ in. long and wide; pale rose-purple, spotted maroon-purple; 10 or 12 stamens. Icon. Pl. Koisikav. *3*: t. 203 (1917). Liukiu and Kawanabe Islands and southern Japan. Not in cultivation.—A much branched shrub, with persistent leaves.

BARBATUM SERIES

The members of this series are generally characterized by possessing hairy or bristly leafstalks. They come from relatively mild climates and are designated in the English list as somewhat tender, being mainly suitable for warm gardens. There are several beautiful forms among them. The series is divided into four subseries which follow geographical lines in their classification.

R. BARBATUM

In this country, until recently, they were little grown except in California where the early blooming *Rhododendron strigillosum* has been reported as being very much appreciated. Nine species are now listed as tested on the West Coast. *R. barbatum* seems to be the species most used in crosses, and several of its hybrids bear merit stars. The crosses on record to date have been mainly with the Arboreums or Thomsoniis and their derivatives. The Barbatum series is considered to be most nearly allied to the Arboreum series,* having lesser affinities with the series Irroratum, Thomsonii and Taliense.

Subseries Barbatum

This group is confined to the Himalayas, such as Nepal, Bhutan and Sikkim, at altitudes around 10,000 feet. They possess a tree-like habit, coarse bristles, large flower trusses and deep red tubular flowers. The species are variable, but mainly distinguished from one another by the extent of their indumentum. *Rhododendron barbatum* is highly regarded in England, receiving the four stars of the highest merit class.

Rhododendron argipeplum Balfour & Cooper (silver robed). 6 ft. tall. Flowers 1½ in. long, incompletely known, color not described. Found growing under Abies in Bhutan at 11,000 ft.

Rhododendron barbatum Wallich (barbed), syn: R. lancifolium Hooker f. *B*. Tree 30 to 60 ft. high in native habitat. (See accompanying text-figure.) Inflor. (a). Flowers (4), 1 in. long, deep crimson or blood red, with nectar pouches black-crimson. Hooker's Rhodo. Sikkim Himal. t. 3 (1849). Nepal and Sikkim, 10,000 ft.—A well known, but tender, species with bright red flowers in small trusses. Millais says it needs protection in most parts of England. Does not bloom at all

* Hutchinson, J. A. Rehder and H. J. Tagg. The Species of Rhododendron. London, 1930.

until more than 10 or 15 years old. Evidently the tenderness is to large extent in
the flower buds which open very early (February to April in England), for the
plant is said to withstand zero temperature, but is difficult to grow. **X**

Rhododendron imberbe Hutchinson (not bearded). *C.* 8 ft. tall. Inflor. (a), 15 fls.
Flowers (68), 1¾ in. long; red, spotted and blotched with darker red. Western-
central Himalaya, 9,000 ft.—Featured by freedom from bristles.

Rhododendrum Smithii Nuttall (after Sir J. E. Smith, English botanist). *B.* 10–15
ft. tall. Inflor. (a), 10–15 fls. Flowers (73?), 1¾ in. long, deep red with crimson
in the nectar pouches. East Sikkim and Bhutan, 8,000–12,000 ft.—Much like
R. barbatum, but is smaller, more hairy and has darker foliage. **X**

SUBSERIES CRINIGERUM

Yunnan and adjoining portions of southeastern Tibet is the home of the
two closely related species comprising the subseries Crinigerum. They have
several distinct floral and foliage characters by which they are separated from
those of the other series. *Rhododendron crinigerum* is regarded as an attractive
garden species.

Rhododendron Bainbridgeanum Tagg & Forrest. *B.* 3–6 ft. tall. Inflor. 6–8 fls.
Flowers 1½ in. long, white or creamy yellow, sometimes flushed rose, blotched
crimson, spotted outside. Open thickets and margins of forests. Southeastern Tibet,
10,000–13,000 ft.

Rhododendron crinigerum Franchet (bearing hairs), syn: R. ixeuticum Balfour
f. & W. W. Smith. *B.* 8–12 ft. tall. Inflor. (a?), 12 fls. Flowers 1½ in. long, white
or flushed rose, with deep basal blotch. Open pine forests in southeastern Tibet and
northwestern Yunnan, 10,000–13,000 ft.—Some plants flowering in England have
been heavily spotted on a creamy ground. A desirable feature is that it flowers at
an early age. An intermediate form, approaching *R. glischrum,* is var. *euadenium.*

SUBSERIES GLISCHRUM

This group comes from northeastern Upper Burma and Yunnan. The species
are classified according to the bristles they bear, many of which are glandular.
They have large leaves, large flowers and coarse bristles. As in the Subseries
Barbatum, several species are tree-like. Again, variation within species is said
to be considerable.

Rhododendron diphrocalyx Balfour (calyx like a chariot board), syn: R. burri-
florum Balfour f. & Forrest. *B.* 5–15 ft. high. Inflor. (a), 20 fls. Flowers 1½ in.
long, bright red or light crimson, with crimson spots and basal blotch. Thickets,
western Yunnan, 10,000–11,000 ft.—The calyx is very large and conspicuously one-
sided, giving almost a "bonbon" appearance to the flower.

Rhododendron erosum Cowan (eaten away). *B.* Early blooming shrub up to 20 ft. Allied to *R. barbatum,* but with broad, rounded leaves; soft woolly indumentum when young. Flowers deep rich crimson to rose pink, and a large deep pink calyx. Notes Bot. Gard. Edinburgh *19* :225 (1937). Tibet.

Rhododendron exasperatum Tagg (exasperating). *C.* 10–15 ft. tall. Inflor. (a?). Flowers 1½ in. long, rusty brick-red. In Abies and rhododendron forest, Assam, 10,000–12,000 ft.—An unusual flower color is described.

Rhododendron glischroides Tagg & Forrest (similar to glischrum). *C.* 6–15 ft. tall. Inflor. (b?), 6–10 fls. Flowers (62?) 1½ in. long, white or cream, sometimes flushed with rose, crimson basal blotch. In thickets, Burma, 10,000–11,000 ft.—This differs from *R. glischrum* in its indumentum. Variety *arachnoideum* has a fine white coating like a cobweb of white underneath the leaves.

Rhododendron glischrum Balfour f. & Smith (sticky). *B.* Up to 25 ft. tall, small tree. Inflor. (a), 10 fls. Flowers (62) 1½ in. long, deep rose, with a crimson blotch at base. Bot. Mag. *150*: t. 9035. Open places in thickets and pine woods, N.W. Yunnan and Burma, 13,000–14,000 ft.—The leaves bear a covering of bristles, many of them glandular. It has hairy shoots but paler yellow-green foliage than *R. barbatum.* There is some variation in the flower color, from magenta-pink to white, and care must be taken in selecting desirable individuals, as some colors are not pleasing.

Rhododendron habrotrichum Balfour f. & Smith (with soft hairs). *B.* 4–10 ft. tall. Inflor. (a?). Flowers 2 in. long, white or pale rose. Millais, Rhodos. *2*: 150 (1924). Rhododendron forests and thickets, W. Yunnan, 10,000 ft.—Rather difficult to grow. Very hairy stems and dark green leaves. English results indicate its preference for plenty of watering, with a soil of rich leaf-mould and semi-shaded conditions.

Rhododendron hirtipes Tagg (shaggy footed). *B.* A small tree of 20–25 ft. Inflor. lax umbel with 3–5 fls. Flowers 1½ in. long, whitish to rose pink, spotted with carmine and broadly striped outside with pink and white. Moss-clad, wooded cliffs and shady ravines, S.E. Tibet, 13,000 ft.

Rhododendron rude Tagg & Forrest (rough). *B.* 8–9 ft. tall. Inflor. racemose umbel with 10 fls. Flowers 1–1¼ in. long, purplish crimson, with a darker line running from the apex of each lobe. Thickets in N.W. Yunnan, 12,000 ft.

Rhododendron spilotum Balfour f. & Farrer (stained). *C.* Small tree. Inflor. racemose umbel with 8 fls. Flowers 1½ in. long, pink with crimson basal blotch. Alpine woods in N.E. Upper Burma.

Rhododendron vesiculiferum Tagg (vesicle bearing). *B.* A small tree. Inflor. (a?) 10–15 fls. Flowers 1¼ in. long, purplish rose, with a basal blotch of deep crimson or purple. Steep sheltered slopes in S.E. Tibet, 9,000–11,000 ft.

Subseries Maculiferum

Separated geographically as well as physically from the others, the subseries Maculiferum, of Szechuan and Hupeh, plus three Formosan species, shows special distinction. All are smallish shrubs, with smaller lax flower trusses in place of the large compact ones of the Himalayan species. Incidentally, this sub-group, along with the eastern representatives of the Arboreum series, shows some kinship with the northern Caucasicum subseries—which may or may not be significant in improving both sorts by hybridization. The colors range from white to deep red, through various shades of pink and magenta. *Rhododendron strigillosum* is especially attractive, but blooms too early in spring to succeed in a cold garden, it is said.

Rhododendron anwheiense Wilson (from Anwhei). *A.* A spreading shrub to 12 ft., having 6–10 flowers to a truss, white or flushed with pink and sometimes having spots of purplish red. From Anwhei Province, in eastern China, in rocky places, 5,000–6,000 ft.

Rhododendron longesquamatum Schneider (with long scales), syn: R. Brettii Hemsley & Wilson. *B.* 3–10 ft. tall sometimes larger. Inflor. (a?), 12 fls. Flowers 1½ in. long, pink to rose, with deep crimson blotch. Woodlands, W. Szechuan, 10,000–12,000 ft.—Said to be of slow growth.

Rhododendron maculiferum Franchet (bearing spots). *B.* Small tree or shrub, 5–30 ft. tall. Lax umbellate racemes of 7–10 fls. Flowers 1¼ in. long, white or faintly flushed rose, with a deep purple basal blotch breaking into lines and a few spots. Cliffs and woods, Szechuan and W. Hupeh, 8,000–10,000 ft.—Small flowers in medium sized trusses, but appearing as if pure white with deep black-purple blotches at the base. A pretty shrub, according to English horticulturists.

Rhododendron monosematum Hutchinson (with one mark). *B.* A compact shrub of 5 ft. Inflor. between (a) and (b), with 12 fls. Flowers (65) 2 in. long, white suffused with rose pink, purple basal blotch. Bot. Mag. *142*: t. 8675. Mt. Wu, Szechuan.

Rhododendron Morii Hayata (after U. Mori, collector in Formosa), syn: R. pachysanthum Hayata. *B.* 15–25 ft. tall. A loose cluster of 12–15 flowers. Flowers 1½–1¾ in. long, white or flushed rose, with crimson spots and a faint blotch. Forests in Formosa, 6,000–10,000 ft.

Rhododendron nankotaisanense Hayata (from Nankotaisan, Formosa). *C.* A small bush with an umbellate corymb of flowers, 1 in. long, color not given. Formosa, 10,000 ft.—Allied to R. *Morii,* but incompletely known.

Rhododendron ochraceum Rehder & Wilson (yellowish). A 9 ft. shrub with crimson flowers.

Rhododendron pachytrichum Franchet (with thick hairs). *B.* 6–18 ft. tall. Racemose umbel of 7–10 fls. Flowers 1¼ in. long, white to pale rose, with deep purple blotch. Woods in western Szechuan, 7,000–10,000 ft.—There are forms with green buds and others with the buds reddish-purple. Forms having flowers with a purplish magenta tint should be avoided.

Rhododendron pseudochrysanthum Hayata (false *R. chrysanthum*). *C.* 1–9 ft. tall. 9 or more flowers in a racemose umbel. Flowers 1¼–1½ in. long, pink spotted crimson with rose colored lines on the outside along the petal ridges. Formosa, 6,000–13,000 ft.—Another Formosan species, allied to *R. Morii.* **X**

Rhododendron strigillosum Franchet (beset with bristles). *C.* 5–8 ft. tall. Inflor. (a), with 8–12 fls. Flowers (73) 1½ to 2¼ in. long, deep red or bright scarlet, with crimson nectar pouches. Bot. Mag. *146*: t. 8864. W. Szechuan, in thickets and woodlands at 7,000–10,000 ft.—An outstanding species in the subseries. The color is variable and there are forms ranging from a mediocre pink to almost white, all of which should be avoided. At times the shrub attains a height of 20 ft. It has been called the Chinese *Rhododendron barbatum,* but its flower trusses are looser, with larger individual bells. In the good garden forms the flowers are of a very brilliant crimson-scarlet. The objection to this species in England is that it blooms in February or early March there, and so cannot be grown except in mild regions. This species was recommended by E. H. Wilson for use as breeding material. **XX**

BOOTHII SERIES

A Himalayan group of small shrubs, some of which are epiphytic, coming from Bhutan, Yunnan and Upper Burma. Yellow is the common color of the flowers, with vivid magenta in one species. Several are described as being very pretty, but all, of course, are tender. The flowers vary from three-quarters to one and one-half inches long and the plants are generally only two to four feet high when mature. Several of the species are variable in color. The yellows are interesting, but the other colors seem rather dreary.

Their nearest allies appear to be the members of the Glaucum series, although the Maddeniis are thought also to be connected.

R. BOOTHII

This series has been studied and rearranged by Cowan and Davidian (1948). Members of the Boothii series are happy in cultivation at San Francisco.

Subseries Boothii

Rhododendron Boothii (after T. J. Booth, collector in Bhutan, 1850). *F.* An epiphytic shrub. (See accompanying text-figure.) Inflor. 7–10 fls. Flowers about 1 in. across, lemon yellow, no spots. Bot. Mag. t. 7149. Grows on oaks in Bhutan, 5,000 ft.—It will probably do best in cultivation as a cool greenhouse plant.

Rhododendron chrysodoron Tagg (golden gift). *E.* Up to 5 ft. Flowers 1 in. long, broadly bell-shaped, lemon yellow, not spotted, in clusters of 7–10. Epiphytic shrub. Bot. Mag. t. 9442. Bhutan, 5,000 ft.—A cool greenhouse plant.

Rhododendron Dekatanum Cowan & Davidian (after Mrs. DeKat). Shrub up to 4 ft. Inflor. 3–fld. umbel. Flowers 1 in. long, bright lemon yellow. S. Tibet, 11,500 ft.

Rhododendron mishmiense Hutchinson & Ward (from Mishmi). *E.* Epiphytic, with 3–4 fls. in a cluster. Flowers 1¼ in. long, bright lemon yellow, heavily spotted with reddish brown. Assam, 7,000–8,000 ft.

Rhododendron sulfureum Franchet (sulphur colored). Syn.: R. theiochroum Balfour f. & W. W. Smith; R. cerinum Balfour f. & Forrest; R. commodum Balfour f. & Forrest. *E.* 2–4 ft. tall. Inflor. (d). Flowers (12) ¾ in. across, bright yellow. Bot. Mag. t. 8946. Moist shady ledges. Yunnan, 9,000–10,000 ft.—The illustration indicates that it is a pretty species. Requires good drainage, but plenty of water in summer and some shade. This is a variable species.

Subseries Megeratum

Rhododendron leucaspis Tagg (white shield). *C.* 1–2 ft. tall. Inflor. (d), 1–3 fls. Flowers (12), 1¼ in. long, 2 in. across, pure white. Gard. Chron. *85*: 135, fig. 67 (1929); Bot. Mag. t. 9665. Steep grassy slopes, Tibet, 10,000 ft.—This is fairly hardy and flowers at a very early age. It also blooms early in the spring and this makes it need protection from late frosts. It is small and bushy, but has large milk-white flowers. **XX**

Rhododendron megeratum Balfour f. & Forrest (passing lovely), syn: R. tapeinum Balfour f. & Forrest. *C.* 1–2 ft. tall, often prostrate. Flowers solitary, terminal, 1½ in. long, bright yellow. On boulders and ledges of cliffs or forming prostrate cushions on alpine granitic precipices; sometimes epiphytic on old fir-trees. Yunnan and Burma, 12,000–13,000 ft.—Fastidious.

Subseries Tephropeplum

Rhododendron auritum Tagg (with long ears). *C.* A shrub up to 6 ft. tall. Inflor. terminal umbel of 4–7 fls. Flowers (2), 1 in. long, creamy white or sulphur-yellow, tinged pink. Tibet, 8,000 ft. Closely allied to *R. xanthostephanum.* **X**

Rhododendron chrysolepis Hutchinson & Ward (with golden scales). *E.* Small epiphyte with 5 fls. in a cluster. Flowers 1¼ in. long, bright canary yellow, not scented. Upper Burma, 7,000–8,000 ft.

Rhododendron tephropeplum Balfour f. & Farrer (ashy robe), syn: R. spodopeplum Balfour f. & Farrer; R. deleiense Hutchinson & Ward. *B.* 2–4 ft. tall. Flowers terminal, 4–6 in a cluster, 1¼ in. across, vivid magenta-rose with crimson-purple tube. Bot. Mag. t. 9343. Ledges of limestone cliffs and rocky slopes, S.E. Tibet and Upper Burma, 14,000 ft.—Said to be a charming small bush, growing on limestone cliffs, blooming abundantly after it becomes a foot or so tall. One form has almost white flowers. Mr. Joseph Gable reports that it failed with him in southern Pennsylvania. **X**

Rhododendron xanthostephanum Merrill (golden garland), syn: R. sureum Franchet; R. messatum Balfour f. & Forrest. *D.* Up to 9 ft. Leaves lanceolate. 3–5 flowers in cluster, tubular-campanulate, yellow, pale or bright. Bot. Mag. t. 8882. Yunnan and Burma, 7,000–13,000 ft.

CAMELLIAEFLORUM SERIES

Another group of tender, sometimes epiphytic, small shrubs from the Himalayas, comprising two species, of which one is still imperfectly known and the other apparently of little horticultural significance.

Mr. de Rothschild says that the members of this series are of little interest to gardeners. The inflorescence is terminal and is characterized by having very few flowers. This series belongs among the lepidote or scaly-leaved rhododendrons and, according to Hutchinson, shows some signs of affinity with the Maddenii series. There are apparently no hybrids on record between this and any other series and I have never heard of any attempt being made to cross one of these

R. CAMELLIAEFLORUM

species with any other species. *Rhododendron camelliaeflorum* has small white flowers, but the flowers of *R. lucidum* have never been described and were not seen by Booth when he first collected a specimen of the plant. We may probably consider these species as having no useful horticultural possibilities.

There are very few series among the rhododendrons that do not include at least one species of some distinction or of some potential usefulness. In this respect, however, the Camelliaeflorum series seems unpromising. But one can never predict when a new species or variety may be discovered which will possess merits beyond all expectation. The history of the genus is rich in such cases. Then, too, plants which at first seem unpromising later become useful or even valuable horticultural subjects when found adaptable to new uses or as the parents of distinctive hybrids. So one should not altogether overlook the hidden virtues of such species as these if he lives in a climate where they may easily be grown.

Rhododendron camelliaeflorum Hooker f. (camellia-like flowers), syn: R. sparsiflorum Nuttall; R. Cooperi Balfour f. *D.* 2–6 ft. tall, often epiphytic. Inflor. (see accompanying figure). Flowers (9), 1 in. across, white, tinged pink. Hooker's Rhodo. Sikkim Himal. t. 28. Bot. Mag. t. 4932. Bhutan, Sikkim, 9,000–11,000 ft.—Reported a slow grower.

Rhododendron lucidum Nuttall (shining). A shrub with terminal inflor., imperfectly known and the flowers not yet described. Bhutan.

CAMPANULATUM SERIES

R. WALLICHII

These are Himalayan species which, in cultivation, are about the size of the members of the Ponticum series and having flowers not unlike them. The flower truss is not so much elongated as in the latter, however. The Campanulatum series is also not unlike the series Arboreum and Barbatum. In the wild, some species are tree-like. The series has one yellow-flowered species, *Rhododendron lanatum,* while the other species are all lilac, rose or white. *Rhododendron campanulatum* is perhaps the best known species in the group. In this series, again, the warning is needed against employing any but the best selected forms, because of variability within the species.

This series was worked over in 1949 by Cowan and Davidian. Three new species, *R. miniatum, R. Sherriffii,* and *R. tsariense* were added, while *R. aeruginosum* was reduced to varietal rank.

Rhododendron campanulatum D. Don (bell-shaped). *A.* Inflor. compact (a) or sometimes (b), 8 or more flowers, broadly campanulate (59) or (62) up to 2 in. across, with a tremendous amount of variation as to intensity of color, ranging from white to mostly lilac or rosy shades of purple. Bot. Mag. t. 3759. Himalayas from Kashmir to Bhutan, 9,000–14,000 ft.—This variable species has long been cultivated and has also been used in hybridization. It has a good truss and foliage, and its spotted pattern can be interesting in the best forms. With few exceptions, however, the different forms that this writer has seen appear to be characterized mainly by a sad, unattractive lavender or purplish color which would not, in his opinion, be as good by comparison as the average wild form of *R. catawbiense*. To be certain, a buyer should choose carefully in order to get a desirable clone when selecting plants of this species. In Britain, the species blooms early and should be protected from late frosts. Var. *aeruginosum* Hooker f., differs from the species in that the young leaves of the variety have a metallic lustre and are of an interesting blue color. Useful chiefly as a foliage plant.

Rhododendron fulgens Hooker f. (shining). *B.* 4–8 ft. tall, of rounded habit. Inflor. (a). Flowers (68) 1½ in. long, 1¾ in. across, deep blood-red, with 5 black-red nectaries. Bot. Mag. t. 5317. Forming thickets on mountain slopes and spurs. Sikkim and Nepal, 12,000–14,000 ft.—An early blooming species with bright scarlet flowers in small, compact trusses, very attractive, but said to be slow to reach blooming size. Flowers in early March in England. It has a more compact truss than the other species of this series. The small rounded trusses give the flowers almost the effect of a pompon dahlia, writes de Rothschild.

Rhododendron lanatum Hooker f. (woolly). *C.* Bush or small tree 10–15 ft. tall. Inflor. (b?). Flowers 1¾ in. long, pale sulphur yellow with spots of crimson-purple. Hooker's, Rhodo. Sikkim Himal. t. 16. Rocky spurs of mountains and gullies, Sikkim Himalaya, 10,000–12,000 ft.—In England this species is reported as fastidious and difficult to keep in good health, according to the comment of the Rhododendron Association. It is a thin shrub with smallish leaves which have a light brown under-surface. It seems to need plenty of leafy, woods soil plus a good mulch. Var. *luciferum* Cowan has larger, more pointed leaves. Wool under leaves is used by Tibetans for their lamps.

Rhododendron miniatum Cowan (cinnabar red). Shrub to 15 ft. Leaves with fawn indumentum. Flowers funnel-campanulate, about 1 in. long in lax clusters of 4–6; fleshy, deep crimson, sometimes with magenta patches at base. R.H.S. Rhod. Yr. Bk. 4:172 (1949). Tibet.—Smaller leaves than *R. fulgens*. Large fleshy calyx.

Rhododendron Sherriffii Cowan (after Major G. Sherriff, botanical explorer). *B.* A 12-ft. shrub. Flowers in clusters of 4–6, 1½ in. long, fleshy; deep rich carmine, with a glaucous crimson calyx. R.H.S. Rhod. Yr. Bk. 4:172 (1949). Tibet, 12,500 ft.—The undersides of the leaves bear a thick, dark brown woolly indumentum. Said to be a distinctive and beautiful species, blooming in April in Britain.

Rhododendron tsariense Cowan (from Tsari, S.E. Tibet). *B.* Height 2–9 ft., with densely tomentose branchlets, and leaves densely woolly beneath. Flowers 2–5 in a cluster, bell-shaped, 1–1½ in. long; pink or white. S.E. Tibet, 10,000–14,500 ft.—Differs from *R. lanatum* in flower color and has smaller leaves.

Rhododendron Wallichii Hooker f. (after Nathaniel Wallich, Supt. Calcutta Botanic Garden). *B* (*C* in England). 8–10 ft. tall. Inflor. (see accompanying text-figure). Flowers (68), 1¾ in. long, lilac, with deep rose dots. Bot. Mag. t. 4928. Interior of Sikkim Himalaya.—Although in England this species is classified as *C* in hardiness, with *R. campanulatum* as *B,* when grown on Cape Cod *R. Wallichii* proved somewhat hardy, while *R. campanulatum* was not hardy at all. This is often regarded as a variety of *R. campanulatum.*

CAMPYLOGYNUM SERIES

R. CAMPYLOGYNUM

Small shrublets, usually under one foot in height, with small nodding flowers, bell-like in shape and only an inch or less across. They are quite unique and appear as dwarf, rather compact mounds, suitable for the rock garden or on the edge of a planting. Although peculiar, they are not unattractive, with rather interesting foliage and a flower color that is difficult to describe—a pale rose-beige in effect, with a waxy "bloom" on the outside, occasionally becoming darker. Restudied by Cowan and Davidian, three former species have been reduced to varieties of *R. campylogynum,* which now remains the only species in this series. These plants cannot be regarded as hardy in the American Northeast, although they have succeeded in southern Pennsylvania. *R. campylogynum* is shown as Figure 4 in the color plate facing page 334.

Rhododendron campylogynum Franchet (bent ovary), syn: R. caeruleoglaucum Balfour f. & Forrest; R. damascenum Balfour f. & Forrest; R. glauco-aureum Balfour f. & Forrest. *A.* Shrub up to 18 or 24 inches, frequently smaller, with a terminal inflorescence of 1 to 3 flowers. Flowers (23), ¾ in. long, pale salmon-rose-purple (a rosy sun-tan effect) to almost black-purple, with a glaucous "bloom" on the outside. The small leaves are usually glaucous beneath. The campanulate flowers are borne in a nodding position on longish flower stalks. The plants thrive on peat at Edinburgh. Var. *myrtilloides* (Balfour f. & Ward) Cowan & Davidian does not differ essentially from the type except in smaller flowers. Var. *celsum* Davidian has an erect habit and is said to grow up to 4 ft. high. Var. *charopoeum* (Balfour) Davidian has flowers slightly larger than the type, while var. *cremastum* (Balfour) Davidian is about 2 ft. high, but with leaves somewhat larger than the type and pale green on both sides. Bot. Mag. t. 9407A. Moist open situations of the Tali Range, W. Yunnan, 9,000–12,000 ft. A.M., F.C.C.—It likes the rocks, needs to have its roots cool and moist, and requires light, according to an authority. **X**

CAMTSCHATICUM SERIES

Three species of tiny plants from the Arctic region of the Pacific. They inhabit the Bering Sea district bordering Alaska and Siberia. *Rhododendron camtschaticum* appears to be the only species in cultivation and this might become a rock garden plant if its requirements were fully understood. It is deciduous. This group is so distinct that it was once regarded as outside the genus *Rhododendron,* yet *R. camtschaticum* has been crossed with *R. glaucum.*

Its flowers are borne on young leafy shoots and not in special buds as in the rhododendrons belonging to other series. Although it has been growing with great success in Scotland, *Rhododendron camtschati-*

R. CAMTSCHATICUM

cum appears to be a difficult subject. Upon several occasions, seedlings have been propagated in this country by Mr. Gable, who reports that the plants always die after a few months. It grows interestingly on rocks in the Edinburgh Botanic Garden and appears happy there. While not unattractive, it is still too insignificant to be regarded in cultivation as anything much more than a collector's item, unsuited for warm summers.

Rhododendron camtschaticum Pallas (from Kamchatka), syn: Therorhodion camtschaticum Small; Rhodothamnus camtschaticus Lindley. *A.* 6 in. tall. See accompanying text-figure. Inflor. (x). Flowers (15), 1 in. long, 1½ in. across, rose-purple, spotted. Bot. Mag. t. 8210. Alaska, both sides of Bering Strait, extending south to an island off the coast of British Columbia and along the Sea of Okhotsk to northern Japan.—According to reports, this species needs full sun and (in England) a rather dry position. It is hardy, but seems to be temperamental in a mild climate. Does well among stones in a rockery at Edinburgh.

Rhododendron glandulosum Stanley ex Small (glandular), syn: Therorhodion glandulosum Stanley. *A?* A low shrub forming dense clumps a few inches high. Flowers ¾ in. long, rose-purple. Alaska.—A little known species.

Rhododendron Redowskianum Maximowicz (after Redowski). *A?* 4 in. tall, with flowers ¾ in. long. Kew Bull. (1921), 204, fig. 1. Manchuria.—Very much like *R. camtschaticum,* but with smaller leaves and other differences.

CAROLINIANUM SERIES

R. CAROLINIANUM

This is a group of medium-sized North American evergreen rhododendrons. Some of the plants are occasionally smallish, but, as a whole, they are not at all in the small, dwarfish or "little" class as implied in many published descriptions. The smallest species in the group will attain a height of six feet when fully mature, while the tallest species, incongruously named *Rhododendron minus,* is said to be the most rapidly growing American rhododendron and has been known to reach a height of considerably more than 20 feet, although its usual stature is about ten feet.

The members of this group are exceedingly useful for horticultural purposes in America and should be better known and more widely used, are reliably hardy in New York State and New England and, with smaller leaves and a finer texture, may be employed in some situations where the Catawba and Maximum types, with their coarser leaves, do not appear advantageously. Their flowering dates differ from these others also, alternating with them in such a way that continuity of bloom may be secured where *Rhododendron carolinianum, catawbiense, minus* and *maximum* are planted together to succeed one another during their flowering periods.

Rhododendron carolinianum would be much more popular if its superior forms were better known. Many people think of it as merely a compact rhododendron with small trusses of rosy-purple flowers. This, of course, is the prevailing wild form of the type species. But it also comes in a pure white form, var. *album,* which is often tinged with cream or greenish yellow in the bud and which does not bear the slightest trace of purple or magenta. This form occurs abundantly in the wild and differs sufficiently from the type species to almost constitute a separate species. Compared with the type, var. *album* has lighter green leaves, blooms about one week later, is a somewhat less vigorous grower, behaves differently in crosses and comes quite true from seed unless crossed with other than white-flowered forms. In my opinion, *Rhododendron carolinianum* var. *album* is the most valuable of the series Carolinianum and certainly one of the finest of American rhododendrons.

There are other color variations of the Carolina rhododendron. One of these has a distinct yellowish tinge mixed with rose-pink in the buds and freshly opened flowers, producing a delicate salmon-pink effect. The color plate of var. *foliatum* (following p. 78) shows this color form. This effect is usually lost, however, when the flowers become old, as they become more purplish and the yellow pigment fades out. Then there are various shades of pink, occasionally a very clear rose without the purple tinge. The commonest form of *Rhododendron carolinianum* is a light rose pink, being scarcely more than a faint blush-pink when the plants are flowered in the greenhouse in mid-winter. I do not know that any of the color forms, except var. *album*, have been designated by special names. Good examples of the various flower colors, such as the salmon or peach-pink form and the clear rose type, should be selected, named and disseminated as clonal varieties. As in all the other variable groups of rhododendrons, care should be taken to select superior individuals rather than average plants if the choicest sorts are desired.

Rhododendron minus blooms from four to six weeks later than *R. carolinianum*, usually starting late in June, sometimes early July with some variation between individuals. In general, it fills the gap between the last Catawba rhododendrons and the first Maximum blooms. Its color is much darker than that of *R. carolinianum*, standing between magenta-pink and bright magenta. I consider that *R. minus* has flowers of a richer, brighter magenta, decidedly less toward a magenta lilac color, than the well known wild color of *R. catawbiense*. When planted in a woodland setting the color is not unattractive and appears rather pleasing. Small reports an albino form, but I have never seen this and it is not in the trade; it might be valuable if acquired, as some people object to the prevailing magenta color.

Rhododendron minus is a much looser shrub than *R. carolinianum*, besides being later to bloom and taller in stature. It also occurs much less abundantly in the wild. In nature, the relationship between these two species is somewhat analagous to that existing between *R. catawbiense* and *R. maximum*. *Rhododendrons catawbiense* and *carolinianum* grow on the uplands, while *Rhododendrons maximum* and *minus*, both later bloomers, frequent the shaded ravines and streambanks of the foothills. The former are often quite compact in habit, the latter often rather scrawny. When not in bloom, *R. minus* is difficult to distinguish from *R. carolinianum*, but *R. minus* may generally be detected by its more acuminate leaves, which tend to be twisted between the middle and apex, and by its looser, more straggling habit.

Rhododendron Chapmanii is little known and its hardiness has not yet been thoroughly tested. It is likely to be more tender than the other species, but has excellent possibilities for the Lower South. Its flowers look, from the horticultural standpoint, much like those of *R. carolinianum*. It grows on the low pinelands of western Florida, where one would scarcely expect to find a rhododendron, and is very limited in its distribution.

It seems probable that the best examples of these species have not yet reached Europe and that the growers of England and elsewhere have not come to fully recognize the merits of this series, which, in many respects, is superior to certain of the well known Asiatic importations. Since *Rhododendron carolinianum* and *R. minus* have withstood winter temperatures colder than 20 degrees below zero Fahrenheit in my garden and elsewhere, they may be classed as winter-hardy. Probably ecological conditions abroad, especially in Britain, are unfavorable for *R. carolinianum*. No plants that I have observed there have seemed to be happy, thrifty or floriferous as compared with those regularly seen in the eastern United States. No doubt this accounts for the relatively low merit rating accorded this species.

Members of the Carolinianum series all bear brown dots or scales on the under sides of their leaves. Their relationship to other series is a matter of doubt, but they are said to show some affinity to the Heliolepis series of China. It is certain that they have no phylogenetic relationship with the other evergreen rhododendrons of America. They are difficult to cross outside their own series, but a few interseries hybrids are on record. Most interesting have been some crosses made by the author and also by Mr. Joseph Gable between this series and the Obtusum azaleas. Mine have not lived to bloom.

Rhododendron carolinianum Rehder (from Carolina). CAROLINA RHODODENDRON. *A.* 3–6 ft. tall; up to 15 ft. in var. *foliatum*. Inflor. compact (a), but smaller and sometimes looser (see color plates), 4–10 fls. Flowers (55) about 1½ in. across, from pure white to pale rose, rose, and lilac-rose, commonly light purplish-rose; sometimes with a creamy, or salmon tint in the buds and freshly opened flowers (see color plate of var. *foliatum*); plain or inconspicuously dotted with yellow. Woods and mountain summits, Blue Ridge Mts. of the Carolinas and Tennessee. Bot. Reg. *1* : t. *37*.—This shrub tends to be rather compact and grows to 6 ft. tall, although it is usually about 4 ft. when seen in cultivation. It grows relatively fast from seed after the first few months. It blooms about May 20th at New York City, along with *Rhododendron Kaempferi* and the *R. caucasicum* hybrid 'Boule de Neige.' It is also amenable to forcing in the greenhouse, where it makes a handsome blooming plant, in pot or tub, in early March. Other characteristics of this species have been described above in the discussion of the series and also in Chapter VIII. Variety *album* Rehder has pure white flowers, sometimes tinged with creamy or greenish yellow, and tends to be slightly less vigorous than the type, with leaves a brighter green (not so much inclined to be bronzy) and blooming a week later in the season. It appears not to be merely an albino form of the type, but, rather, a special race or strain, almost deserving of designation as a separate species. It is, however, a choice garden form, probably of greater merit than the type species. Variety *foliatum* Rehder is a looser, tall growing form than the type, attaining a height of 15 ft. Its colors are the same as those of the type, including the yellow-tinged form shown in the color plate following page 78, which is not restricted to var. *foliatum* but occurs in the type also. It is a long-jointed form, probably inferior to the type for ornamental planting, but with a possible use in backgrounds. *R. carolinianum* does not display its true beauty in Britain.

Rhododendron Chapmanii A. Gray (after Dr. A. W. Chapman, botanical explorer, who discovered the species, 1840). CHAPMAN'S RHODODENDRON. *C?* Up to 6 ft. tall, with erect rigid branches. Inflor. similar to *R. carolinianum*. Flowers (55), up to 1½ in. across, rose-pink, often of a peach blossom effect, crisped margins. Jour. N.Y. Bot. Gard. *23*: 127. Pl. 275 (1922). Western Florida, in sandy pine lands near the Gulf Coast, at sea-level.—This limited species, which is verging upon extinction, occurs in a region where one would not expect to find rhododendrons. Although its nearest allies live in the Appalachian region, associated with hardwood forests, and at considerable elevations, *Rhododendron Chapmanii* occurs in a separate region, far south of the Blue Ridge, and at sea-level in sandy pine-barrens. In cultivation, it blooms about the same time as *R. carolinianum,* and its general appearance is very like that of the other members of the series. Proof of its hardiness in the North has not been established, but it should doubtless be much better adapted to conditions in the Lower South than are the Appalachian species, and so has a wide potential usefulness in that region. It is, as yet, very little known and is probably not in the trade. Hand-pollination should induce the production of seeds, which should be sown liberally in order to save this species from possible extinction. It probably has no advantages over *R. carolinianum* for culture in the North, and would perhaps be of little use as a parent of hybrids.

Rhododendron minus Michaux (smaller), syn: R. punctatum Andrews; R. Cuthbertii, Small, PIEDMONT RHODODENDRON. *A.* Shrub of loose habit, 6–10, and sometimes to 20 ft. tall. Inflor. (d), 4–10 fls. Flowers (55), up to 1½ in. across, purplish rose, between magenta-pink and bright magenta (not lilac). Andrews Bot. Rep. *1*: t. 36. Intro. in England 1786 by John Fraser. Sandy woods, inner Coastal Plain to lower Blue Ridge, North Carolina to Georgia and Alabama; frequents the lower, rather than the higher, mountain situations.—Michaux's term *minus* is a misnomer for this species, because, as previously noted, it is the tallest and most rapid growing of the series. Although its color is against it as a garden plant, I consider it very valuable for the woodland, especially for its late bloom which occurs the last week of June. It runs through some of the variations of *Rhododendron carolinianum,* showing forms with either loose or compact flower trusses, but seems to be fairly constant in color. White forms are not in the trade and apparently have not been named, but have been reported. *R. minus* has withstood a temperature of −20°F. in my tests and so appears to be perfectly hardy in the North. I have made some very successful crosses between *R. minus* ♀ and *R. carolinianum* ♂. The blooming date is intermediate between those of the parents and occurs about the first week in June on Long Island. An interesting feature of my cross is that the F_1 progeny grow larger and more vigorously than either of the parent species, although tetraploidy does not appear to be involved. This is the only instance of so-called hybrid vigor, or heterosis, that I have observed in this genus. This cross, made in 1928, is labeled "208." The flowers are shell pink.

CINNABARINUM SERIES

R. KEYSII

Although distinctive and rather lovely things, it is doubtful if these species will prove useful in the eastern United States. Seedlings were grown to blooming age by Mr. Dexter on Cape Cod, but were unable to withstand the climatic conditions for more than a short time. Young plants are now being tested elsewhere. They do well in England, however, and are useful on our Pacific coast, although a bit sensitive to winter cold at Seattle. At any rate, they are decidedly worth while wherever they can be grown.

The shape of the flower is unusual, being almost cylindrical in some forms. The colors, also, are unusual. *Rhododendron cinnabarinum* is described as cinnabar-red. It has a variety with orange or yellow-tipped-red flowers and another with rosy red flowers. Its variety, *Royalei,* has a plum colored effect. *R. concatenans* is especially interesting.

Rhododendron cinnabarinum Hooker f. (cinnabar-red). *B.* A shrub up to 6 ft. tall. Inflor. (s). Flowers (2b), very tubular, 1½–2 in. long, cinnabar-red or brick-red (or orange or rose in varieties). Hooker's Rhodo. Sikkim Himal. t. 8 (1849). Sikkim Himalaya, 10,000–12,000 ft.—A fine free flowering species, somewhat variable, highly esteemed in England. The Rhododendron Association recommends planting it so that the setting sun can be seen through the flowers. In var. *Blandfordiaeflorum* Hooker the flowers are yellow, tipped with red and the calyx is rimlike. It is illustrated in Bot. Mag. t. 4930. Another form is var. *Roylei* Hooker (syn: R. Roylei Hooker), with intense plum red flowers which are more open than those of the other forms, but somewhat shorter. This form is illustrated in Bot. Mag. t. 4788. Var. *aestivale,* var. *pallidum* and var. *purpurellum* are additional color variants. **XX**

Rhododendron concatenans Hutch. (linking together). *B.* Shrub up to 6 ft. with neat glaucous leaves. Inflor. (t), with 7 or 8 fls. in a loose truss. Bell-shaped corolla with 5 half-spreading lobes. Flowers somewhat like (2b), 1½–2 in. long, half open; coppery yellow, sometimes faintly tinged purplish on outside, but deep buff yellow in effect (see color plate). S.E. Tibet.—This is one of the choicer treasures of the rhododendron world and has quite the deepest yellow color I have seen in an evergreen species. Its habit resembles that of *R. cinnabarinum*. It is suspected of being a hybrid. **XX**

Rhododendron igneum Cowan (flaming). A shrub up to 12 ft. with bright salmon-pink flowers; allied to *R. Keysii*.

Rhododendron Keysii Nuttall (after Keys). C. A leggy shrub, attaining a height of 12 ft. Inflor. (see accompanying text figure). Flowers (1a), ¾ in. long, bright red, tipped with yellow. Bot. Mag. t. 4875. Summits and ridges of the Himalayan Mts., Bhutan, 9,000–16,000 ft.—This is a taller form and said to be attractive, but the plants in cultivation have come from the lower part of its range and are not so hardy as those from higher altitudes. They require a sheltered position. The flowers are shorter than those of *R. cinnabarinum*. Both species have a thick, fleshy corolla. **X**

Rhododendron xanthocodon (yellow bell). C. Height 15–25 ft., slender, with pale green leaves. Flowers rich green-yellow, bell-shaped and somewhat between flower types of Cinnabarinum and Triflorum series. **X**

DAURICUM SERIES

The two species comprising this series are almost similar enough to be regarded as geographical forms of the same species and have been so recorded in much of the literature. *Rhododendron mucronulatum* is perhaps the more desirable for ordinary culture, but I am inclined to believe that many of the seedling plants in the trade under this name are merely chance hybrids between this species and *R. dauricum,* having little or no superiority over the latter. Hand pollination of desirable plants with pollen from others of similar type is probably the best means of propagating superior stock. The best flower forms, or types with persistent leaves, should be propagated in this manner or else asexually as clonal varieties.

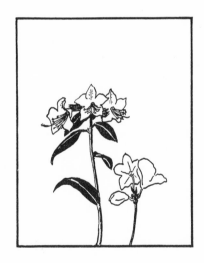

R. DAURICUM

The two forms do not differ strongly. The flowers are slightly larger in *Rhododendron mucronulatum* and, I believe, are more inclined to have wavy margins. It is sometimes asserted that the flowers of *R. dauricum* are deep rose-purple and pink, while those of *R. mucronulatum* are rose colored, but I believe there are few of either that are actually rose colored. One very fine individual appeared some years ago at Cornell University among plants raised from Korean seed of *R. mucronulatum*. This rose-colored form is being propagated under the name of 'Cornell Pink'. All have been various shades of magenta or lilac, the best forms, to be sure, being a quite bright, pleasant magenta, very pleasing in the early spring when few other brightly colored flowers are in bloom. *R. dauricum* is supposed to have leaves that are somewhat more persistent than those of *R. mucronulatum* which are quite deciduous, and a definitely evergreen form of the former exists in var. *sempervirens*. *R. mucronulatum* is supposed to bloom a week or so earlier than *R. dauricum* and is thus the earliest flowering hardy rhododendron grown in the northeastern United States. It blooms on April 1st in New York City. In milder regions and in England the flowers open so early that the spring frosts often ruin them, but this seldom happens in the North. Under glass, they will bloom in January.

These rhododendrons grow from four to eight feet tall and are quite floriferous.

This series occupies an interesting position on the borderline between the azaleas and the true rhododendrons. Their sometimes deciduous, sometimes evergreen foliage, their ten stamens and other floral characters and their ability to cross with both azaleas and rhododendrons, which I have noted in my experiments, marks them as a transition group which will doubtless provide some very interesting data when their phylogenetic relationships are worked out and when hybridization experiments, now in progress, are completed.

Rhododendron dauricum Linnaeus (from Dauria, Siberia), syn: R. dahuricum De Candolle; R. Fittianum Balfour f.; Azalea dahurica Hort. *AA* (*B* in England). Up to 8 ft. tall. Inflor. (m). Leaves deciduous or evergreen. Flowers (14), ¾ in. long, magenta-rose. Bot. Mag. t. 636. N.C. to N.E. Asia and Japan.—This very early species is entirely hardy, but sometimes blooms so early as to be injured by frosts. It has been sufficiently discussed above. The evergreen form is known as var. *sempervirens* Sims and is said to have darker flowers. Var. *roseum* is rose.

Rhododendron mucronulatum Turczaninow (with a sharp point), syn: R. dauricum var. mucronulatum Sims. *A*. See color plate, page 367. 7 to 8 ft. tall. Inflor. (m). Leaves deciduous. Flowers (14), 1½ in. long, 1½ in. across, bright rosy purple. Bot. Mag. t. 8304. Northern China, Manchuria, Korea and northern Japan, about 1,000 ft.—This Korean form is considered superior to the preceding species and is slightly earlier to bloom. The flowers are larger, the color brighter. Variety *acuminatum* Hort., which blooms a fortnight later, is of slightly different habit. Variety *ciliatum* Nakai has leaves and petioles ciliate and a few appressed hairs above. 'Cornell Pink' is a rose-colored sport, and several similar variants are known as var. *roseum*. **X**

EDGEWORTHII SERIES

Although these plants are mostly epiphytes from Upper Burma and Yunnan, some of them, at least, seem to be capable of use in warm English gardens, suggesting that they might be grown also in mild regions elsewhere. As might be imagined, they require shade and a good mulching of leaves when grown under garden conditions, but are found in a diversity of situations when growing wild in their tropical habitat. Some of them are lovely things, but should generally be considered as greenhouse subjects only. Considerable difference exists between species in size of plant, size of flower, color and other characters. *Rhododendron bullatum* is considered the best.

R. EDGEWORTHII

Rhododendron bullatum Franchet (puckered leaves). *D.* Up to 8 ft. tall. Flowers (63?), 2–2½ in. long, white or tinged with pink, sweet-scented. Gard. Chron. 1923: p. 243. Ledges and crevices of cliffs. Yunnan, 8,000–10,500 ft. A beautiful, large-flowered greenhouse species, some forms being hardier than others and able to endure mild conditions outdoors. It is the Chinese relative of *R. Edgeworthii*. There is heavy tomentum on the plant. **X**

Rhododendron Edgeworthii Hooker f. (after M. P. Edgeworth, Bengal Civil Service). *F.* See text-figure. 8–10 ft. An epiphyte on old trees. Inflor. 2–3 fls. Flowers (63), 3–4 in. long, white or tinged with pink, scented. Hooker's Rhodo. Sikkim Himal. t. 21, or Bot. Mag. t. 4936. Sikkim and Bhutan Himalayas, 7,000–10,000 ft. —Makes a thin, straggling bush of 8 to 10 ft. in cultivation. **X**

Rhododendron pendulum Hooker f. (hanging). *C.* A straggling, epiphytic shrub which lives on trees and hangs down with trailing branches. Inflor. (y). Flowers (9), small, white, tinged inside with yellow. Hooker's Rhodo. Sikkim Himal. t. 13. Sikkim Himalaya, 10,000–12,000 ft.

Rhododendron sciaphilum Balfour f. & Ward (shade loving). *F.* Dwarf, 1½–2 ft. tall. Flowers 1¾ in. long, white. On dead tree-trunks or on the ground in deep shade, rain forests in eastern Upper Burma, 7,000–8,000 ft.

Rhododendron seinghkuense Ward (from the Seinghku Valley). *E.* An epiphytic undershrub. Flowers ¾ to 1 in. long, bright sulphur-yellow with red-brown anthers. On moss-bound forest trees. Burma, 6,000–10,000 ft. **X**

FALCONERI SERIES

R. FALCONERI

With those of the Grande series, to whom they are closely related, the members of this group are very distinct from all other rhododendrons. Both groups mentioned occupy the same geographical territory, extending from Nepal through the Himalayas to Upper Burma, Yunnan and Szechuan. All have large leaves and are known as the "big-leaved" sorts.

Needless to say, these series fall into the class of rhododendrons which succeed only in warm English gardens, or moist, mild situations of like character elsewhere. Even there they prefer sheltered, wooded locations and are much better off when planted in a site where they will not start too soon in the spring, for they bloom early and are easily injured by late spring frosts.

The members of the Falconeri series have characteristically bell-shaped or mortar-shaped flowers which have from seven to ten corolla lobes ("petals"), 12 to 18 stamens and a seven- to 18-chambered ovary. Their leaves are large and tomentose on the under surface. The Falconeri series is separated from the Grande series mainly by differences in this tomentum beneath the leaves. The colors of the flowers extend from white, cream and pale yellow, through varying intensities of rose, to lilac, rose-purple and magenta-purple. The flowers range from one to two and one-half inches long and the plants are mostly small trees over ten feet tall, in one species, however, attaining a height of 40 feet under natural conditions. They grow in Cornwall and on the British West Coast.

Rhododendron Falconeri itself is said by some to be among the finest of all rhododendrons. Discovered in 1837, it is very well known in England. Cox states that the plants one purchases, of this series as with all the other large-leaved sorts, should be in good condition when bought, otherwise they transplant badly. They are tree-like in habit and will develop a trunk of a foot or more in diameter. When cut back severely these tree rhododendrons will not start growth again from the base as will other species. It requires 15 years or more for them to reach blooming size from seeds.

Rhododendron arizelum Balfour f. & Forrest (notable or conspicuous). *C.* 10–20 ft. tall. Inflor. (compare text-figure for the series). Flowers (69), 8-lobed, 1¾ in. long, white, creamy yellow or yellow tinged rose; basal blotch of crimson. Open sites in rhododendron forests, W. Yunnan, N.E. Upper Burma and S.E. Tibet, 10,000–12,000 ft.—Some forms have appeared which have flowers as deeply yellow as *Rhododendron lacteum.*

Rhododendron basilicum Balfour f. & W. W. Smith (royal), syn: R. megaphyllum Balfour f. & Forrest; R. regale Balfour f. & Ward. *B.* 10–30 ft. tall. Inflor. (as above). Flowers (69), 8-lobed, 1¼ in. long, fleshy, pale yellow or tinted crimson; crimson blotch. Spec. Rhodo. p. 238. In rhododendron forests, W. Yunnan, 10,000–11,000 ft.—The only member of this series having flat petioles, somewhat winged. X

Rhododendron coriaceum Franchet (leathery), syn: R. foveolatum Rehder & Wilson. *B.* 10–25 ft. tall. Inflor. (as above), lax. Flowers 5–7-lobed, 1½ in. long, white or flushed with pink; crimson blotch. In rhododendron forests, Yunnan and S.E. Tibet, 10,000–13,000 ft.—Characterized by thinnish branches, long narrow leaves tapering toward base and gray-white leaf indumentum. Nearest relative is *R. rex.*

Rhododendron decipiens Lacaita (deceptive). *C.* A small tree. Flowers (69), about (1¼?) in. long, purple-rose. Sikkim.—An imperfectly known species, close to *Rhododendron Hodgsonii* and possibly a natural hybrid between this and *R. Falconeri.*

Rhododendron eximium Nuttall (excellent). *C.* A small tree to 30 ft. tall. Inflor. (a), 12–20 fls. Flowers (69), fleshy, 8–10-lobed, 1¾ in. long, tinted with rose or pink. Bot. Mag. t. 7317; Spec. Rhod. p. 243. In forests on rocky spurs, often forming thickets, in Oola Mts. Bhutan, 10,000–11,000 ft.—The young leaves are covered with a bright orange indumentum, so attractive that this surpasses the flowers in beauty, it is said. It is reported to be a slow grower. It makes its new growth late in the season and should be provided with extra water at this time if needed. A sheltered position is recommended at all times. It resembles *R. Falconeri.*

R. Falconeri Hooker f. (after Hugh Falconer, Garden Supt., in India, 1832). See text-figure. *C.* A large shrub or tree attaining 40 to 50 ft. Leaves from 8 to 12 in. long, with a dense rust-colored indumentum beneath. Inflor. 20 or more fls. Flowers (69), 8–10- (usually 10) lobed, 1½ to 2¼ in. long, creamy white to pale yellow, sometimes tinged with lilac; dark purple blotch at base. Hooker's Rhodo. Sikkim Himal. t. 10. Bot. Mag. t. 4924. The Himalayas from Nepal to Bhutan, about 10,000 ft.—This species is said by some to be one of the world's finest shrubs when seen in its native habitat. It succeeds fairly well in most warm and sheltered British gardens, being best in the South and West. Young plants are growing under sheltered conditions in the United States, but I know of none that have reached flowering size. It resents dry summers, especially after the plants reach flowering size, which is at 12 to 20 years. It is reported to be subject to bark splitting during cold winters and starts so early in the spring that it may be damaged by late frosts. Its very large leaves become disfigured by exposure to wind. For all these reasons, Rhododendron Falconeri needs a well sheltered position. *R. Falconeri,* as well as some other members of its series, apparently is difficult to cross with species in other series, but a few successful hybrids have been made. It was discovered by Griffith in 1837 and by Hooker in 1848 and has long been in cultivation. **XX**

Rhododendron fictolacteum Balfour f. (false lacteum), syn: R. lacteum var. macrophyllum Franchet. *B.* A shapely tree, 15–45 ft. tall. Inflor. (Cf., figure above.) Flowers (69), 7–8-lobed, 1½ in. long, 2½ in. across, white, creamy white or tinted with rose; spotted and blotched with deep crimson. Bot. Mag. t. 8372, as *R. lacteum*. In corries on hillsides and edges of pine forests, Yunnan and S. W. Szechuan, 10,000–13,000 ft.—Widely distributed and variable, this species is one of the hardiest of the series when cultivated in England. When small it is said to be a shy bloomer. Forms with large and small flowers exist, so it is necessary to choose the best when buying. The flowers have a tremendous range of variation in different individuals, most of them being extremely unattractive and of a dirty purplish tinge. **X**

Rhododendron galactinum Balfour f. (milky). *A.* A small tree, 15–22 ft. tall. Flowers 7-lobed, 1¼ in. long, pale rose, with basal blotch, lines and spots of deep crimson. Millais Rhodo. 2:94. Szechuan.—This is less attractive but hardier than the other species. In a controlled cross with *Rhododendron catawbiense album* as the seed parent, *R. galactinum* produced a few weak seedlings which soon died.

Rhododendron Hodgsonii Hooker f. (after B. H. Hodgson, one time resident in Nepal). *B.* A rounded shrub, 12–20 ft. tall. Inflor. (a). Flowers (69), 7–8-lobed, 1¼–1½ in. long, dark magenta-purple when first opening, but fading to pale, dull magenta-lilac, with a few darker basal blotches. Bot. Mag. t. 5552. On rocky spurs and in valleys of the Himalayas, from Nepal to Bhutan, 10,000–12,000 ft.—The fine foliage of shiny green is more attractive than the flowers.

Rhododendron lanigerum Tagg (woolly). *D.* A small gnarled tree. Flowers (69?) 5-lobed, 1½–2 in. long, rose-purple. In middle and upper forests, Assam, 10,000–11,000 ft. **X**

Rhododendron preptum Balfour f. & Forrest (distinguished). *D.* 6–8 ft. tall. Flowers (69?) 1¼ in. long, creamy white, deep crimson blotch. N.E. Upper Burma. —Incompletely known.

Rhododendron rex Léveillé (king). *B.* 15–20 ft. tall. Inflor. 20–30 fls. Flowers (69?), 2 in. long, rose color, with darker blotch and spots. N.E. Yunnan and S.W. Szechuan.—The Chinese form of *R. Hodgsonii*. The flower is good. **XX**

Rhododendron sino-Falconeri Balfour f. (Chinese *Falconeri*). *D.* 20 ft. tall. Flowers (69?) 8-lobed, 2 in. long, pale yellow. In forests, Yunnan, 9,000 ft.

FERRUGINEUM SERIES

This small group comprises some of the few native rhododendrons of Europe. These are all from the mountains of southern Europe, above 4,000 feet. *Rhododendron ferrugineum* and *R. hirsutum* are familiar as the "alpine roses" of the Alps, occurring near together and hybridizing freely in the wild. They appear to have been artificially hybridized with members of the Caroliniana-num series from America. *Rhododendron Kotschyi* is a related form from Transylvania and northern Bulgaria. The members of this series are said to be difficult to grow in the United States, although presumably hardy. Millais reported that they were very subject to a fungous disease, and this may

R. HIRSUTUM

be the factor responsible for their failure. Where successful, they are adaptable for rock gardens. In Edinburgh *R. ferrugineum* is beautiful in both its sprightly rose and its pure white color forms. Its habit and foliage are compact and good, not leggy as elsewhere described, and it is quite the sort of plant admired by landscape architects. If not directly adaptable to American conditions, it should prove useful as a parent of hardy hybrids. I believe it has been overlooked. Its color is better than expected. See color plate, page 334.

Rhododendron ferrugineum Linnaeus (rust colored). ALPINE ROSE. *A.* Small shrub, sometimes 3 to 5 ft. tall. Rather leggy habit. Inflor. (u) but small. Flowers (2a) ¾ in. long, rose. Bot. Cab. t. 65. Alps of southern Europe, from the Pyrenees to Austria.—The Alpenrose of Switzerland. Variety *album* Sweet has white flowers. Variety *atrococcineum* Millais has flowers almost scarlet, and in var. *variegatum* Millais the leaves are edged with cream. An upright form is var. *erectum* Millais. A form with larger flowers and leaves than the type is var. *major* Millais. A form with purple flowers is var. *atropurpureum* Millais.

Rhododendron hirsutum Linnaeus (hairy). HAIRY ALPINE ROSE. *A.* 3–5 ft. tall, and similar to *R. ferrugineum,* but hairy. Inflor. (u). Flowers (2a) but with wider limb, ½ in. long, rose to nearly scarlet. Bot. Mag. t. 479. Alps of southern Europe.—This is said to come from limestone regions and be able to endure calcareous soil. It needs moisture near its roots. Variety *album* Schinz & Kell., has white flowers and var. *laciniatum* Schroet., has jagged leaves.

Rhododendron Kotschyi Simkovics (after Kotschy, an Austrian botanist), syn: R. **myrtifolium** Schott & Kotschy, not Loddiges, which is a hybrid by same name. *A.*

A low shrub with twiggy branchlets. Inflor. (u). Flowers between (7) and (8), base-like (2a) but with wider limb, ½ in. long, purplish pink. Bot. Mag. t. 9132. Transylvanian Alps and northern Bulgaria, 5,000–7,000 ft.

FORTUNEI SERIES

R. FORTUNEI

A large and important series, containing some of the best known and most horticulturally valuable species. This group is divided into six subseries as indicated below. Except for a few outlying members, all the species in this series come from China, centering in Szechuan and extending east as far as Chekiang.

The plants are of medium size, from six to 25 feet high—usually around ten feet—and with smoothish, oval leaves. The flowers usually have six or seven lobes to the corolla, and from 12 to 25 stamens, rarely ten. The series is characterized by large-sized flowers which are of white, pink or rose, having no conspicuous markings and without deep red or yellow pigmentation. The flowers are commonly somewhat funnel-shaped or funnel-bell-shaped.

The other series which most closely resemble the Fortunei series are the Thomsonii, Arboreum and Irroratum groups. Members of the Ponticum series have been hybridized extensively with some of the Fortunei species.

Certain members of the Fortunei series have long been cultivated in England, but have been little used in America. Although only half-hardy in the regions of New York and Philadelphia, several of these species are being readily and successfully grown in sheltered places as far north as Boston. There is a large area in the eastern United States, south of New York City, where, with a little protection, a number of good species of the Fortunei series may be successfully grown. They are worth the trouble in providing special protection when grown as fancier's plants. The experience of American growers does not exactly coincide with the observations of the English Rhododendron Association in measuring the hardiness of these species, due to climatic differences. For instance, some species rated *C* for England are as hardy here as those marked *B,* probably due to absence of frost injury in spring. Of such species as *Rhododendron Fortunei, R. decorum, R. discolor, R. Fargesii* and *R. sutchuenense,* we may say: "hardy in warm gardens and in protected spots near the seacoast where extremes of temperature do not occur." These species are being grown successfully in many places on the Pacific Coast.

Although the Dexter hybrids and other hybrid developments, and certain selected strains within the Fortunei series have given promise of becoming useful cultivars for the American East, this has not caused me to alter my original opinion that the species themselves are not to be recommended for this region except in special situations.

SUBSERIES CALOPHYTUM

Two woodland species from western Szechuan, of which one, *Rhododendron calophytum,* is considered very fine. This is distinguished from the other subseries by its bell-shaped flowers, bulged at the base, broad discoid stigmas, oblanceolate leaves which taper at the base and by other special features. They are early bloomers in spring and have light colored flowers blotched at the base.

Rhododendron calophytum Franchet (beautiful plant). *B*. 15 ft. in cultivation, but up to 50 ft. tall in the wild. Inflor. (a), 30 fls. Flowers (59) 2–2½ in. long, white or rose, with dark crimson blotch and spots. Bot. Mag. t. 9173. Millais Rhodo. 2 : 260. Woodlands, W. Szechuan, 7,000–10,000 ft.—Large leaves and large flower trusses. "Without a doubt, this is one of the finest of all rhododendrons," says Cox, while Millais says words to the same effect and Wilson recommends the species for breeding. "It has the typical long tapering leaves of the series, and yet is always easily distinguishable, for the leaves are more closely packed than in any other member of the series and form what are almost rosettes." It blooms early, which makes it unsuitable where there are spring frosts. It needs shade and moisture at its roots, but does not require so much atmospheric moisture as the large leaved species from India. It takes 7 or 8 years to flower. The pedicels are strikingly red. An encouraging feature about this species is that it grew successfully for Mr. C. O. Dexter on Cape Cod, it has lived several years for Mr. Gable in southern Pennsylvania, and others are raising it. It should have plenty of protection. I consider its flower color rather disappointing. **XX**

Rhododendron Openshawianum Rehder & Wilson (after Rev. H. Openshaw, of the American Baptist Mission in China). Hardiness not determined. Up to 18 ft. tall. Flowers (59?), 1½–2 in. long, white, blotched. Woodlands in W. Szechuan, 7,000–10,000 ft.

SUBSERIES DAVIDII

Four species from Szechuan and Hupeh, characterized by long, rather narrow leaves, comprise this group. *Rhododendron Davidii* itself has an elongated inflorescence as shown in the figure cited below; the rachis is relatively long and the flowers are funnel-shaped. In the other species the inflorescence is more umbellate or corymbose. *Rhododendron sutchuenense,* a handsome species, is regarded as an excellent plant for form and foliage on the West Coast and is accorded three stars on the English list, giving it preference over the other species in the subseries.

Rhododendron Davidii Franchet (after l'Abbé Armand David, early collector in W. China). See figure (g). Perhaps not in cultivation. 9–15 ft. tall. Inflor. (g). Flowers (66) 2 in. long, rose or lilac, spotted purple. Nouv. Arch. Mus. Paris ser. *2,* vol. 10; Pl. David. *2*: pl. 11. (1888). Woodlands in W. Szechuan, 10,000 ft. —Said to be a slow grower.

Rhododendron Huianum Fang (after Prof. H. H. Hu, China). Shrub to 15 ft. with lilac flowers. Contrib. Biol. Lab. Sc. Soc. China, Bot. Ser. *12*:38 (1939), Szechuan. —Not in general cultivation.

Rhododendron planetum Balfour f. (wandering). *C.* 4–12 ft. tall. Inflor. (a) 10 fls. Flowers (66) 1½–2 in. long, pink without markings. Bot. Mag. t. 8953. Szechuan. —This appeared as a rogue at the Coombe Wood Nursery among seed sent from Szechuan by E. H. Wilson, under a wrong number.

Rhododendron praevernum Hutchinson (before the spring). *B.* A medium-sized compact shrub, much like *R. sutchuenense.* Inflor. (a?). Flowers (66?) 2 in. long, white or tinted rose, with a wine-red blotch and spots. Gard. Chron. *73*: 159. In woods, Hupeh, 5,000–7,000 ft.—This is growing on Cape Cod.

Rhododendron sutchuenense Franchet (from Szechuan). *B.* A large shrub 10–20 ft. high in the wild. Inflor. between (a) and (b). Flowers (59) 2–3 in. long, lilac-rose, spotted with deeper rose; sometimes lilac-white. Bot. Mag. t. 8362. Woodlands in Szechuan and Hupeh, 5,000–8,000 ft.—A good plant with handsome foliage and pale rosy flowers. There is a form with magenta flowers which should be avoided. It needs shade and blooms so early that protection from late frosts is desirable. Seedlings are growing on Cape Cod, but has failed south of Philadelphia. Variety *Geraldii* has deeper rose colored flowers and a magnificent chocolate blotch at the base. *Rhododendron sutchuenense* is said to be growing under woodland conditions on Long Island. Highly recommended in England. **X**

Subseries Fortunei

This subseries contains 13 species, three of which are very well known and appear, in seedlings, to offer real possibilities for American culture. These are *Rhododendron decorum, R. discolor* and *R. Fortunei.* The latter is said to be the first Chinese true rhododendron introduced in western gardens and, in its several forms, is worthy of attention.

Variants or hybrids, presumably of this series and known to the author, are notable for a delightful gardenia-like fragrance and are hardy on Cape Cod. A delicacy of coloring, with clear opal-like rose and lavender tints free from grayishness, characterizes some of the flower forms to be found within the Fortunei subseries. These tints do not assume a darkening or "washy" character nor show evidence of a "dirty" form of magenta or lilac as do, for instance, some of the *R. catawbiense* variations. The wide-open character of the flowers of *R. discolor* and some of the others, which may be four inches or more across, renders the plants particularly delightful when in bloom, because the flowers are not only large but graceful as well, frequently having wavy margins.

In western China the members of this subseries grow on hillsides in woodlands and about the margins of woods at altitudes of 4,000 to 10,000 feet. *Rhododendron Fortunei* itself is an eastern representative, growing in Chekiang at 3,000 feet. In cultivation, they need protection. Members of this subseries are the parents of many choice hybrids, and more, I believe, are still to come which ought to be valuable for American gardens.

Rhododendron Chengianum Fang (after Dr. Cheng). A shrub to 20 ft. with white flowers. Ic. Pl. Omeisium *1*:t.31 (1942). China.

Rhododendron chlorops Cowan (green eye). *B.* 6 to 10 ft. tall, with leathery leaves. Inflor. a lax umbel of 6–8 flowers, 1½ in. long, fleshy; cream or pale yellow, with a greenish base marked with rows of purple spots and blotch. Notes Roy. Bot. Gard. Edinburgh *21*:143 (1953).—Presumably from Yunnan, but described from plants in cultivation.

Rhododendron decorum Franchet (ornamental), syn: R. Franchetianum Léveillé; R. hexamerum Handel-Mazzetti; R. Giraudiasii Léveillé; R. Spooneri Hemsley & Wilson. *C.* 6–20 ft. tall. Inflor. (a), 8–10 fls. Flowers (67) 1½–2 in. long, white to soft rose with or without greenish or pinkish spots. Bot. Mag. t. 8659. In scrub on hillsides and in woodlands, Yunnan and Szechuan, 8,000–11,000 ft.—The flowers are sweet scented. This species, which is a close ally of *R. Fortunei,* is widely distributed and exceedingly variable. Different strains, said Mallais, have widely divergent times of bloom, ranging from April to July or even later in England. Formerly hybrids of *R. decorum* were considered of little value, but several good ones have more recently appeared. The form sent from China by Wilson seems to be superior to those of Forrest and Farrer, the latter being quite tender. While *R. decorum* has succeeded well on the West Coast, and will grow in mild protected spots in the Middle Atlantic Coast area, it cannot be regarded as more than a fancier's pet in the American Northeast and its merits do not justify the care required to grow it in this region. Other observers may disagree with this opinion. **X**

Rhododendron diaprepes Balfour f. & W. W. Smith (distinguished), syn: R. rasile Balfour f. & W. W. Smith. *C* (or *D*). 10–25 ft. tall. A loose inflor. of 7–10 fls. (b?).

Flowers (67?) up to 4 in. long and as much as 5 in. across, white or faintly flushed with rose, slightly scented. Open sites and margins of forests in S.W. Yunnan and N.E. Upper Burma, 10,000–11,000 ft.—This species, regarded as the finest of the Fortunei series, is a large-leaved and large-flowered expression of *Rhododendron decorum,* coming from the moister monsoon area and somewhat less hardy than the latter. In England it suffers from bark splitting and is considered hardy only in the extreme West. Young seedlings, which are possibly chance hybrids, are growing successfully on Cape Cod. **X**

Rhododendron discolor Franchet (different colors), syn: R. mandarinorum Diels; R. Kirkii Hort. *B.* 20 ft. tall ultimately. Inflor. between (a) and (b). Flowers (67), resembling also (54) and (63), 2–3 in. long, up to 4 in. across, white or pale pinkish, tube yellowish green at base, scented. Bot. Mag. t. 8696. Woodlands, Szechuan and Hupeh, 4,000–7,000 ft.—A relatively late blooming species and one that is recommended as most desirable of the Fortunei series for general cultivation in England. It blooms the first week in July. In some localities its late summer growth is against it, but it is a highly desirable species and of potential value as a parent of hybrids. Mr. J. C. Williams of England called it "Wilson's second-best discovery." Its scent is not the least of its charms. *R. discolor* is excellent for the American West Coast, but cannot yet be considered hardy in most parts of the East. Otherwise it is a very excellent species. **XX**

Rhododendron Faithae (for Faith, a woman's name). Hardiness not rated. Height 12–20 ft., with peeling bark. Flowers large, white, fragrant, glandular outside.

Rhododendron Fortunei Lindley (after Robt. Fortune, a famous early collector in China). FORTUNE'S RHODODENDRON. *B.* 10–12 ft. tall, sometimes 20 ft. Inflor. between (a) and (b). See color plate and text-figure accompanying series. Flowers (67) 1½–2 in. long, 2¾–3½ in. across, pale lilac rose, fragrant. Bot. Mag. t. 5596. Chekiang, eastern China, about 3,000 ft.—This outlying species, uncommon in its native habitat, has been of unusual value in cultivation. It is one of the hardiest of the Chinese rhododendrons, has large flowers of clear but delicate color and gives a delightful fragrance. Its general appearance is pleasing. In sheltered situations, such as Cape Cod and certain protected spots on Long Island, *Rhododendron Fortunei* is doubtless entirely feasible as a garden subject. It seems to be reliably hardy also south of Philadelphia. Certain seedlings appear to succeed even at Boston. It blooms just after *Rhododendron carolinianum* and about a fortnight ahead of the main group of Catawba hybrids. There are later blooming forms, however. A clone called 'Sir Charles Butler' (see color plate, page 335) is perhaps a mere form of the species. *R. Fortunei* is not the equal of *R. discolor* and generally is no hardier. **X**

Rhododendron glanduliferum Franchet (gland bearing). An imperfectly known species from Yunnan having white flowers 2 in. long. It is close to *R. Fortunei,* but much more glandular, the glands assuming the appearance of bristles.

Rhododendron Hemsleyanum Wilson (after W. B. Hemsley, English botanist). Apparently not in cultivation. A small tree of 18 ft. with white flowers 2 in. long, collected in 1910 on Mt. Omei, Szechuan, by E. H. Wilson, who wrote: "A remarkable, fine and distinct rhododendron only met with on Mt. Omei and very rare even there."

Rhododendron Houlstonii Hemsley & Wilson (after G. Houlston, friend and helper of E. H. Wilson), syn: R. Fortunei var. Houlstonii Rehder & Wilson. B. 6–12 ft. tall flowers (67?), about 2 in. long, pale pink or white flowers. Mixed woods, Hupeh and E. Szechuan, 4,500–7,000 ft.

Rhododendron platypodum Diels (broad stalked). *C.* Close to *R. decorum,* but with pinkish red flowers.

Rhododendron serotinum Hutchinson (autumnal). *B.* A straggling shrub of 10 ft. Inflor. between (a) and (b). Flowers (67) 2¼ in. long, white, blotched, spotted and tinged with red. Blooms August to October. Bot. Mag. t. 8841. China.—This is remarkable as the latest rhododendron to bloom, but is said to be worthless in all its other features.

Rhododendron vernicosum Franchet (shiny), syn: ·R. adoxum Balfour f. & Forrest; R. lucidum Franchet, not Nuttall. *B.* A spreading shrub 6–25 ft. tall. Inflor. (b). Flowers (66) 1½ in. long, clear pink (or in varieties white to bright rose), with or without crimson markings. Bot. Mag. t. 8834. In open thickets or open situations in forests, W. Szechuan, W. and N.W. Yunnan, 9,000–11,000 ft.— There are four geographical forms: vars. *araliaeforme, euanthum, rhantum* and *Sheltonae,* all hardly distinguishable from the type species.

Subseries Griffithianum

One well known species from Sikkim and Bhutan, notable for its handsome large white flowers, constitutes this subseries. It is distinguished from other subseries by its large, smooth calyx. *Rhododendron Griffithianum* itself is not at all hardy, being, in reality, only a greenhouse subject, but it has been a parent of several notable garden hybrids, among which 'Loderi,' 'Kewense' and 'Pink Pearl' are some of the most famous. It is said to be the largest flowered of any of the Himalayan rhododendrons and is certainly one of the most magnificent.

Rhododendron Griffithianum Wight (after Wm. Griffith, Supt. Calcutta Botanic Garden, 1842), syn: R. Aucklandii Hooker f. *E.* In cultivation 4–12 ft. tall. Inflor. lax (b). Flowers (63), 1½ to 2½ in. long and as much as 4½ to 6 in. across, white with greenish spots, sometimes touched with pink; edges often crenulate (frilled); slightly fragrant. Bot. Mag. t. 5065. Himalayan Mts., Sikkim and Bhutan, 7,000–9,000 ft.—This superb but tender species is variable and has several different forms. It has been a parent of many valuable hybrids. **XX**

SUBSERIES ORBICULARE

A small group which does not fit into the other subseries and may have some affinity with the Thomsonii series. The flowers are rose with a bluish tinge. Its chief horticultural distinction is in its round foliage and exceedingly round, symmetrical habit of growth. One comes from western Szechuan and requires protection.

Rhododendron cardiobasis Sleumer (with heart-shaped base). Shrub to 10 ft. with leaves shaped like those of *R. orbiculare*. Flowers large, with 7 lobes, in lax trusses of 6 or 7, white and rose colored. Kwangsi, S. China.—Not in cultivation.

Rhododendron orbiculare Decaisne (circular leaves), syn: R. rotundifolium David. *A*. A rounded, much branched bush up to 9 or 10 ft. tall; in cultivation about 6 ft. high and 13 ft. in diameter. Inflor. between (a) and (b). Flowers (70) 1½ in. long, rose, often with a bluish tinge. Bot. Mag. t. 8775. Woodlands and thickets, W. Szechuan, 8,000–10,000 ft.—The chief beauty of the plant is said to be its round leaves and perfectly symmetrical form, resembling the outline of a clipped yew. It needs some shelter and plenty of space to develop this feature. The flowers are good. It has been recommended by Wilson for breeding purposes. It is growing on Cape Cod. **XX**

SUBSERIES OREODOXA

A group of four species characterized by smaller flowers than are found elsewhere within the series, a neat shrublike habit, more or less elliptic-shaped leaves and less flowers in a truss. *Rhododendron Fargesii* does well on Long Island and Cape Cod when grown in sheltered situations. A disadvantage in England is that most of these species bloom too early in the spring and become injured by frost.

Rhododendron erubescens Hutchinson (blush red). *B*. Height not given. Inflor. (b). Flowers (70) 1½ in. long, white. Bot. Mag. t. 8643. China.—A relative of *R. Fargesii* raised from seed collected by E. H. Wilson. The flowers are rose-carmine outside, white inside and it blooms in April. Resents sun and requires shade.

Rhododendron Fargesii Franchet (after Père Paul Farges, French missionary in Szechuan). *B*. From 3 to 18 ft. tall. Inflor. (b). Flowers (58) 1½ in. long, usually pink, but sometimes white to deep rose, spotted red. Bot. Mag. t. 8736. In woodlands, 7,000–10,000 ft., Szechuan and Hupeh.—Considered attractive and of interest because it will grow on Cape Cod, Long Island and elsewhere in the eastern United States, in warmish, sheltered situations. In England it is so floriferous that, unless the dead flowers are picked off, the plant will injure or kill itself through excessive seed production. **X**

Kurume Azalea 'Hinodegiri'

Rhododendron Schlippenbachii

Rhododendron oreodoxa Franchet (glory of the mountains). *B*. A shrub or small tree, 6–10 ft. tall. Inflor. (b). Flowers (66) 1½ in. long, pale rose with or without purple spots. Bot. Mag. t. 8518 as R. haematocheilum. Woodlands, W. Szechuan and Kansu, 7,000–10,000 ft.—This species flowers early and needs protection from late frosts, although its buds are relatively frost-resistant. The buds have a peculiar habit of showing color before they start to open. Very floriferous after reaching a certain height. Wilson recommended this as a parent for breeding. The species has a wide range in Szechuan and Kansu, where the following geographical forms have been reported, all scarcely distinguishable from the type species: Var. *haematocheilum* Craib, var. *Limprichtii* Diels and var. *Reginaldii* Balfour f. **X**

Rhododendron praeteritum Hutchinson (passed over). *C*. Height not given. Inflor. between (a) and (b). Flowers (70) 1¼–1½ in. long, pink or white flushed pink, spotted with carmine. Gard. Chron. *71* (1922), fig. 73; *73* (1923), fig. 67. Western Hupeh.—Very close to *R. oreodoxa*.

FULVUM SERIES

This small series, which after revision contains only two species, comes mainly from Yunnan, with some collections from southeastern Tibet, and thus are not too hardy. They are closely related to those of the Campanulatum series, being large shrubs with an indumentum under the leaves, that of *R. fulvum* being uniquely composed of mop-shaped fawn-colored hairs. There is considerable variation among them, both in flower color and in foliage, as well as in character of plant and in floriferousness, so that the good ones are quite good and the poor ones quite poor. *R. fulvum* is regarded as a handsome plant in its best forms, with a unique and effective appearance.

Rhododendron fulvum Balfour f. & W. W. Smith (tawny), syn: R. fulvoides Balfour f. & Forrest. *B*. 3–20 ft. Flowers 1–1½ in. long, white flushed pale to deep rose, with or without crimson blotch at base, spotted or unspotted, in trusses of 8–15. Indumentum under leaves of mop-like hairs (i.e. capitellate hairs, held together in bundles like a mophead), yellowish to deep cinnamon, almost orange. Bot. Mag. t. 9587. Thickets and margins of forests, W. Yunnan, 8,000–11,000 ft.— This species takes its name from the bright orange-like indumentum beneath the leaves, which always makes the plant a conversation-piece. **X**

Rhododendron uvarifolium Diels (with Uvaria-like leaves), syn: R. monbeigii Rehder & Wilson; R. niphargum Balfour f. & Ward; R. dendritrichum Balfour f. & Forrest. *C*. Up to 30 ft. Leaves with a thin or thick white or ash-gray indumentum. Flowers campanulate, to 1½ in. long, white or pale rose or pink, with or without crimson blotch at base, spotted or not spotted. In rhododendron forests, N.W. Yunnan, 7,000–8,000 ft. Bot. Mag. t. 9480 as R. niphargum. Var. *griseum* Cowan has leaves thicker and broader, with whitish silky indumentum.

GLAUCOPHYLLUM SERIES

R. GLAUCOPHYLLUM

These are mostly dwarf shrubs growing high in the Himalayan Mountains of Sikkim, southeastern Tibet, Upper Burma and Yunnan, from 10,000 to 13,000 feet above sea-level. They have thick scaly evergreen leaves, glaucous (covered with "bloom") on the under side. Four of the species have yellow or yellowish flowers, while five have pink or purple flowers. With the exception of *Rhododendron Genestierianum*, which attains 12 feet, the species are all under four feet tall, the majority being only one or two feet high. The flowers are relatively small, not being over one inch long and less than one and one-half inches across in the largest flowered species. Some have aromatic foliage.

Mr. de Rothschild states that while some of the Glaucophyllums (formerly called Glaucums) are among the best dwarf shrubs, other members of this series are scarcely worth the space they occupy. *Rhododendron charitopes* he considers a splendid small bush for edgings or for the rock garden, and *R. Genestierianum,* although rather tender, is interesting and attractive, being the unusual combination of a rather tall plant bearing quantities of small flowers, plum colored and glaucous. Cowan and Davidian (1948) have divided this series into two subseries and have reduced *R. charitostreptum, R. hypolepidotum* and *R. pruniflorum* to varietal rank.

Subseries Glaucophyllum

Rhododendron brachyanthum Hutchinson (short flowers). *A.* 2–5 ft. tall. Inflor. (v). Flowers (25) ¾ in. long, pale or greenish yellow. Bot. Mag. t. 8750. Yunnan, 9,000 ft.—Of little garden value. Var. *hypolepidotum* Franchet, syn: R. charitostreptum Balfour f. & Ward. This differs from the type in having leaves that are densely scaly on the under side. **X**

Rhododendron charitopes Balfour f. & Farrer (graceful of aspect). *B.* Up to 1 ft. tall. Flowers 1 in. long, clear apple-blossom pink, speckled with crimson. Upper Burma, 10,000–12,000 ft.

Rhododendron glaucophyllum Rehder (bluish-gray leaf), syn: R. glaucum Hooker f. Calyx leafy. *B.* 2–4 ft. tall. Flowers (12), up to 1 in. long, pale old rose color (pink), not scented. Bot. Mag. t. 4721. Sikkim, 10,000–12,000 ft.—A small shrub with very aromatic foliage, having a resinous smell. Long in cultivation. Good for the front of the border. Var. *tubiforme* Cowan & Davidian has a long tubular corolla.

Rhododendron shweliense Balfour f. & Forrest (from the Shweli River). *B.* 2–2½ ft. tall, with aromatic foliage. Flowers 2/3 in. long, pale pink, tinged yellow. Open cliffs and rocky slopes, Shweli-Salween divide in W. Yunnan, 10,000–11,000 ft.

Rhododendron tsangpoense Ward (from the Tsangpo River). *B.* Small shrub 1–2 ft. tall, forming dense tangled scrub. Flowers 1 in. long, dull pink or deep cerise. Steep alpine slopes, Tibet, 12,000–13,000 ft. Var. *curvistylum;* Var. *pruniflorum* (Hutchinson) Cowan & Davidian (syn: R. sordidum Hutchinson) has overlapping scales on under side of leaves.

SUBSERIES GENESTIERIANUM

Rhododendron Genestierianum Forrest (after Père Genestier, French missionary in Tibet), syn: R. mirabile Ward. *E.* Up to 12 ft. tall. Flowers ½ in. long, plum purple, covered with a glaucous bloom, small. In cane brakes and on open rocky slopes, W. Yunnan.—This species is taller and considerably more tender than the others of this series. The small bright green leaves are white underneath and the small flowers are not unlike those of *R. campylogynum.*

Rhododendron micromeres Tagg (with small parts). *C.* A shrub up to 6 ft., usually epiphytic. Inflor. terminal. Flowers rotately campanulate, creamy yellow or white, ½ in. long, in clusters of 3–8. S.E. Tibet.

GRANDE SERIES

This series, most closely related to the Falconeri group, comprises relatively tender species mostly coming from the rain-frosts. They form trees or large shrubs at elevations of from 8,000 to 10,000 feet above sea-level and are characterized by having large leaves. In cultivation they require complete shelter from all direct wind. It generally requires many years for a plant to attain blooming age. The flower colors run from white and pale yellow to rose, red and magenta. The flowers average about or under two inches in length and are generally borne in fair-sized trusses of 20 or more. The leaves are evergreen and large, often being two feet long in *Rhododendron sinogrande.* The tallest tree

R. GRANDE

rhododendron known belongs in this series. It is *R. giganteum* and attains a height of 80 feet in the forests of southwestern Yunnan where it is native.

Rhododendron coryphaeum Balfour f. & Forrest (leading), syn: R. semnum Balfour f. & Forrest. *C.* 15–20 ft. tall. Inflor. (a?). Flowers (69?) 1¾ in. long, creamy white, with basal blotch and spots of crimson. Rhododendron and pine forests, N.W. and W. Yunnan, 12,000 ft.

Rhododendron giganteum Forrest (gigantic). *E.* The largest tree rhododendron, attaining 80 ft. Flowers funnel-campanulate, 2½ in. long, deep rose crimson without spots, basal blotch of crimson; fleshy; borne in trusses of 20–25. Open forests, S.W. Yunnan, 9,000 ft.—The giant among rhododendrons, requiring many years to develop into blooming size. **X**

Rhododendron grande Wight (large), syn: R. argenteum Hooker f., R. longifolium Nuttall, Waldemaria argentea Klotzsch. SILVERY RHODODENDRON. *E.* Tree to 30 ft. Inflor. (a). See figure for series. Flowers (69) 2–2½ in. long, white or cream with purple blotches, pink in bud. Bot. Mag. t. 5054. Forming forests at 8,000–10,000 ft., Sikkim and Bhutan.—The only Himalayan species in the series and a magnificent plant in its natural habitat. The silvery leaved *Rhododendron argenteum* was formerly considered a separate species, but more recently has been merged with *Rhododendron grande.* **XX**

Rhododendron Macabeanum Watt MS. (descript. Balfour f.) (after Macabe). *B.* A tree up to 45 ft. tall. Flowers about 2 in. long, pale yellow or creamy white, with large purple spots. Naga Hills, Manipur. **XX**

Rhododendron magnificum Ward (distinguished). *E.* A tree up to 45 ft. Thin brown indumentum on under surfaces of large leaves. Inflor. large trusses of 15–30 tubular-campanulate flowers, rose-purple. Burma-Tibet frontier.

Rhododendron Mollyanum Cowan (after the Duchess of Montrose). *B.* A tree to 30 ft. Silvery-white plastered indumentum on under surfaces of large leaves. Inflor. large trusses of 15 pink flowers with crimson basal blotch. S.E. Tibet.

Rhododendron peregrinum Tagg (foreign). *C.* A small tree, height when mature not known. Flowers 1¾ in. long, white, tinted rose, blotched, spotted and lined with bright red. S.W. Szechuan.—This appeared as a rogue among seeds of another species sent from China by E. H. Wilson.

Rhododendron praestans Balfour f. & W. W. Smith (excellent). *C.* 20–30 ft. tall. Flowers 1½ in. long, magenta rose, or flushed with that color; crimson blotch. Pine forests and shady cliffs, Yunnan, 11,000–13,000 ft.

Rhododendron protistum Balfour f. & Forrest (first of the first). *E.* 25–45 ft. tall. Flowers 2 in. long, creamy white, flushed rose, in trusses of 20–30. Mixed forests, N.W. Yunnan, 10,000–13,000 ft.

Rhododendron pudorosum Cowan (very bashful). Tree to 25 ft. Large bud-scales are persistent. Flowers large mauve-pink with a basal patch of magenta. Notes Bot. Gard. Edin. *19*:239 (1937).

Rhododendron semnoides Tagg & Forrest (resembling *R. semnum*). A small tree up to 15–20 ft. tall. Flowers 1¾ in. long, white, flushed rose, with a crimson blotch. Rhododendron forests in S.E. Tibet, 12,000–13,000 ft.—Allied to *R. coryphaeum* and *R. praestans*.

Rhododendron sidereum Balfour f. (excellent). *D.* Up to 30 ft. tall. Inflor. (a?). Flowers (69?) 1½ in. long, creamy white to clear yellow, crimson blotch at base. Mixed forests in N.E. Upper Burma and W. Yunnan, 9,000–10,000 ft.—Resembles *R. grande,* which it represents on the Burmese frontier.

Rhododendron sinogrande Balfour f. & W. W. Smith (Chinese *R. grande*). *D.* A tree, 20–30 ft. tall. Inflor. (a), about 20 flowers to a truss. Flowers (69) 2–2½ in. long, dull creamy white with crimson blotch. Bot. Mag. t. 8973. In rhododendron forests, W. Yunnan, N.E. Upper Burma and S.E. Tibet, 10,000–14,000 ft.—An even finer species than *Rhododendron grande,* of which it is a Chinese relative. It is remarkable for its very large leaves, some examples in cultivation exceeding 30 in. in length. The earlier introductions were tender, but later collections have brought forth hardier forms, notably Forrest's No. 20,387. Variety *boreale* is a northern form, said to be of better color than the type, soft yellow throughout without markings or pale yellow with a crimson blotch at base. The hardier forms are not so tender as *R. grande.* One hardly knows where *R. sinogrande* might succeed in North America, but it should have a mild climate with abundant summer rainfall. It is surely worth testing wherever there is a possibility of success, for it is a magnificent foliage plant. Young plants are at Berkeley, Calif. **XX**

Rhododendron Watsonii Hemsley & Wilson (after W. C. Haines-Watson, Chinese Customs). *C.* 7–8 ft. tall. Flowers 1½ in. long, white with crimson blotch. In thin conifer forests, W. Szechuan, 9,000–10,000 ft.—An aberrant member of the series, not closely allied to the others.

HELIOLEPIS SERIES

R. RUBIGINOSUM

A group, mainly from Yunnan, resembling the Triflorum series. Cox says that, although the flowers are not striking, the plants have a sturdy bushy habit and a wholesome aromatic scent, which makes them horticulturally desirable. In height they may vary from six to 30 feet, the flowers being funnel-shaped and ranging through violet, mauve and red in color, often being spotted. *Rhododendron rubiginosum* is said to tolerate limestone soil, provided that it is grown from seed upon such a medium. Although *R. invictum* comes from the relatively northern province of Kansu, it is rated as less hardy than most of the others by the British authorities.

The status of *R. rubiginosum* and *R. heliolepis* is doubtful so far as the eastern United States is concerned, but both are hardy in the Pacific northwest, where they seem to do well in nearly any location.

Rhododendron brevistylum Franchet (with a short style), syn: R. porrosquameum Balfour f. & Forrest. *A*. Up to 10 ft. tall. Flowers 1½ in. long, pale to deep rose with crimson markings. Open alpine pastures, Yunnan, 12,000–13,000 ft.

Rhododendron desquamatum Balfour f. & Forrest (bereft of scales), syn: R. catapastum Balfour f. & Forrest; R. stenoplastum Balfour f. & Forrest; R. squarrosum Balfour f. *B*. Up to 25 ft. tall. Flowers 1½ in. long, mauve, spotted, relatively large for the series. W. Yunnan to N. Burma, 10,000 ft.

Rhododendron fumidum Balfour f. & W. W. Smith (smoke colored). *C*. About 6 ft. tall. Flowers bell-shaped, 1 in. long, dull violet, N.E. Yunnan, about 10,000 ft.

Rhododendron heliolepis Franchet (glittering scales), syn: R. plebeium Balfour f. & W. W. Smith. *B*. Up to 10 ft. tall. Flowers widely funnel-shaped, 1 in. long, red or rose colored (shades of old rose) with darker spots; sometimes almost white; borne in small, loose trusses. Yunnan, 10,000–11,000 ft.—Foliage intensely aromatic. Blooms in June after most other species have finished.

Rhododendron invictum Balfour f. & Farrer (unconquered). *D*. Up to 6 ft. tall. Flowers widely funnel-shaped, 1 in. long, purple. Alpine coppice, Kansu, 8,000–9,000 ft.

Rhododendron Leclerei Léveillé (after Leclere). *C.* Flowers widely funnel-shaped, ¾ in. long, blue (might this not actually be violet or bluish magenta?). High plateau, Yunnan, 10,000 ft.

Rhododendron oporinum Balfour f. & Ward (autumn flowering). *B.* Flowers 1 in. long, rose pink, with a dark red blotch at base. Open ridges, E. Upper Burma, 11,000–12,000 ft.

Rhododendron pholidotum Balfour f. & W. W. Smith (scaly). *B.* Up to 8 ft. tall. Flowers widely funnel-shaped, 1¼ in. long, rose to rose-purple, spotted. Open sites, N. Yunnan, 10,000–12,000 ft.

Rhododendron rubiginosum Franchet (full of rust). *A.* See text-figure for series. Up to 30 ft. tall. Flowers (20) 1¼ in. long, mauve, spotted brown. Bot. Mag. t. 7621. Open situations in forests, Yunnan, 7,500–11,000 ft.—Quite desirable and very floriferous. Blooms in May. Said to tolerate limestone soils.

IRRORATUM SERIES

A large series of shrubby, rather than tree-like plants, which, in general characteristics, probably most resemble those of the series Arboreum and Fortunei. Included in this series are several exceptional species, of which *Rhododendron eriogynum*, *R. facetum* and *R. Kyawi* are highly regarded. Unfortunately, they are tender outside the mildest regions of England and so, like other soft-leaved species, can be of little direct use in most parts of North America. They have scarlet, crimson or rose flowers, not scented, usually tubular in form and with prominent spotting. The series is divided into two subseries, of which the subseries Parishii is nearly distinct enough to be called a separate series.

R. IRRORATUM

Subseries Irroratum

The two subseries are separated on the basis of indumentum character. In this group the mature leaves have no indumentum, except in three species (*Rhododendron agastum*, *R. leptopeplum* and *R. pennivenium*) in which it is present but thin and never stellate. The leaves are usually acute or acuminate at the apex in this subseries, in which it differs from the usually rounded leaves of the next subseries.

Rhododendron Aberconwayi Cowan (after Lord Aberconway). *B.* A medium-sized shrub to 8 ft. Inflor. (b), racemose, 6–12 flowers (57) 1–1½ in. long, open, flatly-campanulate or saucer-shaped; white or tinged pink, with pink or crimson specks on upper petal. Leaves are of an unusually rigid, leathery texture, with margins mark-edly recurved, brittle. Eastern Yunnan. R.H.S. Rhod. Yr. Bk. *3*:42–43. 1 illus. (1948). **XX**

Rhododendron agastum Balfour f. & W. W. Smith (charming). *D.* 10–20 ft. tall. Flowers 2 in. long, rose color, with basal blotch of crimson which breaks into lines and spots. Oak and pine forests, W. Yunnan, 6,000–9,000 ft.

Rhododendron Annae Franchet. *B.* 4–6 ft. tall. Flowers 1 in. long, creamy white, flushed rose, purple spotted, Kweichow, 4,500 ft.

Rhododendron anthosphaerum Diels (round flowered). *C.* 20–30 ft. tall. Inflor. between (a) and (b) but smaller. Flowers (20) 1½–2 in. long, rose magenta with crimson markings and a black-crimson blotch. Bot. Mag. t. 9083. Open sites in pine forests, N.W. Yunnan, 10,000–11,000 ft. *R. hylothreptum* is a subspecies.

Rhododendron araiophyllum Balfour f. & W. W. Smith (narrow leaved). *D.* A slender shrub 9–16 ft. tall. Flowers cup-shaped, 1¼–1½ in. long, white or tinged with rose, crimson blotch. Mixed forests in W. Yunnan, 9,000–10,000 ft.—Said to be one of the best of the Irroratums, with neat foliage and a graceful appearance.

Rhododendron cerochitum Balfour f. & Forrest (covered with wax). *C.* About 20 ft. tall. Flowers 2 in. long, rose, with or without a few deeper markings. Rhodo-dendron and pine forests, W. Yunnan, 10,000–11,000 ft.

Rhododendron dimitrum Balfour f. & Forrest (with double cap). *D.* 6–7 ft. Flowers 1½ in. long, deep rose with crimson spots. Open thickets, mid-western Yunnan, 10,000 ft.

Rhododendron epapillatum Balfour f. & Cooper (without a nipple). Hardiness not recorded. Up to 17 ft. tall. Flowers 2 in. long, pale rose with deeper tinted spots and faint blotch. Bhutan, 6,000 ft.

Rhododendron eritimum Balfour f. & W. W. Smith (highly prized). *C.* 18 ft. tall. Flowers 1½ in. long, dark crimson or a lighter rose magenta, blotched at base. Open thickets, Yunnan, 9,000 ft.—Four forms have been classed as subspecies of *Rhododendron eritimum,* as follows: *Rhododendron chawchiense* Balfour f. & Farrer, with smaller flowers of a blue-magenta color; *R. gymnogynum* Balfour f. & Forrest, with crimson flowers and smaller leaves; *R. heptamerum* Balfour f., with large deep crimson flowers, hardiness *D;* and *R. persicinum* Handel-Mazzetti, with flowers of peach-blossom color and more pointed, smaller leaves.

Rhododendron Hardingii Forrest (after Harding). *E.* 6–8 ft. tall. Flowers cup-shaped, 1½ in. long, white, flushed pink, crimson spots. Margins of forests, N.W. Yunnan, 7,000 ft.

Rhododendron irroratum Franchet (covered with dew). *B.* Shrub or small tree to 25 ft. Inflor. between (a) and (b). See text-figure for series. Flowers (61) 1½–2 in. long, white or creamy yellow, tinged rose, with crimson or greenish spots. Bot. Mag. t. 7361. Shady pine and rhododendron forests, W. Yunnan, 9,000–10,000 ft.—Regarded as a fine rhododendron, but early flowering and needing shelter.

Rhododendron Kendrickii Nuttall (after Dr. Kendrick, friend of the botanist Nuttall). *E.* Small tree 15–25 ft. tall. Flowers (67) but smaller than illustration, 1¼ in. long, pink or deep red, spotted, fleshy and having petals with wavy margins. Bot. Mag. t. 5129 (var.). Forming thickets in Bhutan, 7,000–9,000 ft.—Variety *latifolium* Hooker is a broader leaved variety.

Rhododendron laxiflorum Balfour f. & Forrest (loose-flowered). *B.* 12–20 ft. tall. Flowers 1½ in. long, white, unspotted. Mixed thickets, W. Yunnan, 8,000 ft.

Rhododendron leptopeplum Balfour f. & Forrest (with smooth covering). *C.* 9–14 ft. tall. Flowers 1½ in. long, creamy white, flushed rose, blotched and spotted crimson. Rhododendron forests, Yunnan, 13,000 ft.—The upper surface of the leaves are waxy.

Rhododendron lukiangense Franchet (from the Lukiang Valley). *B.* A medium-sized shrub. Flowers 1¾ in. long, rose to magenta-rose, blotched and spotted crimson. Thickets and pine forests, N.W. Yunnan, 10,000 ft.—Four geographical forms are recognized as subspecies: *Rhododendron admirabile* Balfour f. & Forrest (admirable), from S.W. Szechuan, has larger deep rose flowers, with or without a few spots. *Rhododendron adroserum* Balfour f. & Forrest (eglandular) has smaller, less acuminate leaves than the type, while the rose flowers are conspicuously spotted and flushed magenta-crimson toward the margins. *Rhododendron ceraceum* Balfour f. & W. W. Smith (wax-like), from S.E. Tibet, is distinct in several particulars, having its leaves ridged longitudinally on the upper side and glossy beneath, while the flowers are magenta-rose with a small blotch. *Rhododendron gymnanthum* Diels (naked flowers) has narrow leaves with acuminate apices, flowers rose with crimson markings and comes from a higher altitude, in rocky situations at 13,000 ft.

Rhododendron mengtszense Balfour f. & W. W. Smith (from Mengtze). *E.* A tree of 20 ft. Flowers 1½ in. long, purple-red, blotched deep crimson. In mountain forests in S.E. Yunnan, 7,000 ft.

Rhododendron ningyuenense Handel-Mazzetti (from Ningyuen). *D.* Medium sized shrub. Flowers 1½ in. long, whitish rose. Mixed forests, Szechuan, 8,000–10,000 ft.

Rhododendron ombrochares Balfour f. & Ward (lover of rain). *E.* Medium sized tree. Flowers 1½–2 in. long, cherry crimson marked with deeper spots, fleshy. Open places in forests, N.E. Upper Burma, 7,000–8,000 ft.

Rhododendron pankimense Cowan (from Pankim La, Assam). A shrub to 10 ft. Flowers crimson, with darker spots and no blotch. Assam.

Rhododendron papillatum Balfour f. & Cooper (covered with nipples). *D.* A small bush. Flowers 1¼ in. long, pale cream, blotched at base, pink spots. Under Abies, Bhutan, 10,000 ft.

Rhododendron pennivenium Balfour f. & Forrest (pinnately veined). *C.* 9–20 ft. Flowers 1½ in. long, deep crimson, with deeper spots. Pine and mixed forests, Yunnan, 11,000 ft.

Rhododendron pogonostylum Balfour f. & W. W. Smith (bearded style), syn: R. adenostemonum Balfour f. & W. W. Smith. *E.* About 15 ft. tall. Flowers 1½ in. long, pink, spotted with dark red. In forests, S.E. Yunnan, 7,000–8,500 ft.

Rhododendron Ramsdenianum Cowan (after Sir John Ramsden). *C.* A tree to 30 ft. Inflor. trusses of 12–15 tubular-campanulate flowers (61), crimson or deep rose, blotched or unblotched; not spotted.

Rhododendron Shepherdii Nuttall (after H. Shepherd, Curator Liverpool Botanic Garden, d. 1854). *E.* Height to 12 ft. Inflor. (a). Flowers (59?), deep scarlet, spotted dark crimson. Bot. Mag. t. 5125. Oola Mts., Bhutan.

Rhododendron spanotrichum Balfour f. & W. W. Smith (few hairs). Small tree to 20 ft. Flowers 1½ in. long, crimson, with a darker blotch at base. In forests, S.E. Yunnan, 7,500 ft.

Rhododendron tanastylum Balfour f. & Ward (with a long style). *C.* A bush or thin tree 8–20 ft. tall. Flowers 1½–2 in. long, deep crimson, sometimes spotted, fleshy. In open thickets and forests, E. Upper Burma and adjacent W. Yunnan, 9,000–11,000 ft.

SUBSERIES PARISHII

This group is composed of a few species and has its headquarters in the wet monsoon-forest region of Upper Burma. It contains some gorgeous, but tender representatives. The prevailing color is red, sometimes intensely vivid scarlet or crimson of unusual clearness and purity. Besides being a rain-forest group, this subseries is distinct from the other subseries in several characters, notably the presence of a stellate indumentum and a somewhat rounded leaf-apex. The flowers are fleshy, while the leaves are larger and of softer texture than those typical of the Irroratum subseries.

Rhododendron agapetum Balfour f. & Ward (delightful). *E.* A scraggly tree of 15–20 ft. Flowers 1¾ in. long, crimson-scarlet, fleshy. On limestone cliffs in half shade, E. Upper Burma, 6,000–7,000 ft. **X**

Rhododendron Elliottii Watt MS. (after Elliott). *E.* A small straggling tree, height to 12 feet. Inflor. (a) or (b). Flowers (58), 1¾ in. long, deep scarlet with darker spots. Naga Hills, Manipur, 9,000 ft. Kingdom Ward's form 7725 has magnificent flowers of bright scarlet-red which it transmits to hybrid progeny. Bot. Mag. t. 9546. **XX**

Rhododendron eriogynum Balfour f. & W. W. Smith (with a woolly ovary). *D.* A shrub or small tree of 10 ft. Flowers 1¾ in. long, bright red with darker markings. Open thickets, Yunnan, 9,000 ft.—Very much like *R. facetum* (below). They have magnificent clear, bright red flowers in June. They are tender, however, and may not be grown except in favored localities. *Rhododendron eriogynum* failed in southern Pennsylvania, and is considered hardy only in the mildest parts of England. There is some variation and later introductions or selected strains may bring hardier sorts. They grow late in the season, and their new growth does not ripen-off properly before winter. It is said that they resent transplanting. **XX**

Rhododendron facetum Balfour f. & Ward (elegant). *D.* 15–20 ft. tall. Flowers 1¾ in. long, scarlet with deeper colored spots, fleshy. Rain forests, N.E. Burma and W. Yunnan, 9,000 ft.—The remarks made for *R. eriogynum* will probably apply equally to this species, which is hardly to be distinguished from the former. (See color plate page 334.) **XX**

Rhododendron Kyawi Lace & W. W. Smith (after Maung Kyaw, a Burmese collector), syn: R. prophantum Balfour f. & Forrest. *E.* 15–20 ft. tall. Inflor. (a). Flowers (45) 1¾–2¼ in. long, bright crimson or rose scarlet, an intermediate color between *R. eriogynum* and *R. Griersonianum,* fleshy. Spec. Rhod., p. 366. In mixed forests in enclosed ravines, N.E. Upper Burma, 6,000–9,000 ft.—This is called a "truly magnificent rhododendron" and blooms in late July or early August. The drawback, of course, is that it is tender. **XX**

Rhododendron Parishii C. C. Clarke (after Rev. C. S. P. Parish, Chaplain at Moulmein). *F.* A small tree 18–25 ft. tall. Inflor. (a) or (b). Flowers (58?) 1½ in. long, red, lined deeper along the petals. Burma, 6,200.—Leaf shape distinct.

Rhododendron schistocalyx Balfour f. & Forrest (with split calyx). *C.* 12–15 ft. tall. Flowers 1¾–2 in. long, bright rose to crimson. In rhododendron thickets, W. Yunnan, 10,000–11,000 ft.

Rhododendron venator Tagg (hunter). Height 8–12 ft. Bushy. Flowers hunting-coat red (hence its name), in trusses of 4 to 6. China, 7,000–8,000 ft. Blooms in late May.

JAVANESE, MALAYAN AND TROPICAL RHODODENDRONS *

R. BROOKEANUM

Except for a few species which have entered into a race of Javanicum hybrids, namely, *R. jasminiflorum, R. javanicum, R. Lobbii, R. malayanum, R. multicolor,* and *R. Teysmannii,* which are all glasshouse subjects, these tropical rhododendrons have little importance in temperate-zone horticulture. Moreover, material on them is often scanty, especially in America. Since this is definitely a horticultural work and not in any sense a taxonomic monograph, a listing of these species is being entirely omitted. Also, the other tropical species in general, except where included in some of the series groupings, are being deliberately excluded. Altogether, there are some 200 or more species noted as coming from the tropics, most of which have not yet been put into series groups. Many of them are epiphytes and all are probably strictly warmhouse plants. A dozen or so new species have been recently named.

Furthermore, there is every indication that a whole new section of the genus, consisting of hundreds of species from the Malayan region, including those from Java, Borneo, New Guinea, Papau, and the Philippines, as well as Formosa and other islands, many of which are imperfectly known, will emerge from studies now in progress and in prospect in these regions. Generally, they will not be of horticultural importance for the temperate zone. It has been noted that in order to bloom in cultivation the species from New Guinea require the day length to be adjusted to 12 hours each of light and darkness, which is approximately the day length experienced by these plants in their native habitat.

The cultivated sorts are used primarily as conservatory plants, growing at temperatures of not lower than 55° or 60°F. and requiring plenty of moisture and shade in summer. Sandy soil, chiefly peat mixed with sand, is recommended

* In H. Sleumer's systematic treatment of the genus Rhododendron, which has been summarized in Part III of this book, the numerous rhododendrons from Southeast Asia, not otherwise accounted for in previously existing series groups, are gathered together under appropriate Sections and Subsections. Groups have been newly constituted with a typical species named to serve as a standard-bearer for each of the groups, which are thus somewhat analogous to Series. Besides many new species in new categories, a number of new species have been found which fit into the previously existing series. A great many natural hybrids have also been found. Much of this material will eventually be placed in a monograph of the rhododendrons of Southeast Asia now in preparation by Dr. Sleumer. Meanwhile two important papers in English have been published by Dr. Sleumer, containing the technical descriptions of many new species. These are cited in the footnote on p. 461. No attempt has been made to include them all in this book.

by the English growers. At Kew the Javanicums grew luxuriantly when planted in ground beds in the greenhouse, but they did not flower. When grown in pots or tubs, however, they bloomed well. They flower almost continuously throughout the year, new flowering shoots being formed constantly. The plants get to be about six feet high. Some of the species, and particularly the hybrids, are of great beauty, but it is questionable if they are adapted for any kind of commercial production as florists' flowers or plants. This is a point, however, that calls for further investigation. Propagation is effected by cuttings of half-ripened wood, rooted in a propagating case. A list of clonal varieties is presented in Chapter XXIII and a brief account of the parentage of the hybrids in Chapter XIX. A list of species is as follows:

R. acuminatum. Borneo.
R. agathodaemonis. New Guinea.
R. album. Java.
R. anagalliflorum. New Guinea.
R. Andersoni. Borneo.
R. angiense. New Guinea.
R. angulatum. New Guinea.
R. annamense. Annam.
R. apoanum, syn: R. jasminiflorum F. Villar. Philip. Is.; Java.
R. arfakianum. New Guinea.
R. Armitii. New Guinea.
R. asparagoides. New Guinea.
R. asperum. New Guinea.
R. astrapiae. New Guinea.
R. Baenitzianum. New Guinea.
R. bagobonum. Philip. Is.
R. Beyerinckianum. New Guinea.
R. Beyerinckianum, var. longepetiolatum. New Guinea.
R. Bodenii. New Guinea.
R. brachygynum. Philip. Is.
P. brevitubum. Borneo.
R. Brookeanum. Bot. Mag. t. 4935. Borneo.
R. buxifolium. Borneo.
R. calceolarioides. New Guinea.
R. callichilioides. New Guinea.
R. calocodon. Malay Peninsula.
R. candidapiculatum. New Guinea.
R. Carringtoniae. New Guinea. Var. majus.
R. carstensense. New Guinea.
R. catanduanense. Philip. Is.

R. chapaense. Indo-China.
R. Chevalieri. S. Annam.
R. Christi. New Guinea.
R. citrinum. Java.
R. Clementis. Philip. Is.
R. coelorum. New Guinea.
R. Coenenii. New Guinea.
R. Commonae. New Guinea.
R. comptum. New Guinea.
R. coniferum. New Guinea.
R. Copelandii. Philip. Is.
R. correoides. New Guinea.
R. coruscum. Malaya.
R. crassifolium. Borneo.
R. culminicolum. New Guinea.
R. curviflorum. New Guinea.
R. cyrtophyllum. New Guinea.
R. dasylepis. New Guinea.
R. Devrieseanum. New Guinea.
R. Dielsianum. New Guinea.
R. dubium. Malaya.
R. durionifolium. Borneo.
R. elegans. Malaya.
R. Englerianum. New Guinea.
R. ericoides. Borneo.
R. excelsum. S. Annam.
R. filamentosum. New Guinea.
R. flavoviride. New Guinea.
R. Fleuryi. Annam.
R. fortunans. Borneo.
R. Frassenianum. New Guinea.
R. fuchsioides. New Guinea.
R. Gardenia. New Guinea.
R. Gibbsiae. New Guinea.

R. Giulianettii. New Guinea.
R. glabrifilum. New Guinea.
R. glabriflorum. New Guinea.
R. gorumense. New Guinea.
R. gracile. Borneo.
R. gracilentum. New Guinea.
R. Habbemai. New Guinea.
R. hameliiflorum. New Guinea.
R. Hansemanni. New Guinea.
R. hatamense. New Guinea.
R. Hellwigii. New Guinea.
R. Herzogii. New Guinea.
R. hirtolepidotum. New Guinea.
R. honbanianum. Annam.
R. inconspicuum. New Guinea.
R. jasminiflorum Hooker. Bot. Mag. t. 4524. Malacca.
R. javanicum Benn. Java.
R. Keysseri. New Guinea.
R. kinabaluense. Borneo.
R. Klossii. Malaya.
R. Kochii. Philip. Is.
R. Konori. New Guinea.
R. Korthalsii. Sumatra.
R. laetum. New Guinea.
R. langhianense. Annam.
R. laoticum. Indo-China.
R. laureola. New Guinea.
R. Lauterbachianum. New Guinea.
R. leptanthum. New Guinea.
R. leptocladon. Indo-China.
R. leucobotrys. Malaya.
R. leytense. Philip. Is.
R. Lindaueanum. New Guinea. Var. *latifolium.*
R. lineare. Borneo.
R. linnaeoides. New Guinea.
R. Lobbii. Borneo.
R. loboense. Philip. Is.
R. Lochae. Australia.
R. Loerzingii. Java.
R. Loheri. Philip. Is.
R. lompohense. Celebes.
R. longiflorum. Borneo.
R. Loureirianum. Cochin-China.
R. Lowei. Borneo.
R. maboraense. New Guinea.

R. Macgregoriae. New Guinea.
R. malayanum, Jack, syn : R. celebicum ; R. lampongum ; R. tubiflorum DC. Sumatra, Java, Celebes. Var. *axillare.* Borneo.
R. malindangense, syn : R. Quadrasianum var. malindangense. Philip. Is.
R. Maxwelii L. S. Gibbs (not *R. pulchrum* var. *Maxwellii.* Borneo.)
R. megalostigma. New Guinea.
R. melantherum. New Guinea.
R. microphyllum. New Guinea.
R. mindanaense. Philip. Is.
R. minimifolium. New Guinea.
R. Mollianum. New Guinea.
R. Moszkowskii. New Guinea.
R. multicolor. Sumatra.
R. neriifolium. New Guinea.
R. nhatrangense. Annam.
R. Nieuwenhuisii. Borneo.
R. nodosum. New Guinea.
R. Nortoniae. Philip. Is.
R. nubicola. New Guinea.
R. obscurinervium. Borneo.
R. oreadum. New Guinea.
R. orion. Malay Peninsula.
R. papuanum. New Guinea.
R. pauciflorum. Malay Peninsula.
R. perakense. Malay Peninsula.
R. Petelotii. Indo-China.
R. phaeochiton. New Guinea.
R. podocarpoides. New Guinea.
R. Poilanei. Indo-China.
R. Prainianum. New Guinea.
R. Pulleanum. New Guinea.
R. purpureiflorum. New Guinea.
R. pusillum. New Guinea.
R. radians. Celebes.
R. rarum. New Guinea.
R. retusum. Sumatra, Java.
R. Robinsonii. Malay Peninsula.
R. rugosum. Borneo.
R. salicifolium. Borneo.
R. saravanense. Indo-China.
R. saruwagedicum. New Guinea.
R. saxifragoides. New Guinea.
R. Schadenbergii. Philip. Is.

R. Schlechterii. New Guinea.

R. Schultzei. New Guinea.

R. Scortechinii. Malay Peninsula.

R. spathulatum. Malay Peninsula.

R. spectabile. Philip. Is.

R. spondylophyllum. New Guinea.

R. Stapfianum, syn: R. lacteum. Borneo.

R. stenophyllum. Borneo.

R. Stolleanum. New Guinea.

R. subcordatum. Borneo.

R. subsessile. Philip. Is. Var. *baucoense.*

R. taxifolium. Philip. Is.

R. Teysmannii. Sumatra.

R. torricellense. New Guinea.

R. Toverenae. New Guinea.

R. triumphans. S. Annam.

R. tuberculiferum. New Guinea.

R. uliginosum. New Guinea.

R. ultimum. New Guinea.

R. undulaticalyx. New Guinea.

R. Vanhoeffeni. New Guinea.

R. Vanvuurenii. Celebes.

R. variolosum. Borneo.

R. velutinum. Borneo.

R. Versteegii. New Guinea.

R. verticillatum. Borneo.

R. villosulum. New Guinea.

R. Vonroemeri. New Guinea.

R. Warianum. New Guinea.

R. Wentianum. New Guinea.

R. Whiteheadii, syn: R. Curranii. Philip. Is.

R. Wilhelminae. Java.

R. Williamsii. Philip. Is.

R. Wolastonii. New Guinea.

R. Wrayi. Malay Peninsula.

R. Wrightianum. New Guinea. Var. *cyclopense;* var. *ovalifolium;* var. *piliferum.*

R. xanthopetalum. Philip. Is.

R. Zoelleri. New Guinea.

R. Zollingeri, syn: R. tubiflorum Zoll. Java.

LACTEUM SERIES

Excepting *Rhododendron Wightii,* which is a Himalayan species, the members of this series are all Chinese, coming from Yunnan or the regions of Tibet or Burma which are directly adjacent. Some of its members are not unlike certain familiar hardy species in so far as size and inflorescence are concerned. The Lacteum series is related to the series Campanulatum and Taliense, while certain of the species in the Ponticum series also bear a resemblance to the various Lacteums. They are shrubs, ranging from six to 20 feet high, with variations toward dwarfness. The flowers are white or rose, except in two species where they are yellow. The Lacteums are distinguished from related

R. LACTEUM

series on the basis of indumentum, and in cultivation identification is easy because of differences in general appearance, hardiness and geographical habitats from which they have been derived. Plants belonging to the Lacteum series are separable from those of the Ponticum series, (subseries Caucasicum), by their less elongated inflorescence and less leathery leaves. They do not bear the thick felt on their leaves which the Talienses possess and they do not have smooth ovaries like the Campanulatums.

The yellow species, *R. lacteum* and *R. Wightii,* have been used in crosses and one of the best hybrids is the clone 'Mariloo' (see color plate). This was derived from 'Dr. Stocker' (*R. caucasicum* × *Griffithianum*) × *R. lacteum.* A magnificent plant of *R. lacteum* grows in Windsor Great Park. Although variation exists, the plants I have seen of *R. lacteum* are far superior to those of *R. Wightii,* which are of gawky habit, drooping truss and pallid color.

Rhododendron aberrans Tagg & Forrest (wandering). *B.* 6–15 ft. Flowers about 1¼ in. long, white, flushed rose, with copious crimson markings. Open conifer and rhododendron forests, W. Yunnan, 11,000–12,000 ft.—Very similar to *R. Traillianum,·*but with smaller leaves and flowers. Not in general cultivation.

Rhododendron agglutinatum Balfour f. & Forrest (stuck together). *B.* To 15 ft., rarely higher. Under surface of leaves covered with a thin brown agglutinate or suede-like indumentum. Inflor. a racemose umbel of 10–12 fls. Flowers (62) 1–1½ in. long, white or creamy, flushed rose or pink, with or without crimson markings.

Rhododendron Beesianum Diels (after Messrs. Bees, Cheshire nurserymen), syn: R. colletum Balfour f. & Forrest; R. emaculatum Balfour f. & Forrest; R. microterum Balfour f. *B.* Small tree or shrub up to 20 ft. Inflor. in trusses of 10–25 flowers, broadly campanulate (59), 1½–2¼ in. long; white to magenta-rose, with or without crimson spots and blotch. Yunnan, Szechuan and Tibet. 11,000–14,000 ft.

Rhododendron dictyotum Balfour f. ex Tagg (netted veined). *B.* 9–12 ft. tall. Flowers campanulate, 1½–2 in. long, whitish, often with copious crimson spots; borne in trusses of 8–15. Open pine forests and rhododendron thickets, S.E. Tibet, 11,000–13,000 ft.

Rhododendron dignabile Cowan (deemed worthy). 3–15 ft. Inflor. truss with 8–15 flowers, campanulate (62), 1–1¾ in. long; pink, cream or white, with or without purplish spots and blotch. Tibet, 11,000–14,500 ft. Not in general cultivation.

Rhododendron dryophyllum Balfour f. & Forrest (leaves like an oak), syn: R. aiopeplum Balfour f. & Forrest; R. helvolum Balfour f. & Forrest; R. intortum Balfour f. & Forrest; R. levistratum Balfour f. & Forrest; R. sigillatum Balfour f. & Forrest; R. theiophyllum Balfour f. & Forrest; R. vicinum Balfour f. & Forrest. *B.* 3–25 ft. Flowers about 1½ in. long, white, tipped or flushed rose, few crimson markings; in trusses of 15. Open pine forests, N.W. Yunnan, 11,000–14,000 ft.

Rhododendron dumosulum Balfour f. & Forrest (bushy). *A.* A low shrub 2–3 ft. high. Flowers ¾ in. long and 1¼ in. across, white, faintly flushed, copious crimson spots; borne in small umbels of 8 flowers. Open moorlands, N.W. Yunnan, 13,000 ft.—A smaller species from a high altitude and more exposed habitat.

Rhododendron lacteum Franchet (milky), syn: R. Mairei Léveillé. *C.* See text-figure for series. A tree up to 30 ft. tall. Inflor. (a) very round, with 20–30 fls. Flowers (73) 1¾ in. long, clear canary yellow (or creamy white in some forms), unspotted. Bot. Mag. t. 8988 and Spec. Rhod. p. 380. In rhododendron forests, Tali Range and N.W. and N.E. Yunnan, 12,000 ft.—A prominent British rhododendron authority regards this as perhaps the finest yellow rhododendron capable of being grown in English gardens, but somewhat slow growing and difficult. It seems hardy in sheltered positions and its color is rather deeper than that of *Rhododendron campylocarpum,* another highly-rated yellow species. It flowers early in the spring, however, which makes it especially undesirable where spring frosts prevail.

A good plant of *R. lacteum* in bloom with its fine yellow flowers is truly impressive, though probably rare. Such a plant may be seen, however, alongside superior blue forms of *R. Augustinii,* blooming together at Windsor Great Park in England. Unfortunately, *R. lacteum* has a frightful reputation as an unhappy and temperamental subject in cultivation—a neurotic rhododendron! This prevents it from achieving first place. Nevertheless, this is a very fine yellow rhododendron and is a parent of at least one good hybrid clone, 'Mariloo' (see color plate facing page 79), which is said to be rather fussy, too. They say it does better when grafted on something else than when on its own roots, for both parent and hybrid are reputed to be weak growers and short-lived. Specimens I have seen of 'Mariloo,' however, look very lush. Perhaps there is an answer. **XX**

Rhododendron nakotiltum Balfour f. & Forrest (having the wool plucked off). *C.* 6–12 ft. tall. Flowers 1½ in. long, pale rose, blotched and spotted; 12–15 flowers in a truss. Pine forests, N.W. Yunnan, 11,000–12,000 ft.

Rhododendron phaeochrysum Balfour f. & Smith (dark golden), syn: R. lopophorum Balfour f. & Forrest; R. dichropeplum Balfour f. & Forrest; R. syncollum Balfour f. & Forrest. *B.* A shrub up to 15 feet. Flowers (58) in trusses of 8–15, and up to 2 in. long; white or creamy white, flushed rose or rarely yellow, purple and pink. Yunnan and Tibet.—Very close to *R. dryophyllum* and variable, but with indumentum agglutinate, not felty, and with larger flowers.

Rhododendron pomense Cowan (from Pome, S.E. Tibet). A shrub to 4 ft. with a thin indumentum and campanulate pink flowers, 2 in. long. S.E. Tibet, 11,000 ft.—Has a large unequal calyx. Not in general cultivation.

Rhododendron Przewalskii Maximowicz (after a Russian traveler). *A.* A shrub to 9 ft. Flowers (58) or (59) up to 1¾ in. long; white or rose pink, with or without spots, in trusses of 10–15. Kansu, Tibet and Szechuan, China.

Rhododendron Traillianum Forrest & W. W. Smith (after G. W. Traill). *B.* Up to 30 ft. Flowers 1¼ in. long, white or flushed rose or pink, with or without crimson spots. Rhododendron forests, N.W. Yunnan, 11,000–12,000 ft. Bot. Mag. t. 8900.—Distinguished from other species by characters of the indumentum.

Rhododendron Wightii Hooker f. (after Robert Wight, M.D., Madras Botanic Garden). *B.* A small tree 10–15 ft. tall. Inflor. a large rounded but very lax truss of 12–20 flowers, (59) with base like (68), 2 in. long, pale yellow, heavily blotched and spotted crimson. The flowers tend to droop downward. Bot. Mag. t. 8492. Hooker's Rhodo. Sikkim Himal. t. 27. Wooded valleys and on spurs of mountains, E. Himalayas, Nepal, Bhutan, 12,000–14,000 ft.—The only Himalayan member of the series. The flowers differ from those of *R. lacteum* in being spotted, and the leaves differ in being narrower. *R. Wightii* is easier to grow than *R. lacteum*, according to all reports, but is otherwise much less desirable. All the examples that this writer has seen have exhibited a very poor habit of growth, being sparse, leggy plants, gangling in habit and with droopy trusses of indifferent pale yellow flowers. You can make the flowers look good in a photograph by pointing the camera upward into their faces; hence, some attractive pictures are in circulation. But don't be deceived—the plant itself is not so attractive.

LAPPONICUM SERIES

VAR. CANTABILE

The Lapponicum series constitutes one of the larger natural groups of rhododendrons. They are dwarf shrublets, mostly from the higher altitudes of western China, where they form a low matted growth over hundreds of square miles of alpine moorlands, producing in May, as Kingdon Ward says, "a chromatic storm-tossed surf—rose, pink, purple, lavender and amber, through which one may wade ankle-deep for days on end. The majority of the species belong to the series Lapponicum, and the term 'Lapponicum Sea' is not inappropriate for this rainbow ocean of blossom." * This in the mountains of Yunnan and Szechuan, above 14,000 feet, and more sparsely, in the alpine moorlands and meadows of the Tibetan Marches. The series is rare in the eastern Himalaya, does not occur at all in central and eastern China, but is represented by an arctic species which occurs in Lapland (whence the name

* Rhododendrons for Everyone, London, 1926.

"lapponicum"), northeastern Asia and North America. This species extends even to the United States where it is found growing wild near the summit of Mount Washington, New Hampshire. The Lapponicum series is therefore the most widely distributed of any in the genus.

In their native climes, many of the Lapponicums endure cold temperatures of considerable severity, but coupled with this are other ecological conditions difficult to duplicate in gardens. Deep winter snows, abundant summer rains, the cool moist air of high altitudes, constant moisture from melting snow, abundant bright light without hot sunshine and a short growing season are some of the characteristic features of their homelands. The Lapponicum rhododendrons are adapted to just such conditions and hence, in most instances, cannot be expected to obtain optimum happiness in the average garden. A few of them appear promising, many are still imperfectly known or understood and almost all can be accepted as suitable garden subjects for this country only after a great deal more testing than they have yet received. Some of them appear to do well here in an open moraine or wet rock garden, with no mulch other than stones. In England, however, many sorts have passed their probationary period and are being successfully grown. As the drier regions of western China are more fully explored, we may obtain additional species in the Lapponicum group which will have added possibilities for America. At present, copious moisture seems to be the best treatment for them in the United States.

It is said in England that the Lapponicums will not endure sun scorching and that they grow best in a damp atmosphere without much sunlight when cultivated at low altitudes. Certain results obtained in America indicate that alpine rhododendrons need plenty of light, but that it must be combined with very copious irrigation. Some of the Lapponicums vary in height and floriferousness according to the amount of sun or light exposure they receive. *Rhododendron hippophaeoides,* one of these, is said to retain its dwarf prostrate habit if grown *en masse* in an exposed position, but will assume a much taller habit if grown as a single specimen in a more protected situation. In the moister parts of the Chinese alps the number of species is considerable and the distribution of any one sort is strictly limited, while in the drier regions there are fewer species, but each species extends over a large area.

The range of flower color is very wide, with, however, the mauve or rosy purple colors predominating as in nearly every group of rhododendrons. There are four species with yellow flowers. Among other colors, dark violet, plum-purple, purplish blue, deep crimson and bright magenta are some of the more unusual hues appearing in addition to the commoner shades of rose, pink and purple. In nature, the species vary from a few inches to two feet in height. *Rhododendron hippophaeoides,* the tallest species, sometimes attains four feet in cultivation. The branchlets are short, the leaves small and evergreen, and the small flowers are borne in terminal clusters of only a few blossoms.

It is obvious that this group, as well as certain others from the very high regions, requires special conditions for successful growth. What these conditions are, for America at least, seems to differ with climate. On the West Coast it is stated that they are miserable unless grown in full sun. Yet in Britain, Cox says that Lapponicums should not be permitted to receive an undue amount of sun and that if placed in an open or exposed situation at all they should be planted in clumps and the clumps planted close together. With increased exposure they become dwarfer in habit. *Rhododendron hippophaeoides* has been grown successfully outdoors at the New York Botanical Garden, but probably resents the hot dry summers. I would not call it a particularly handsome subject, yet it has interesting miniature-sized clusters of magenta-lilac flowers and blooms at New York City about May 1st, or two weeks after *Rhododendron mucronulatum*. *Rhododendron lapponicum* grows in certain wooded gardens on Long Island and elsewhere. It is an inconspicuous plant, a few inches high, with small flowers of the familiar purplish-magenta color. Several of the Chinese Lapponicums have been tried from seed in the eastern United States and, while most of them have failed in the initial trials, later results have been better. Mr. G. G. Nearing in Delaware and Mr. J. B. Gable in southern Pennsylvania have succeeded with a number of Lapponicums, while other Lapponicums have not behaved so well. Evidently, we must learn by experience which of the species are best adapted to American conditions. It is noteworthy that one or two species difficult in England have done better here. But it is too early to arrive at reliable conclusions, at present.

At any rate, the Lapponicum series is an interesting one. The plants have the unique advantage of being easy of propagation by means of cuttings and the further virtue of coming into bloom within 18 months from seed. This, plus their wide range of color, their compact habit of growth and their potential value as rock garden subjects may give them considerable future importance either directly or as the progenitors of hybrid races. Like most arctic and alpine species, geared to a short growing season, these plants tend to exhaust themselves in a vain attempt to adjust to a longer growing period. In my observation, only a few of the species are of attractive colors.

Rhododendron achroanthum Balfour f. & W. W. Smith (paler colored flowers), syn: R. propinquum Balfour f. & Ward. *A.* 2 ft. Flowers ½ in. long, dull deep magenta-red. Open cliffs, Yunnan, 12,000–13,000 ft.

Rhododendron alpicola Rehder & Wilson (dweller in high mountains), syn: R. oreinum Balfour f. *A.* Up to 3 ft. Flowers funnel-shaped, ½ in. long, lavender-purple. Moorlands, W. Szechuan, 12,000–15,000 ft.

Rhododendron Ammundsenianum Handel-Mazzetti (after E. Ammundsen, a missionary in Yunnanfu, China). An undershrub, 12 inches tall, of which little is presently known.

Rhododendron blepharocalyx Franchet (with a fringed calyx). *A*. A small erect shrublet. Flowers narrowly tubular, 1/3 in. long, mauve. E. Tibet.

Rhododendron bulu Hutchinson (a native name in Assam). A 5-ft. shrub, with white or pinkish widely funnel-shaped flowers. Assam.—Not in general cultivation.

Rhododendron capitatum Maximowicz (flowers in a head). *A*. Up to 3 ft. Flowers mauve, in clusters of 5. Kansu.

Rhododendron chamaezelum Balfour f. & Forrest (growing on the ground). *A*. Matted shrub 6 to 8 in. high. Flowers ½ in. long, yellow or pale yellow. N.W. Yunnan, 12,000 ft.

Rhododendron chryseum Balfour f. & Ward (golden yellow), syn: R. muliense Balfour f. & Forrest. *A*. 1–1½ ft. high. Flowers open, ½ in. long, bright yellow. Open grassy slopes, Yunnan, 12,000–14,000 ft.—Said to be one of the best yellow alpines and very pretty when planted among the lavender forms of the series, but has failed when tried in southern Pennsylvania.

Rhododendron compactum (compact). *A*. Height 1–2½ ft. Flowers bright purplish rose.

Rhododendron complexum Balfour f. & W. W. Smith (interwoven). *A*. Matted shrublet 1–2 ft. Flowers ½ in. long, deep rose-purple. Open stony pastures, Yunnan, 12,000 ft.

Rhododendron cuneatum W. W. Smith (wedge-shaped). *A*. Up to 4 ft. Flowers 1 in. long, widely funnel-shaped in clusters of 4, deep rose. Limestone cliffs, Yunnan, 11,000–12,000 ft.

Rhododendron dasypetalum Balfour f. & Forrest (hairy petals). *A*. Up to 2½ ft. Flowers ¾ in. long, bright purplish rose. Open stony pastures, N.W. Yunnan, 11,000 ft.—Called "one of the less interesting of the series."

Rhododendron diacritum Balfour f. & W. W. Smith (separated), syn: R. pycnocladum Balfour f. & W. W. Smith. *A*. Matted shrublet up to 2 ft. Flowers 1/3 in. long, deep rose-purple with white throat. Open places on cliffs and on humus-covered boulders, Yunnan, 13,000–14,000 ft.—First proved tender in eastern United States, but now does well on a wet moraine exposed to full sun and with no mulch except stones (Nearing).

Rhododendron drumonium Balfour f. & Ward (from woods). *B*. Small tufted shrub of 2 ft. Flowers ½ in. long, mauve. Open stony places in pine forests, Yunnan, 10,000–12,000 ft.—This does well in Mr. Nearing's wet moraine, openly exposed.

Rhododendron Edgarianum Rehder & Wilson (after Rev. J. H. Edgar, Tibetan Missions), syn: R. oresbium Balfour f. & Forrest. *A*. Up to 3 ft. Flowers ½ in. long, rose-purple. W. Szechuan, 12,000–15,000 ft.

Rhododendron fastigiatum Franchet (projecting point). *A*. A small erect shrublet. Flowers ½ in. long, light purple. Yunnan.—Millais calls it a compact plant for the rock garden, which flowers quickly from seed, has an unusual color and often blooms in autumn.

Rhododendron fimbriatum (fringed). *A*. Coarser than *R. scintillans* and having more purple in the flowers, but otherwise similar.

Rhododendron flavidum Franchet (somewhat yellow), syn: R. primulinum Hemsley. *A*. Small shrub, intricately branched. Inflor. (z). Flowers (55) 2/3 in. long, pale yellow. Bot. Mag. t. 8326. W. Szechuan and E. Tibet.—A dainty species which comes early in the spring. Var. *psilostylum* has duller green leaves, smaller calyx and fruit.

Rhododendron glomerulatum (somewhat clustered). *A*. Dwarf, resembling *R. russatum* var. *cantabile*. Flowers light purple-mauve.

Rhododendron hippophaeoides Balfour f. & W. W. Smith (resembling sea buckthorn). *A*. About 2 to 3 ft. high, with a few rather leggy branches. Inflor. (z). Flowers (26) about 1 in. across, pale lilac to rose, not spotted. Gard. Chron. 77: 94 (1925). Yunnan.—This species seems able to survive at New York City (N.Y. Bot. Garden) and in southern Pennsylvania (Joseph B. Gable) and in New Jersey (G. G. Nearing). It may be worth growing in places where a medium dwarf shrub is desired. The small clusters of flowers impress one as miniature trusses of *Rhododendron catawbiense*. The color is lilac, however, and not a very attractive shade in the examples I have seen, while the plants lack the compactness that is desirable in a dwarf species. In other words, I should judge that the species is interesting as a new sort, but nothing to justify extravagant praise and but doubtfully worthy of the four asterisks that have been accorded it by the English Rhododendron Association. It is said to be comparatively easy to grow and tolerant of extra moisture, often occurring in boggy ground in China. The watchword here seems to be "plenty of moisture." **X**

Rhododendron idoneum Balfour f. & W. W. Smith (suitable). *A*. A cushion-like shrublet up to 18 inches high. Flowers ½ in. long, deep purplish blue, with white inside the throat. Cliffs and stony pastures, Yunnan, 13,000–14,000 ft.—Remarkably floriferous, says Millais.

Rhododendron impeditum Balfour f. & W. W. Smith (tangled), syn: R. semanteum Balfour f. *A*. Low shrublet. Inflor. (z). Flowers (26), ⅔ in. long, mauve or light purplish blue. Gard. Chron. *78*: Suppl. p. 41 (1925). Open peaty pastures, Yunnan, 15,000–16,000 ft.—Seedlings of this species, said to be an attractive rock-garden plant, have survived and bloomed in S. Pennsylvania and New Jersey, but are of doubtful hardiness northward. **XX**

Rhododendron intricatum Franchet (webby). BLUET RHODODENDRON. *A*. An intricately branched shrublet, low. Inflor. (z). Flowers (26). 1/3 in. long, mauve. Bot. Mag. t. 8163. W. Szechuan, grasslands and moors, 12,000–15,000 ft.—Flowers quickly from seed. May also be propagated from cutting of ripened wood taken in July and rooted in mixed sand and peat. **X**

Rhododendron lapponicum Linnaeus (from Lapland). LAPLAND RHODODENDRON. *A*. A dwarf shrub from a few inches to 1 ft. high. Inflor (r) but of a more prostrate habit. Flowers (27) 1/3 in. long, purplish. Bot. Mag. t. 3106. Arctic regions and mountaintops, Lapland, Sweden, Labrador and Mt. Washington in the United States.—This dwarf from the arctic tundras and cold mountaintops has been cultivated in some wooded gardens on Long Island and elsewhere. Probably its conditions in nature are similar to those for *R. camtschaticum*. It may be tolerant of moisture.

Rhododendron litangense Balfour f. (from Litang Valley). *A*. Up to 2 ft. Flowers ½ in. long, dull plum purple. S.W. Szechuan, 12,000–14,000 ft.

Rhododendron lysolepis Hutchinson (with loose scales). *A*. A dwarf shrublet. Flowers 1 in. across, deep violet or pinkish violet. Seedlings cultivated at Kew, wild habitat not recorded.

Rhododendron microleucum Hutchinson (small, white). *A*. Small shrub with white flowers. **X**

Rhododendron nigropunctatum Bureau & Franchet (marked with black spots). *A*. Small shrub, intricately branched. Inflor. (r). Flowers (26b) 1/3 in. long, pale purple. Bot. Mag. t. 8529. Szechuan, 10,000–15,000 ft.

Rhododendron nitidulum Rehder & Wilson (shining). *A*. Up to 4 ft. Flowers ½ in. long, violet-purple. W. Szechuan, 10,000–12,000 ft.—A variety of this, var. *nubigenum* Rehder & Wilson has a lower habit, smaller leaves and colored calyx.

Rhododendron nivale Hooker f. (snowy). *A*. A prostrate shrublet. Inflor. (r) but with more prostrate habit. Flowers (26b) ½ in. long, bright magenta. Hooker's Rhodo. Sikkim Himal. t. 26 (1849). Sikkim and S. Tibet, 15,000–18,000 ft.

Rhododendron orthocladum Balfour f. & Forrest (with straight twigs). *A*. Up to 4 ft. Flowers ½ in. long, mauve, openly funnel-shaped. Open places on limestone cliffs, N. Yunnan, 11,000–12,000 ft.—Reported hardy in mid-Atlantic Seaboard States.

Rhododendron paludosum Hutchinson & Ward (marshy). *A.* An intricately branched shrublet, height not given. Flowers shortly and openly tubular, 1/3 in. long, bright violet. In masses in open bogs, Tibet, 12,000 ft.

Rhododendron parvifolium Adams (small leaves). *C.* Shrublet up to 1½ ft. Flowers 2/3 in. long, pale rose-magenta. Gartenflora t. 904. Cold alpine marshes in N.E. Asia, from eastern Altai to Kamchatka and the Island of Sakhalin.—This is the Asiatic prototype of *Rhododendron lapponicum.* Its var. *albiflorum* Herd has white flowers.

Rhododendron peramabile Hutchinson (very lovely). *A.* Height 2½ ft. Flowers deep violet mauve. Resembles a luxuriant form of *R. intricatum.* Perhaps from Yunnan.

Rhododendron polifolium Franchet (many-leaved). *A.* Small shrub, height to 2 ft. Flowers 1/3 in. long, mauve, widely funnel-shaped. W. Szechuan.

Rhododendron polycladum Franchet (many branches). *A.* Up to 4 ft. Flowers ½ in. long, openly funnel-shaped, purple. Grasslands in Szechuan.

Rhododendron ramosissimum Franchet (very branched), syn: R. yaragongense Balfour f. *A.* Up to 3 ft. Flowers 1/3 in. long, dark purple, openly funnel-shaped. Moorlands, W. Szechuan, 11,000–13,000 ft.—Reported hardy in open moraine and wet rock garden, Delaware.

Rhododendron ravum Balfour f. & W. W. Smith (gray), syn: R. cheilanthum Balfour f. & Forrest; R. sclerocladum Balfour f. & Forrest. *A.* Up to 4 ft. Flowers ¾in. long, deep rose. Open shrub, Yunnan, 10,000 ft.

Rhododendron rupicola W. W. Smith (from stony places). *A.* 1–2 ft. high. Flowers ½ in. long, deep purple crimson, openly funnel-shaped. Limestone cliffs, Yunnan, 13,000 ft.—Similar to *R. achroanthum* but with more numerous stamens.

Rhododendron russatum Balfour f. & Forrest (reddened), syn: R. osmerum Balfour f. & Forrest MSS. *A.* Up to 4 ft. Inflor. (2). Flowers (26) deep purple-blue with white throat. Gard. Chron. *81*: 333 (1927). Open moist stony pastures, N.W. Yunnan, 12,000 ft.—Said to be one of the most striking of the alpines. It probably deserves a high rating as a rich violet-colored dwarf, very floriferous and eminently suited for planting in drifts or masses in a heath garden. (See Figure 15 on color plate opposite page 334.) It blooms impressively at Wisley, England. There are many close relatives. One gets tired of so many different but similar Lapponicums in the blue-purple range, but this is probably one of the few that will endure with time. It is very effective when planted in drift-like masses, spreading out to make a low heather-like ground cover. I would like to see it alongside a yellow-blooming species. The former *R. cantabile* Balfour f., with flowers in the truss more numerous than in the type, but linked with intermediate forms, has been reduced to varietal rank and is now called *R. russatum* var. *cantabile* (see text figure at head of this series, also Bot. Mag. t. 8963). **XX**

Rhododendron scintillans Balfour f. W. W. Smith (sparkling). *A.* Small shrub, 2–3 ft., erect branches. Inflor (z). Flowers (26) ½ in. long, lavender-blue, the best forms approaching a royal blue. Gard. Chron. *75*: 78 (1924). On open pastures and cliffs, Yunnan, 11,000–14,000 ft.—This is another one of the finest Chinese alpine rhododendrons, very attractive, rather light and ethereal in effect. As there is some variation among seedlings, only the best should be propagated, and these should properly be handled as clones, being named, sold and described as such. This is easily accomplished in the Lapponicum series, because these plants strike root readily from cuttings. Seedlings produced by Mr. Gable failed in southern Pennsylvania, but further tests are being made. There is doubt as to the possibility of growing this species successfully in the eastern United States. **XX**

Rhododendron setosum D. Don (bristly). *A.* Small shrub, height to 4 ft. Flowers up to 1 in. long, bright purple-pink. Hooker's Rhod. Sikkim Himal. t. 20. Bot. Mag. t. 8523. Sikkim and S. Tibet, 11,000–16,000 ft.

Rhododendron spilanthum Hutchinson (with spotted flowers). A 3 ft. shrub with solitary purplish flowers and small narrow leaves. Assam.—Probably not in general cultivation.

Rhododendron stictophyllum Balfour f. (with spotted leaves), syn: R. batangense Balfour f. *A.* Small shrublet, height to 2 ft. Flowers ⅓ in. long, mauve to rose, W. Szechuan.—The very small leaves are densely scaly on both sides.

Rhododendron tapetiforme Balfour f. & Ward (carpet-like). *A.* Small shrublet forming a carpet. Flowers ½ in. long, pink. Tibet-Yunnan frontier, 15,000 ft.—Hardy in Britain; questionable in eastern United States.

Rhododendron telmateium Balfour f. & W. W. Smith (from the marshes), syn: R. vicarium Balfour f. *A.* Up to 3 ft. Flowers ½ in. long, deep rosy purple with white throat. Open situations, Yunnan, 10,000–12,000 ft.—Very small leaves. Attractive.

Rhododendron thymifolium Maximowicz (thyme-like leaves). *A.* A small erect shrub with very tiny leaves. only about 1/3 in. long. Flowers 1/3 in. long, mauve. Kansu.—Perhaps the smallest leaved rhododendron; attractive as a rock garden subject.

Rhododendron Tsai Fang (after H. T. Tsai, Chinese collector). A 12 in. shrub with purplish white flowers in clusters of 5–7. Contrib. Biol. Lab. Sc. Soc. China, Bot. Ser. *12*:66 (1939).—Not in general cultivation.

Rhododendron verruculosum Rehder & Wilson (warty). *A.* Up to 3 ft. Flowers ½ in. long, purple. Sunny places among rocks, W. Szechuan, 1,000 ft. **X**

Rhododendron violaceum Rehder & Wilson (violet colored). *A.* Up to 4 ft. Flowers ½ in. long, violet-purple. Moorlands, W. Szechuan, 12,000–13,500 ft.

Rhododendron Websterianum Rehder & Wilson (after F. G. Webster of Boston, Mass.). Up to 3 ft. Flowers ¾ in. long, rosy purple. Moorlands of W. Szechuan, 10,000–14,000 ft.—Poor results thus far on the Atlantic Seaboard.

Rhododendron Yungningense Balfour f. (from Yungning). *A.* 1–3 ft. high. Flowers 1/3 in. long, deep purple. Mountains of S.W. Szechuan, 13,000–14,000 ft.

LEPIDOTUM SERIES

R. LEPIDOTUM

Another group of dwarfish species coming from rather high altitudes, but in this case, mainly from the Himalayas and from southern Tibet. This series bears some resemblance to the Glaucum and Lapponicum groups. A distinguishing character of the Lepidotums is found on their leaves, which are completely covered beneath by overlapping scales. Two of the species have yellow flowers, while those of the others are either purple, reddish or pink.

These species have not proved successful in the trials that have been made in the eastern United States, so it is assumed that the various Lepidotums are of little promise in that particular region. This series has been revised by Cowan and Davidian and two subseries set up, based upon differences in foliage and inflorescence. Baileyi has a racemose truss with more flowers, larger leaves and crenulate scales. Lepidotum rarely has over three flowers, in an umbel, with small leaves and entire greenish scales.

SUBSERIES BAILEYI

Rhododendron Baileyi Balfour f. (after Col. F. M. Bailey, a traveler in Tibet), syn: R. Thyodocum Balfour & Cooper. *B.* Up to 6 ft. Infl. terminal, racemose, with 5–18 fls., ½ in. long, rotate, reddish purple or deep purple, with or without darker spots. Leaves 1¼–2½ in. long, rust colored beneath. Bot. Mag. t. 8942. S. Tibet, 9,000 ft.

SUBSERIES LEPIDOTUM

Rhododendron lepidotum Wallich (beset with scales), syn: R. obovatum Hooker f.; R. salignum Hooker f.; R. lepidotum var. chloranthum; R. sinolepidotum Balfour f.; R. cremnastes Balfour f. & Farrer; R. eleagnoides Hooker f.; R. lepidotum var.

elaeagnoides Franchet. WILLOW-LEAVED RHODODENDRON. *A.–C.* See text-figure for series. Up to 3–4 ft. Inflor. (v). Flowers (10), about 1 in. across, pale yellow or greenish yellow, pink or purple. Hooker's Rhod. Sikkim Himal. t. 23. Himalayan Mts., Kashmir to Bhutan, S. Tibet, 7,000–15,000 ft.—Owing to the wide altitudinal and geographical range of this species, its hardiness varies depending upon its native habitat. Millais said the flowers are poor in color and sparse in number. Reported tender in eastern North America. Other species have been placed under *R. lepidotum* as intermediate forms have been discovered and specific distinctions have broken down. Several distinct types may be listed as: (1) a small shrub 1–2 ft. high with purple flowers; (2) a dwarf form to 12 in. with purple flowers; (3) a yellow-flowered form similar to (1), formerly *R. salignum;* (4) a dwarf compact form with yellow flowers, formerly *R. elaeagnoides;* and (5) a taller bush to 3 ft. with yellow flowers. Several forms have been illustrated under synonyms in Bot. Mag. t. 4657, t. 4802 and t. 6450.

Rhododendron Lowndesii Davidian (after Col. D. G. Lowndes). A little shrublet, possibly deciduous, 4 in. high. Infl. terminal, 1 or 2 fls., corolla rotate-campanulate, ½–¾ in. long, pale dull yellow spotted with yellow ochre. Nepal, 4,600 ft.

MADDENII SERIES

Captain F. Kingdon Ward,* referring to hardiness, says, "there is little hope of anything which answers to the family name of Maddenii, Stamineum or Irroratum," *Rhododendron ciliatum,* one of the hardier of the Maddenii species, will grow throughout England, it is said, but is likely to be injured by spring frosts. In America, they should all probably be regarded as subjects for the cool greenhouse or its equivalent. In nature they occur at levels considerably lower than those of the hardier Chinese and Himalayan species, few species being found at altitudes above 10,000 feet. The wild plants grow in the Himalayas, Sikkim, western Yunnan, Burma and adjacent regions, two species oc-

R. MADDENII

curring in the Chinese province of Kweichow. None come from Szechuan. Some botanists regard the Maddenii series as the group out of which the Triflorum series perhaps originated.

* Rhododendrons for Everyone, London, 1926.

These species are large or medium-sized shrubs, with evergreen leaves which are densely scaly below. They have large flowers, funnel-shaped and often waxy or fleshy, with five lobes ("petals") and from ten to 25 stamens. The colors range from white and greenish white, cream and yellow to flesh, pink, light rose or violet tinted. Many are blotched inside with yellow or orange. One or two species have yellowish throats. A few have red spotting inside and some have pink or red bands on the back angles of the lobes. Many are fragrant, some quite deliciously sweet and one with a nutmeg scent. In height the plants vary, in different species, from three to 20 feet, the majority being between six and ten feet tall. There are three subseries, separated from one another on stamen number, calyx and leafstalk characters.

Millais states that cuttings of *Rhododendron formosum,* if taken in summer, root readily in sandy peat in a close frame. Some species are well adapted for use as conservatory plants for a 60° house. *Rhododendron Nuttallii* is considered one of the choicest species, while *R. Taggianum* is a very promising newcomer.

SUBSERIES CILIICALYX

Rhododendron amandum Cowan (lovable). Shrub to 6 ft. Close to *R. ciliatum,* with pale yellow flowers. Notes Roy. Bot. Gard. Edinburgh *19*:245 (1937). Tibet.

Rhododendron burmanicum Hutchinson (from Burma). *F.* 6 ft. tall. Flowers (68) greenish yellow or greenish white, sweet-scented. Mt. Victoria, S.W. Burma.

Rhododendron carneum Hutchinson (flesh-colored). *F.* 8 ft. Inflor. (b) or (c). Flowers (76) 2½ in. long, flesh colored or whitish pink. Bot. Mag. t. 8634. Open grassy hillsides, Upper Burma, 7,500 ft. **X**

Rhododendron ciliatum Hooker f. (fringed). FRINGED RHODODENDRON. *C.* 3 ft. Inflor. (c). Flowers (4) 1½–2 in. long, white or tinged rose. Bot. Mag. t. 8634. Sikkim, 9,000–11,000 ft.—Said to be rich red in the bud. Perhaps the most floriferous rhododendron and restraint is recommended. Its hybrid with *R. dauricum* is a well known clone called 'Praecox.'

Rhododendron ciliicalyx Franchet (fringed calyx), syn: R. atentsiense Handel-Mazzetti. *F.* Up to 10 ft. Inflor. (c). Flowers (76) 1–1¼ in. long, white or rose. Bot. Mag. t. 7782. Sides of rocky hills, W. Yunnan, 7,300 ft.—Scented. **X**

Rhododendron ciliipes Hutchinson (fringed at the base). *E.* Height not given. Solitary flowers, 2¼ in. long, white, fragrant, with a green or yellow blotch. On cliffs and humus covered boulders, Yunnan, 10,000 ft.

Rhododendron Cubittii Hutchinson. *F.* Wide funnel-shaped flowers 2¾ in. long, white, tinged. N. Burma, 5,800 ft.—Up to 8 ft. tall.

Rhododendron Cuffeanum Craib (after Lady Wheeler Cuffe who discovered it in 1913). *F.* Inflor. (b). Flowers (76) 2½ in. long, white with large yellow blotch. Bot. Mag. t. 8721. Mt. Victoria, S.W. Burma.

Rhododendron dendricola Hutchinson (dweller on trees). *F.* A 9 ft. epiphyte. Inflor. (c). Flowers (71) 3¼ in. long, white, tinged pink, orange marks on lower lobes. Notes Roy. Bot. Gard. Edin. *12*: 61 (fig. 8). Generally epiphytic on trees, N. Burma.

Rhododendron formosum Wallich (beautiful), syn: R. Gibsonii Paxton. *F.* Height to 10 ft. Inflor. (c). Flowers (76) 2¼ in. long, white, tinged yellow and rose, 5 red stripes outside; sweet-scented. Bot. Mag. t. 4457. From Assam (not Formosa), 5,000–5,500 ft.—Will root from summer cuttings.

Rhododendron inaequale Hutchinson (of unequal size). *F.* 3–6 ft. Flowers large, white, fragrant. Assam, 4,000–5,500 ft.—Name refers to unequal leaf-scales.

Rhododendron iteophyllum Hutchinson (willow leaved). *F.* Up to 6 ft. Flowers 2¼ in. long. Assam, 2,000 ft.

Rhododendron Johnstoneanum Watt (after Mrs. Johnston, Manipur, 1882). *D.* Large bush. Flowers 2¼ in. long, white, spotted red, yellow blotch; very fragrant. Assam; Manipur, 6,000–11,000 ft. **X**

Rhododendron lasiopodum Hutchinson (woolly-footed). *E.* 16 ft. high. Flowers 1¾ in. long, white, yellow inside the base; fragrant. Pine forests, W. Yunnan, 8,000–9,000 ft.

Rhododendron Ludwigianum Hosseus. *F.* Up to 4½ ft. Flowers 2½ in. long, white and rose. Thailand, 6,600 ft.

Rhododendron Lyi Léveillé (after J. Lyi, Chinese collector). *D.* 6 ft. Inflor. (b). Flowers (76) 2 in. long, white with yellowish blotch, scented. Bot. Mag. t. 9051. Kweichow, China.

Rhododendron missionarum Léveillé (of the missionaries). *E.* Shrub, height not given. Flowers 2 in. long, violet or white. On rocks, N.E. Yunnan, 9,000 ft.

Rhododendron notatum Hutchinson (marked). *F.* Small epiphytic bush. Flowers 2 in. long, white marked with a purplish pink band on angles; scented. On trees and rocks in river bed, N.E. Burma, 3,500–5,500 ft.

Rhododendron pachypodum Balfour f. & W. W. Smith (thick footed). *E.* 5 ft. Flowers 2 in. long, yellow. Open scrub and pastures, W. Yunnan, 9,000–10,000 ft.

Rhododendron Parryae. *E.* A "medium-sized" tree to 10 ft. high, with strongly scented white flowers and a smooth purplish bark.

Rhododendron pilicalyx Hutchinson (hairy calyx). *E.* 4 ft. Flowers 2¾ in. long, white with a little pink, S.E. Yunnan, 8,000 ft.

Rhododendron pseudo-ciliicalyx Hutchinson (false ciliicalyx). *F.* Height not given. Flowers 2½ in. long, white or rose. Habitat uncertain, probably Yunnan.

Rhododendron roseatum Hutchinson (rosy). *E.* Up to 10 ft. Flowers 2 (?) in. long, white, faintly flushed rose outside. Open scrub, W. Yunnan, 9,000 ft.

Rhododendron rufosquamosum Hutchinson (with reddish scales). *F.* 3 ft. Flowers 2¾ in. long, white, pink in the bud. S.W. Yunnan, 4,800 ft.

Rhododendron scopulorum Hutchinson (of the crags). *F.* Bushy shrub 6–8 ft. high. Flowers 1¾ in. long, probably pink. Boulder screes and thickets, E. Tibet, 6,000 ft.

Rhododendron Scottianum Hutchinson (after M. B. Scott, a Kew botanist, d. 1917). *F.* Up to 12 ft. Flowers large, white, with yellow blotch, sometimes flushed on the outside with rose. Open rocky places, W. Yunnan, 6,000–8,000 ft.—Sweet-scented.

Rhododendron Smilesii Hutchinson (after its discoverer, F. H. Smiles). *F.* Tree up to 20 ft. Flowers 1¼ in. long, white. N. Thailand.

Rhododendron supranubium Hutchinson (above the clouds). *E.* Up to 12 ft. Inflor. (c). Flowers (67) 1¼ in. long, dull white with rose outside; fragrant. Notes Roy. Bot. Gard. Edinburgh *12*:68 (fig. 9). Ledges of cliffs and dry rocky spots, Yunnan, 10,000–12,000 ft.—Comes from a higher altitude in the Chinese Alps than any other member of its series.

Rhododendron Surasianum Balfour f. & Craib. *F.* 12 ft. Flowers about 3 in. long, pale pink. Rocky ground in open evergreen jungle, N. Thailand, 4,500 ft.

Rhododendron taronense Hutchinson (from the Taron Gorge). *F.* An epiphytic shrub, 10–15 ft. high. Flowers 2 in. long, white with large yellow blotch; slightly fleshy; fragrant. Growing high in the trees of the jungle, Yunnan, 4,000–5,000 ft. **X**

Rhododendron Valentinianum Forrest (after Père S. P. Valentin, Missionary in China). Small shrub 2–3 ft. high. Flowers 1¼ in. long, bright butter yellow. Open scrub, Yunnan, 11,000 ft.—An attractive species allied to *R. ciliatum.* **X**

Rhododendron Veitchianum Hooker (after the English nurserymen by that name). VEITCH'S RHODODENDRON. *F.* 8 ft. Inflor. (b), white. Flowers (76) but with a very frilled margin, 2¾ in. long, slightly tinged with green outside. Bot. Mag. t. 4992. On rocks or epiphytic on trees, Burma, Tenasserim and Thailand, 4,000–5,500 ft.— The flowers illustrated in the Botanical Magazine are very beautiful with their frilled petals. Millais said it is handsome, easy of cultivation, flowers young and is a good plant for the cool greenhouse. It has given rise to several hybrids.

Rhododendron walongense Ward (from Walong, Assam). A shrub to 10 ft. with funnel-shaped white flowers in clusters of 3 or 4.—Not in general cultivation.

SUBSERIES MADDENII

Rhododendron brachysiphon Balfour f. (short tubed). 8 ft. Flowers 1¾ in. long, pink, scented. Bhutan, 6,000–7,000 ft.

Rhododendron calophyllum Nuttall (beautiful leaf). *F.* About 5 ft. Inflor. (c). Flowers (30) 1½ in. long, probably white, scented. Notes Roy. Bot. Gard. Edinburgh *12*:23. Oola Mts., Bhutan, 6,000–7,000 ft.—Not in cultivation, those passing for it being *R. Maddenii,* which it resembles.

Rhododendron crassum Franchet (fleshy). *D.* Up to 20 ft. Flowers 2¼–3½ in. long, white. W. Yunnan and Upper Burma, 7,500–12,000 ft.—This sweet-scented shrub flowers in June and is said to be the only Maddenii that is fairly hardy and satisfactory outdoors in England. **X**

Rhododendron excellens Hemsley & Wilson (superb). *F.* 10 ft. Inflor. (c). Flowers (64) 3 in. long and about the same in diameter, white, blooming in July in its native habitat. Notes Roy. Bot. Gard. Edinburgh *12*:30 (1919). S. Yunnan. —A very rare species.

Rhododendron Maddenii Hooker f. (after Lt. Col. Madden, d. 1865). *E.* See text-figure for series. 6–9 ft. Flowers 1¾ in. long, white with a faint flush of rose on the outside and in the bud. Bot. Mag. t. 4805. Sikkim and Bhutan, 5,000–9,000 ft.—Very sweet-scented and, according to Millais, very good for the cool greenhouse. Forms have been recorded under the following varietal names: var. *longiflorum,* with longer pedicels; var. *Jenkinsii,* with a longer style; var. *tubiflorum;* var. *virginale;* and var. *Walkeri.* **X**

Rhododendron manipurense Balfour f. & Watt (from Manipur), syn: R. Maddenii var. obtusifolium Hutchinson. *D.* Shrub of 15 ft. Inflor. (b). Flowers (76) up to 4 in. long, large pure white. Naga Hills, Assam, 8,000–10,000 ft.

Rhododendron odoriferum Hutchinson (fragrant). *E.* Shrub (8 ft.?). Inflor. (c). Flowers (64) white, tinged green inside, flushed rose outside, scented. Gard. Chron. *82*:31 (1927). S. Tibet, 8,000 ft.

Rhododendron polyandrum Hutchinson (many stamens). A bush of 3 ft. Inflor. (c). Flowers (30) 2¾ in. long, white. Notes Roy Bot. Gard. Edinburgh *12*:26 (1919). Bhutan, 8,500 ft. **X**

Subseries Megacalyx

Rhododendron Dalhousiae Hooker f. (after Lady Dalhousie). *F.* Epiphyte. Inflor. (c). Flowers (64) about 3½ in. long, pale yellow, white tinged, fragrant. Bot. Mag. t. 4718. Sikkim, Bhutan, 6,000–8,000 ft.—Millais said that this species is one of the most beautiful and sweet scented of the Himalayan rhododendrons, but is tender except in the mildest parts of England. In its native home it grows as an epiphyte, but will succeed well in soil when grafted or if grown from seed. It is a beautiful, large lemon-scented species for the cool greenhouse, where it is easy of culture and enjoys plenty of syringing and moisture. **X**

Rhododendron Headfortianum Hutchinson (after the Marquess of Headfort). To 3 ft. with white flowers, spotted and flushed rose. Bot. Mag. *163*:9614 (1942). S.E. Tibet, Assam.

Rhododendron Levinei Merrill (after C. O. Levine, Canton Christian College). Shrub to 13 ft. with funnel-campanulate flowers in clusters of 2 or 3, white, fragrant. —Not in general cultivation.

Rhododendron liliiflorum Léveillé (lily-like flowers). *F.* Inflor. (c). Flowers (64) 3 in. long, white, scented. Edinburgh Notes *12*:32 (1919). Kweichow.—An incompletely known species.

Rhododendron Lindleyi T. Moore (after Dr. John Lindley, famous botanist). *E.* Epiphyte. Inflor. (c). Flowers (64) 3 in. long, white, scented. Notes Roy. Bot. Gard. Edinburgh *12*:40 (1919). Sikkim, Bhutan, 6,000–10,000 ft.—A rare and tender species.

Rhododendron megacalyx Balfour f. & Ward (large calyx). *E.* Bushy tree of 10–16 ft. Inflor. (c). Flowers (64) 2¼ in. long, white, nutmeg-scented, large. N.E. Upper Burma, 7,000–9,000 ft.—Said to be fine where it can be grown. Early forms were quite tender; later importations have possibilities. **X**

Rhododendron Nuttallii Booth (after Thomas Nuttall, famous botanist, 1786–1859). *F.* Eventually 30 ft. high. Inflor. (b). Flowers (64) 4 in. long, white, suffused with yellow in the tube and slightly tinged pink on the petals. Bot. Mag. t. 5146. Bhutan, 4,000–5,000 ft.—This species has the largest flowers of any of its kind in a clear light yellow or nankeen yellow. It is a magnificent thing and very fragrant, but should be regarded as a greenhouse plant, as it can be made to live outdoors only in the most favored parts of southern England, against a warm wall. **XX**

Rhododendron Species Illustrated Opposite: 1. *R. cinnabarinum* (Cinnabarinum Series) 2. *R. ambiguum* (Triflorum Series) 3. *R. dichroanthum* subspecies *apodectum* (Neriiflorum Series) 4. *R. campylogynum* (Campylogynum Series) 5. *R. trichostomum* var. *ledioides* (Anthopogon Series) 6. *R. Wardii* (Thomsonii Series) 7. *R. facetum* (Irroratum Series) 8. *R. Griersonianum* (Auriculatum Series) 9. *R. Augustinii* (Triflorum Series) 10. *R. concatenans* (Cinnabarinum Series) 11. *R. scyphocalyx* (Neriiflorum Series) 12. *R. ferrugineum,* white and rose forms (Ferrugineum Series) 13. *R. racemosum* (Virgatum Series) 14. *R. discolor* (Fortunei Series) 15. *R. russatum* (Lapponicum Series)

Rhododendron Species

Rhododendron Fortunei 'Sir Charles Butler'

Rhododendron rhabdotum Balfour f. & Cooper (striped). *E.* 12 ft. Flowers 3 in. long, cream colored and striped with red on the outside. Bhutan, 8,000 ft. **XX**

Rhododendron sinonuttallii Balfour f. & Forrest (Chinese Nuttallii). *F.* This white flowered shrub from S.E. Tibet is almost the counterpart of the Bhutan species, *R. Nuttallii,* except for some minor differences in pubescence and other slight botanical characters. It is very handsome. **XX**

Rhododendron Taggianum Hutchinson (after H. F. Tagg, Edinburgh Botanic Garden). *E.* Height to 8 ft. Inflor. (b). Flowers (58) 3¼ in. long, pure white, yellow blotch, slightly fleshy, deliciously fragrant. New Flora and Silva *4* (1): 5 (1931). Margins of open conifer forests and among scrub on rocky slopes, N.E. Upper Burma, 10,000–11,000 ft.—It is noted in Spec. Rhod. that this beautiful species will probably prove to be the gem of Mr. Forrest's 1925 collection. **X**

MICRANTHUM SERIES

This series consists of only one species, a very distinct form covering a wide range in northern China and showing no particular affinity with any other rhododendron. Although it looks more like a ledum than a rhododendron and the flower might, at first glance, be taken for a small spiraea, it is not unattractive. It is singularly useful because of its hardiness. E. H. Wilson used to say that, of the countless Chinese rhododendrons tested at the Arnold Arboretum, *Rhododendron micranthum* was the only evergreen sort that had proved reliably hardy there. Coming from a naturally bleak region, *R. micranthum* appears to be as hardy as the most rugged American sort. While its small white flowers are inconspicuous, it may prove to be useful as a landscape plant. Some persons regard it as horrid, while others commend it.

R. MICRANTHUM

Rhododendron micranthum Turczaninow (small flowered). *A.* Bush with lanky branches (or sometimes fairly compact), up to 6 ft. or so. Inflor. (f). See text-figure. Flowers (21) about ¼ in. long to ⅝ in. across, milky white. N. Korea to Manchuria and north and west China, from W. Szechuan to the Pekin district. Bot. Mag. t. 8198.—Evergreen leaves, about 1½ in. long by ½ in. broad, covered with overlapping scales below; oblanceolate. The small flowers are borne in many-flowered terminal racemes. Some plants, at least, of this species are self-incompatible, but set seed readily from pollen of another individual. May be propagated satisfactorily in America from seed.

MOUPINENSE SERIES

R. MOUPINENSE

The fact that these small shrubs from Szechuan are usually epiphytic and are closely allied to the Maddenii and Triflorum series should be ample commentary on their probable unfitness as garden subjects in North America. *Rhododendron moupinense,* however, is hardy in the British Isles if given a little shelter and may survive elsewhere in cultivation. Its principal disadvantage is that it blooms too early and hence is often injured by spring frosts. The flowers are azalea-like.

It is grown in California, where it blooms in January, and it may be useful elsewhere upon the West Coast. In Delaware, Mr. G. G. Nearing had difficulty in keeping it alive under glass frames. *Rhododendron moupinense* has been used as a pollen parent in crosses with *R. ciliatum,* the resulting hybrid having pinky white flowers and bearing three merit stars. It has also been crossed with *R. spinuliferum.* The closest allies of the Moupinense series appear to be the series Maddenii and Triflorum.

Rhododendron dendrocharis Franchet (graceful tree). An epiphytic shrub, possibly not in cultivation. Flowers 1¼ in. long, bright rosy red. E. Tibet and Szechuan, 7,000–9,000 ft.

Rhododendron moupinense Franchet (from Moupin). *B.* This is a small spreading shrub up to 4 ft., sometimes epiphytic in nature. See text-figure. Flowers (63) but smaller, about 1½ in. long, white and azalea-like, fragrant, sometimes pink or deep rose. Bot. Mag. t. 8598. E. Tibet and Szechuan.—Considered desirable where it can be grown, but blooms early (February or earlier in England) and thus is suitable only for warmer regions and when protected from late frosts. It appeared to be of very doubtful hardiness on Cape Cod in Mr. Dexter's tests. A rock-garden subject, but needs shade. **X**

Rhododendron petrocharis Diels (gracing the rocks). A small shrub with white flowers, growing on rocks in Szechuan at 5,500 ft. Imperfectly known.

NERIIFLORUM SERIES

This group contains a relatively large number of species, classified according to sub-groups and sections (the latter being omitted in this treatment). Its closest affinity is with the series Taliense, Thomsonii and Fortunei. Having unspotted flowers, this series may be distinguished from Taliense by that character. From Thomsonii it is separable by the broad, characteristic Thomsonii leaf. From Fortunei it is recognized by its densely hairy ovary.

The Neriiflorum series is an important group, comprising several magnificent species. They come from western or northwestern Yunnan, southeastern Tibet and northeastern Upper Burma at altitudes rang-

R. FORRESTII

ing from 10,000 to 14,000 feet. In height the plants vary from creeping undershrubs a few inches high to bushes or small trees as much as 12 feet tall. The inflorescence is commonly in the form of an umbel and is never congested. In color the flowers range from white to pink, rose, deep crimson, bright scarlet, brick-red, salmon, orange, yellow to lemon-yellow. They are noted for brilliancy and purity of tone in color. Forms of *Rhododendron dichroanthum* are apricot-colored. Unfortunately, very few color figures of the species in this series have appeared as yet. Many of the species are of relatively recent introduction and several are but imperfectly known. See color plate, page 334.

Several of these species are said to be among the best of the Asiatic rhododendrons in cultivation. Nevertheless, says Cox, they are not the easiest to grow, especially when very young, as they hold back unless very favorably situated. They cannot endure drought, they need shelter and a rich soil with coolness at their roots and should be planted two feet apart in groups. They are slow growing and never become very large, so that they may be planted in the shelter of large plants. Considering their natural habitat, it would be surprising if any of these species should prove to be reliably hardy in the northeastern United States unless crossed with hardier sorts. Seedlings of some species of this series are being grown in this region, however, and we shall eventually learn more of their ability to withstand American conditions. It is possible that some of these seedlings are chance hybrids and not true representatives of the series.

This group as a whole appears very heterogeneous, suggesting that there may be considerable variation within the species as well as the possibility of natural hybrids between different species within the series. In classification, the series Neriiflorum has been divided into four subseries, the separating lines being drawn on the basis of leaf-shape, indumentum and habit of growth.

SUBSERIES FORRESTII

Although generally regarded as dwarf or creeping shrubs, this group contains intergrading variants as tall as 3 feet or more. The colors run through rose and crimson to bright scarlet. The fact that they will cross with species of standard or ordinary garden height has made these species, especially *R. Forrestii* var. *repens,* very valuable parents in producing offspring of dwarfish habit and bright red flowers.

Rhododendron chamae-Thomsonii (Tagg & Forrest) Cowan & Davidian (dwarf Thomsonii), syn: R. repens var. chamae-Thomsonii Tagg & Forrest. To 3 ft. and upright; large rounded leaves and a truss of 1–5, tubular-campanulate crimson flowers. There are dwarfer forms linking this species with *R. Forrestii.* R.H.S. Rhod. Yearbook for 1951–52, p. 66. Tibet and Yunnan. Var. *chamaethauma* Cowan & Davidian (syn: R. repens var. chamaethauma Tagg) has leaves smaller than the type.

Rhododendron erastum Balfour f. & Forrest (lovely). *A.* A prostrate creeper, only a few inches high, very narrow-leaved. Flowers about 1 in. long, clear begonia-pink. Stony alpine meadows, N.W. Yunnan, 14,000 ft.

Rhododendron Forrestii Balfour f. ex Diels (after George Forrest, botanical explorer, 1873–1932). *B.* A prostrate, creeping, woody undershrub, 6–18 in. high. Inflor. (zz). Flowers (31), 1⅛ in. long, deep crimson or scarlet, borne solitary or in pairs and relatively large for the size of the plant. Leaves in the typical form are red or purple underneath. Alpine meadows and moorlands, N.E. Yunnan and S.W. Tibet, 13,000–14,000 ft.—This species and its variant, the former *R. repens,* as well as its related neighbor, *R. chamae-Thomsonii,* have all been studied and revised by Cowan and Davidian in an effort to eliminate the chaos which had confused these various forms. Under the new revision, the former species *R. repens* is now reduced to varietal status and becomes *R. Forrestii* var. *repens* (Balfour f. & Forrest) Cowan & Davidian. The most distinguishing difference between the typical species and its variety is the color of the undersurface of the leaf, which is pale or glaucous green in the variety, as against red or purple in the species. There is also var. *tumescens* Cowan & Davidian, which is characterized by a dome-shaped habit of growth with its outer branches creeping and with leaves larger than the others. Intergrading forms between this and *R. chamae-Thomsonii* are suspected. Horticulturally these plants are of considerable interest. The dark green leaves and bright scarlet trumpet-shaped flowers of var. *repens,* exceptionally large for such a small prostrate creeper, have given this plant a unique fame, but one which is also linked with a reputation for somewhat fastidious growth. In its hybrids, however, it seems to be valuable, for the color is transmissible to other more tractable garden species, while its dwarf habit imparts a more compact habit of growth to the combination. Naturally the species is somewhat slow of growth and requires a moist though well-drained soil. In America, culture seems to be limited to the West Coast, but there is hope that some of the hybrids will prove adaptable to the Northeast. The American hardiness rating is presently H-3. **XX**

Rhododendron porphyrophyllum Balfour f. & Forrest (purple leaved). *A.* A creeping woody undershrub about 2 ft. high, rooting freely. The flowers are deep rose and about 1½ in. long. Like *R. Forrestii* the leaves are purple beneath. Stony alpine pastures and ledges of cliffs, S.E. Tibet and N.W. Yunnan, 13,000 ft.

Rhododendron serpens Balfour f. & Forrest (creeping). *A.* A creeping shrub, rooting freely from the prostrate stems, with the ascending stems rising from a few inches to 1½ ft. high. Flowers usually in pairs, about 1 in. long, deep rose or paler. Open rocky alpine meadows, S.E. Tibet, 14,000 ft.

Rhododendron trilectorum Cowan (commemorating the three collectors Ludlow, Sherriff and Taylor, 1938). A species closely akin to *R. Forrestii* var. *repens,* but differing in decurrent leaf lamina, glabrous ovary, and pale yellow flowers. A prostrate shrub in 12 inches. S.E. Tibet. Notes Roy. Bot. Gard. Edinburgh XXI (*3*): 144 (1953).—Not in general cultivation.

Subseries Haematodes

These are small to medium-sized shrubs, ranging from three to ten feet high. The leaves are broadly obovate (inverted egg-shaped) with a rounded apex and a woolly indumentum on the under side. This indumentum is reddish brown. The flowers are very fleshy and are usually red or deep crimson, rarely yellow or white. *Rhododendron haematodes* is considered one of the best of the cultivated members of the series.

Rhododendron Beanianum Cowan (after W. J. Bean of Kew). *B.* An 8-ft. shrub with bristly stems. Flowers scarlet, crimson or pink. Var. *compactum* is less scraggly and is without bristles on branches and petioles. New Flora and Silva *10*:246 (1938). Tibet, Burma. **X**

Rhododendron catacosmum Balfour f. in MS. (descript. Tagg) (adorned). *B.* 6–9 ft. tall. Flowers 1½–2 in. long, crimson-rose. Among scrub in alpine side valleys, S.E. Tibet, 13,000–14,000 ft.—This is said to be a magnificent member of the subseries.

Rhododendron chaetomallum Balfour f. & Forrest (with fleecy hair). *C.* 4–5 ft. Flowers 1½ in. long, deep crimson in the type species, varying to yellow in other forms. Open thickets and among rocks, S.E. Tibet and N.W. Yunnan, 11,000–13,000 ft.—This species is quite variable in both flower and leaf characters. Its name has reference to the indumentum on its leaves. Variety *glaucescens* Tagg & Forrest is 5 ft. tall with deep rich crimson flowers. Variety *hemigynum* Tagg & Forrest has bright crimson flowers. Variety *xanthanthum* Tagg & Forrest is 2–4 ft. tall with larger creamy-yellow flowers flushed more or less rose-pink, especially on the margins. The latter should be carefully distinguished from *Rhododendron citriniflorum,* a yellow-flowered species in this same series, which has thin, glandular flowers in contrast to the fleshy, non-glandular flowers of *R. chaetomallum* var. *xanthanthum.* The latter comes from a somewhat higher altitude than the type species and is presumably hardier.

Rhododendron chionanthum Tagg & Forrest (snowy flowers). *B.* 3 ft. tall. Flowers 1½ in. long, white. Alpine meadows and rocky slopes, N.E. Upper Burma, 13,000–14,000 ft.

Rhododendron coelicum Balfour f. & Farrer (heavenly). *C.* A low bush or rarely a small stout tree. Flowers 1½ in. long, bright scarlet, fleshy, borne in compact trusses of 12–15 flowers. On precipices or making tangle in the canebrake, N.E. Upper Burma, 11,000 ft.

Rhododendron haematodes Franchet (bloodlike). *B.* Up to 10 ft. tall; usually small, spreading. Leaves dark green, felty beneath. Inflor. (b) or (c), 6–8 fls. Flowers (32) 1¾–2 in. long, crimson or brilliant scarlet-crimson. Bot. Mag. t. 9165. Rocky open situations on alpine meadows, Yunnan, 11,000–12,000 ft.—Regarded as one of the very best Chinese rhododendrons. It flowers late and is hardy in England. Although it is slow in developing, it is said to be worth waiting for. Some plants grown in America appear partially hardy, while others do not. It is possible that some of the seedlings tested are not true to type. In cultivation the species is a small bush. Its American hardiness rating is H-4, tender. **XX**

Rhododendron hemidartum Balfour f. MS. (descript. Tagg) (half flayed). *B.* About 4 ft. Flowers 1¾ in. long, deep rich crimson without markings, borne in a compact umbel of 10. Rocky alpine meadow among rhododendron scrub, S.E. Tibet, 13,000–14,000 ft.—The name of this species refers to an irregularly developed indumentum on the foliage which gives it a peculiar appearance, leaving certain bare areas on the leaves.

Rhododendron mallotum Balfour f. & Ward (fleecy), syn: R. aemulorum Balfour f. *B.* Up to 12 ft. tall in nature. Flowers 1½ in. long, dark crimson, fleshy; borne in compact umbels of 14. Open rocky slopes and margins of thickets, W. Yunnan and N.E. Upper Burma, 10,000–11,000 ft.

Rhododendron pocophorum Balfour f. MS. (descript. Tagg) (fleece bearing). *B.* 4–10 ft. Flowers 2 in. long, crimson, sometimes faintly spotted; borne in compact trusses of 15–20. Open rocky slopes amidst scrub, S.E. Tibet, 12,000–15,000 ft.

SUBSERIES NERIIFLORUM

The species in this subseries are smallish or medium-sized shrubs, closely related to one another but exceedingly varied. They are characterized by elliptic or narrow pointed leaves, with or without an indumentum, which, if present, is loose-woolly and gray or dark cinnamon. The flowers are very fleshy and range from scarlet and crimson to yellow in color. *Rhododendron neriiflorum, R. sperabile* and *R. sperabiloides* are all considered valuable species. They are rated H-4 (tender) in America.

Members of this group are on the "failure" lists of Messrs. Dexter, Gable and Nearing, so may be considered unlikely candidates for a place in the horticulture of the eastern

R. NERIIFLORUM

United States. Although they are grown in San Francisco, they are considered fastidious there, requiring shade, above and below, as well as plenty of water.

Rhododendron Albertsenianum Forrest (after M. O. Albertsen, Chinese Maritime Customs). *B.* 4–7 ft. tall. Flowers 1¼ in. long, bright crimson-rose without markings, frilled on the margins; borne in trusses of 5–6. Open forests, W. Yunnan, 10,000 ft.

Rhododendron euchroum Balfour f. & Ward (with a good color). *C.* 1½–2 ft. Flowers 1¼ in. long, bright brick-red, fleshy; borne in trusses of 4–5. In damp shady situations under bamboos, E. Upper Burma, 10,000 ft.—Although attractive in description, this species is unknown in cultivation.

Rhododendron floccigerum Franchet (woolly). *B.* 3–5 ft. Flowers 1¼ in. long, crimson; in lax trusses of 4–7. Open moist situations among scrub and boulders, Yunnan, 13,000 ft.—The leaves have a characteristic woolly tomentum which disappears at maturity, leaving a white glaucous surface on the under sides of the leaves. Although the typical color of the flower is deep or lighter crimson, it varies in some areas to rose and even to a yellow with rose margins. Variety *appropinquans* lacks an indumentum and has glandular shoots and petioles.

Rhododendron neriiflorum Franchet (flowers like oleander). *C.* 3–9 ft. Inflor. (b). Flowers (32), 1½–1¾ in. long, bright crimson or scarlet. Bot. Mag. t. 8727. In shady rocky situations in side valleys and in open meadows and pine forests, mid-west Yunnan, 9,000–12,000 ft.—The typical plant is about 5 ft. tall and is of free flowering habit, making an attractive sight when its scarlet flowers are in bloom. Even small plants will bloom. It is, however, a slow grower and needs a sheltered position when grown in England. Its hybrids are much better than the species. The leaves are lightish green and have a very white undersurface. It is relatively variable and has several forms, some of which are said to be hardier than others. However good its best forms may be, I have seen many plants of *R. neriiflorum* which, in my opinion, were neither impressive nor beautiful. **XX**

The following are recognized as subspecies:

Rhododendron agetum Balfour f. & Forrest (wondrous), which differs in having more pointed leaves and certain other minor characteristics.

R. euchaites Balfour f. & Forrest (with beautiful hairs), a choice woodland form attaining a height of 15–20 ft. and having larger flowers than the type, bright crimson scarlet. Yunnan and Burma. **XX**

Rhododendron phaedropum Balfour f. & Farrer (of bright appearance), a 15-ft. shrub, which has, like *R. floccigerum,* only traces of indumentum and flowers which vary from straw yellow to crimson.

Rhododendron phoenicodum Balfour f. & Farrer (with purple-red trumpet), *C,* having smaller leaves and flowers than the type.

Rhododendron sperabile Balfour f. & Farrer (to be hoped for). *C.* 3–6 ft. Flowers 1½ in. long, scarlet, in clusters of 4–5. On granite screes and in ravines, N.W. Upper Burma, 10,000–12,000 ft.—An attractive plant, but said to be not quite so good as *Rhododendron haematodes,* although new and better forms are being raised, some of which may surpass the former. Variety *weihsiense* has longer, narrower leaves and a lighter indumentum.

Rhododendron sperabiloides Tagg & Forrest (like sperabile). Hardiness *C* (H-4 in U.S.), and statement made that it seems to take kindly to the British climate. 2–4 ft. high. Flowers about 1 in. long, deep to light crimson; borne in umbels of 6–8. In alpine scrub in side valleys, S.E. Tibet, 12,000–13,000 ft.—Has smaller flowers than *Rhododendron sperabile* and is distinguished by its eglandular stems and petioles, and by other botanical characters.

Subseries Sanguineum

As a rule, the shrubs in this sub-group are from two to five feet tall. The leaves are either without any indumentum or, if present, it is usually thinly plastered and white to fawn colored. The flowers are an inch and one-half or so in length and vary tremendously in color. Some of them are exceedingly attractive, among which may be mentioned the various forms of *Rhododendron aperantum, R. apodectum, R. dichroanthum, R. sanguineum* and *R. scypho-*

calyx. However, they are mostly too slow of growth for horticultural purposes and some are unattractive in color. Ward says that *R. aperantum,* 25 years after its introduction, had still never flowered in Britain. Nevertheless, *R. dichroanthum* has gone on the record as a parent of 'Fabia,' one of the more interesting modern hybrids.

Rhododendron aperantum Balfour f. & Ward (limitless). *A.* Dwarf spreading shrub about 6 to 20 in. high. Flowers (60) 1¾ in. long, various shades from white to rose, deep rose, orange and yellow, sometimes flushed or margined; borne in a lax cluster of 4. In open stony alpine meadows and ledges of cliffs, N.E. Upper Burma, 12,000–14,000 ft.—A slow growing dwarf, eventually making mats from 1 to 20 ft. across. The color variations occur without reference to geographical habitat in nature and are so numerous that no attempt has been made to give them varietal names. Suitable for rock gardens. Behavior in the eastern United States not yet known.

Rhododendron citriniflorum Balfour f. & Forrest (citron-like flowers), syn: R. chlanidotum Balfour f. & Forrest. *B.* Dwarf shrub, 2–4 ft. Flowers (29) bright lemon-yellow. New Flora and Silva *4* (1):5 (1931). Ledges of cliffs and on open rocks, W. Yunnan, 13,000 ft.—Characterized by its yellow flowers and very heavy indumentum, fawn colored. Variety *chlanidotum* n. comb., has longer leaves.

The following are recognized as subspecies of *R. citriniflorum:*

R. aureolum Cowan (ornamented with gold). Ovary glandular. Flowers yellow, yellowish-rose or rose.

R. horaeum Balf. f. & Forrest (beautiful). To 6 ft. with 3–5 flowers, deep rose-crimson.

R. rubens Cowan (red). Ovary glandular, flowers red.

Rhododendron dichroanthum Diels (2-colored flowers). *B.* 2–6 ft. high. Flowers (33) 1½ in. long, apricot or orange flushed salmon-rose, varying from deep orange, dull orange to salmon-pink. Bot. Mag. t. 8815. Dry open rocky meadows and open shady situations, Tali range mid-western Yunnan, 11,000–12,000 ft.—Millais calls this a very beautiful rhododendron and one of the best. Apparently, it is variable, so that it is worth while to purchase only the superior forms. These are available as clonal varieties, since the species strikes root easily from cuttings and nurserymen have been propagating it in this manner.

The following are subspecies of *R. dichroanthum:*

R. apodectum Balf. (acceptable). *A.* Flowers shaded dull rose-orange; 2 weeks later than *R. dichroanthum.* See color plate, page 334.

R. herpesticum Balf. f. & Ward (spreading). *B.* Dwarf shrublet, 1–2 ft. high. Flowers 1¼ in. long, dull yellow to orange-red.

R. scyphocalyx Balf. f. & Forrest (cup-shaped calyx). *B.* 5 ft. Inflor. 3–5 fls. in truss, rose-orange to coppery brown. The coppery-colored form is interesting and is nearer brown than any other evergreen rhododendron I have seen (see color plate).

R. septentrionale Cowan (belonging to the north). *B.* 4 ft. Flowers yellow, flushed rose or lemon yellow.

Rhododendron eudoxum Balfour f. & Forrest (of good report). *C.* About 6 ft. high with thin, twiggy branches. Flowers 1¼ in. long, deep clear crimson-rose, in clusters of 5–6. Open rhododendron thickets, N.W. Yunnan and S.E. Tibet, 11,000–13,000 ft.—This is the central species about which the following variant, classed as a subspecies, revolves:

Rhododendron brunneifolium Balfour f. & Forrest (brown colored foliage), *C,* with a brown indumentum and a very small calyx.

Rhododendron fulvastrum Balfour f. & Forrest (tawny). *A.* A small shrub of 2 ft. Flowers 1¼ in. long, pale lemon-yellow without markings, borne in clusters of 4. Rocky slopes and ledges of cliffs in ravines, S.E. Tibet, 14,000 ft.
The following are subspecies of *R. fulvastrum:*

R. epipastrum Balf. f. & Forrest (sprinkled over). 5 ft., with smaller dark rose flowers.

R. mesopolium Balf. f. & Forrest (gray in middle). 2 ft., flowers rose, pink or crimson.

R. trichomiscum Balf. f. & Forrest (bristly twigs). 3 ft., bristly branchlets. Flowers pale rose-pink.

R. trichophlebium Balf. f. & Forrest (hairy veined). 3 ft., flowers bell-shaped, crimson.

Rhododendron parmulatum Cowan (with small shield). *B.* To 4 ft. high. Inflor. tubular-campanulate. Flowers pale creamy-white, creamy yellow, white or white tinged pink, with crimson spots. Bot. Mag. t. 9624.

Rhododendron sanguineum Franchet (blood-red). *B.* An undershrub of 3 ft. Flowers 1¼ in. long, bright crimson, borne in terminal umbels of 3–4. Among scrub in open situations and margins of pine forests, W. Yunnan and S.E. Tibet, 13,000–14,000 ft.—The flower trusses are large for the size of the leaves. This is a lovely species, but, like all the other Neriiflorums, it does not flower early, grows slowly and requires shelter, care and patience on the part of the gardener. Variety *didymoides* has small rose flowers and is intermediate in many characters between *R. sanguineum* and *R. didymum. Rhododendron sanguineum* seedlings have failed when tested in southern Pennsylvania.

The following are subspecies of *R. sanguineum:*

R. aizoides Cowan (evergreen). Fls. yellow; bud-scales persistent.

R. atrorubrum Cowan (black-red). *A.* To 3 ft. Fls. black-crimson; bud-scales deciduous.

R. cloiophorum Balf. f. & Forrest (wearing a collar). *B.* To 4 ft. Fls. yellowish-rose or rose colored, with darker margins.

R. consanguineum Cowan (related to *R. sanguineum*). *B.* To 4 ft. Fls. dark crimson or carmine; bud-scales deciduous.

R. didymoides Tagg & Forrest (like *R. didymum*). *B.* To 3 ft. Fls. rose or yellow, margined crimson; bud-scales persistent.

R. didymum Balf. f. & Forrest (twofold). *B.* Dwarf alpine, 2–3 ft. Fls. 1 in. long, black-crimson.

R. haemaleum Balf. f. & Forrest (blood-red). *B.* To 4 ft. Fls. deep black-crimson. S.E. Tibet.

R. himertum Balf. f. & Forrest (lovely), syn: R. nebrites, R. poliopeplum. *A.* To 3 ft. Fls. 1½ in. long, yellow, bell-shaped; bud-scales deciduous.

R. leucopetalum Balf. f. & Forrest (with white petals). *B.* A pure white form with very woolly pedicels and ovary.

R. melleum Cowan (of honey). Ovary glandular. Fls. yellow; bud-scales not persistent.

R. mesaeum Cowan (intermediate). *B.* 5 ft. Fls. black-crimson; bud-scales persistent.

R. roseotinctum Balf. f. & Forrest (tinged with rose). *B.* Dwarfer than the type, glandular, with smaller flowers margined with deep rose, producing a picotee effect.

R. sanguineoides Cowan (like *R. sanguineum*). *B.* Fls. crimson; bud-scales persistent.

Rhododendron temenium Balf. f. & Forrest (from a sacred place near Doker La, Tsarong, in E. Tibet). *B.* To 4 ft. Inflor. tubular-campanulate. Flowers deep crimson or purplish-crimson. Blooms in mid-season. Tibet.
    The following are regarded as subspecies:

R. albipetalum Cowan (white-petalled). Ovary glandular; flowers white.

R. chrysanthemum Cowan (golden-flowered). *B.* Ovary not glandular; flowers yellow.

R. dealbatum Cowan (whitened). Ovary glandular; flowers white.

R. gilvum Cowan (pale yellow). *B.* To 4 ft. Flowers yellow.

R. glaphyrum Balf. f. & Forrest (polished). *C.* Without glands and with glabrous foliage. Has a wide variation in color, ranging from rose to white and yellow.

R. pothinum Balf. f. & Forrest (much desired). *B.* To 4 ft. Flowers bell-shaped, deep or purplish-crimson or carmine.

R. rhodanthum Cowan (red flowered). *B.* To 7 ft. Flowers pale rose, crimson brown markings.

OVATUM SERIES

R. OVATUM

For most practical purposes the members of this series might well be regarded as azaleas, although the Ovatum series forms a natural group readily separated from the Azalea series by its character of axillary flowers, borne singly. Nevertheless, the Ovatums closely approach the Azaleas in appearance and otherwise. The series, as yet, seems to have assumed little horticultural importance outside of the Orient. Of the five species in the group, three come from eastern China and nearby small islands, while the remaining two come from the region of Yunnan and Tibet. It has been suggested that some affinity exists between the members of the Ovatum series and the outlying American species *R. albiflorum* and possibly also the Stamineum series.

Rhododendron Bachii Léveillé. *E.* A twiggy bush 6 ft. or more high. Intermediate in character and geographical range between the typical *Rhododendron ovatum* of eastern China and the Yunnanese *Rhododendron leptothrium,* having the leaves of the former and the calyx of the latter. Flowers soft rosy-lilac. Hupeh, Kiangsi and Kweichow Provinces, China.

Rhododendron hongkongense Hutchinson (from Hongkong), syn: Azalea myrtifolia Champion. CHAMPION'S RHODODENDRON. *F.* Shrub of general habit of *Rhododendron ovatum.* Inflor. (n). Flowers (76) white with violet specks. Bot. Mag. t. 4609. On rocks, Black Mt., Hongkong and Kwangtung, 2,400 ft.—Winter flowering (?), evergreen, azalea-like shrub.

Rhododendron leptothrium Balfour f. & Forrest (with thin leaves), syn: R. australe Balfour f. & Forrest. *E.* 6–10 ft. tall. Leaves lanceolate, handsome bright green. Flowers deep magenta-rose, crimson markings. W. Yunnan, 7,000–11,000 ft.

Rhododendron ovatum (Lindley) Planchon (egg-shaped). *C.* A shrub up to 12 ft. high. Leaves evergreen, broadly ovate. Inflor. (n). Flowers (13) white or white and pink-spotted (sometimes lilac?), about 1½ in. across. Bot. Mag. t. 5064. Chusan Islands and Chekiang, eastern China.—Millais and others mention that this is a difficult subject, being a shy bloomer and not too hardy. This is doubtless a matter of several ecological conditions and not merely a question of temperature; in fact, the species might be better adapted to certain parts of America than to conditions in the British Isles where the observations relative to hardiness were made.

Rhododendron Vialii Delavay & Franchet (after Père Paul Vial, French missionary in Yunnan). *E.* 6–10 ft. Inflor. (n). Flowers about 1 in. long, crimson. Spec. Rhod. p. 566. S. Yunnan, 4,000–6,000 ft.

PONTICUM SERIES

Although this is not one of the larger series, its horticultural importance is perhaps greater than that of any other group of evergreen rhododendrons. It might be better called the Catawbiense series, since in America, at least, the catawba rhododendron and its hybrids is by far the outstanding species in the entire group so far as cultivation is concerned. In nature, *Rhododendron maximum* probably occurs most abundantly. But *Rhododendron ponticum* is certainly of small importance in America, at least, where its use is confined to grafting stock, and, from the standpoint of the American grower, it has probably been a detriment rather than an advantage as an ancestor of the garden hybrids.

R. CATAWBIENSE

The general characteristics of this group are familiar to most gardeners, since it embraces some of our best-known species including the relatively hardy large-shrub sorts from America, Europe and Asia. Most of them may be described as medium-sized, while one very dwarf form, the yellow *Rhododendron chrysanthum* from Siberia, is included. The series as a whole is characterized by a candelabra-like inflorescence, a tendency toward long pedicels and lobes of the corolla which are cut deeply enough to equal the length of the corolla-tube. The group is divided into two subseries, one with smooth leaves and the other having a distinct indumentum—a woolly or rusty under-surface on the leaves.

At present, the Ponticum series is considered to include only these two sub-series, one of them being exclusively Asiatic. With few exceptions, all members of both sub-groups are reliably hardy and four of these have furnished the "backbone" of the garden hybrids of the past. The "blood" of one or more of these hardy species must still be relied upon to furnish hardihood to almost every large-flowered hybrid race intended for cultivation in northeastern United States, regardless of how unfavorably plant breeders may look upon these sorts as breeding stock. In Great Britain it is fashionable now to avoid the use, for breeding purposes, of any variety having the least infusion of Catawba ancestry. Their chief drawback is the constant recurrence of the wild or magenta-lilac color. Whether this may eventually be avoided by the use of tested material which is genetically free from this color factor is very doubtful. But some of the other hardy species, rather than *R. catawbiense,* may work better. For the colder regions of America there is yet no substitute, as breeding stock, for the hardy members of this series, since these are, with few exceptions, the only evergreen rhododendrons well adapted to withstand the rigors of the climate.

There is no reason for belittling the value or beauty of the members of this series. Fads for other sorts may come and go, but these "ironclad" species will long remain important and indispensable in cold climates. If they are sometimes criticized for their lack of clear bright colors, it is often through lack of knowledge of the better varieties or because of the improper placement of the plants which emphasizes their shortcomings. I make bold to say that we are well on the way toward remedying the color difficulty through hybridization. In the meantime, it is a reason for real criticism, not of the plants but of gardeners, especially in America, that so little attention has been paid to certain worthy but little known hardy members of the series. I refer to *Rhododendron Smirnowii, R. Metternichii, R. caucasicum, R. brachycarpum* and possibly others. We have too few hybrids in which *Rhododendron caucasicum* has a part and the same statement is true of *R. maximum.* The use of these two species would lengthen the blooming season of the Catawba hybrids at each end, and neither would introduce lilac or magenta coloration. Of course, their slowness of growth is a disadvantage, but not a serious one. *Rhododendron chrysanthum,* being a low, prostrate species difficult to grow, is in a different category from the rest, but its color and the possibility of desirable hybrids from it should prompt a further search for useful strains, which might be found in the wild. Even among the well-known species, such as *Rhododendron catawbiense* and *R. maximum,* wide variation in character, vigor and color exists among wild plants and seedlings, so that careful selection of superior individuals would yield much in initiating noteworthy strains and races. As pointed out elsewhere, bad impressions of these species are sometimes created by the poor wild stock sold by certain irresponsible peddlers and collectors, as well as through the long lists of mediocre and out-of-date varieties which some nurserymen still persist in propagating. Practically all the species in this series are variable. It is my opinion that the superior strains and individuals of the various wild sorts should be selected, isolated and propagated as clones. Among the hybrids only the best varieties should be placed on the market and advertised as "named sorts." The others are not much better than the average run of seedlings.

The members of this series, of course, are not equal to the Fortunei hybrids and other highly favored groups of a more tender constitution when color, fragrance, beauty, size and some other characters are concerned. But in a cold climate the one indispensable prerequisite is hardiness and without this we cannot expect any species or hybrid to be successful in the colder parts of North America. Hence the value of the members of this series. Abroad, they are considered passé, for better things are now available, but it will be a long time before we can dispense with them in America.

Subseries Caucasicum

The species in this group are geographically distributed as follows: (1) From the Caucasus: *Rhododendron caucasicum, R. Smirnowii* and *R. Ungernii*. (2) From the mountains of northern and central Japan: *Rhododendron brachycarpum* and *R. Fauriei*. (3) Also from Japan: *Rhododendron Degronianum, R. Makinoi* and *R. Metternichii*. (4) From Formosa or islands near Japan: *Rhododendron hyperythrum* and *R. yakusimanum*. (5) From Siberia, Manchuria and northern Japan: *Rhododendron chrysanthum*. (6) From eastern Szechuan and Hupeh in western China: *Rhododendron adenopodum*.

It will be noted that, with one exception, these species all occur outside the world's great rhododendron center—western China. Six out of the ten occur in or near Japan, while three are confined to the Caucasus.

We should become better acquainted with nearly all the species in this subseries, few of which have been adequately tested in America and none of which are well known. *Rhododendron Smirnowii* is perhaps the most used and this, in its best forms, is something highly desirable for cold gardens.

Rhododendron adenopodum Franchet (glandular pedicel). B. 4–10 ft. Flowers 1½ in. long, pale rose, more or less spotted; borne in an elongated truss. Under surface of leaves clad with a loosely felty grayish to pale fawn tomentum, mixed

with long stalked glands. Thin woods, E. Szechuan and Hupeh, 5,000–7,000 ft.—
This is the only Ponticum in China and not closely allied to any other Chinese
rhododendron. It is regarded as a fine plant and blooms in April.

Rhododendron brachycarpum D. Don (short fruited). FUJIYAMA RHODODENDRON.
A. 6 to 10 ft. Inflor. (a). Flowers (56) 1 in. long and about 2–2¼ in. across,
usually pinkish white, sometimes creamy, flushed pink, spotted green. Bot. Mag. t.
7881. North and central mountain regions, Japan.—Characterized by a very short
style and a thin pale-fawn indumentum which disintegrates readily. This species,
which flowers in June, has proved perfectly hardy near Boston and also at Rochester.
Although young plants appear to be a bit fastidious in some places, they are quite
easily handled in others. The flowers that I have seen, although good, do not equal
those depicted in the color plate of the Botanical Magazine cited, and Millais states
that this illustration flatters the truss too much. The flowers are usually pinkish-
white and not cream-colored as illustrated. Its hardiness and comparatively unob-
jectionable color make it a potentially valuable species. Cream-colored forms, if
available, would, of course, be of considerable value. The color forms which have
been given names are var. *lutescens* Koidzumi, with glabrous leaves and flowers
white to yellowish, and var. *rosaeflorum* Miyoshi, with pink flowers. Millais regards the foliage of *Rhododendron brachycarpum* as superior to that of *R. catawbiense*. Potentially useful for hybridization in northeastern America.

Rhododendron caucasicum Pallas (from the Caucasus). CAUCASIAN RHODODEN-
DRON. *A.* A dwarfish shrub with thick branches, seldom more than 3 ft. high.
Leaves rust-colored beneath. Inflor. (a). Flowers (53) 1½ in. long, 1½ in. across,
rosy white or yellowish, with greenish spots; petals waved. Bot. Mag. t. 1145. The
Caucasus, 6,000–9,000 ft.—This species is better known through its hybrids than
in its original form and the type is very rare in cultivation. Cultivated forms often
show distinct yellow coloration and it is a question whether this has come from a
yellow form of the wild species or from hybridization with *Rhododendron chrysanthum*. Since *Rhododendron caucasicum* was introduced in 1803, soon after the introduction of *R. chrysanthemum* (1796), it seems possible that an early crossing of
these two species might have occurred. Variety *stramineum* Hooker f. with straw-
yellow flowers and fulvous spots is thought by some writers to have originated in
such a cross with *R. chrysanthum*. This variety is considered a parent of the clone
known as 'Cunningham's sulphur.' Variety *flavidum* Regel is another straw-
yellow variety, having greenish spots. Perhaps both *stramineum* and *flavidum*
should be regarded as clones. Other forms, mostly hybrid clones, are in cultivation.
The forms which have come to my attention have all been relatively early-flowering, blooming in May with *Rhododendron carolinianum*. *Rhododendron caucasicum*
and its varieties constitute, in my opinion, a very promising group and should be
more employed in breeding experiments. One of their foremost qualifications is
the fact that they are hardy in the north. Besides this they flower somewhat early,
but not too early, and they do not carry an objectionable magenta pigmentation.
They seem to be unusually fertile in crosses, occasionally even self-fertile. Lastly,
they may serve as a useful source for yellow pigmentation. *Rhododendron caucasicum* has entered into the Catawba hybrid race as described elsewhere in this work.

Rhododendron chrysanthum Pallas (golden flowered), syn: R. officinale Salisbury. *A?* or *B?* A dwarf alpine or arctic shrub of 6 to 12 in., prostrate or semi-prostrate with short ascending branches. Inflor. an umbellate corymb of 5–8 flowers on erect stalks. Flowers about 1 or 1¼ in. long, pale yellow, with the upper lobe spotted and somewhat larger than the others. Flora Rossica t. 30 (1784). Siberian-Mongolian mountains and Manchuria, Altai to Kamchatka, Korea, north and central Japan.— To quote Millais: "This small moisture-loving species was introduced from Dahuria in 1796. It occurs along the whole of the Siberian-Mongolian chain of mountains and throughout Manchuria. In Siberia it is common on the Altai and to the east it extends to Kamchatka and Okhotsk and the islands of the Bering Sea, and southward to Yezo and the high mountains of north and central Japan. . . . It is cultivated by the Japanese in several hill-stations. Professor Bayley Balfour states that its principal home in Japan is the Hiva and Etchm range, but it is also common in the Nikko Hills." *Rhododendron chrysanthum* is reported difficult to grow and rare in cultivation. It is reputed to demand a blanket of snow in winter and moist sphagnum moss in summer. Young seedlings seem to thrive in America if given much moisture, but are slow in development. It is not an effective plant from the standpoint of appearance and is a shy bloomer. Yet it appears to have been an important parent of the yellow Caucasicum hybrids and might well be the subject of further experimentation. Variety *niko-montanum* Komatsu is an erect growing variety from Japan. The species stands apart from the other members of the series, its closest affinity probably being with *R. caucasicum.*

Spurious seeds of *R. brachycarpum* are on the market under the name of *R. chrysanthum.* To be genuine the plant must have leaves under two inches long and a flat flower truss. (See G. G. Nearing in Bull. Amer. Rhod. Soc. 9:40. 1955.)

Rhododendron Degronianum Carrière (after M. Degron, Director of French posts in Yokohama, 1896), syn: R. Metternichii var. pentamerum Maximowicz; R. japonicum Schneider var. pentamerum Hutchinson. *A.* A compact rounded bush 3–4 ft. clad to the base with foliage. Inflor. (a). Flowers (54) 1½ in. long, 1¾ in. across, soft pink, unspotted or spotted very faintly, deep pink lines along the middle of the petals. Bot. Mag. t. 8403. Japan.—This is the correct name for the plant usually grown as *Rhododendron Metternichii,* from which it differs in its 5-parted corolla (*R. Metternichii* has 7 lobes, etc.). It is common in Japan. It is hardy at the Arnold Arboretum where it was introduced in 1892 by Professor Sargent under the name of *Rhododendron Metternichii* var. *pentamerum.* It is doubtful if the true *R. Metternichii* is in cultivation, its place being taken by *R. Degronianum* and *R. Makinoi.*

Rhododendron Fauriei Franchet (after Père Louis F. Faurie, French missionary in China). *B.* 5–10 ft. Inflor. (a?). Flowers about 1 in. long, white or yellowish, with a pinkish flush on the median lines, green spotted. Japan.—Sometimes regarded as a variety of *Rhododendron brachycarpum,* this species differs chiefly in the lack of indumentum on the under surface of the mature leaf.

Rhododendron hyperythrum Hayata (reddish), syn: R. rubropunctatum Hayata. Flowers 1½–2 in. long and broad, purple spotted. Formosa.—A species probably not in cultivation and probably not hardy.

Rhododendron Makinoi Tagg (after T. Makino, Japanese botanist), syn: R. stenophyllum Makino. *B.* A rounded bush 3–7 ft. tall, "remarkable for the lateness (August–September) of the new annual growths and for the curved sickle-like leaves." Leaves white woolly tomentose beneath. Flowers 1½ in. long and the same across, clear soft pink with or without crimson dots. Japan.—This plant has been in cultivation for some time under the name of *Rhododendron Metternichii* var. *angustifolium* or as a narrow-leaved variety of *R. Degronianum,* but is now regarded as a distinct species. It is considered desirable.

Rhododendron Metternichii Siebold & Zuccarini (after Prince Metternich, Austrian diplomat), syn: R. japonicum Schneider. LEATHERLEAF RHODODENDRON. *A* (*B* in England). 3–8 ft. tall. Inflor. (a?). Flowers rose, more or less spotted with deeper rose; 7 "petals" and 14 stamens. Flora Japon. vol. 1 (1835) t. 9. Mountains of northern Japan.—It is doubtful if the true species is in cultivation, the ordinary form grown under the name being *Rhododendron Degronianum* or *R. Makinoi.* This is easily identified by its 7-parted flower. Coming as it does from the north of Japan, there is little reason to doubt that this is as hardy as *R. Degronianum* which has endured conditions at the Arnold Arboretum for some years.

Rhododendron Smirnowii Trautvetter (after M. Smirnow, friend of Baron Ungern-Sternberg, its discoverer). SMIRNOW RHODODENDRON. *A.* Shrub 4–6 ft., or small tree to 15 ft. or more. Inflor. (a). Flowers (51) 1½ in. long, 2 in. across, rose or rosy purple, sometimes with waved margins. Young stems and foliage white woolly tomentose, under surface of mature leaves clad with a persistent dense woolly tomentum, sometimes becoming pale brown. Ovary tomentose. Bot. Mag. t. 7495. The Caucasus, 5,000–8,000 ft.—This woolly-leaved hardy species, in its best forms, is an excellent thing and somewhat better than illustrated in the color plate cited, in which the color was somewhat too lilac. There is variation, but in superior individuals the color is a fairly clear rose-pink, the flowers good-sized, widely opened and interestingly moulded with rather wavy margins. The lace-bugs and other insects dislike the woolly tomentum beneath the leaves and hence avoid this species. An excellent plant is growing in the Arnold Arboretum collection, where the species is perfectly hardy. When crossed with smooth-leaved sorts, such as *Rhododendron catawbiense,* the woolly tomentum usually disappears in the first generation offspring, but there is reason to believe that it reappears among the F_2 seedlings. Self-fertilized seed gives plants of reduced vigor and open-pollinated seed from plants in mixed collections is apt to produce almost entirely non-woolly offspring, so it is best to hand-pollinate, crossing 2 individual plants of *R. Smirnowii,* if you desire vigorous and true-to-type seedlings. *Rhododendron Ungernii* is the nearest ally to *R. Smirnowii* which differs from the former in its tomentose ovary. Blooms in June with *R. catawbiense.*

Rhododendron Ungernii Trautvetter (after Baron Ungern-Sternberg). *A.* 12–20 ft. Inflor. (a). Flowers (53) 1¼ in. long, 2 in. across, pale pink or white, faintly spotted. Ovary glandular and not tomentose. Blooms in July. Bot. Mag. t. 8332. The Caucasus, 5,000–8,000 ft.—Rather slow growing, reputed to be very hardy, but never showy, as new growth often hides the late blooming flowers. Millais quotes Mr. J. C. Williams: "*R. Ungernii,* when it is grown well as at Tregrehan, is a noble plant and loves to flower in July. There it is a faultless green-white and, under certain conditions, smells strongly of sandal-wood." Seedlings are said to damp off easily. It is most closely related to *R. Smirnowii,* differing from it in characters of ovary and leaf-apex, as well as in time of bloom. It is said to be hardy in the northeastern United States, but is rare. The altitudinal range of *R. Smirnowii* in its native Caucasian habitat is higher than that of *R. ponticum* and lower than that of *R. caucasicum.*

Rhododendron yakusimanum Nakai (from Yakusima Island). *A.* A compact rounded shrub to 3 ft. with tight round trusses of white flowers, bright rose in bud without trace of purple; tan indumentum under leaves; related to *R. Degronianum* and *R. Makinoi,* from Yakusima Island, Japan. Western gardeners know this species mainly from one superb plant at Exbury, England, which may not be typical. It is a free-flowering, beautifully shaped mound, only 3 ft. tall at 15 years. Seedlings do not come true. (See Quar. Bull. Amer. Rho. Society *14*:9–15. Jan. 1960.)

Subseries Ponticum

The species in this group need no introduction to most rhododendron growers; they are, perhaps, the most widely known rhododendrons of any group within the entire genus. *Rhododendron catawbiense* and *R. maximum* are, of course, the most familiar true rhododendrons from America and were among the very first to be introduced into cultivation. The former is a mid-season bloomer and the latter blooms late in the season. Both are reliably hardy in the "ironclad" sense of that term. Their respective merits and defects are discussed elsewhere. *Rhododendron ponticum,* naturalized in England and little used for anything but grafting stock in this country, is unable to withstand northern winters here, doubtless because of its failure to close its leaves at low temperatures (see Chapter IX). Its color is not desirable enough to make it worth while as a subject for cultivation. *Rhododendron macrophyllum* is thought by some to be handsomer than *R. catawbiense,* which it most nearly resembles and of which it appears to be a western form. *R. macrophyllum,* even when coming from the northern part of its native range, does not appear hardy in the northeastern states.

A good deal of variation exists within the species, so that some of the characters commonly used for classification break down when variant individuals appear. Wavy margins on the flowers occur on certain seedlings along with plain margins on other individuals in nearly all the species, as well as in other subseries. This occurs notably in *Rhododendron Smirnowii.* This seems to be a heritable character, travelling independently. Dwarf forms and geographical races occur also, as will be noted. There are considerable variations in flower color. In *Rhododendron catawbiense,* the common lilac color is occasionally replaced by a fairly clear pink, pure white or intermediate shades, these variations occurring among wild plants. The best white form of *R. catawbiense* is especially good and ranks, in my estimation, as one of the very finest hardy rhododendrons. Similarly, in *R. maximum,* a pure white-flowered form appears quite commonly in the wild, and there are rose-colored forms also, besides the prevailing apple-blossom pink type. If the best forms of all these species were selected and grown, the popular estimation of these plants would be considerably enhanced. There are many other species, of course, much better for use in Great Britain and in other mild climates than the species listed here, but in the rigorous weather of the northeastern United States, these hardy sorts necessarily are the "backbone" of the collection.

Rhododendron catawbiense Michaux (from the Catawba River). CATAWBA RHODO-
DENDRON. *A.* Shrub of 6 ft. or more, rarely to 20 ft., generally broader than high.
Inflor. (a) racemose truss of 15–20 fls. Flowers (56), but variable in form, often
resembling (51), (53), (54) or (57); 1½ in. long, 2–2½ in. across, lilac-purple,
sometimes purplish rose, more or less spotted with greenish or brownish yellow.
Leaves with a rather broader base than other species of this series, oblong-oval to
oval. Bot. Mag. t. 1671. Slopes and summits of mountains, bluffs and cliffs, southern
Alleghenies, West Virginia southward to Georgia and Alabama, covering extensive
areas in western North Carolina and adjacent regions; up to about 6,000 ft.—One
of the hardiest and best known of all rhododendrons, introduced by J. Fraser in
1809 and thereafter becoming one of the leading cultivated species and ancestor
of countless hybrids. All things considered, *Rhododendron catawbiense* must be
accorded a place among the handsomest and most important of North American
native shrubs. There are scores of handsomer species, I will admit, but few are near
so hardy. As it occurs in nature it is a beautiful plant, floriferous, shapely in habit
and showy when in bloom, because the good-sized flowers, in large trusses, are
borne well on the outside of the plant and are not concealed by the foliage. The
sole criticism, of any consequence, against *Rhododendron catawbiense* is that its
color, being purplish in all excepting the pure white form, is unattractive when
grown in gardens or placed alongside clearer colors of brighter hue. I have discussed this feature in another chapter and have pointed out how most of this bad
color effect may be overcome by proper planting design, especially by using quantities of conifers and other foliage plants of dark green among the rhododendrons
and by keeping *R. catawbiense* away from bright colors and architectural features
with which it may clash. Aside from this one feature, the Catawba rhododendron is
a most meritorious plant and one which, because of its hardiness, must necessarily
persist as a leading horticultural species wherever severe climates make the use of
other sorts impracticable. Unfortunately, the common white clones when crossed,
as *white* $\times$ *white,* do not breed true, but produce lavender seedlings in F_1. As mentioned elsewhere, this species frequents the slopes and summits of mountains, under
conditions of more drought, exposure and sunlight than those of its associate,
Rhododendron maximum, which prefers the more protected areas, such as ravines,
stream banks and the sheltered sides of mountains or shady wooded areas. Although
Rhododendron catawbiense does not range so far northward in its native habitat, it

seems equal in hardiness to *R. maximum* and even somewhat better adapted to open sites. There is a good deal of variation among wild plants in almost every character, but, of course, the predominating number approximate the average or typical description as given for the type species. In color the flowers vary from a fairly deep purple, through almost all intermediate grades of light purple and lavender to pure white, nearly all having a purplish tinge. The only form entirely free from this tinge is the white form and this tends to be pinkish in the bud. Occasionally a plant occurs which has fairly clear rose-pink flowers, but even these are inclined to turn purplish as the flowers age. *Rhododendron catawbiense* takes kindly to cultivation and its typically rounded, bushy habit of growth makes it valuable as a landscape material. Old plants sometimes attain a considerable size. Variety *album* Waterer is a white flowered form of the type which occurs rarely in the wild. So far as I know, only 1 clone is in the trade and this is the form which was introduced, presumably, by Waterer many years ago and is sold extensively as 'Catawbiense Album.' I believe this clone to have originated as a seedling, and that it is of hybrid origin. It appears, from numerous observations, to be equally as hardy as the wild type and similar to it in nearly every respect except color. However, several other plants with pure white flowers have been found growing wild in the Carolina mountains and I have one of these growing in my experimental garden. A pure white selection, grown as a clone, is 'La Bar's White.' A form with pinkish buds is 'Glass White' and one of its seedlings is 'Catalga.' The Waterer plant referred to, which is the common form sold as 'Catawbiense Album' is, in my opinion, one of the very finest hardy rhododendrons on the "ironclad" list and should be much more commonly used. Persons objecting to the color of the type species should plant this rhododendron instead, as it has all the virtues of the purple Catawba without its purplish effect. It is tinged with pink in the bud, but becomes pure white with yellowish green spots when the flowers open. It is entirely free from the "dirty" tinge so common in the light colored Catawba rhododendrons which are slightly flushed with purple (see color plate). It does not turn purplish when the flowers age. A dwarf form of the type *R. catawbiense* which grows near the summit of Mt. Mitchell, 6,684 ft., is known as var. *compactum* Hort. This is a compact shrub which does not exceed 3 ft. in height, even when grown in gardens at low altitudes and hence is a useful hardy plant for foregrounds. I suspect that it grows slowly. A form growing in the Piedmont region is var. *insulare*. The Catawba rhododendron blooms about the first week of June at New York City, and about June 7th to 15th at Boston and Asheville, N.C. A large list of hybrid clones, in which the character of *R. catawbiense* predominates, is presented in Chapter XXIII, designated as Catawba hybrids.

Rhododendron macrophyllum G. Don (with big flowers), syn: R. californicum Hook. WEST COAST RHODODENDRON. B. 6 to 12 ft. high, sometimes to 20 ft. Inflor. (a). Flowers (56) 1½ in. long, 2–2¼ in. across, good purplish rose, paler toward the center, spotted yellowish or brownish, rich carmine in bud, margins crisped or waved. Bot. Mag. t. 4863. On mountains, California, Oregon, Washington to British Columbia, 1,500 ft.—This is the western representative of *Rhododendron catawbiense* and thought by some to be a finer plant. But it is not hardy in New England or New York State and is probably of very doubtful hardiness anywhere north of

Philadelphia, although hardier strains may exist. A form with smaller white flowers, smaller capsules and larger, more pointed leaves is sometimes distinguished as var. *album.* The rose form is a better color than *R. catawbiense.*

Rhododendron maximum Linnaeus (largest), syn: R. procerum Salisbury; R. purpureum G. Don; R. Purshii G. Don. ROSEBAY RHODODENDRON (GREAT LAUREL). *A.* 4 to 15 ft. high in the north and often a tall bush or small tree to 30 ft. or more in the Appalachian Mts.; commonly about 12 ft. high in cultivation. Rather loose in habit of growth. Leaves narrow-oblong to oblong-lanceolate. Flower buds, ovary and pedicels glandular and very sticky. Inflor. (a), see color plate, following p. 78. Flowers (52), 1–1½ in. long, 1–2 in. across, not waved or crisped, typical rose-pink at the margins shaded to white in the center resembling the color pattern of apple blossoms, bright rose color in the bud, spotted with greenish yellow on the upper lobe; in variations, the color ranging from pure white to deep rose. Blooms about July 1st. Bot. Mag. t. 951. Damp deep woods, edges of acid bogs, shady mountainsides, ravines, banks of streams; rare from Nova Scotia, Maine and Quebec to Ontario and Ohio, but very common through the Alleghenies from New York to Georgia and Alabama; present in most of the New England States and very plentiful in the mountains of Virginia, West Virginia, the Carolinas and Tennessee; sea-level to 5,000 or 6,000 ft.—The special advantages of this species are its hardiness, its late-blooming quality which furnishes flowers after most of the other species have ceased to bloom, its comparative freedom from objectionable "magenta" color and the value of its height in background plantings. Its disadvantages are that it is sometimes rather loose and coarse in habit of growth, it is not so floriferous as *Rhododendron catawbiense* and the flowers are often hidden by new leaf-growth which develops before blooming time. Its flowers, also, are somewhat smaller than those of *Rhododendron catawbiense,* the trusses are less showy and less graceful and the leaves are longish and tend to hang down more conspicuously in cold weather. Then, too, it is often a slow grower, particularly in its northern forms. For cold climates, for background or forest plantings and for areas in which many inexpensive plants are needed, *Rhododendron maximum* is a godsend. Although it needs semi-shade and shelter from sweeping winds, this species will stand considerable amounts of cold temperature. Collected material which has been cut back and re-grown by collecting-nurserymen is generally reasonable in price and far superior to poorly collected stock which has not been cut back or re-grown. The latter kind should usually be avoided. Slight differences exist between the plants native in the north (Pennsylvania and northward) and those occurring in the regions of greatest concentration (the Virginias and Carolinas). The southern forms appear to be slightly more vigorous than those of the north, the leaves are somewhat broader and the flowers are sometimes a trifle larger, while the plants, of course, grow taller in the south than in the north. Their height seems to depend somewhat, also, upon site and water relations. In general, the southern forms are most to be recommended for cultivation as their greater vigor produces handsomer plants, while they appear hardy enough to withstand New England conditions as well as those which are indigenous to the locality. The type shown in the color plate herewith is of the vigorous southern strain with broadish leaves. The plant from which it was painted is a large, old specimen growing in central New York where the winter temperature sometimes goes to nearly 30 degrees below zero Fahrenheit. Its spreading branches hang down from above. Although it lacks the showiness of other types, *Rhododendron maximum* is not to be despised. It was introduced in 1736 and has produced some, but not many, late-blooming hybrids. The close-grained heartwood is sometimes used for making tool handles and the root for tobacco pipes. Its floral parts are often very sticky and it has a much larger calyx than its allies. In America *R. maximum* is often purchased from collectors in carload lots for planting in parks and on large estates. Variety *album* Pursh is a totally white-flowered form which occurs quite abundantly in nature and is an excellent kind to use. It is subject to minor variations and differs from the typical form only in the absence of pink color from its flowers. A clonal variety is on the market under the name of 'Maximum Album' but this is a Waterer hybrid. It is sold by the trade mainly in England and Continental Europe, where it probably originated, and, although it contains some *maximum* characters and blooms late, is very evidently a hybrid in which *Rhododendron ponticum* has had a part. Its flowers are somewhat larger than those of the true *Rhododendron maximum* var. *album* and in some respects it is superior, but it is not reliably hardy north of New York City. In order to avoid confusion between this hybrid clone and the wild variety which is the prevailing sort used in America, I propose to now designate the hybrid, as a horticultural clone, 'White Maximum' and continue calling the wild form, which is not a clone, by its proper name as a botanical variety, *Rhododendron maximum* var. *album*. Another form occurring in the wild is var. *roseum* Pursh, which has crimson-rose flowers and is simply a deeper-colored form of the type species. This, also, is relatively common in the wild and is sold by collectors and others. Here again a situation similar to that of var. *album* exists, for a hybrid, presumably of European origin, is also on the market under the name of 'Maximum Roseum,' a clone.* Like the 'White Maximum' hybrid, this clonal variety differs from the wild sort in bearing a slightly larger flower and lacks the hardiness of the wild variety. It is again necessary, therefore, to establish the hybrid variety under a horticultural clonal name which will distinguish it from Pursh's wild *R. maximum* var. *roseum*. There is another wild form, var. *purpureum* Pursh, with purple flowers, with which I am not familiar. The various hybrids of *R. maximum* are listed in the next chapter. A derivative has been called *Rhododendron Ashleyi* Coker.†

* 'Maximum Roseum' (see color plate, following p. 366) is a synonym for 'Ponticum Roseum.'

† *Rhododendron Ashleyi* Coker in Jour. Elisha Mitchel Scientific Society, *51*(1):189 (August 1935), is described as a new species. "This very remarkable plant is almost certainly an extreme mutant of *R. maximum*," says the author. The flower has the same color as *R. maximum*, blooms at the same time and many other features of the two species are similar. Its distinctive characters are: entirely separate petals and sepals instead of the usual lobed corolla, and a slow compact growth, resulting in densely set leaves. Several plants were found in one vicinity, all having these same characters and all apparently sterile with weak, slow growth. Abnormal forms, comprising variants of many sorts, are not uncommonly found among seedlings of *Rhododendron maximum* and *R. catawbiense*. These probably result from genetical interactions or other phenomena involving the genes or the chromosomes occurring in certain parent plants or between individual parents. In this instance it seems most likely that some parent plant in the locality has been "throwing" these abnormal forms among its seedling progeny. Weak growth, resulting in a dwarf or compact habit, is more often than not associated with such morphological abnormalities. If such conditions obtain here, it would seem that *Rhododendron Ashleyi* is merely an extreme variant within the species *R. maximum* and not the beginning of another species. The best form will probably be perpetuated as a clone.

Rhododendron ponticum Linnaeus (from Pontus, Asia Minor). B (*A* in England). A spreading, much branched shrub up to 15 ft. Leaves rather narrow, oblong-lanceolate. Inflor. (a), 10–15 fls. in a corymb. Flowers (50) 1½–2 in. long and as much across, lilac-purple, sometimes pinkish purple, greenish yellow spots on upper lobe. Bot. Mag. t. 650. Asia Minor, the Caucasus and Armenia, with European representatives in Spain and Portugal.—The typical plant occurs in Asia Minor with a curious extension to the Iberian Peninsula where it grows on the Pyrenees mountains. The species was introduced to cultivation in England in 1763 and is so well adapted to that country that it has become extensively naturalized there and Millais warns growers that it is difficult to keep in check there in sandy soils, because it spreads rapidly by seeds and layers. The largest bush on record measured 281 ft. in circumference and was over 20 ft. high. This was a cultivated plant in England. Suckers spring up and eventually kill the main stem; this is why *Rhododendron ponticum* is objectionable as a grafting-stock in regions where its suckers are not regularly killed back. Despite its great hardiness in England, *Rhododendron ponticum* is quite tender in the northeastern United States, being unsafe north of Philadelphia. This tenderness does not seem to affect its value as a grafting-stock, however, and is a positive advantage for it kills back the suckers which would otherwise overrun the plant and ruin it. As noted in Chapter IX, the leaves of *Rhododendron ponticum* fail to respond to thermal stimuli by curling up in cold weather and this failure to protect themselves is doubtless one explanation of their tenderness. In addition to the tenderness occasioned by its leaf behavior, I suspect that *Rhododendron ponticum* does not possess those inherent qualities of hardiness with which *R. catawbiense* and *R. maximum* have been endowed by long centuries of natural selection in a cold habitat. As an ancestor of hardy hybrids, therefore, *Rhododendron ponticum* has probably had a detrimental influence. The fact that many of our garden hybrids contain the "blood" of *Rhododendron ponticum* is a point against them and plant breeders who are working for American strains should avoid the use of parents whose ancestry comprises any appreciable percentage of this European species. The color of *Rhododendron ponticum* is scarcely better than that of *R. catawbiense* and, since it does not even possess the factor of hardiness, this species has positively nothing of advantage to offer the American breeder. Its use in this country is practically confined to grafting-stock, for which it is used extensively. Its vigor of growth is something of an advantage and has been noted, particularly, in connection with the sand-culture experiments of Dr. Shive and his associates, cited in another chapter. As American propagators come to produce more own-root rhododendrons, the importance of *Rhododendron ponticum* as a grafting stock will possibly wane.

Several varieties have been described. Variety *baeticum* (syn: R. baeticum) is the form which is grown in Spain and Portugal. Var. *album* is a form with white flowers. Variety *cheiranthifolium* has very narrow leaves which are wavy at the margin. It is said to be dwarf and compact. Variety *lancifolium* Hort. (?) is also dwarf and compact with flat narrow leaves. Variety *variegatum* Hort. (?) has variegated foliage. A sterile double-flowered clone, presumably a hybrid, is known as 'Fastuosum Flore Pleno.'

SALUENENSE SERIES

Very low evergreen shrublets from the high altitudes of Burma, Yunnan and south-eastern Tibet, not unlike the Lapponicums, from which they differ, however, by having a very large and fringed calyx rather than a small one and with wide open rather than funnel-shaped flowers. The flowers are purplish or dark reddish crimson and are conspicuously large for the size of the plant, being about two inches across. They bloom in May in England, where several are much esteemed, but at least *R. prostratum* and *R. saluenense* seem not to have succeeded when grown as seedlings in southern Pennsylvania. Their evergreen leaves are gray-green.

R. CALOSTROTUM

Cox says that these are "charming little plants" and states that they should be planted in clumps in a fairly moist position where they do not get full sun. Like the members of the Lapponicum series, they root readily from cuttings, so that desirable individuals may be easily perpetuated in this way. They bloom when young from seed.

Rhododendron calostrotum Balfour f. & Ward (with a beautiful covering), syn: R. pipapium. *A.* Shrublet up to 12 in. high. Habit and inflor. (see figure for series). Flowers (34) in. long, bright reddish purple, open flat corolla. Bot. Mag. t. 9001. N.E. Burma, 11,000–12,000 ft. Var. *calciphilum,* with leaves smaller than the type, is found in limestone regions, Burma.

Rhododendron chameunum Balfour f. & Forrest (lying on the ground), syn: R. colobodes Balfour f.; R. seriocacalyx Balfour f.; R. pamprotum Balfour f. & Forrest; R. humifusum Balfour f. *A.* Small shrublet, up to 12 in. high. Flowers 1 in. long, deep purple-rose, crimson markings. Open stony pastures, W. Yunnan, 11,500 ft. Var. *cosmetum,* purple rose flowers, a variant of *R. chameunum* from N.E. Burma has been called R. charidotes.

Rhododendron fragariflorum Ward (strawberry-flowered). *C.* Shrublet to 6 in. high, forming carpets. Flowers ¾ in. long, crushed-strawberry color, slightly fragrant. S. Tibet, about 15,000 ft.

Rhododendron keleticum Balfour f. & Forrest (charming). *A.* Semi-prostrate shrublet up to 6 in. Flowers 2/3 in. long, deep purplish crimson, darker markings. Open peaty and stony pastures and on cliffs, S.E. Tibet.

Rhododendron nitens Hutchinson (shining). *A.* Dwarf to 1½ ft. Flowers deep pinkish purple or pink magenta, with crimson spots. Blooms late. Gard. Chron. Ser. 3, *99*:10. (1936). Yunnan.

Rhododendron prostratum W. W. Smith (low growing). *A.* Prostrate shrublet up to 4 in. high. Inflor. (cf. figure for series). Flowers (34) ¾ in. long, pink-violet, slightly spotted red. Bot. Mag. t. 8747. On rocks and in moist peaty soil, Yunnan, 15,000–16,000 ft.

Rhododendron radicans Balfour f. & Forrest (rooting stems). *A.* A prostrate shrublet, 2–4 in. high. Flowers ¾ in. long, purple. Open stony moorlands, S.E. Tibet, 14,000–15,000 ft.—Said to be an attractive rock garden subject and blooms later than most alpine rhododendrons. **X**

Rhododendron saluenense Franchet (from the Salween River), syn:. R. amauro-phyllum Balfour f. & Forrest; R. humicola Wilding. *A.* Undershrub about 4 ft. high. Inflor. (see figure for series). Flowers (34) 1 in. long, deep purple-crimson, darker markings. Bot. Mag. t. 9095. Cliffs and on boulders, N.W. Yunnan, 12,000–13,000 ft. **X**

SCABRIFOLIUM SERIES

R. SCABRIFOLIUM

Smallish evergreen shrubs, one species attaining eight feet, from high altitudes in Yunnan, with nearly tubular or funnel-shaped flowers ranging from white to pink and crimson in color. The foliage is softly pubescent, evergreen and scaly below. Its nearest ally is the Virgatum series. The flowers bloom early in the year. *Rhododendron pubescens* and *R. spinuliferum* seem to be preferred above the others in the classification of the British Rhododendron Association. They are mostly quite tender.

They comprise another group of high-altitude dwarf species which will probably prove difficult in the east. Mr. Nearing, however, has flowered *R. hemitrichotum* outdoors in a north-facing cleft of a rock garden in Delaware and finds it very pretty. *Rhododendrons spinuliferum*, *pubescens* and *mollicomum* are said to be popular among the California rhododendron fanciers. Hybrids are on record between *R. spinuliferum* and *Rhododendrons lutescens*, *moupinense* and *racemosum*. The Scabrifolium series is considered to be allied to the Virgatum series.

Rhododendron hemitrichotum Balfour f. & Forrest (half hairy). *B*. 2–4 ft. high. Numerous small white or pale pink flowers, deeper in the margin, tipped bright brick red in the bud. Jour. Roy. Hort. Soc. *48*: 64 (1923). Open rocky pastures, S.W. Szechuan, 12,000 ft.

Rhododendron mollicomum Balfour f. & W. W. Smith (soft haired). *B*. Up to 6 ft. Flowers rose or crimson. Open thickets, Yunnan, 10,000–11,000 ft.

Rhododendron pubescens Balfour f. & Forrest (downy). *B*. 3–6 ft. Flowers ½–¾ in. long, pinky white. In thickets and scrub, S.W. Szechuan, 10,000 ft. **X**

Rhododendron scabrifolium Franchet (rough leaves). *C*. A small shrub with narrow dark green leaves, hairy (see figure for series). Flowers (5b), ¾ in. long, pink or white. Bot. Mag. t. 7159. Yunnan, 5,000–7,000 ft.—Covered in February with numerous tubular small pink or white flowers.

Rhododendron spiciferum Franchet (bearing spikes). *C*. Small shrub, up to 3 ft. Flowers ½ in. long, many, pink. Yunnan.

Rhododendron spinuliferum Franchet (bearing spines), syn: R. Duclouxii Léveillé. *D*. Up to 8 ft. Inflor. (see figure for series). Flowers (1b) 1 in. long, tubular, crimson to brick red; stamens protruding. Bot. Mag. t. 8408. Shady thickets, Yunnan, 6,000–8,000 ft.

SEMIBARBATUM SERIES

Only one member, an azalea-like species from central and southern Japan, is included in this series. It is distinct in several characters. Its flowers, however, are quite insignificant. Its nearest allies are thought to be the members of the Ovatum series. To all intents and purposes this is, horticulturally, an azalea. The leaves are deciduous and the flowers are borne singly. Its stamens, two of which are shorter than the rest, have been considered to be unique in the genus, but unequal stamens are also found in *Rhododendron Vaseyi*.

This species has been tested in Delaware and found to be successful there if kept under a lath house. It failed when tested in southern Pennsylvania. It would probably succeed on the West Coast, but I do not know whether it is grown there. Like *R. albiflorum,* this species occupies a lone position in its class and series and is probably not sufficiently attractive to merit much attention.

R. SEMIBARBATUM

Rhododendron semibarbatum Maximowicz (partially bearded), syn: Azalea semi-barbata Kuntze; Azaleastrum semibarbatum Makino; Mumeazalea semibarbata Makino. *A*. A deciduous shrub from 2 to 10 ft. high. Inflor. (see figure). Flowers (11) borne singly, ¾ in. across, yellowish white or white, flushed pink, red dots. Bot. Mag. t. 9147. In the mountains, central and southern Japan.—The flowers are insignificant and partly hidden by the foliage. The leaves color in autumn before they fall.

STAMINEUM SERIES

R. STAMINEUM

This is another group on the borderline between azaleas and true rhododendrons. This series comes from low altitudes in Burma, southern China and the Island of Formosa and is said to be closely related to the Ovatum series. Some of the species are from Thailand. Naturally, none of the members of this series can be expected to be hardy. All are rated *F* for England. I find very little comment about these species in the literature and note that only *Rhododendron stenaulum, R. pectinatum* and *R. Wilsonae* are accorded the distinction of an asterisk in the Rhododendron Association's list. Most members of the series are not cultivated. Although the flowers are often fragrant, they are not especially large. The colors range from white to rose and red. The stamens are numerous and prominent. The leaves are evergreen. Some of them may be desirable for the greenhouse.

Rhododendron Cavaleriei Léveillé (after J. Cavalerie, French collector in China). *F*. 6–9 ft. Flowers 1¼ in. long, white to rose. Kweichow.

Rhododendron Championae Hooker (after Mrs. Champion). MRS. CHAMPION'S RHODODENDRON. *F*. Height to 18 ft. Inflor (c). Flowers (76) 2½ in. long, pink. Bot. Mag. t. 4609. Mt. Victoria, Hongkong; also Fukien.

Rhododendron Esquirolii Léveillé (after J. Esquirol, French collector in Burma). *F*. Flowers rose-violet. Yunnan.—Imperfectly known.

Rhododendron Feddei Léveillé (after F. Fedde, German botanist). A 12-ft. shrub with small flowers, color not stated. Probably not in cultivation.

Rhododendron Hancockii Hemsley (after W. Hancock, Chinese Imp. Customs). *F*. 3–6 ft. Flowers 3 in. long, white with yellow on the upper lobe. Hooker's Icon. Plant. t. 2381. Woods, S. Yunnan, 5,000–6,000 ft.

Rhododendron Henryi Hance (after Rev. B. C. Henry), syn: R. Dunnii Wilson. *F*. Flowers 1½ in. long, pink. Kwangtung, China.

Rhododendron Latoucheae Franchet. (Named after Madame de la Touche who with her husband collected in Fukien in 1898.) *F*. Height, color and illustration not given. Flowers 1¾ in. long. Mountains around Kuatun (Fukien?), China.

Rhododendron leiopodum Hayata (smooth-footed). *F*. Height not given. Flowers 1¾ in. long, pink to white. Rocky mountainsides, Formosa.

Rhododendron leucobotrys Ridley (with white clusters). *F*. Flowers 1½ in. long, white. Kedah Peak (Malay Peninsula?), 2,800–4,000 ft.

Rhododendron moulmeinense Hooker (from Moulmein), syn: R. siamense Diels; R. Klossii Ridley. MOULMEIN RHODODENDRON. *F*. Inflor. (i) with many flowers, giving appearance of type (b). Flowers (19) on long pedicels, 1¼ in. long, red. Bot. Mag. t. 4904. Burma, Thailand and the Malay Peninsula, 5,000 ft.

Rhododendron oxyphyllum Franchet (pointed leaves). *F*. Up to 15 ft. Flowers 2 in. long, 3 in. across, white with yellow inside, fragrant. Gard. Chron. *70*: 74 (1921). S. Yunnan and Thailand, 3,500–5,000 ft.—Mr. Joseph Gable writes: "It has flowered for six weeks or so, but one at a time, and fills the whole room with fragrance. It is absolutely tender and a plant for frost-free climates and green-houses only. The flowers are 3–3¼ in. across, white with a yellow throat and deep yellow blotch on the upper lobe."

Rhododendron pectinatum Hutchinson (toothed like a comb). *F*. A tree to 20 ft. with fragrant tubular-funnel-shaped white flowers, having a pale yellow blotch and being borne in clusters of 2 to 4. Gard. Chron. Ser. 3, *101*:119 (1937). Yunnan.

Rhododendron stamineum Franchet (with many stamens), syn: R. Chaffanjonii Léveillé. *E*. 6 ft. Inflor. (see figure for series). Flowers tubular, about 1 in. long, white, with very prominent stamens; scented. Bot. Mag. t. 8601. Yunnan, Szechuan, Hupeh and Kweichow.

Rhododendron stenaulum Balfour f. & W. W. Smith (narrow grooved), syn: R. Mackenzianum Forrest. *F*. Up to 16 ft. Flowers 2 in. long, soft purplish rose with a greenish yellow blotch; fragrant. Gard. Chron. *81*: 193 (1927). In thickets in mixed forest, W. Yunnan, 9,000 ft.

Rhododendron taiense Hutchinson (from Thailand). A 30-ft. tree with large funnel-shaped flowers.—Imperfectly known.

Rhododendron Tutcherae Hemsley & Wilson (after Mrs. W. J. Tutcher, Hong-kong). *F*. A tree to 40 ft. in height. Flowers 1½ in. long, violet. In forests, Mengtze, in S. Yunnan, 6,000 ft.—Flowers borne singly or in pairs.

Rhododendron Westlandii Hemsley (after A. B. Westland, Hongkong). *F*. Small tree to 20 ft. Flowers lilac, sweetly scented. Lantao Island, near Hongkong, 2,500 ft.

Rhododendron Wilsonae Hemsley & Wilson (after Mrs. Wilson, wife of E. H. Wilson). *D*. 4–6 ft. Flowers 1½ in. long, flesh pink. Woods in W. Hupeh, 5,000–6,000 ft.—Although Wilson called this "one of the most beautiful and distinct of Chinese rhododendrons," Millais and Wilding considered the small flesh-pink flowers rather unattractive.

TALIENSE SERIES

R. PRINCIPIS

A Chinese series from Yunnan, Szechuan and Kansu (plus adjoining parts of Burma and Tibet), having a marked resemblance to the hardy evergreen rhododendrons familiar to us in the Ponticum series. They are also allied to the series Campanulatum, Lacteum and Arboreum. Their flower clusters are somewhat more compact than those found in the typical Ponticum series, the rachis being relatively short.

This is one of the largest series in number of species discovered to date and is divided into four subseries for purposes of classification. A distinguishing character of the Taliense rhododendrons is their dense woolly or felty indumentum, usually red to tawny, which occurs beneath the mature leaves. It is rarely white and, if so, is of a thick spongy nature. The leaves are evergreen. The flowers are thin (not fleshy) and are spotted or blotched. Although rose is the common color of the flowers, bright yellows and creams occur, as well as many whites and inter-mediate shades between light pink and purple.

The plants are medium-sized (three to 12 feet or so in height) in three of the subseries and these occur mainly between 8,000 and 12,000 feet above sea-level. The other subseries, Roxieanum, consists largely of dwarf species and these occur, in nature, at somewhat higher altitudes. Most of the species in the series are of recent introduction and only a very few have been grown in America, so perhaps it is unwise to attempt any evaluation of their horticultural merits as yet. Unfortunately, very few have been figured in illustrations to date. Cox describes the habit of some as spreading, being broader than tall and possessing a good sturdy appearance. They tend to be slow growing and slow to flower. This is their greatest handicap.

Subseries Adenogynum

This section is characterized by the large, fringed calyx with prominent "glands," the ovary also being glandular. Besides this, there is a tendency toward glandulosity of varying degree in other parts of the plant. With the exception of *Rhododendron codonanthum*, which is yellow, the species all have white or pink flowers.

Rhododendron adenogynum Diels (glandular ovary). *A.* 9 ft. Flowers near (62), 1¾ in. long, white, tinged rose or magenta, or shaded rose at base, many crimson spots. Spec. Rhod. p. 632. In terminal umbels of 10 fls. In clumps on grassy mountain slopes, N.W. Yunnan, 11,000–12,000 ft.—The central species of this subseries.

Rhododendron adenophorum Balfour f. & W. W. Smith (gland bearing). *A.* 4–8 ft. Flowers 1¼ in. long, rose with few crimson markings. Open situations on rocks, stony pastures, ledges of limestone cliffs and margins of pine forests, Mid-Yunnan, 12,000 ft.

Rhododendron alutaceum Balfour f. & W. W. Smith (leathery in texture). *A.* 12–14 ft. Flowers 1¼ in. long, rose with crimson spots and blotch. Open thickets, N.W. Yunnan, 12,000 ft.

⚬ *Rhododendron Balfourianum* Diels (after Sir I. B. Balfour, late Regius Professor of Botany, Edinburgh). *B.* 4–8 ft. Flowers 1½ in. long, pale rose with crimson markings. Open meadows and rhododendron forests, W. Yunnan, 11,000–12,000 ft. —Has a broadish leaf and plastered indumentum. Var. *aganniphoides* has a spongy indumentum.

Rhododendron Bureavii Franchet (after Edouard Bureau, collector in China). *B.* 6 ft. Flowers 1½ in. long, rose or reddish with crimson markings. Open pastures and margins of pine forests, Yunnan, 10,000–12,000 ft.—Dark green foliage with woolly brown indumentum on the under side and on the young shoots. Said to be an attractive foliage plant. Leaves broadly elliptic.

Rhododendron Bureavioides Balfour f. (resembling *R. Bureavii*). *C.* 4–10 ft. Flowers 1¾ in. long, rose, crimson spots, deep basal blotch. A northern expression of *R. Bureavii* from Szechuan, with larger leaves and flowers and other slight differences.

Rhododendron circinnatum Cowan & Davidian (coiled). Large shrub to 25 ft. with a thick cinnamon-colored indumentum. Notes Roy. Bot. Gard. Edinburgh. *19*:179 (1936). Tibet.—Imperfectly known.

Rhododendron codonanthum Balfour f. & Forrest (with a bell-shaped flower). *B.* 2–3 ft. Flowers 1¼ in. long, bright yellow with crimson markings; small leaves. In open scrub on rocky hillsides. N.W. Yunnan, 12,000–13,000 ft.—Not in cultivation. In the wild it is a small plant and a very shy bloomer.

Rhododendron cruentum Léveillé (color of gore). *C.* A small tree. Flowers 1 in. long, white or white flushed rose, wavy margins. N.E. Yunnan.—A close relative of *R. Bureavii.*

Rhododendron detersile Franchet (clean). About 3 ft. Flowers 1¼ in. long, reddish, hairy within. E. Szechuan, 7,000–8,000 ft.

Rhododendron detonsum Balfour f. & Forrest (shorn). *B.* 9–12 ft. Flowers 1¾ in. long, rose-pink with few crimson spots; in lax umbels. Margins of mixed forests, Yunnan, 9,000–11,000 ft.—Probably not hardy in the eastern U.S. where it has failed when tested. An undescribed plant, arising as a sport in cultivation and called *Rhododendron xenosporum,* is thought to be a form of this.

Rhododendron dumicola Tagg & Forrest (dweller in thickets). *A.* 3–4 ft. Flowers 1¼ in. long, white flushed rose, faint crimson blotch. Rocky slopes and alpine thickets, N.W. Yunnan, 14,000 ft.

Rhododendron elegantulum Tagg & Forrest (small and elegant). *C.* 4–5 ft. Flowers pale purplish pink with darker spots, 1¼ in. long. Open sheltered slopes, among larch, fir, etc., S.W. Szechuan, 12,000–13,000 ft.

Rhododendron Faberi Hemsley (after Rev. Ernst Faber, collector in China). *B.* Flowers 1½ in. long, variable. Mt. Omei, Szechuan.—Very close to *R. Prattii* and confused with it in cultivation.

Rhododendron Faberioides Balfour f. (resembling *R. Faberi*). Flowers 1½ in. long. W. Szechuan.—Perhaps only a variety of *R. Faberi.*

Rhododendron mimetes Tagg & Forrest (imitative). *B.* Flowers 1½ in. long, white, faintly flushed and margined rose, crimson markings; lax truss. Among rock and scrub on slopes in gullies and in thickets and margins of forests, S.W. Szechuan, 11,000–12,000 ft.—Variety *simulans* has broader, cordate leaves and a splitting indumentum.

Rhododendron Prattii Franchet (after A. E. Pratt, explorer in China). *B.* Flowers 1½–2 in. long, white with pink spots. Close to *R. Faberi.* Szechuan.

Rhododendron wuense Balfour f. (from Mt. Wu). An imperfectly known shrub, up to 18 ft. high, with trusses of few flowers, 1¼ in. long, color not described. Not far from *R. Faberi.* Western China.

SUBSERIES ROXIEANUM

This is a dwarfish subgroup with very short annual growths, narrow leaves frequently incurved on the margins, a dense indumentum, a small calyx, white

Rhododendron carolinianum

Rhododendron calendulaceum

Typical form (center) and some of its natural variants

Maximum Hybrid 'Maximum Roseum'

Catawba Hybrid 'Purpureum Grandiflorum'

Rhododendron Kaempferi

Rhododendron Vaseyi

Double Ghent Azaleas

'Rosetta'   'Mina Van Houtte'   'Narcissiflora'

Rhododendron mucronulatum

to rose flowers with conspicuous spots, persistent bud-scales, and a congested truss. Two species sometimes have creamy or yellow flowers. It requires a long time for any of these plants to reach flowering size.

Rhododendron bathyphyllum Balfour f. & Forrest (leafy). *A.* 3–5 ft. Flowers 1½ in. long, white with many crimson spots. Rocky slopes, S.E. Tibet, 13,000 ft.

Rhododendron comisteum Balfour f. & Forrest (to be taken care of). *A.* 2–3 ft. Flowers 1½ in. long, rose with a few crimson spots. Open pastures, slopes and ledges of cliffs, S.E. Tibet, 13,000–14,000 ft.

Rhododendron cucullatum Handel-Mazzetti (hooded), syn: R. coccinopeplum Balfour f. & Forrest. *A.* 3–8 ft. Flowers 1 in. long, white with crimson spots. Cliffs, rocky slopes and pastures, S.W. Szechuan and N.E. Yunnan, 12,000 ft.

Rhododendron globigerum Balfour f. & Forrest (bearing a globe), syn: R. porphyroblastum Balfour f. & Forrest. *B.* 3–6 ft. Flowers 1 in. long, white with crimson markings. Thickets and rocky slopes, S.W. Szechuan, 11,000–12,000 ft.

Rhododendron gymnocarpum Balfour f. MS. (descript. Tagg) (with naked fruits). *A.* 2–3 ft. Flowers 1½ in. long, deep claret crimson with deeper markings. In cane-brakes and among rocks, S.E. Tibet, 14,000 ft.—As its name implies, this species has a practically smooth ovary. American hardiness rating H-3.

Rhododendron iodes Balfour f. & Forrest (violet colored). *B.* 6–8 ft. Flowers 1¼ in. long, white with crimson spots, without blotch. In open cane and rhododendron thickets, S.E. Tibet, 12,000 ft.—This species has a rusty tomentum and I can find nothing in its description to indicate violet coloration as implied by the name, except perhaps the rusty tomentum.

Rhododendron lampropelum Balfour f. & Forrest (bright covering). *A.* 2–3 ft. Flowers 1¼ in. long, white, faintly flushed rose, crimson spots. On open rocky pastures and cliffs, S.W. Szechuan, 12,000–14,000 ft.

Rhododendron microgynum Balfour f. & Forrest (small ovary). *B.* 4 ft. Flowers 1 in. long, dull soft rose faintly spotted with crimson. Open rocky slopes, S.E. Tibet, 12,000 ft.

Rhododendron perulatum Balfour f. & Forrest (with persistent bud-scales). *A.* 2–4 ft. Flowers 1¼ in. long, pale to deep rose, without markings. On open rocky slopes and by streams, 11,000–14,000 ft., S.E. Tibet.—Scales of leaf-buds persist for several years.

Rhododendron pronum Tagg & Forrest (prostrate). *A.* A low prostrate shrub only 3 to 10 in. high. Flowers 1½ in. long, creamy yellow with copious deep crimson markings; wavy margins; in trusses of 8–12. Moist rocky slopes and on humus covered boulders in side valleys and peaty moorlands, Mid-West Yunnan, 12,000–15,000 ft.

Rhododendron proteoides Balfour f. & W. W. Smith (resembling *Protea*). *B.* 1–3 ft. Flowers 1¼ in. long, pale canary-yellow with crimson markings, copiously spotted; sometimes pale cream, flushed rose or a deeper rose tint. Leaves small and revolute. Open situations among boulders, Yunnan, 12,000–13,000 ft.

Rhododendron Roxieanum Forrest (after Mrs. Roxie Hanna of Tali-fu, China, friend of George Forrest), syn: R. aischropeplum Balfour f. & Forrest; R. poecilo-dermum Balfour f. & Forrest; R. recurvum Balfour f. & Forrest. *B.* 4–9 ft. Flowers 1 in. long, creamy white or faintly flushed rose, crimson markings. Leaves with thick, rust-colored felt underneath. Open moist pasture among rocks, Yunnan, 12,000 ft.—The central species of the subseries. Like all the rest, it is slow growing and slow to flower.

The specimen at Inverewe, Scotland, is a very choice, compact, round plant, 3 ft. high, with very narrow, dark, shiny leaves, felty underneath. It is well-filled with round, compact trusses of white flowers having a faint suggestion of dots in the throat. It is an exceptionally close, neat evergreen bush—the answer to a landscape architect's prayer. Its only drawback, aside from climatic factors, is that it requires 15 years to attain this stature.

Rhododendron russotinctum Balfour f. & Forrest (tinged with red). *B.* 6–8 ft. Flowers 1½ in. long, white flushed rose, crimson spots. Open pine forests, N.W. Yunnan, 13,000 ft.—Not closely connected with the other species of this series. Long slender annual growths.

Rhododendron triplonaevium Balfour f. & Forrest (with triple moles). *B.* 5–9 ft. Flowers 1¼ in. long, white or flushed, crimson blotch with triradiate markings; wavy margins. Open pine forests, N.W. Yunnan, 11,000–12,000 ft.

Rhododendron tritifolium Balfour f. & Forrest (familiar leaved). *C.* 6–9 ft. Flowers 1½ in. long, white suffused rose, with crimson blotch and few spots. Open thickets and pine forests, N.W. Yunnan, 11,000–12,000 ft.—A glandular expression of *R. triplonaevium*.

SUBSERIES TALIENSE

This group is characterized by having a calyx which is small to the point of minuteness and which is not glandular. The ovary also is smooth and without glands. The flowers are usually white, varying to a rosy tint or to creamy yellow sometimes, and they are distinctly spotted. The species are all said to be of very slow growth and are horticulturally unpromising.

Rhododendron aganniphum Balfour f. & Ward (snowy). *A.* 15 ft. Flowers 1¼ in. long, white or flushed rose, with crimson spots. In rhododendron scrub, S.E. Tibet and N.W. Yunnan, 14,000–15,000 ft.

Rhododendron agglutinatum Balfour f. & Forrest (stuck together). *C.* 15 ft. Flowers 1¼ in. long, white, creamy or tinged rose, with crimson markings. Rhododendron forests and in open rocky slopes and thickets, S.W. Szechuan, 11,000–13,000 ft.—Indumentum agglutinate.

Rhododendron Clementinae Forrest (after Clementine, wife of George Forrest). 4–10 ft. Flowers 1½–1¾ in. long, creamy white flushed rose to bright rose with crimson markings. Open thickets, N.W. Yunnan and S.W. Szechuan, 11,000 ft.— Unique in that the flowers are usually 6- or 7-parted, with 14 stamens. It is said to be somewhat fastidious.

Rhododendron doshongense Tagg (from Doshong Mountain). *B.* A tangled shrub 2–3 ft. high. Flowers 1¼ in. long, pink with dark purple spots. Along the alpine top ridges, S.E. Tibet, 12,000–13,000 ft.

Rhododendron flavorufum Balfour f. & Forrest (yellow to brown). *A.* 2–6 ft. Flowers 1¼ in. long, white or soft rose, few crimson spots. Cliffs and rocky slopes and margins of pine forests, S.E. Tibet, 12,000–14,000 ft.

Rhododendron glaucopeplum Balfour f. & Forrest (shining covering). *B.* 6–8 ft. Flowers 1¼ in. long, bright rose with conspicuous crimson markings. In cane brakes, Yunnan, 11,000 ft.

Rhododendron principis Bureau & Franchet (of the prince). See figure for the series. A small tree, height not given. Flowers 1¼ in. long, color not given. Tibet, 10,000 ft.—Imperfectly known and not in cultivation.

Rhododendron Purdomii Rehder & Wilson (after W. Purdom, collector in China). A robust shrub, height not given. Flowers 1–1¼ in. long. Imperfectly known. From Shensi, Mid-China.—Not unlike *R. brachycarpum* of the Ponticum series.

Rhododendron schizopeplum Balfour f. & Forrest (with split covering), syn: R. fissotectum Balfour f. & Forrest. *A.* 3–12 ft. Flowers 1¼ in. long, rose with deep crimson spots. In open thickets, rocky situations and margins of forests, N.W. Yunnan, 12,000–14,000 ft.—The buff or brown indumentum beneath the leaves splits irregularly.

Rhododendron sphaeroblastum Balfour f. & Forrest (with rounded buds). *B.* 3–6 ft. Flowers 1½ in. long, white with crimson spots; pink in bud. Rocky slopes in open thickets and openings in conifer forests. S.E. Szechuan, 11,000–14,000 ft.

Rhododendron syncollum Balfour f. & Forrest (glued together). *B.* 5–10 ft. Flowers, 1¼ in. long, washed rose, deepest on the margins, crimson spots. Open rhododendron forests and thickets. West-N.W. Yunnan, 11,000–13,000 ft.

Rhododendron taliense Franchet (from the Tali Range). *B.* A loosely branched shrub of 4–8 ft. Flowers 1¼ in. long, creamy yellow or cream flushed rose with deep crimson markings; margins wavy; borne in compact umbels of 10–15. Open and rocky situations, mountain meadows and ravines and side valleys, Tali Range, W. Yunnan, 10,000–12,000 ft.

Rhododendron vellereum Hutchinson MS. (fleecy). *B.* 6–15 ft. Flowers 1¼ in. long, white or flushed rose, with carmine or purple spots. Steep sheltered slopes among spruce, larch and birch, S.E. Tibet, 10,000–14,000 ft.

SUBSERIES WASONII

Although the members of this group approach those of the Taliense subseries in general appearance, they have tomentose ovaries. These plants also have somewhat broad leaves and lack conspicuous glands. They are confined to the provinces of Szechuan and Kansu in their natural distribution. Six of these 7 species are reported to be in cultivation and are said to be somewhat faster growers than the majority of the other species in the Taliense series.

Rhododendron coeloneurum Diels (with impressed nerves). Height about 12 ft. Flowers unknown. Szechuan.—This is an incompletely known species, supposed to belong in the subseries Wasonii, but at present insufficiently described for accurate placing.

Rhododendron inopinum Balfour f. (unexpected). *B.* A low bush. Flowers about 1 in. long, creamy white with a deep crimson blotch and crimson spots; variable from white to cream and some forms have no blotch. Szechuan.

Rhododendron paradoxum Balfour f. (unexpected). *B.* 4–7 ft. Flowers 1½ in. long, white, with a deep crimson blotch breaking out into short lines of spots. Szechuan.

Rhododendron rufum Batalin (rust). *B.* A shrub or small tree. Flowers 1–1¼ in. long, white or pinkish purple, spotted with crimson. In forests, Szechuan and Kansu, 10,000–11,500 ft.

Rhododendron Wasonii Hemsley & Wilson (after Lt. Comm. C. Wason, R.N., friend and helper of E. H. Wilson). *B.* Bush about 4 ft. Inflor. a lax umbel about like (c). Flowers smaller than (73), 1–1½ in. long, pinkish rose or creamy white, spotted within; one form with creamy yellow flowers. Bot. Mag. t. 9190. On rocks in conifer forests, W. Szechuan, 9,000–11,000 ft.—Variety *Rhododactylum* is a form of *R. Wasonii* with pinkish flowers.

Rhododendron Weldianum Rehder & Wilson (after Gen. S. M. Weld, U.S.A.). *B.* 6–14 ft. Flowers about 1 in. long, in umbellate racemes of 6–12. Flowers are white spotted. Woodlands, W. Szechuan, 9,000–10,000 ft.

Rhododendron Wiltonii Hemsley & Wilson (after E. C. Wilton, Chinese Consular Service). *B.* 3–15 ft. Flowers about 1¼ in. long, whitish or flesh pink, with red spots or a small blotch. Leaves dark green, bullate, felted reddish brown below. Thin woods and thickets, W. Szechuan, 7,000–9,000 ft.—Said to be a handsome foliage plant. Two forms are in cultivation, one having broader leaves.

THOMSONII SERIES

There is but one tall species and one dwarf species in this series—all the other members are practically of medium height. They come mainly from the western Chinese provinces of Yunnan and Szechuan, with extensions elsewhere in adjoining mountainous regions. Some live in Sikkim, Nepal or Bhutan and others in southeastern Tibet. Best known is *Rhododendron Thomsonii,* a species long cultivated in England where it thrives in situations that are not too severe. As the name-bearer for this series, however, it is not a representative prototype for the series as a whole. In fact, there is considerable variation between the members, and arbitrary lines have to be drawn to define the limits

R. CAMPYLOCARPUM

of the series, which at several points seems to have a close affinity with species of other series, notably Fortunei, Irroratum, Barbatum, Taliense and Neriiflorum.

In a careful study of this series by Cowan and Davidian (1954), some rearranging was done and the number of subseries was increased from five to six. In general terms the series may be described as composed almost entirely of medium height shrubs, having leaves that are usually broad in proportion to their length, more or less rounded at the ends and frequently cordate at the base. The leaves usually appear smooth, although often minutely hairy, but the pedicels, calyx, ovary and style commonly have a marked development of glands. Instead of a dense truss, the inflorescence tends to occur as a few-flowered cluster. The flowers themselves are of several types—saucer-shaped, funnel-shaped, bell-shaped or broadly tubular, no one type being general throughout the series.

In some respects the Thomsonii series most resembles the Fortunei series. The latter, however, has six to eight divisions of the flower (corolla lobes), while Thomsonii has only five. The Thomsonii leaves are more rounded.

This series contains a number of horticulturally important species. *Rhododendron Thomsonii* has been highly praised and much employed by British hybridists over a long term of years. More recently, *R. campylocarpum* and, later, *R. Wardii* and *R. caloxanthum* have become prominent sources of yellow color in garden hybrids. *R. Williamsianum,* with its compact, dwarfish habit of growth and its attractive foliage, has become a horticultural favorite, not only for its own value, but also for its usefulness as a parent of compact-growing garden hybrids. Most of these do very well on the American West Coast as well as in the rhododendron-growing areas of England, Scotland and Wales. Their hybrid progeny possesses greater hardiness, since these species are crossable with most of the common hardy species.

Many of these species appear very variable, both in flower color and in habit, and it behooves the buyer of seedlings to choose the best or, more sensibly, to confine his purchases to superior clones. In *R. Thomsonii*, for instance, I have seen a dozen poor, gawky-looking plants to one that has a good habit of growth. It is only the excellent plants that one hears about, but the world is full of inferior ones.

SUBSERIES CAMPYLOCARPUM

This group is characterized by bell-shaped flowers, up to 1¾ inches long, yellow, pink or white, and by a style that may be either glandular at the base (or up to one-half its length) or eglandular.

Rhododendron callimorphum Balfour f. & W. W. Smith (lovely shaped), syn: R. cyclium Balfour f. & Forrest; R. hedythamnum Balfour f. & Forrest. *B.* 4–9 ft. Inflor. (b). Flowers (59) 1¾ in. long, soft rose with a crimson blotch, deep rose in the bud. Small round leaves. Bot. Mag. t. 8789. Open rocky slopes, W. Yunnan, 10,000 ft.—An attractive free-flowering smallish or medium sized shrub, well known in cultivation abroad. **X**

Rhododendron caloxanthum Balfour f. & Farrer (beautiful yellow flower). *C.* 3–5 ft. Flowers 1¼ in. long, citron or sulphur yellow when fully open, flushed and tipped orange-scarlet in the bud. A small bush. Open slopes, precipice ledges and alpine scrub, N.E. Upper Burma, 11,000–12,000 ft. *R. caloxanthum* may be constitutionally hardier than *R. campylocarpum,* but because of its earlier bloom it may be more subject to spring frosts, which gives it a less hardy rating in Britain. American rating H-2. **X**

Rhododendron campylocarpum Hooker f. (bent fruits). HONEYBELL RHODODENDRON. *B.* A small rounded bush of 4–8 ft. Inflor. similar to (a) but with only 6 to 8 flowers and inclined to be more lax (see figure for series). Flowers (68) 1½ in. long and about 2 in. across, clear canary-yellow to pale yellow, with or without faint crimson basal blotch, sometimes tipped with orange in the bud. Introduced 1851. Hooker's Rhod. Sikkim Himal. t. 30; Bot. Mag. t. 4968. In rocky valleys and open spaces, E. Nepal and Sikkim Himalaya, 11,000–14,000 ft.—This, says Capt. F. Kingdon Ward, is "one of Sikkim's most precious gifts." It was one of Sir Joseph Hooker's original importations from the Himalayas, having been introduced in 1851. It has long been cultivated, in a very limited way, in England, where it was long regarded as a somewhat difficult and fastidious species, but has more recently come to be esteemed as the best yellow-flowered species for general cultivation and is widely accepted as such, having proved reasonably amenable to cultivation there if carefully handled. There are at least two distinct forms, one being a smallish, compact shrub with clear yellow flowers and the other a much taller, looser-growing form with pale flowers and some orange or crimson blotching. The latter is said to be the originally introduced type. Several writers state that *Rhododendron campylo-carpum* injures itself by blooming too abundantly, and that it requires extra nourishment in the form of leaf-mold and cow-manure in proportion as it produces flowers. Disbudding may also be practiced. Millais advises against allowing it to flower too freely in successive years. A situation which is open but well protected from winds and draughts and which has a cool rooting medium and which is somewhat cool in summer is the site generally advocated by the British growers who have had experience with this species. In this country the results of such tests as have been made have not been at all encouraging, but it is perhaps too soon to pass final judgment upon the matter. In view of the general experience in this country with most Himalayan species, however, it seems unlikely that *Rhodo-dendron campylocarpum* or any of the other species coming from its native region will ever be directly useful outdoors in the northeastern United States. Our only chance of securing plants with the characters of these tender sorts would seem to rest in the possibility of implanting some of these characters into hardy sorts by means of hybridization. So far as *Rhododendron campylocarpum* is concerned, quite a number of hybrids have been made or are now in the making, some of which may be of promise while others are distinctly mediocre. Some of these will be noted among the clonal varieties in the next chapter. From the records of these crosses it would seem that *Rhododendron campylocarpum* (as, indeed, most of the other yellow forms recorded) produces an intermediate type of inheritance with respect to the yellow pigmentation in first-generation offspring. There seems to be no complete dominance or recessiveness, but rather a faint touch of yellow in the hybrids. Crossed with a pink, the result reported is a flower with an apricot or orange-like color; crossed with a white, the result reported is ivory or cream. *Rhododendron campylocarpum* blooms in June in its native habitat and a month or so earlier in England. Its flowers are slightly fragrant. American hardiness rating H-3. **XX**

Rhododendron myiagrum Balfour f. & Forrest (the fly catcher). *C.* 3–5 ft. Flowers 1 in. long, white with a few spots and a faint basal blotch, in clusters of 4–5. Open canebrakes and thickets, W. Yunnan, 10,000 ft.—The pedicels are so glandular and sticky that in Yunnan they become plastered with small flies.

Rhododendron panteumorphum Balfour f. & W. W. Smith (quite lovely), syn: "R. selense" Diels not Franchet; R. telopeum Balfour forma telopeoides Balfour f. ex Tagg. *B.* 2–9 ft. Leaves oblong, flowers 1½ in. long, campanulate, pale yellow, pistil glandular, in trusses of 4–8. S.E. Tibet and Yunnan, 11,000–14,000 ft.

Rhododendron telopeum Balfour f. & Forrest (conspicuous). *B.* 3–10 ft. tall. Flowers 1½ in. long, bright to pale yellow with a faint crimson blotch. Margins of thickets and in scrub, S.E. Tibet, 12,000 ft.—This species intergrades with *R. campylocarpum* and *R. caloxanthum*. There is a form with less rounded leaves known as f. *teloeoides*.

Subseries Cerasinum

Medium-sized shrubs with oblong leaves and campanulate flowers which may be cherry-red, brilliant scarlet or creamy white with a broad cherry-red band. The style is glandular to the tip.

Rhododendron Bonvalotti Bureau & Franchet (after Gabriel Bonvalot, traveler in Tibet). Leaves leathery, oblong, about 2 in. long and ½ in. broad. Flowers campanulate, 1 in. long, presumably rose. S.W. Szechuan.—An imperfectly known species.

Rhododendron cerasinum Tagg (cherry-colored). *B*. A shrub 4–10 ft. high. Leaves 2–4 in. long and 1 in. wide, oblong (or oblong-elliptic) and leathery. Flowers bell-shaped, 1½ in. long, fleshy, beautiful bright cherry-red (or scarlet or creamy-white with a broad cherry-red band at the summit in certain variants), the base pouched with 5 deep purple nectaries. Anthers dark brown. In dense rhododendron thickets or on the edge of forests of Abies, S.E. Tibet, Assam, Burma, 10,000–12,000 ft.— This choice plant, about 4 ft. high in cultivation, grows in Edinburgh where it blooms in June. Bot. Mag. t. 9538. The flowers are as brilliantly colored as glowing embers of fire. The trusses, however, are skimpy, with only about five flowers. **X**

Subseries Selense

The leaves of this subgroup are oblong and their ends tend to be pointed. The flowers are funnel-shaped or funnel-campanulate, 1 to 2 inches long, and rose-pink or white. They are handicapped by requiring many years to flower from seed, and have achieved little horticultural importance.

Rhododendron calvescens Balfour f. & Forrest (becoming bald). *C*. 3–6 ft. Flowers 1½ in. long, rose, without blotch or spots. Open thickets, S.E. Tibet.—The leaves have traces of a scurfy indumentum.

Rhododendron dasycladoides Handel-Mazzetti (like *R. dasycladum*). A little-known shrub, 6–12 ft. high, with oblong leaves, a tomentose ovary, branchlets and leaf stalks, a truss of 5–8 pinkish, campanulate flowers, 1 in. or so long. Szechuan, 7,000–14,000 ft.

Rhododendron dasycladum Balfour f. & W. W. Smith (hairy boughs), syn: R. rhaibocarpum Balfour f. & Smith. *B*. 6–10 ft. Flowers (62) 1½ in. long, rose, pink or white, with or without a crimson basal blotch; spotted or unspotted, open thickets. N.W. Yunnan and S.E. Tibet, 12,000 ft.—Characterized by setose-glandular twigs.

Rhododendron erythrocalyx Balfour f. & Forrest (with a red calyx), syn: R. beimaense Balfour; R. cymbomorphum Balfour; R. eucallum Balfour; R. truncatulum Balfour f. & Forrest; R. docimum Balfour f. & Forrest. *B*. 3–8 ft. Flowers

1–1½ in. long, funnel-campanulate, creamy white, or sometimes yellow, with or without a basal crimson blotch, sparsely spotted with crimson or unspotted. Open thickets and pine forests, N.W. Yunnan and S.E. Tibet, 11,000–13,000 ft.—Several supposed species have now been found to represent one single variable species and their names have been relegated to synonymy. This population is linked with *R. selense*, with overlapping characters. The above synonyms were formerly listed under *R. erythrocalyx* as subspecies. Since intermediate forms between these and the typical species have been discovered, these names have now been discarded and the plants are considered as variants.

Rhododendron esetulosum Balfour f. & Forrest (hairless), syn: R. manopeplum Balfour f. & Forrest. *B*. 3–5 ft. Leaves thick, coriaceous, with a thin veil of hairs underneath. Flowers 8–10 in a lax truss, creamy white, or flushed rose, spotted with crimson or unspotted, 1½ in. long. Bouldery slopes, Yunnan, 13,000–14,000 ft.

Rhododendron eurysiphon Tagg & Forrest (broad tube). *B*. 3–5 ft. Inflor. an open umbel of 3–5 fls. Flowers 1½ in. long, creamy white or very pale rose, more or less heavily flushed deep magenta and spotted with crimson. Rhododendron thickets, scrub and stony slopes, S.E. Tibet, 13,000 ft..

Rhododendron jucundum Balfour f. & W. W. Smith (pleasant), syn: R. blandulum Balfour f. & W. W. Smith. *B*. 6–20 ft. Branchlets and petioles usually setose-glandular. Flowers 1¼ in. long, rose, pink or white, 5–8 in a truss. Open rocky situations, mountain meadows and margins of pine forests, W. Yunnan, 10,000–12,000 ft.

Rhododendron Martinianum Balfour f. & Forrest (after J. Martin of Caerhays, Cornwall). *B*. 3–6 ft. Flowers about 1¾ in. long, pale rose, borne in open umbels of 2 or 3. Open rocky pastures, thickets and scrub, S.E. Tibet and N.W. Yunnan, 11,000–12,000 ft.—The bush is said to be desirable in leaf and character and the flowers of an attractive color.

Rhododendron selense Franchet (from the Sie La), syn: R. axium Balfour f. & Forrest; R. chalarocladum Balfour f. & Forrest; R. dolerum Balfour f. & Forrest; R. metrium Balfour f. & Forrest; R. nanothamnum Balfour f. & Forrest. 4–9 ft. Flowers 1¼ in. long, pink or rose, spotted or unspotted, with or without a crimson blotch at base. Summits of hills, W. Yunnan, 10,000–12,000 ft.—A number of variant forms, formerly regarded as subspecies, have now been reduced to synonyms. However, the following are considered varieties: Var. *duseimatum* (Balfour f. & Forrest) Cowan & Davidian, with tomentose ovary and oblong-lanceolate leaves; var. *pagophilum* (Balfour f. & Ward) Cowan & Davidian, with small elliptic leaves and small flowers, sometimes dark rose or crimson, but with intergrading characters; and var. *probum* (Balfour f. & Forrest) Cowan & Davidian, with white, unmarked flowers.

Rhododendron setiferum Balfour f. & Forrest (bristle bearing). *B*. 5–9 ft. Flowers 1¾ in. long, creamy white, crimson lines at base. Open thickets and in pine forests, N.W. Yunnan, 12,000–13,000 ft.

Rhododendron vestitum Tagg & Forrest (clothed). *B*. 4–5 ft. with twisted branches of short annual growth. Flowers 1¼ in. long, white flushed rose, marked crimson; deep rose in bud. Oval leaves with a distinct tawny indumentum. In cane brakes, S.E. Tibet, 14,000 ft.

SUBSERIES SOULIEI

R. SOULIEI

The members of this subgroup are fairly easy to determine, being rather distinct. The leaves are leathery and rounded, the flowers are saucer-shaped to bowl-shaped, quite widely open, sometimes blotched with red but not spotted and, in most species, the color is yellow. The chief distinguishing characters of this subseries are the very open flowers and the styles which are entirely glandular to the tip. The flowers are inclined to be fleshy. *R. litiense* and *R. Wardii,* both excellent yellow rhododendrons, are very much alike and probably intergrade, but differ in their typical forms in that *R. litiense* has oblong or oblong-oval leaves, waxy underneath, while *R. Wardii* has leaves that are orbicular or ovate and glabrous underneath. Either might be confused with the yellow species of the Campylocarpum series, with which they are probably closely affiliated, but the difference is determined by the glandular or eglandular nature of the style. However, intergrading forms exist here, also. None of them are very different.

Rhododendron litiense Balfour f. & Forrest (from the Li-ti-ping, Yunnan). *B*. 4–9 ft. Flowers up to 1½ in. long, saucer-shaped and lemon yellow, in trusses of 5–7. Leaves are oblong or oblong-oval, waxy underneath. In shady forests and margins of pine woods, Yunnan, 9,000–13,000 ft.—This is so close to *R. Wardii* that it is often confused, and is also a very fine plant. One might suppose that they are merely geographical forms of the same species, but with *R. litiense* having a more limited distribution. **X**

Rhododendron puralbum Balfour f. & W. W. Smith (very white). *B*. 12–15 ft. Flowers (62?), 1½ in. long, pure white. In rhododendron and mixed scrub, northeast of the Yangtze bend, Yunnan, 11,000–14,000 ft.—Apart from color, this species resembles *R. Wardii.*

Rhododendron Souliei Franchet (after Père J. A. Soulie, French missionary in Tibet), syn: R. cordatum Léveillé. *B*. 6–12 ft. See figure for series. Flowers (62)

1–1½ in. long, about 3 in. across, white to a soft or deeper rose (some say bluish rose). Bot. Mag. t. 8622. Woodlands and thickets, W. Szechuan, 9,000–11,000 ft. —This species appears to be highly thought of in England where it is one of the few rhododendrons that do better on the east coast than on the west. It blooms there in May. The behavior of seedlings in the cooler portions of this country seems not to have been satisfactory to date. Ward states that it will flower when five years old. There are several superior clones, among them the Exbury and Windsor Great Park forms. **XX**

Rhododendron Wardii W. W. Smith (after F. Kingdon Ward, collector and explorer), syn: R. gloeoblastum Balfour f. & Forrest; R. oresterum Balfour f. & Forrest; R. Mussoti Franchet; R. croceum Balfour f. & W. W. Smith; R. prasino-calyx Balfour f. & Forrest; R. astrocalyx Balfour f. & Forrest. *B.* Shrub up to 20 ft. (much less in ordinary cultivation) with flowers in loose trusses of 5–14, open cup or saucer-shaped, broader than (62), 1½ in. long and up to 2 in. across, clear yellow, with or without a small crimson basal blotch (see Fig. 6 in color plate, facing page 334), rather fleshy in substance. Open thickets and forests, Mekong-Salween Divide, W. Yunnan, 12,000–14,000 ft.—A number of related plants, first described as distinct species, have proved to be variants differing from the type only in minor characteristics, all of which are linked to *R. Wardii* by intermediate forms. Most of these distinctions have proved to be unreliable and inconstant, hence their names have all become synonyms under *R. Wardii* in the recent revision by Cowan & Davidian.

SUBSERIES THOMSONII

This is the central group of the series. The leaves are leathery, the calyx large, the flowers broadly tubular to bell-shaped and usually red in color. The flowers are often spotted and are characterized by large nectar pouches at the base of the corolla. The species occur from eastern Nepal to western Yunnan, some coming from southeastern Tibet, Bhutan and northeastern Upper Burma. One naturally does not expect much in hardiness from a group out of this general region. Yet *R. Thomsonii* is well regarded for hardiness in Britain, where, with a little shade it does well and is a sight worth seeing when in bloom. Seedlings in this country have failed, at least in one instance, when

R. THOMSONII

undertaken by a careful grower in southern Pennsylvania. It seems unlikely that any of the members of this group will be successful along the Atlantic

Seaboard, but they have distinct possibilities for the West Coast. An unusually large percentage in this subseries have been accorded the distinction of special merit in the British classification.

Rhododendron cyanocarpum W. W. Smith (with blue fruits), syn: R. Thomsonii var. cyanocarpum Franchet; R. hedythamnum Balfour f. & Forrest var. eglandulosum Handel-Mazzetti. *B*. 5–20 ft. Flowers 2–2¼ in. long, white or creamy-white flushed rose, or a rich soft rose color. Open moist situations, mountain meadows and margins of pine forests, W. Yunnan, 10,000–13,000 ft.—This species has round blue-green leaves like *R. Thomsonii*. A form with a densely glandular ovary is var. *eriphyllum* Balfour f. MS. **X**

Rhododendron eclecteum Balfour f. & Forrest (to be chosen out). *C*. About 7 ft. tall. Flowers 1¾ in. long, white to deep rose, sometimes rose-magenta or rarely yellowish; unspotted or more or less spotted; fleshy. Rhododendron thickets, S.E. Tibet, 13,000 ft.—Variety *brachyandrum* has dark, much-spotted flowers and shorter stamens. Variety *bellatulum* has smaller leaves, bright rose-colored flowers and puberulous stamens. Other wild variations have appeared with almost sessile leaves and whitish or rose-pink flowers, showing that the species is quite variable. **X**

Rhododendron Hookeri Nuttall (after Sir Joseph D. Hooker, famous botanist and early collector in the Himalayas). *C*. An erect shrub of 12–14 ft. Inflor. (a). Flowers (60), about 1½ in. long, deep crimson with 5 deep red blotches at the base. Bot. Mag. t. 4926. Discovered by Booth in 1852. Forming thickets, Oola Mts., Bhutan, 8,000–9,000 ft. Peculiar lines of hairs on the veins of the under side of the leaves distinguish this species. These hairs occur in tufts like small barbs. This is a rhododendron for the cool greenhouse and not for outdoor culture here or abroad. Its flowers are of an intense blood-red color and it is said to be a magnificent species. **XX**

Rhododendron hylaeum Balfour f. & Farrer (belonging to forests). *B*. A round-headed tree up to 25 ft. Flowers 1¾ in. long, pale rose, more or less dappled a deeper tint. N.E. Upper Burma, 10,500 ft.

Rhododendron Lopsangianum Cowan (after Nga-Wang Lopsang Tup-Den Gyatso, the late Dalai Lama of Tibet). *B*. A low compact shrub, up to 6 ft. Truss loose, of 3–5 flowers, tubular campanulate, fleshy, 1¾ in. long, deep crimson, with a crimson calyx surrounding base. Tibet, 8,500–14,000 ft.—A smaller plant, much like *R. Thomsonii* but with smaller flowers. Discovered in Tibet in 1936 by Ludlow and Sherriff.

Rhododendron Meddianum Forrest (after George Medd, Bhamo, Upper Burma). *C*. 6 ft. or more tall. Flowers 1½–2¼ in. long, deep crimson, 5-pouched at the base, fleshy; wavy margins. In open rhododendron scrub, W. Yunnan and N.E. Upper Burma, 10,000–11,000 ft.—This is the Chinese form of *R. Thomsonii*, with less rounded leaves and larger flowers of a deeper color. Variety *atrokermesinum* has flowers that are still darker and larger. A form is reported blooming in Cornwall which has flowers of bright hunting-coat scarlet. This is probably a splendid species, but it was not discovered until 1917. **XX**

Rhododendron populare Cowan (popular). Small tree to 15 ft. Narrow, oblong leaves, small calyx and crimson flowers up to 1½ in. long, with or without deeper spots. Tibet, 11,500–15,000 ft.—Another new discovery of Ludlow and Sherriff.

Rhododendron Stewartianum Diels (after L. B. Stewart, Curator, Edinburgh Botanic Garden), syn: R. niphobolum Balfour f. & Farrer. *B.* A graceful bush of 3–7 ft. Leaves small, gray-green. Flowers 1¾ in. long, variable in color, ranging from pure white or shades of soft primrose yellow through various shades of rose to deep crimson; sometimes margined; with or without markings. In bamboo brake, rhododendron thickets and rocky slopes at 10,000–14,000 ft., in N.E. Upper Burma, W. Yunnan and S.E. Tibet.—Farrer is quoted as describing a whole hillside of this species, with no two bushes of the same color. It is evidently extremely variable and is also regarded as very beautiful. It is usually a plant of smaller stature than its allies and has smaller leaves. Var. *aiolosalpinx* (Balfour f. & Forrest) Cowan & Davidian, with exceptionally large calyx and leaves. Var. *tantulum* Cowan & Davidian, with minute calyx and small leaves. **X**

Rhododendron Thomsonii Hooker f. (after Thomas Thomson, Supt. Calcutta Botanic Garden, 1854–1861). *B.* A bush of 6–14 ft., with roundish smooth blue-green leaves. See figure for series. Flowers (4) but somewhat larger, 2–2¼ in. long, deep blood-red, spotted; fleshy and waxy. Bot. Mag. t. 4997. Discovered by Hooker in 1849. Sikkim and Nepal, 11,000–13,000 ft.—This species was one of Hooker's sensational introductions from the Sikkim Himalayas in 1859 and has been justly acclaimed as magnificent. It has long been grown in Britain and is a parent of some of the finest hybrids. A fine specimen exists at the Edinburgh Botanic Garden, and there are others. But this species is variable and I have seen many more poor specimens than good ones. In its best forms it is large, lush and well covered with flowers and foliage, but more often it has a gangling and leggy habit of growth, and scattered flowers of a color so dark they must be caught by transmitted sunlight to show their ruby-like hue, too often hidden by the plum-color coating of the exterior. They do not bloom early in life. They will not do for America except on the West Coast. Var. *candelabrum* has paler flowers, a small calyx and a glandular ovary. Var. *pallidum* has rose-pink flowers with magenta patches at the base, and a big calyx like the type. In buying *R. Thomsonii* remember that only the finest clones can live up to the glowing reports that have been written. **XX**

SUBSERIES WILLIAMSIANUM

This new subseries was erected by Cowan and Davidian to accommodate just one species, *Rhododendron Williamsianum,* a beautiful and compact plant, now much used in hybridization.

Rhododendron Williamsianum Rehder & Wilson (after Mr. J. C. Williams of Cornwall, England, rhododendron expert). *B.* 3–5 ft., branching horizontally to form a flattish bush. Inflor. a loose umbel of 3–6 nodding flowers, not unlike the subseries type. Flowers (66), 1¼–1½ in. long, nearly 2 in. in diameter, pale rose or beautiful clear shell pink. Leaves heart-shaped at the base, with a blue cast when mature, the young leaves and shoots bronze. Bot. Mag. t. 8935. In thickets, Szechuan, 8,000–10,000 ft.—This species, which deviates somewhat from the general type of the others, is regarded as a most attractive species. Its small, horizontal, spreading habit makes it desirable for rockeries or foreground planting wherever it will endure the climate. In Great Britain it is much esteemed and Ward regarded it as one of the dozen best species in existence. It is often quite low and sprawling, almost prostrate. It blooms in April or May and is quite easily propagated from cuttings. Only half-hardy in eastern United States, and doubtfully successful north of Philadelphia, it is, nevertheless, a parent of some fairly hardy hybrids. In regions where it might succeed, it surely deserves a careful trial. A whole new race of hybrids is arising from it.

TRICHOCLADUM SERIES

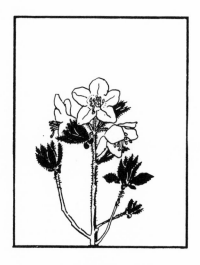

R. TRICHOCLADUM

A group of semi-deciduous small shrubs with yellow flowers, not unlike the azaleas. They come from Yunnan, northern Burma and southern Tibet, where they grow in open situations in the mountains at fairly high elevations, usually above 11,000 feet. The flowers are small to medium-sized, borne in clusters of two to four with the corolla one inch or less in length and scaly on the back of the lobes. In each species, the color is some form of yellow. The Trichocladums have ten stamens. Some, at least, are hardy enough for England when grown outdoors. "Although not in the front rank," says Cox of *Rhododendron trichocladum,* it "is a useful rhododendron."

The flowers of this series, as I have seen them at shows, have looked like little woody potentillas. They were quite unimpressive and would not inspire me to grow them except as curiosities. Three species reported on the West Coast are classed in hardiness as H-4, and earlier reports from the East Coast indicated failure.

Rhododendron chloranthum Balfour f. & Forrest (green-yellow). *A.* 2–4 ft. Deciduous. Flowers ¾ in. long, yellow, tinged green at base, borne in clusters of about 4. Open situations, N.W. Yunnan, 11,000 ft.

Rhododendron lepidostylum Balfour f. & Forrest (scaly style). *B.* About 1 ft. high. Subevergreen. Flowers about 1 in. long, pale yellow, borne in twos. Open situations, W. Yunnan, 11,000–11,500 ft.

Rhododendron Cowanianum Davidian (after Dr. John MacQueen Cowan of the Royal Botanic Garden, Edinburgh). A shrub to 5 ft. Flowers short-campanulate, reddish-purple. Nepal.

Rhododendron lithophilum Balfour f. & Ward (stone lover). *B.* 2–3 ft. Flowers ¾ in. long, pale sulphur-yellow. Among granite boulders, N.E. Burma, 12,000 ft.

Rhododendron lophogynum Balfour f. & Forrest (crested ovary). *C.* 2–3 ft. Flowers (12) 1 in. long, yellow. Open rocky slopes and cliffs, Yunnan, 10,000–11,000 ft.

Rhododendron mekongense Franchet (from the Mekong River). *B.* Deciduous. Up to 4 ft. Flowers 1 in. long, pale yellow, tinged green. Margins of forests, E. Tibet and Yunnan, 11,000 ft.

Rhododendron melinanthum Balfour f. & Ward (honey flowered). *B.* 6–8 ft. Deciduous. Flowers ¾ in. long, yellow. E. Upper Burma, 12,000–14,000 ft.—Said to be the finest of the Trichocladums.

Rhododendron oulotrichum Balfour f. & Forrest (with curly hairs). *B.* 2–4 ft. Deciduous. Flowers ¾ in. long, yellow. Dry open pastures, W. Yunnan, 10,000 ft.

Rhododendron rubrolineatum Balfour f. & Forrest (lined with red). *B.* Deciduous. Up to 5 ft. high, yellow, lined and flushed with rose on the outside. Open pastures, N.W. Yunnan, 11,000–12,000 ft.—Closely approaches the Triflorum series in character.

Rhododendron semilunatum Balfour f. & Forrest (half crescent shaped). *C.* Deciduous. 2–3 ft. Flowers ¾ in. long, deep yellow. Open situations, S.E. Tibet.

Rhododendron trichocladum Franchet (hairy twigs), syn: R. xanthinum Balfour f. & W. W. Smith; R. brachystylum Balfour f. & Ward. *A.* About 3 ft. Deciduous. See figure for series. Flowers (12) about 1 in. long, greenish yellow, spotted with dark green. Bot. Mag. t. 9073. In mountains, W. Yunnan, 7,500 ft., N.E. Burma, 12,000–13,000 ft.

Rhododendron viridescens (greenish). *B.* A newly described species with glaucous evergreen leaves and pale yellow flowers.

TRIFLORUM SERIES

R. TRIFLORUM

An extensive aggregation of smallish or medium-sized shrubs in which certain members have deciduous leaves, while others are evergreen or semi-evergreen. The species mostly come from Yunnan and Szechuan; they are rare in the Himalayas and do not occur at all in eastern China. One outlying species, *Rhododendron Keiskei,* occurs in Japan. Hutchinson * thinks that the Triflorums have been derived from the Maddenii series. Besides their deciduous leaves, they show other characters which remind one of azaleas.

Most of them are taller than two feet and less than ten or 12 feet in height. They tend to be slender. Several are inclined to have a lax habit with "lanky" or "leggy" branching. Others are quite twiggy and a few are compact. The flowers are not large, being usually smallish, and may be of yellow, white, pink, mauve or purplish color, commonly spotted with red. There are ten stamens and these protrude beyond the corolla. The ovary is always densely scaly. A complete key to the species of the series is given in *The Species of Rhododendron* (1930), p. 759. The group is divided into five subseries.

All the members of this series appear to best advantage when grown in clumps of several plants rather than when planted individually, owing to their slender, often scraggly habit. In the wild most of them grow exposed to the full sun, but this, of course, at high altitudes where the heat of the sunlight is not a factor, since the weather is never hot at such elevations. Several of the species will endure drought better than most Chinese rhododendrons and this factor may prove to be the keynote of their behavior in America, where a few show some slight promise of success.

There seems to be a good deal of variation in color, even among plants of the same species. Many of them root readily from cuttings, so when good forms appear there is little reason why they cannot be easily multiplied and disseminated as horticultural clones under cultivar names. Observers have noted many peculiar intermediate colors among the different species, some of these hues being hard to describe, and a recommendation has been made that care be used in combining the various colors in plantings as they may clash.

* Species of Rhododendron, p. 758.

The leaves are commonly thinnish and almost azalea-like in appearance. I seriously question, however, if these plants are as good as azaleas for cultivation or effect anywhere in America. Good-sized plants, placed in groups, are doubtless interesting and handsome, but the few small individual specimens I have seen were anything but effective. The yellow species are also said to be disappointing. One "blue" form is outstanding.

SUBSERIES AUGUSTINII

Rhododendron Augustinii Hemsley (after Dr. Augustine Henry, botanist, formerly in China). *B.* Shrub of 6–10 ft., with rather "leggy" habit. Inflor. (i). Flowers (19) mauve or lilac-purple, sometimes bluish violet, with yellowish green spots; 1½–2 in. long, in clusters of 3. Bot. Mag. t. 8497. Common in rocky situations exposed to the sun, W. Hupeh and Szechuan, up to 9,300 ft.—This is a so-called "blue" rhododendron, which, however, is variable and, according to Ward, is more often "a dull morose blue or dirty violet, or washy lavender." The bluest form is said to be that collected by Wilson under number 4238, but this, unfortunately, is reported to be the most tender. When the color is good, this species is regarded as absolutely first class. The lilac-purple or gray-blue forms are regarded as being worth growing, but, says Cox, "care should be taken that the pink-lilac form does not get into your garden, for the color is muddy and the appearance of muddiness is increased by yellow spots on the upper lobe." Luckily, the species will root readily from cuttings, so that superior individuals may be easily propagated and sold as clonal varieties. Buyers should be sure to get only the more desirable clones. The best specimens are blue as the bluest lilac bloom and are on everybody's "best" list. Color may vary slightly with season. At the 1955 British rhododendron show the plant from Windsor Great Park rated first, Rothschild's second and Aberconway's third. Half-hardy on Long Island and Cape Cod. American rating H-3. (See color plate.) **XX**

Rhododendron chasmanthum Diels (with gaping flowers), syn: R. chasmanthoides. *C.* 3–8 ft. Flowers 1½ in. long, pale lavender-rose with olive markings, sometimes varying from pale lavender to deep lavender-mauve in individual plants. Open situations in side valleys, N.W. Yunnan and S.E. Tibet, 10,000 ft.—Blooming a week later than *R. Augustinii,* but with rather more of a truss. Considered attractive. **X**

Rhododendron hirsuticostatum Handel-Mazzetti (hairy ribs). *D.* Flowers 1¼ in. long, whitish rose, not spotted. S.W. Szechuan, 6,500–8,000 ft.—Close to *R. yunnanense.*

Rhododendron trichophorum Balfour f. (bearing hairs). *B.* About 10 ft. Flowers pinkish mauve. Possibly a natural hybrid between *R. Augustinii* and *R. villosum.*

Rhododendron villosum Hemsley & Wilson (shaggy). *B.* 5–20 ft. Flowers bright magenta purple, light purple or rose. W. Szechuan, 7,000–11,000 ft.—There seems to be a good bit of variability in the color of the different forms. One is of a rich dark purple, rare in rhododendrons, but difficult to place unless care is taken to group it with whites or yellows.

Subseries Hanceanum

Rhododendron afghanicum Aitchison & Hemsley (from Afghanistan). *D.* Creeping on rocks. Flowers scarcely ½ in. long, whitish green. Jour. Linn. Soc. *19* : t. 21 (1882) ; Spec. Rhod. p. 771. Afghanistan, 7,000–9,000 ft.—Reputed to be poisonous.

Rhododendron Hanceanum Hemsley (after H. F. Hance, Consul at Canton). *C.* Up to 3 ft. Inflor. (i), but more floriferous, appearing somewhat like (p). Flowers smaller than (19) ; somewhat like (36), ¾ to 1 in. long, pale yellow. Bot. Mag. t. 8669. W. Szechuan, 7,000–9,000 ft.—In flower and habit the general appearance is not unlike that of a Kurume azalea in the color illustration cited herewith.

Subseries Oreotrephes

Rhododendron apiculatum Rehder & Wilson (pointed leaves). *C.* About 5 ft. Flowers 1¼ in. long, dark purple. W. Szechuan, 7,800–9,400 ft.

Rhododendron artosquameum Balfour f. & Forrest (with compressed scales), syn: R. cardioeides Balfour f. & Forrest; R. pubigerum Balfour f. & Forrest; R. trichopodum Balfour f. & Forrest. *B.* 2–8 ft. Flowers 1¼ in. long, rose without markings. Spec. Rhod. p. 774. S.E. Tibet, 11,000–12,000 ft.

Rhododendron bracteatum Rehder & Wilson (furnished with bracts). *B.* About 6 ft. Inflor. (i). Flowers (6) ¾ in. long, white, spotted red. Bot. Mag. t. 9031. On cliffs, W. Szechuan, 7,000–10,000 ft.

Rhododendron exquisitum Hutchinson (exquisite). *B.* A 9-ft. shrub with 5–8 widely funnel-shaped pale lavender flowers in a truss. Bot. Mag. t. 9597. **X**

Rhododendron oreotrephes W. W. Smith (mountain dweller), syn: R. depile Balfour f. & Forrest; R. hypotrichotum Balfour f. & Forrest; R. oreotrephoides Balfour f.; R. phaeochlorum Balfour f. & Forrest. *B.* Up to 7 ft. Inflor. (i). Flowers (36) 1¼ in. long, mauve or mauve-pink, often with darker spots. Bot. Mag. t. 8784. Yunnan and S.E. Tibet, 10,000–12,000 ft.—With its small leaves, glaucous above and scaly below, sometimes with a bluish tinge, this plant is said to be attractive especially at blooming time which occurs in early May. Some persons prefer the paler colored forms. It is floriferous and graceful in habit, and it does not seem to demand so much moisture as some. **X**

Rhododendron sycnanthum Balfour f. & W. W. Smith (fig-like flowers). *B.* Twiggy shrub, 3–9 ft. Flowers scarcely 1 in. long, deep rose-lavender with olive-brown markings. Cliffs and rocky slopes, N. and Mid-W. Yunnan, 9,000–11,000 ft.

Rhododendron timeteum Balfour f. & Forrest (to be honored). *B.* Up to 4 ft. General character and habit of *R. oreotrephes.* Flowers purplish rose with a few dark markings. Pine forests, S.W. Szechuan, 11,000 ft.

SUBSERIES POLYLEPIS

Rhododendron Amesiae Rehder & Wilson (after the American Ames family). *A.* A small shrub. Flowers purple. Mupin woods, W. Szechuan, 7,000–9,000 ft.

Rhododendron concinnoides Hutchinson & Ward (like *R. concinnum*). *C.* A small shrub (to 6 ft.?). Inflor. (1?). Flowers (19?) about 1 in. long, pinkish purple on the lobes with darker spotting inside, fading to white at the base. Assam, 8,000–11,000 ft.

Rhododendron concinnum Hemsley (neat), syn: R. yanthinum Bureau & Franchet; R. Benthamianum Hemsley; R. coombense Hemsley; R. ioanthum Balfour f. and R. laetevirens Balfour f. *A.* 6 ft. Inflor. (1). Flowers (19) 1 in. (?) long, purplish, spotted. Bot. Mag. t. 8280. Summit of Mt. Omei, Szechuan.—This is said not to be a good garden subject; its color and habit are not attractive.

Rhododendron polylepis Franchet (many scales), syn: R. Harrovianum Hemsley. *A.* Up to 12 ft. Inflor. (1). Flowers smaller than (19), about 1 in. across, dark purple. Rev. Hort. (1914), p. 324. Common in W. Szechuan and N. Yunnan, 7,500–9,000 ft.—A plant blooming under glass in January had flowers somewhat lighter, lilac-purple, with outside at base and pedicels dark maroon red. Millais said the color will prevent this species from ever becoming popular. The flowers are about the size of those of *R. carolinianum*.

Rhododendron pseudo-yanthinum Balfour f. (false *R. yanthinum*), syn: R. yanthimum var. lepidanthum Rehder & Wilson. *B.* Inflor. (1). Flowers (19), purplish, darker than *R. concinnum*. Bot. Mag. t. 8620. W. Szechuan, 7,500–12,000 ft.— Very much like *R. concinnum,* but with larger, darker flowers, and a more showy garden plant.

SUBSERIES TRIFLORUM

Rhododendron ambiguum Hemsley (doubtful). *A.* A smallish shrub up to 5 ft. Inflor. (1). Flowers (19), 1¼–1½ in. long, lemon-yellow or greenish, spotted with green. Bot. Mag. t. 8400. W. Szechuan, 11,000 ft.—Some forms are better than others. It is not so particular about where it grows and hence will stand rougher treatment than the other Triflorums. But its color is described as nothing to brag about. Indeed, Ward says, "what is wanted is a good yellow Triflorum." It has a greenish tinge, which is destroyed or rendered insipid if combined with brilliant orange or yellow hues, so this should be remembered in planting. Plants of this species have lived for Mr. Gable with protection in southern Pennsylvania. The habit is neat and compact and the flowers bloom in May. It looks like a yellow-green Kurume azalea and might make a good florist's plant. See color plate, p. 334.

Rhododendron bauhiniiflorum Watt, MS. (Bauhinia-like flowers). *B.* Very much like *R. triflorum* and perhaps a variety of it. Manipur, Assam, 8,000–10,000 ft.

Rhododendron caesium Hutchinson (dullish blue). Pale yellow flowers; small, twiggy.

Rhododendron chengshienianum Fang. Flowers yellow.

Rhododendron flavantherum Hutchinson & Ward (with yellow stamens). *C*. 6–10 ft. Flowers ¾ in. long, bright clear yellow with deep orange anthers. On vertical cliffs, Tibet, 8,000–9,000 ft.

Rhododendron kasoense Hutchinson & Ward (from Kaso). *B*. A shrub ordinarily lanky, but more compact if grown in full exposure. Flowers ⅔ in. long, yellow with red anthers. Assam, 7,000–8,000 ft.

Rhododendron Keiskei Miquel (named for I. Keisk, Japanese botanist). *A*. A fairly low shrub, 4–5 ft. Inflor. (i), 3–5 fls. in a cluster. Flowers somewhat smaller than (19), about 1 in. long, lemon-yellow, not spotted. Bot. Mag. t. 8300. Among stones, Simabara and Owari provinces, central Japan. This oriental species is free flowering and suitable for the rock garden. In England it blooms in April. Coming from Japan, this species is one of promise for America, since Japanese species adapt themselves to the climate of the eastern United States much better than do those from China or the Himalayas. *Rhododendron Keiskei* is being grown sufficiently in this country at the present time to constitute a good test of its adaptability and it will be interesting to watch the results. At present we can no more doubt that it will be useful in the East, because it is adapting itself to Long Island, Philadelphia and similar regions very successfully and is a worth while plant. Its flowers are azalea-like, but its habit is a bit on the scraggly side. Some persons will prefer yellow azaleas to the pale greenish yellow of this species. **X**

Rhododendron lutescens Franchet (yellowish), syn: R. costulatum Franchet; R. Lemeei Léveillé; R. Blinii Léveillé. *B*. Up to 5 ft., branches elongated. Inflor. (i). Flowers (19), 1¼–1½ in. long, pale yellow spotted with green, fragrant. Bot. Mag. t. 8851. Thickets and margins of woods fully exposed to the sun, W. Szechuan and Yunnan, up to 9,000 ft.—This is a loose growing shrub with pale yellow flowers singly or in pairs. Cox says it should be planted in a mass if its delicate beauty is to be appreciated and it is best to have a dark background. It should be planted closely enough to form a thicket and may be pruned back if it becomes too straggly. It needs semi-shade. Although it may possibly be made to live south of Philadelphia, I doubt if it is a plant for the eastern part of this country. As it roots easily from cuttings, good strains may be easily propagated and multiplied for group planting. It is an early spring bloomer. The flowers are spotted with light green. In spring the leaves are bright bronzy red as they first appear. A clone called 'Bagshot Sands' is recognized with an award of merit. Apparently variation in hardiness exists; while rated *B* for England, it is classed as definitely tender by the American Rhododendron Society. Cox regards it as a fine yellow, but so early as to be badly frost-injured. Forms up to 15 ft. are known. **XX**

Rhododendron triflorum Hooker f. (3 flowered). *C*. Up to 8 ft. See figure for series. Flowers (19), about 1½ in. long, light yellow spotted with green, fragrant. Rhod. Sikkim Himal. t. 19. Sikkim and Bhutan Himalayas, 8,000–9,500 ft.— Although this species is the standard-bearer for the series, it is of lesser horticultural importance. "It cannot be called beautiful," said Millais. Yet, it has smooth dark red bark which peels and is said to be very attractive when seen against the sunlight. It is probably too tender for outdoor use in this country and not worthy of greenhouse culture. **X**

Rhododendron Wongii Hemsley & Wilson (after Y. C. Wong, Ichang, friend and helper of Wilson). *B.* 4–6 ft. Flowers less than 1 in. long, cream colored. Szechuan, 11,000 ft.

SUBSERIES YUNNANENSE

Rhododendron aechmophyllum Balfour f. & Forrest (with a pointed leaf). *C.* 3–4 ft. An imperfectly known species very much like *R. longistylum.* Mu-li Mts., S.W. Szechuan, 11,000–12,000 ft.

Rhododendron Bodinieri Franchet (after E. Bodinier, French missionary in China). *B.* Flowers 1¼ in. long, rose, spotted with purple. Yunnan and Kweichow.

Rhododendron caeruleum Lévl. (blue), syn: R. eriandrum Léveillé; R. raro-squameum Balf. f. Up to 6 ft. Annual shoots short, purplish, non-scaly. Lvs. elliptic. leathery, 1¼ in. long, slightly scaly below. Flowers in terminal clusters of 3 or 4, ¾ in. long, deep rose-lavender to white. Yunnan.

Rhododendron charianthum Hutchinson (beautiful flowers). *B.* 8–10 ft. Inflor. (i) but with 10 fls. in the cluster. Flowers (19), about 1 in. long, rose, densely spotted with red. Bot. Mag. t. 8665. Habitat unknown, but probably Yunnan or Szechuan. —Said to stand drought better than some of the other species from western China.

Rhododendron chartophyllum Franchet (paper-like leaves). *B.* A semi-deciduous species which, for all practical purposes, may be considered like *R. yunnanense.* Yunnan, 6,000–11,000 ft.—The important plant under this heading is not the type species, but, rather, its variety, *R. chartophyllum* var. *praecox* Davis, which is completely deciduous and is a fine and useful plant. The variety is very floriferous with white or pale pink flowers having markings which are usually crimson but sometimes orange. Cox says that it is valuable for specimen planting as well as in groupings and that it is especially effective if planted facing west with a dark background, so that the late afternoon sunshine will illumine the whole plant. It grows 5–7 ft. tall. It is said to be the only rhododendron in Yunnan that the Chinese living there cultivate in their own gardens. It flowers in late May and may easily be propagated from cuttings.

Rhododendron Davidsonianum Rehder & Wilson (after Dr. W. H. Davidson, Friends' Mission in China). *B.* 6–8 ft. Inflor. (i). Flowers (19), 1–1½ in. long, pink with red spots. Bot. Mag. t. 8759 (as *R. siderophyllum*); poor, pale form in Bot. Mag. t. 8605. Exposed sunny situations, W. Szechuan, 6,000–10,000 ft.—The Exbury plant and other good forms are excellent in Britain, floriferous and a clean pink, but poor forms are leggy in growth and insipid in color. It seems not to do well or have good color in eastern United States. Rating H-4. **XX**

Rhododendron erileucum Balfour f. & Forrest (very white). *D.* 6–9 ft. Flowers white. Open rocky slopes, Yunnan, 9,000–10,000 ft.—Very similar to *R. zaleucum,* of which it may be merely a variety with different leaves.

Rhododendron hesperium Balfour f. & Forrest (western). *B.* 4–6 ft. Flowers 1¼ in. long, smoky rose-lavender, deepest at the base, with olive-brown markings. On ledges of cliffs in ravines, Yunnan, 9,000–10,000 ft.

Rhododendron hormophorum Balfour f. & Forrest (bearing a necklace). *B.* A leggy shrublet to 3 ft. Flowers 1¼ in. long, rose, with brown markings. Open dry stony pastures, S.W. Szechuan, 11,000–12,000 ft.

Rhododendron leilungense Balfour f. & Forrest (from Lei-lung-shan). *C.* 2–3 ft. Flowers ⅔ in. long, pale rose. Rocky dry slopes, Yunnan, 9,000 ft.

Rhododendron lochmium Balfour f. (from a coppice), syn: R. glaucophyllum Balfour f. *B.* A straggling shrub with leggy branches, 6–10 ft. Flowers 1¼–1½ in. long, pink and much like those of *R. Davidsonianum.* W. Szechuan.—Capt. Ward says the leaves are persistent and that the flowers, flushed violet, are faintly tinged with yellow at the back and spotted with ochre-brown. It came in as a "rogue" with other seed.

Rhododendron longistylum Rehder & Wilson (long pistils). *C.* Up to 7 ft. Small pink flowers, ¾ in. long. W. Szechuan.

Rhododendron pallescens Hutchinson (becoming paler). Flowers white, flushed pink, with red spots. Suspected of being a natural hybrid between *R. Davidsonianum* and *R. racemosum.*

Rhododendron pleistanthum Balfour f. MS. (many flowered). *B.* A shrub with violet flowers very much like *R. Davidsonianum,* but differing in botanical characters. On rocks, Yunnan, 8,000 ft.

Rhododendron rigidum Franchet (stiff). *C.* 4–7 ft. Flowers ¾ in. long, very pale rose with crimson-brown markings. Yunnan, 9,000 ft.

Rhododendron Searsiae Rehder & Wilson (after Sarah C. Sears, American artist). *B.* 8 ft. or more. Inflor. (i). Flowers (19), 1¼ in. long, white or mauve. Bot. Mag. t. 8993. W. Szechuan, 7,000–9,400 ft.

Rhododendron siderophyllum Franchet (rust-coated leaves), syn: R. obscurum Franchet. *B.* 4–9 ft. Flowers ½ in. long, whitish to violet. S.W. Yunnan, 6,000–7,000 ft.

Rhododendron stereophyllum Balfour f. & W. W. Smith (with hard leaves). *B.* Up to 6 ft. Very small flowers, pale mauve-rose. Mts. N.E. of Yangtze Bend, Yunnan, 10,000 ft.

Rhododendron suberosum Balfour f. & Forrest (slightly gnawed). *B.* 5–7 ft. Flowers faintly flushed rose with deep rose markings. Very similar to *R. yunnanense,* but with smaller flowers and certain other differences. In open scrub by streams, Yunnan, 12,000–13,000 ft.

Rhododendron tatsienense Franchet (from Tatsienlu). An imperfectly known shrub from W. Szechuan, of medium size with purple flowers less than ½ in. long.

Rhododendron Vilmorinianum Balfour f. (after Vilmorin, the famous French family of plant breeders and seedsmen). *B.* A weak growing shrub, height to 6 ft. Flowers (19) 1¼ in. long, white with ochre spots; yellowish when first open. Flora and Sylva *3*:162 as *R. Augustinii.* Known only in cultivation. Habitat probably in E. Szechuan.

Rhododendron yunnanense Franchet (from Yunnan). YUNNAN RHODODENDRON. *B C.* Shrub to 10 or 12 ft. with leggy branches and leaves which often droop, evergreen or subevergreen. Inflor. (i). Flowers (19), 1½ in. long, pinkish or nearly white, spotted with red; in some forms soft mauve. Bot. Mag. t. 7614. Yunnan, about 9,000 ft.—This species, which some regard as the best in the Triflorum series, has extra interest because it is half-hardy at New York City and on Cape Cod and Long Island, where it will live outdoors with protection. Several plants lived to reach blooming age at the New York Botanical Garden and bloomed outdoors. The species will live, also, in southern Pennsylvania. It blooms in May. It is a desirable plant, but is nothing to become excited about when young, at least, although it may become much finer with age and greater size. English rhododendron enthusiasts consider it very excellent. **XX**

Rhododendron zaleucum Balfour f. & W. W. Smith (very white). *D.* A shrub or small tree up to 35 ft. Inflor. (i). Flowers (52) with numerous fleshy scales on the outside of the corolla, 1½ in. long, white or rose, slightly fragrant. Spec. Rhod. p. 816. Either a shrub on rocky slopes or a tree in the rain-forests, W. Yunnan and E. Upper Burma, 9,000–11,000 ft.—Cox says this species, although not particularly striking, is easy to grow and propagate. It blooms in May. The small green leaves are milky white underneath.

UNIFLORUM SERIES

This is a new series, set up in 1948, to accommodate a group of related species taken from the Lepidotum, Boothii and Glaucophyllum series. They are dwarf shrubs, usually not over 2 ft. high, with evergreen leaves and 1 or 2 flowers in the inflorescence. They come from high altitudes in the Himalayas of Burma, Tibet, Assam and Sikkim.

Rhododendron imperator Hutchinson & Ward (Emperor). *A.* A dwarf, carpet-forming shrublet. Flowers over 1 in. long and about 1 in. across, bright purple, not marked. On exposed bare ledges of granite cliffs, Burma, 10,000–11,000 ft. **XX**

Rhododendron Ludlowii Cowan (after F. Ludlow, a collector in Himalaya). *B.* A small shrub to 12 in. Leaves small. Inflor. 1 or 2 yellow flowers, spotted reddish brown inside.

Rhododendron monanthum Balfour f. & W. W. Smith (one-flowered). *D.* A spreading shrub, 2–3 ft. tall. Flowers ¾ in. long, solitary, terminal, bright yellow. N.W. Yunnan, shady places on margins of pine forests, 10,000–11,000 ft., and on rocky slopes among scrub and on cliffs in S.E. Tibet, 12,000–13,000 ft.

Rhododendron patulum Ward (spreading). *B.* Dwarf to 2 ft. or prostrate shrub. Flowers 1 in., single or in pairs, purple. Lvs. small. Assam frontier, 12,000 ft.

Rhododendron pemaköense (from Pemako, Tibet). *A.* Dwarf undershrub spreading by stoloniferous runners underground and suckering. Flowers pinkish mauve. Considered a rock garden accession. **X**

Rhododendron pumilum Hooker f. (dwarfish). *A.* A semi-prostrate shrublet. Inflor. (v). Flowers (28) ½–¾ in. long, almost pure pink. Rhod. Sikkim Himal. t. 14. Alpine slopes, Sikkim, S. Tibet, Burma-Yunnan border, 10,000–14,000 ft. —Said to be the smallest of the Himalayan species.

Rhododendron uniflorum Hutchinson & Ward (one-flowered). *B.* A subprocumbent shrublet. Flowers solitary, about 1 in. long, purple. Steep grassy slopes, S. Tibet, 11,000–12,000 ft.

VACCINIOIDES SERIES

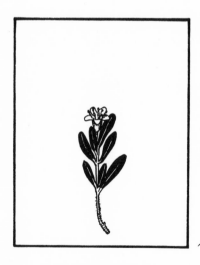

R. VACCINIOIDES

Small-flowered epiphytes from the eastern Himalayas to Formosa and the Philippines. The small flowers, only one-half inch or so long, are of various colors. Its chief claim to distinction lies in the occurrence of very long, thread-like tails at each end of the seeds. The species in this series are probably of no horticultural importance.

The botanists who have classified this group do not venture any conjecture as to its nearest allies. The name and description indicate that the species *R. vaccinioides*, at least, resembles the vaccinium or huckleberry. This brings to mind the thought that our numerous hardy and delightful vacciniums may be suitably and effectively used in plantings with rhododendrons and azaleas, to whom, of course, they are related. Such utilization of good material at hand seems to me to be much more satisfactory in most cold gardens than the use of those exotic species which are none too happy in such climates. Such species as these, however, may be excellent things in suitable regions. Probably near the Malayan sorts.

Rhododendron asperulum Hutchinson & Ward (slightly roughened). *E.* An epiphyte. Flowers 1/3 in. long, pale flesh pink with orange anthers; in clusters of 3. Epiphytic on alder trees or growing on boulders in open pastures, S. Tibet, 7,000 ft.

Rhododendron emarginatum Hemsley (notched at the apex). *E.* Shrub of 2 ft. Flowers ½ in. long, yellow, solitary. Mountains in Yunnan, 6,000 ft.

Rhododendron euonymifolium Léveillé (leaves like Euonymus). A small shrub, imperfectly known, with solitary flowers, ½ in. long. On rocks, Kweichow.

Rhododendron insculptum Hutchinson & Ward (carved). *D.* An epiphyte with solitary axillary flowers ½ in. long, bright orange, with brownish red anthers and an orange style. Rain forest, S. Tibet, 6,000–7,000 ft.

Rhododendron Kawakamii Hayata (after T. Kawakami, collector in Formosa). A shrub 3–5 ft. high, usually epiphytic. Flowers 1/3 in. long, of unknown color, borne in clusters of 3–4. Formosa, 7,000 ft.

Rhododendron quadrasianum Vidal, syn: R. malindangense Merrill. A low bush, sometimes epiphytic. Flowers cylindric, 2/3 in. long, red; solitary. Mountain-tops, Philippine Is., 7,000–8,000 ft.

Rhododendron rosmarinifolium Vidal (rosemary-like leaves). Slender shrub to 12 ft. Flowers 1/3 in. long, red, in clusters of 4. Philippine Islands.

Rhododendron vaccinioides Hooker f. (like Vaccinium), syn: R. sinovaccinioides Balfour f. & Forrest. *C.* A small epiphyte. Flowers (60b) 1/3 in. long, lilac-pink or white tinged pink. Spec. Rhodo. p. 825. Sikkim, 6,000–7,500 ft.; S.E. Tibet, 8,000–12,000 ft.

Rhododendron Vidalii Rolfe (after Vidal, Philippine botanist). A small shrub with pure waxy white flowers, fragrant, in clusters of 5. Philippine Islands.

VIRGATUM SERIES

R. VIRGATUM

A group, at present numbering only three species, related to the Triflorum series, but differing in several respects, notably by bearing its flowers in axillary rather than terminal buds. The members of this series are small erect shrubs or shrublets with leggy branches, coming from Sikkim and Yunnan at altitudes around 8,000 feet.

One species, *Rhododendron racemosum*, seems quite variable and has a hardy form, Rock #59717, a U.S. Government importation, which is hardy, with slight protection, in central New York and other cold regions and is suitable for foreground planting or rock-garden use. Cox says this species appears best if planted in a mass. when it becomes quite effective, while a single plant is not impressive. The other two species in the series very much resemble *R. racemosum,* but, being much more tender, are not so promising as garden subjects. All are variable and it is necessary to be particular about obtaining desirable strains. They are said to be very easy to propagate by cuttings.

Rhododendron oleifolium Franchet (olive-like foliage), syn: R. sinovirgatum Balfour f. *D*. An erect shrub 2–3 ft., with leggy branches. Inflor. (h), evergreen. Flowers (37), about 1 in. long, pink to almost white. Bot. Mag. t. 8802. Yunnan, 8,000–10,000 ft.—This is a Yunnan representative of the Himalayan *R. virgatum*. This species should not be confused with *R. racemosum* var. *oleifolium,* which is a different thing.

Rhododendron racemosum Franchet (flowers in racemes). *A*. A shrublet from a few inches to 3 ft. tall; branches leggy in some forms. Leaves evergreen. Inflor. (u). Flowers (6), ¾–1 in. across, pink to white, not unlike color of trailing arbutus (*Epigaea*). Bot. Mag. t. 7301. Yunnan, 7,000–9,000 ft.—This species, which has long been popular in England, is now of great potential usefulness in the United States, because some hardy forms have been found. One of these forms comes from seed collected by Dr. J. F. Rock as #59717 and seems to be hardy in the latitude of New England if lightly covered for winter protection. Other forms are perhaps as hardy, but several are considerably more tender, among these Forrest's #19404 and the form known as var. *oleifolium,* which has much larger flowers than the type and blooms very early. Both of these latter forms are popular in England, but var. *oleifolium* opens its flowers a little too early for cold gardens even there. Rock's hardy form blooms about May 20th in central New York State. Forrest's #19404 is much dwarfer than the type, being only a few inches high, and has bright pink flowers. Cox recommends planting it in a mass on a slightly shaded bank or in a bed. The plants soon grow together into a thicket, in much the same manner as in China where they are found by the thousand on scrubby hillsides. Rough slopes may be greatly improved by planting *R. racemosum* in bulk. "It is often a mistake," says Cox, "to ignore a rhododendron because it is not showy when planted singly; some thought should always be given about its effect when planted in a mass. *Rhododendron racemosum* is a typical case." * It is said to be easy to propagate and, no doubt, good clonal varieties will be available which can be depended upon for hardiness and other good characteristics. In a species so variable, it is important to avoid poor strains. *Rhododendron racemosum* may become very valuable in all sorts of rockery and wall- or terrace-garden planting. The variety *oleifolium* should be sharply distinguished from *Rhododendron oleifolium,* a different species (see color plate). **XX**

Rhododendron virgatum Hooker f. (willowy twigs). *D.* Up to 6 ft. See figure for the series. Flowers (6), about 1 in. across, pale mauve or shell pink. Hooker's Rhod. Sikkim Himal. t. 26 (1851). Sikkim and Bhutan, 9,000 ft.—The attractive shell-pink variety is Kingdon Ward's collection #6279, but is rather more tender. *Rhododendron virgatum,* on the whole, is too tender to be of promise for American conditions.

* Cox, E. H. M. Rhododendrons for Amateurs. London, 1924.

CHAPTER XXIII

NOTES ON THE CULTIVARS

ONE might wish that rhododendron hybrids could be neatly sorted and classified into distinct racial groups, then listed under well-organized categories in a clear and definite way. Unfortunately, the exact antithesis prevails. Despite the effort of catalogue-makers to categorize the different kinds, the hybridists are working against this, and the broader their crosses become, the greater is the tendency for racial boundaries to become obliterated. While tremendous differences exist among hybrids, especially in matters of size and hardiness, the situation in several areas of the genus comes nearer and nearer to a gigantic melting-pot in which racial and specific identities are lost in the welter of piled-up genes.

Starting with the extreme variability which characterizes many of the natural species at the outset, plus the broad extent to which crossing between species is physically possible in this genus, it is no wonder that any original reference to one particular race or strain is often impossible to distinguish after two or three subsequent generations of successive out-breeding. The ancestry of some better-defined groups has been discussed in Chapter XIX. It will be apparent at once that these group lines can be maintained only on a very provisional basis and that such named groupings as, for example, the Loderi hybrids, Dexter hybrids and the like, named with reference to an originally distinct flock, or grex, are tenable for only so long as these primary combinations remain distinct and are not intermingled in further outside matings.

Yet it is obvious that without some means of distinguishing types, the hundreds and hundreds of hybrids currently alive would become tangled into a hopeless state of chaos. In the first edition of this work, the author endeavored to segregate the hybrids into races based on the various series. Subsequent extensive intercrossings between series have seemed to render this procedure futile. Moreover, diverse races are arising within the same series.

In many instances, a horticultural rather than botanical system of grouping is the more feasible. Races originating at the hands of some breeder or in some locality almost inevitably carry the name of that breeder or locality as a sort of trade-mark. Later, however, such groups pass into limbo, and the best clones become absorbed into broader and more generalized categories. It seems unwise to regard such passing fancies too seriously, and yet they are useful enough for contemporary purposes to be placed in subgroups and given grex names. Inevitably, the eventual overlapping of these groups will tend to break down boundary lines. More realistically, broad categories, such as the Catawba hybrids, are meaningful to many people and follow a long-established pattern.

It would seem to the writer most feasible and wholly in accordance with the International Codes to regard (first) the individual clone as the basis for classification of all rhododendron and azalea hybrids. If an individual plant does not readily conform to the characters of any distinctive group, then such an individual shall be regarded as a clone and shall be permitted to stand alone or as a member-at-large of some very broad category, such as the evergreen elepidote rhododendrons or the miscellaneous deciduous azaleas. For it is in determining which members should belong to what groups, beyond primary crosses, that classification of hybrids becomes difficult and confusing. If segregated too narrowly, the situation becomes too complicated for practical purposes.

It has seemed to me, therefore, that the close alignment of hybrids, especially with reference to their ancestry, should be relegated to the official *Rhododendron Stud Book,* which is an important source of records for breeders and students, but not used as a basis for tabulating the different clones in a horticultural catalogue. Accordingly, I have abandoned any effort here to list the rhododendron hybrids by their Stud Book records. Instead, I am gathering the clones into larger sections, without regard to their immediate racial affiliations, the origins of many being doubtful anyway. The excellent Stud Book, compiled periodically by the Royal Horticultural Society, aided by rhododendron registration officials in various countries, is kept up to date and should be consulted for exact information on hybrid records.

For purposes of general classification, hybrids within the genus might be gathered into a few broad groups as indicated in the following outline:

> Elepidote rhododendrons
> Lepidote rhododendrons
> Javanese, Malayan, and tropical rhododendrons
> Azaleodendrons
> Azaleas
> > Deciduous azaleas (Subseries Luteum)
> > Evergreen azaleas (Subseries Obtusum)
> > Miscellaneous other azaleas

Each of these divisions may be further broken down into subdivisions, somewhat as is done in Chapter XIX where hybrid races were considered. But there will still be a great many clones that will not fit neatly into any such category, since there are multitudes of intergradient forms.

Since no complete list of named clones then existed, this author compiled a long list from various sources which was printed in the first edition of this work. Hundreds of new cultivars have been recorded since then, while vast numbers of the old ones have vanished into oblivion. For purposes of registration, all the known names of rhododendrons and azaleas, including obsolete sorts, have been gathered together by Dr. H. R. Fletcher of Edinburgh, assisted by rhododendron authorities throughout the world, and published in one comprehensive volume with full descriptions under the title of *The International Rhododendron Register.* Since that excellent work is readily available and will be kept current through subsequent revisions, there would seem to be no further need of continuing to list the obsolete and unavailable forms here. It has seemed feasible, instead, to list only those clones which are presently in commerce or are generally grown in gardens, omitting those which are not available or which have been superseded by later introductions. Thus the list is not too large or cumbersome to be workable. Named cultivars constituting fanciers' or breeders' material, not in the trade because held privately or considered obsolete, can be readily located in the *Rhododendron Stud Book,* a portion of the *Rhododendron Handbook* also published periodically by the Royal Horticultural Society, or in the *International Rhododendron Register.* To find the best sorts even more readily, I am inserting lists of clones and species ordinarily available, selected for definite geographical regions, in a subsequent section of this book. New introductions, appearing from time to time, will generally be found described in the publications of the various rhododendron organizations or in the official register as they are introduced. Bearing in mind that considerable time is required for the multiplication of stock sufficient to warrant commercial distribution, good new introductions are generally made known through shows and awards before they become available on the market. The identification of old and obsolete clones no longer familiar is sometimes difficult. A knowledge of the plant's age and, if possible, its source is helpful, and recourse may be had to old prints, old catalogues and to the very full descriptions contained for each clone in the Rhododendron Register. In some instances, however, it will be found that such plants are unnamed seedlings, possibly surplus material from a plant breeder's garden, considered unworthy of formal introduction under a cultivar name. Since rhododendrons are often long-lived, it may be expected that a great many old plants of unknown derivation will always be present in gardens.

For additional facts, so far as these are known, regarding the hybrids listed here, and others, the reader is referred to the *International Rhododendron Register* (noted above) where the parentage, names of introducers, the dates of introduction and, in many cases, the accurate color description as measured by the Horticultural Colour Chart (HCC) of the Royal Horticultural Society are presented. Additional azaleas are described in terms of the Horticultural Colour Chart in Frederic P. Lee's *The Azalea Book* (1958). Color terms, such as "Tyrian rose," usually refer to the HCC color of that definite name. The American Horticultural Council's color "fan" is correlated with the HCC scale. In considering colors, however, one must bear in mind that colors in the same clone may vary with location and age and even between different years on the same plant.

When new rhododendrons arise, there are frequently sister seedlings somewhat like the named sort which are good enough to market. Because new clones multiply slowly, some growers have sold these other plants under the name of the new clone, although they may be somewhat different. This has resulted in further confusion. Under the new rules of horticultural nomenclature, therefore, it is now necessary for such collective names to be designated as "groups," with the symbol "g." or the word "grex" appended to the name. In many instances the name given to a clone is also used as the grex name. In buying plants, therefore, the buyer should specify the clone (or the Award of Merit clone, if it has received an award) in order to insure himself against an inferior seedling. In the following lists, all the plants named are assumed to be clones except where the letter "g." follows the cultivar name. In some instances, the clone is described and the words "also grex" are added to inform the reader that the same name is used for a group. The practice is arising of selecting distinctive individuals from within a group and giving each a separate clonal name, often preceded by the group name. Thus, from an original cross, such as 'Loderi,' for instance, we now have a series of divergent sister forms such as 'Loderi King George,' 'Loderi Venus,' etc. Certain originators, such as Hobbie of Germany and Rothschild of England, have been prolific distributors of group-forms.

The comments made concerning hardiness ratings elsewhere (page 230) apply also to the hybrid lists. Again, the British ratings are employed, and those rated "A" are by no means "ironclad" in the sense of being useful in subzero climates. In the cold parts of America, one should consult the lists of suggested kinds for special geographical locations in Part III of this book.

Names of originators, where known, are given following the names of the cultivars. This often furnishes clues to the character and adaptability of the plant. For instance, the old hybrids of Anthony Waterer often partook heavily of *R. catawbiense* and many of them were of the "ironclad" hardiness class. Seidel's German crosses were likewise on the hardy side. Rothschild and Aberconway produced plants that are mainly in the "B" and "C" hardiness range. The Dutch productions are usually either "A" or "B" as are also the productions of Slocock, Bagshot (J. Waterer Sons & Crisp) and Knap Hill, although "C" is not unusual. American productions are mostly untested in Britain and so are not rated on the comparative scale. Those originating on the American West Coast are generally thought to be in the "B" or "C" classes.

Following is a list of the more important introducers of rhododendrons referred to in the descriptions:

PROMINENT RHODODENDRON ORIGINATORS

Aberconway—Lord Aberconway, Bodnant, Wales.
Bagshot—J. Waterer Sons & Crisp, Bagshot Nursery, England.
Dexter—Charles O. Dexter, Sandwich, Mass., U.S.A.
Endtz—L. J. Endtz & Co., Boskoop, Holland.
Gable—Joseph B. Gable, Stewartstown, Penna., U.S.A.
Gill—Richard Gill, Cornwall, England.
Henny—Rudolph Henny, Brooks, Oregon, U.S.A.
Herbert—Very Rev. Wm. Herbert, England (c. 1830).
Hobbie—Dietrich Hobbie, Linswege ueber Westerstede, W. Germany.
Kew—Royal Botanic Gardens, Kew, England.
Kluis—Anthony Kluis, Boskoop, Holland, and U.S.A.
Knap Hill—Anthony Waterer's Nursery, Knap Hill, Surrey, England.
Koster—M. Koster & Sons, Boskoop, Holland.
Loder—Sir Edmund Loder, Leonardslea, England.
Lowinsky—T. H. Lowinsky, Tittenhurst, Berks, England.
Magor—E. J. P. Magor, Cornwall, England.
Mangles—J. H. Mangles, Surrey, England (1832–84).
Morrison—B. Y. Morrison (U. S. Dept. Agr.), Pass Christian, Miss., U.S.A.
Noble—Charles Noble, Essex, England (c. 1850).
Nearing—Guy G. Nearing, Ramsey, New Jersey, U.S.A.
Ostbo—Endre Ostbo, Bellevue, Washington, U.S.A.
Parsons—Samuel Parsons, Flushing, Long Island, U.S.A. (c. 1870).
Paul—George Paul, Hertfordshire, England (c. 1900).
Pericat—Alphonse Pericat, Collingdale, Penna., U.S.A.
Rothschild—Lionel de Rothschild, Exbury, Hampshire, England.
R.H.S.—Royal Horticultural Society's Gardens, Wisley, Surrey, England.
Seidel—T. J. Seidel, (ex Dresden), Gruengraebchen, W. Germany.
Slocock—W. C. Slocock, Goldsworth Nurseries, Woking, Surrey, England.
Standish & Noble—Sunningdale Nurseries, Essex, England (c. 1850).
Stevenson—J. B. Stevenson, Tower Court, Ascot, England.
van Houtte—Louis van Houtte, Belgium (c. 1860).
van Nes—C. B. van Nes, Boskoop, Holland.
Vuyk—A. Vuyk, Boskoop, Holland.
Waterer—Anthony Waterer, Knap Hill Nursery, England (1853–97).
J. Waterer—John Waterer, Bagshot Nursery, Surrey, England.
Williams—J. C. and P. D. Williams, Cornwall, England.
Windsor Great Park—Crown Estate Commissioners, England.

A LIST OF CULTIVARS CURRENTLY IN USE

RHODODENDRON CLONES AND GROUPS *

A. Bedford (Lowinsky), pale mauve in tube, darker above; dark markings. *A***X**
A. B. Mitford (Waterer), crimson. *A*
Abraham Lincoln (Parsons), red. *A*
Adriaan Koster (Koster), creamy white, small red spot. *B***X**
Afghan, deep blood red. *B*
Afterglow (Slocock), pale pink and mauve; *discolor* hybrid. *B*
Aileen Henderson (Koster), yellow to cream; brown-yellow blotch.
Ajax (Waterer), bright rose. *B*
Alarm (Waterer), deep crimson, white center.
Albatross (Rothschild), white, tinged pink; fragrant; Loderi hybrid. *B***X**
Albert (Seidel), delicate lilac; 'Everestianum' hybrid. *A*
Albert Close (Gable), *maximum* hybrid.
Album Elegans (Waterer), pale mauve, fading to white; late; *maximum* hybrid. *A*
Album Grandiflorum (Waterer), very pale mauve, fading white; Catawba hybrid. *A*
Album Novum (van Houtte), white, tinged lilac, green spots. *A*
Alfred (Seidel), 'Everestianum' selfed; lilac.
Alice (Waterer), deep pink, fading pale rose; *Griffithianum* hybrid. *B*.
Alice Martineau (Slocock), rosy crimson, dark blotch and throat; late. *B*
Alice Street (Koster), light yellow; *Wardii* hybrid. *C*
Allah (Seidel), light lilac-rose; late.
America (Koster), dark red; hybrid of 'Parsons Grandiflorum.' *A*
Amethyst (Dexter), *Fortunei* hybrid.
Ammerlandense g. (Hobbie), *Williamsianum* hybrid, coral rose. *B*
Amy (Bagshot), bright rose; *Griffithianum* hybrid. *B*
Angelo (Rothschild), *Griffithianum* × *discolor;* blush to white. *C*
Anna Rose Whitney (Whitney), *Griersonianum* hybrid.
Annie E. Endtz (Endtz), light pink. *B*
Apple Blossom (Slocock), Fortunei hybrid; pink, yellow center. *B*
Argosy Snow White (Bagshot), *auriculatum* × *discolor*. *B*
Armistice Day (van Nes), scarlet red; *Griffithianum* hybrid. *B*
Arthur J. Ivens (Hillier), *Williamsianum* hybrid; shallow; bell-shaped; rose. *B*
Arthur Osborn (Kew), ruby red; trumpet-shaped, pendulous. *B*
Ascot Brilliant (Standish), red or deep crimson; *Thomsonii* hybrid. *B*
Atrier (Gable), red; *Griersonianum* hybrid. (See 'William Montgomery.')
Atrosanguineum (H. Waterer), Red Catawba hybrid; very hardy. *A*
Auguste van Geert (C. van Geert), purplish red; *ponticum* hybrid. *B*
Aurora (Rothschild), soft pink. *C*
Avalanche (Rothschild), large white; Loderi hybrid; inside basal blotch *C*
Azor (Stevenson), clear pink, brown flecks at base; loose truss. *B*
Bachers Gold (John Bacher), venetian pink shading to saffron yellow.
Bagshot Ruby (Bagshot), ruby red; *Thomsonii* hybrid. *B*
Bahram (Knap Hill), blush, fading white. *B*
Ballerina (Bagshot), large, fringed; white with yellow on upper lobe. *B*
Barclayi Robert Fox (Barclay Fox), deep blood red. *E*
Barnet Glory (syn. of 'Souvenir de D. A. Koster').

* All are clones unless designated "g." in which case a group, or grex, is indicated.

RHODODENDRON CLONES AND GROUPS—*Continued*

Baron Schroeder (J. Waterer), plum color, yellowish center. *A*
Baroness Henry Schroeder (J. Waterer), white, finely spotted. *A*
Bauble (Rothschild), creamy yellow, spotted; *campylocarpum* hybrid. *B*
B. de Bruin (Waterer), rich red, fringed; Catawba hybrid. *A*
Beau Brummell (Rothschild), 30-fld. truss; deep red, speckled; black anthers. *B*
Beaulieu (Bagshot), peach pink, light edge. *C*
Beauty of Littleworth (Miss Mangles), pure white, tinged pink, speckled red. *B*X
Beefeater (R.H.S.), red; *Elliottii* hybrid, late. Geranium lake (HCC 20/1). *B*
Bengt M. Schalin g. (Hobbie), yellow, with red in throat; large flowers. *A*
Bern (John Bacher), mauve, lighter center, prominent blotch, magenta rose.
Berryrose (Rothschild), yellowish or apricot pink; large; fragrant. *B*
Betty Stewart (van Nes), cherry red; upper lobe spotted; suffused white. *B*
Betty Wormald (Koster), pink with pale center; 'Pink Pearl' form. *B*X
Bianchi (Maurice Young), salmon pink. *A*
Bibber (Seidel), carmine red.
Bibiani (Rothschild), bright scarlet, maroon spots. *B*
Biskra (Rothschild), vermilion; lepidote; *Cinnabarinum roylei* hybrid. *C*
Bismarck (Seidel), white with red lines; a Catawba hybrid.
Black Beauty (Slocock), dark velvet crimson or maroon red. *B*
Blandyanum (Standish & Noble, 1850); rosy crimson.
Bluebird (Aberconway), blue (HCC 639/1, veronica violet). *B*X
Blue Danube (Knap Hill), deep mauve purple. *A*
Blue Diamond (Crosfield), showy violet blue; semi-dwarf; *Augustinii* hybrid, *B*XX
Blue Ensign (Slocock), pale lavender blue, black spot. *A*
Blue Peter (Bagshot), light lavender, purple blotch; fringed. *A*X
Blue Tit (Williams), violet blue; smallish flowers; rock garden type. *B*
Boddaertianum (van Houtte), light pink turning white, spotted black. *A*
Bonfire (Bagshot), deep red; *Griersonianum* hybrid. *B*
Bonito (Rothschild), white chocolate blotch. *B*X
Bonzo (Knap Hill), pale pink; compact. *A*
Bo-peep (Rothschild), cream colored; yellow spots within at back. *C*X
Borde Hill (van Nes), dark scarlet. *B*
Boule de Neige (Oudieu, 1878), white, early. Catawba × Caucasicum hybrid. *A*
Bow Bells (Rothschild), *Williamsianum* hybrid; pink, cerise in bud. *B*
Brandywine (Nearing), rose. *R. Keiskei × pubescens.*
Bric-a-brac (Rothschild), white; faint marks on upper lobe; chocolate anthers. *C*
Britannia (van Nes), scarlet, near best; good truss; good habit. *B*XX
Brocade g. (Rothschild), cascade of frilly peach flowers; *Williamsianum* hybrid. *B*
Broughtonii (Broughton, 1840), rosy crimson. *B*
Broughtonii Aureum Azaleodendron; soft yellow, orange spots. *B*
Bulstrode Park (van Nes), bright red; waxy, large fls. *B*
Burgemeester Aarts (Koster), dark red; tall habit.
Buttercup (Slocock), yellow, shaded apricot; *campylocarpum* hybrid. *B*.
Butterfly (Slocock), pale yellow, faintly spotted red; *campylocarpum* hybrid. *B*X
Cadis (Gable), pink.
Camich (Gable), purplish red; spotted.
Captain Jack (R. Henny), currant red. *Eriogynum* hybrid.
Caractacus (Waterer), purplish red; Catawba hybrid; hardy. *A*
Carex Blush (Rothschild), blush pink; spotted. *C*
Carex White (Rothschild), white, spotted. *C*

RHODODENDRON CLONES AND GROUPS—*Continued*

Carita (Rothschild), very pale primrose. *B*

Carmen g. (Rothschild), deep red; one of the best Repens dwarf hybrids. *B*

Caroline (Gable), orchid lavender.

Catalgla (Gable), a selection from Glass's wild *R. catawbiense album. A*

Catawbiense Album (Waterer), white, buds pale lilac; probably a hybrid clone. *A*

Catawbiense Boursault (Boursault), probably a selected form; lilac tinged rose.

Catawbiense Grandiflorum (Waterer), lilac; probably a selected seedling. *A*

Cathaem (Gable), pink, hose-in-hose. *R. catawbiense* × *haematodes.*

Catharine van Tol (van Tol, Boskoop), carmine rose.

Caucasicum Album, *R. caucasicum* × *ponticum* var. *album,* white. *A*

Caucasicum Pictum, pink, dark blotch; frilled. *A*

Cavalcade (Bagshot), red. See 'Mrs. Sassoon.' *B*

C. B. van Nes (van Nes), scarlet; early. *B*

Celeste (Bagshot), solferino purple (HCC 26/3 & 26/2). *B*

Cetewayo (Waterer), dark rich purple. *A*

Chanticleer g. (Rothschild), large, waxy and scarlet. *C*

Charles Bagley (Waterer), cherry red; Catawba hybrid. *A*

Charles Dickens (Waterer, 1865), crimson red; Catawba hybrid; spotted. *A*

Charles Thorold (Waterer), purple, with greenish yellow center. *A*

Charlotte de Rothschild (Rothschild), large fls. frilled; whitish pink; spots.

Chesapeake (Nearing), apricot, fading white; *R. Keiskei* hybrid.

Chevalier Felix de Sauvage (Sauvage), red with dark spots. *B*

China 'A' (Slocock), pale yellow. *B*

Chintz (Waterer), soft pink with ruby spots. *B*

Chionoides (J. Waterer), white, yellow center; *ponticum* hybrid. *A*

Christmas Cheer (Methven), blush; pink buds fading to white. *B*

Cilipinense (Aberconway), pale shell pink; early. *C*

Cis (R. Henny), orange yellow. *C*

C.O.D. (Dexter), white, pale yellow throat; lax habit. Less desirable.

Concessum (J. Byls), bright rose, light center.

Conemaugh g. (Gable), *R. mucronulatum* × *racemosum.*

Conestoga g. (Gable), *R. carolinianum* × *racemosum.*

Conewago g. (Gable), *R. carolinianum* × *mucronulatum,* rose magenta; early. *A*

Conewingo g. (Gable), *R. diphrocalyx* × *haematodes.*

Confection (R. Henny), rose madder (HCC 23/2).

Conical Kate (J. Waterer), clear rosy crimson, yellow blotch. *A*

Constant Nymph (Knap Hill), very pale blush. Syn. 'Donum.' *B*

Coplen's White (Coplen–Gable), white; Catawba hybrid. *A*

Cornell Pink (Skinner), deciduous; a rose selection of *R. mucronulatum. A*

Cornish Cross g. (S. Smith), rose pink. (See 'Exbury Cornish Cross'.) *C*

Cornubia (Barclay Fox), blood red. *C***X**

Corona (J. Waterer), coral pink. *B***X**

Coronation Day (Crosfield), Loderi hybrid; delicate mottled rose, crimson blotch. *C*

Corry Koster (Koster), light pink, spotted crimson; fimbriated. *B*

Countess of Athlone (van Nes), mauve; large truss. *B*

Countess of Derby (White), pale rosy crimson; base spotted. *B***X**

Countess of Haddington, tender; white flushed rose; yellow-brown markings. *F*

Countess of Sefton (Davies), white; tender. *F*

Crossbill (Williams), open bell; yellow tinged red. *C*

C. S. Sargent (Waterer), red. Not so hardy as 'Mrs. Charles Sargent.' *A*

RHODODENDRON CLONES AND GROUPS—*Continued*

Cunninghamii, *R. maximum* × *arboreum* v. *cinnamomeum,* white; spotted.
Cunningham's Sulphur (Cunningham), yellowish; low. A var. of *R. caucasicum. B*
Cunningham's White (Cunningham), white, greenish blotch. *Caucasicum* × *ponticum* var. *album. A*
Cynthia (Standish & Noble, 1870), rosy crimson; still best of its class. *B*
Dairymaid (Slocock), primrose yellow, tinged pink, pink blotch. *B*X
Daisy (Seidel), bright carmine red; *Smirnowii* cross.
Damaris g. (Magor), cream; *campylocarpum* hybrid. See 'Logan Damaris.'
Dame Nellie Melba (Loder), bright pink, crimson dots. *C*
Damozel (Rothschild), deep rose pink. *B*
Darlene (Lem), bright red; *Griersonianum* hybrid.
David (Swaythling), deep blood red; slightly spotted. *B*X
Dawn (Bagshot), white flushed phlox pink. *C*X
Dawn's Delight (Mangles), white, tinged rose, spotted crimson. *C*X
Day Dream g. (Rothschild), deep crimson; bright buds fading to pale. *C*
Delaware (Nearing), apricot, fading to white; *R. Keiskei* × *pubescens.*
Delicatissimum (J. Waterer), white tinged, pale lilac; hardy. *A*
Devonshire Cream (Slocock), creamy yellow, red blotch. *B*
Dexter's #9 (Dexter), *Fortunei* hybrid of unknown parentage; pale amber. *B*
Dexter's Amethyst (Dexter), large lavender flowers.
Dexter's Champagne (Dexter–Vossberg), cream, apricot buds.
Dexter's Favourite (Dexter), pale pink, greenish yellow center.
Dexter's Pink (Arnold Arboretum), phlox pink (HCC 625/2). *A*
Diane (Koster), creamy white, shaded primrose; compact truss. *B*X
Diane Titcomb (Larson), white, edged pink.
Dido g. (Wilding), orange yellow. *B*
Dietrich (Seidel), carmine rose; almost plain.
Diphole Pink (Bagshot), deep rose or cerise pink, spotted brown. *B*
Direcktor E. Hjelm (D. A. Koster), dark carmine rose, bronze blotch.
Disca (Gable), white; *discolor* hybrid.
Diva (Rothschild), carmine scarlet, spotted brownish. *C*
Donald Waterer (Bagshot), deep rose pink, fading in center. *A*
Doncaster (Waterer), vivid crimson scarlet; rather dwarf. *B*
Dora Amateis (Amateis, USA), white, lightly spotted green; *R. carolinianum* hybrid. *A*
Dorothea (Lowinsky), blush-pink white with green center; fragrant. *C*
Dortmund g. (Hobbie), bright yellow, delicate rose. *R. Soulei* × *Wardii. B*
Dr. A. Blok (Endtz), light rose, lighter center. *B*
Dr. Arnold W. Endtz (Endtz), carmine; fimbriated. *B*
Dr. H. C. Dresselhuys (den Ouden), aniline red.
Dr. H. C. Karl Foerster g. (Hobbie), rose to scarlet; *Williamsianum* hybrid. *B*
Dr. H. J. Lovink (den Ouden), aniline red.
Dr. Hogg, dark red.
Dr. Masters (Vander Meulen), an Azaleodendron. Pink, tinged lilac. *A*
Dr. Stocker (North), milky ivory, spotted lemon brown at base. *C*
Dr. V. H. Rutgers (den Ouden), aniline red; fringed.
Dream Girl (Brandt, USA), orange buff, throat blood red.
Duchess of Connaught (J. Mason), bright scarlet crimson. *A*
Duchess of Portland (Fisher Son & Sibray), pure white. *B*
Duchess of Teck (Bagshot), white, edged mauve, bronze blotch. *A*
Duchess of York (G. Paul), salmon pink, green spots. *B*

RHODODENDRON CLONES AND GROUPS—*Continued*

Duke of York (G. Paul), rosy pink, cream spots. *B*

Earl of Athlone (van Nes), bright blood red. *C*X

Earl of Donoughmore (Koster), bright red, orange glow. *B*

Edith (Slocock), rich pink, carmine spots; dark blotch; late. *B*

Edward Dunn (Endre Ostbo, USA).

Edward S. Rand (Waterer), crimson red, yellow eye.

Effner (Seidel), dark violet.

Eidam (Seidel), white, flushed rose.

Eileen (Bagshot), blush, pink edge, yellow blotch. *A*

El Alamein (Kluis), cardinal red (HCC 822/1), brown blotch. *B*

Eleanore (Rothschild), amethyst violet; *Augustinii* hybrid. *C*

Electra (Rothschild), violet blue, lighter than HCC 639/1, greenish blotch. *C*

Elisabeth Hobbie g. (Hobbie), scarlet red; dwarf. *B*

Elizabeth (Aberconway), deep red (HCC 020); dwarfish. *B*XX

Elizabeth Titcomb (Titcomb), white; wavy margins.

Elsa Crisp (Bagshot), soft pink, deeper pink margin. *B*

Elsae (Reuthe), ivory white, crimson basal blotch. Also grex. *E*X

Elspeth (Slocock), pink center, fading to apricot. *B*

Emasculum (Waterer), no stamens; pale purple, rosy lilac. *B*

Emma (Seidel), bright carmine rose, few dark markings.

Ems g. (Hobbie), purple red; dwarfish. *C*

Endsleigh Pink, rosy pink. *C.*

Erika (Seidel), carmine rose; *Metternichii* hybrid.

Essex Scarlet (G. Paul), deep crimson scarlet. *B*

Everestianum (Waterer, 1850), rosy lilac; frilled; spotted; very hardy. *A*

Exbury Angelo (Rothschild), white with green markings. *C*

Exbury Fabia (Rothschild), apricot yellow, flushed salmon pink; large fls. *B*X

Exbury Hawk (Rothschild), clear yellow. *C*

Exbury Lady Chamberlain (Rothschild), yellow, overlaid salmon orange. *C*X

Exbury, see Exbury clones of the following groups: Albatross g., Angelo g., Antonio g., Calstocker g., Cornish Cross g., Fabia g., Hawk g., Matador g., May Day g., Naomi g., Souldis g., Spinulosum g.

Fabia g. (Aberconway), variable forms, A. M. Clone is orange-salmon. *B*X

Fabia Tangerine (Aberconway), vermilion (HCC 18/1); shaded (HCC 20/2 & 16/1). *B*

Faggetter's Favourite (Slocock), cream, flushed pink; scented. *B*X

Fancy (Koster), pale cobalt violet (HCC 637/2), large red blotch. *B*

Fastuosum Flore Pleno (Francoisi Bros.), double; mauve *ponticum*. *A*

Fawn (James), salmon pink, yellow center.

F. D. Godman (Waterer), dark magenta red. *A*

Felise (Adams–Acton), cream, fading white. *C*

Fireball (Gill), rich carmine scarlet. *B*

Fire Bird (Rothschild), salmon red. *B*

F. L. Ames (Waterer), rosy pink, light center. Syn: 'Amphion.' *A*

Flare (Slocock), brilliant salmon red. *B*

Florabunda (Gable).

Flushing (Parsons), crimson. *A*

Fragrans (Paxton), an Azaleodendron. Pale mauve, light in center. *B*

Fragrantissimum, white, tinged pink; tender; scented. *F*

Francis B. Hayes (Waterer), white, chocolate blotch. *A*

RHODODENDRON CLONES AND GROUPS—*Continued*

Frank Galsworthy (Waterer), maroon purple, yellow blotch. *A*

Frederick Waterer (J. Waterer), crimson red. *A*

Fritz Henssler g. (Hobbie), bright rose; *Williamsianum* hybrid. *B*

Full Moon (J. Henny), yellow.

Fusilier (Rothschild), brilliant red. *C*

Gable's Aladdin (Gable).

Gable's Pink No. 1 (Gable), pink, spotted throat; *Fortunei* hybrid.

Gable's pink No. 2 (Gable), pink; *discolor* hybrid.

Galceador (Knap Hill), lilac, with gold eye. *A*

Galloper Light (Rothschild), an Azaleodendron. Cream with gold eye. *B*

Garibaldi (Waterer), bright, light red; frilled. *A*

Gartendirektor Glocker (Hobbie), rose red, darker margins; dwarf. *B*

G. A. Sims (Bagshot), dark pure scarlet; scraggly habit. *B*

G. B. Simpson (Waterer), bluish purple, light center. *A*

General Eisenhower (A. Kluis), deep carmine red (HCC 025); large fls. *A*

General Grant (Parsons c. 1875), soft rose. *A*

General Sir John du Cane g. (Rothschild), rose, dark eye; large. *B*

Geneva (J. Bacher, USA), camellia rose (HCC 622), lighter toward center.

Genoveva (Seidel), pale lilac white, yellowish green blotch.

Geoffrey Millais (Schulz–van Nes), white; lily-shaped. *C*

George Cunningham (Cunningham), white with black spots. *B*

George Grace (R. Henny, USA), light pink.

George Hardy (Mangles), blush fading white. *B*

Gertrud Schaele g. (Hobbie), scarlet red; large flowers; dwarfish. *B*

Giganteum (Waterer), light crimson; Catawba hybrid. *A*

Gill's Crimson (Gill), blood crimson; *Griffithianum* hybrid *C*.

Gill's Gloriosa (Gill), bright cerise. *D*

Gill's Goliath (Gill), carmine pink. *D*

Gill's Triumph (Gill), strawberry red; fading. *D*

Gladys g. (S. R. Clarke), cream, crimson markings. *B*

Glass White, wild white selection of *R. catawbiense;* pinkish in bud. *A*

Glory of Littleworth (Mangles), an Azaleodendron. Lemon, with intense orange blotch; tall. *B*X

Glory of Penjerrick (Gill), deep strawberry red, fading pink. *D*X

Goethe (Seidel), bright rose.

Golden Horn (Rothschild), orange yellow (HCC 18/1), vermilion. *B*

Goldfinch g. (R. Collyer), pink with gold eye. *A*

Goldfort (Slocock), clear yellow, green center, pink edges. *B*

Gold Mohur (Brandt), 'Dream Girl' grex. Barium yellow, greenish spots.

Goldsworth Crimson (Slocock), crimson; vigorous grower. *B*

Goldsworth Orange (Slocock), low shrub; pale orange, tinted pink. *B*

Goldsworth Pink (Slocock), light pink; large; high truss. *B*

Goldsworth Purple (Slocock), purple. *A*

Goldsworth Yellow (Slocock), light yellow, spotted green and bronze. *B*

Gomer Waterer (J. Waterer), rose, tinged lilac; large truss; late. *A*

Govenianum (Methven), an Azaleodendron. Pale purplish rose; scented. *A*

Grand Arab, synonym of 'Vesuvius.'

Grenadier (Rothschild), blood red; *Elliotti* hybrid. Also grex. *D*.

Grosclaude (Rothschild), waxy blood red (HCC 820/1). Also grex. *B*

Gudrun (Seidel), white, slight purple tint, red spotted.

RHODODENDRON CLONES AND GROUPS—*Continued*

Halopeanum (Halope, Belgium), blush, changing to white. Syn. 'White Pearl.' *B*

Handsworth Scarlet (Fisher Son & Sibray), bright red; *caucasicum* hybrid. *B*

Handsworth White (Fisher Son & Sibray), white, faint blush. *A*

Harry Tagg (Edinburgh), a coolhouse plant; large; white, greenish tinge. *F*

Harvest Moon (Koster), cream or lemon yellow, dark red markings. *B*

Hawk g. (Rothschild), fine yellow (HCC 1/3). Clones include: 'Amour,' 'Crest' **X**, 'Exbury Hawk,' 'Beaulieu Hawk,' 'Jervis Bay,' 'Hawk Kestrel,' 'Hawk Merlin.'

Helene Schiffner (Seidel), pure white. *B*

Henrietta Sargent (Waterer), dark rose; compact habit. *A*

Hero (Seidel), pure white with yellow markings.

H. H. Hunnewell (Waterer), purplish red. *A*

Hokessin (Nearing).

Holbein (Seidel), lilac rose.

Holger (Seidel), pale violet, dark green spots.

Hollandia (Endtz), pure carmine. *B*

Holly (Gable).

Homer (Seidel), bright pink.

Hugh Koster (Koster), bright crimson. *B*

Hugh Wormald (Koster), cerise with white stripe; blotched. *C*

Humboldt (Seidel), rose; dark markings.

Humming Bird g. (Williams), dwarfish; *Williamsianum* hybrid. *C*

H. W. Sargent (Waterer), magenta crimson. *A*

Hyperion (Waterer), white, chocolate blotch. *A*

Icarus g. (Rothschild), deep rose bud; flower biscuit color. *B*

Idealist (Rothschild), pale greenish yellow in bold trusses. *B***X**

Ightham (Reuthe), augfast grex; blue. *B*

Ignatius Sargent (Waterer), light rose crimson. *A*

Impeanum (Kew), deep lilac blue; rock garden plant; compact. *A*

Impi (Rothschild), very dark red (HCC 826). *B*

Inamorata (Rothschild), sulphur yellow, spotted crimson blotch; robust. *B*

Independence Day (Waterer), red; pale center, dark spot. *A*

Indiana g. (Rothschild), orange with red markings. *Kyawi* × *scyphocalyx*. *C*

Intrifast g. (Lowinsky), violet blue. *B*

Isaac Newton g. (Hobbie), carmine red; dark lvs.; Repens hybrid; dwarf. *B*

Ivery's Scarlet (Ivery), blood red. *D*

Jacksonii (Herbert, 1835), rosy pink, deeper outside. *A*

Jalisco g. (Rothschild), primrose yellow, crimson markings. *B*

Jalisco Goshawk (Rothschild), mimosa yellow (HCC 60/1), spotted. *B***X**

James Barto (Barto), fuchsine pink (HCC 627/3).

James Burchett (Slocock), white, yellow blotch. *B*

Jan Dekens (Blaauw), rich pink; fragrant. *B*

Jean Marie du Montague. See 'The Hon. Jean Marie de Montague.'

Jervis Bay (Rothschild), Hawk grex; sulphur yellow, red markings. *C*

J. G. Millais (J. Waterer), large; scarlet. *C*

J. H. van Nes (van Nes), soft red. *C*

J. J. de Vink (Koster), rose red (HCC 724), blotched brown. *C*

John Henry Agnew (J. Waterer), pink, chocolate spots.

John Walter (J. Waterer), crimson. *A*

Jordan g. (Rothschild), pale orange. *C*

Joseph Whitworth (J. Waterer), dark purple lake, dark spots. *A*

RHODODENDRON CLONES AND GROUPS—*Continued*

Josephine Everitt (Dexter), pink. Early Dexter selection by S. A. Everitt.

Julie Titcomb (Titcomb), shaded pink to white.

Karkov (Rothschild), carmine rose; faintly spotted. *C*

Kate Greenaway (Bagshot), soft rose. Syn. 'Niobe.' *A*

Kate Waterer (J. Waterer), pink, yellow center; late. *B*

Keay Slocock (Slocock), pale yellow, flushed salmon or cream. *B*

Kettledrum (Waterer), purplish crimson. *A*

Kewense g. (Kew), blush white or pink.

King George (Schulz–van Nes), bright red. *Not* 'Loderi King George.' *C*

King of Shrubs (Endre Ostbo, USA), apricot base, greenish spots, rose margin.

Kluis Sensation (Kluis), bright scarlet, faintly spotted. *B*

Kluis Triumph (Kluis), deep red or terra cotta; *Griffithianum* hybrid. *A*

LaBar's White (R. Harmon), pure white, including buds; *R. catawbiense album. A*

Lady Alice Fitzwilliam, white, with nutmeg fragrance. *F*

Lady Annette de Trafford (Waterer), blush pink, dark brown blotch; *maximum* hybrid. *A*

Lady Armstrong (Waterer), carmine.

Lady Berry (Rothschild), rose opal (HCC 022/3), outside red (018/1). *D*

Lady Bessborough g. (Rothschild), cream with maroon blotch; several clones. *B*

Ladybird g. (Rothschild), pink, freckled yellow inside. *B*

Lady Chamberlain g. (Rothschild), orange red, suffused rose. *C***X**
There are clones as follows: Apricot Lady Chamberlain, Bodnant Yellow, Chelsea, Exbury Lady Chamberlain, Gleam, Golden Queen, Lady Chamberlain Etna, Lady Chamberlain Seville, Oriflamme, Salmon Trout.

Lady Clementine Mitford (Waterer), peach pink; darker edge; large. *A*

Lady Clermont (Waterer), light or rosy red; dark blotch.

Lady Decies (J. Waterer), blush lilac, yellow eye. *A*

Lady de Rothschild (Waterer), white flushed blush pink, spotted crimson. *B*

Lady Eleanor Cathcart (J. Waterer), clear pale pink, purplish red blotch. *A*

Lady Grey Edgerton (Waterer), pale lilac, silvery blush. *A*

Lady Longman (H. White), clear pale pink, chocolate eye. *A*

Lady Montagu (Rothschild), large flowers; pink; darker outside. *C*

Lady Primrose (Slocock), clear lemon yellow, red spots. *B*

Lady Roseberry (Rothschild), rosy red within, crimson outside; Roylei hybrid. *C*

Lady Stuart of Wortley (Koster), rosy red; *Griffithianum* hybrid. *C*

Laetevirens, magenta rose; *carolinianum* hybrid. Synonym: 'Wilsoni.'

Lake Labish (R. Henny), Neyron rose (HCC 623); *Loderi* hybrid.

Lamplighter (Koster), rose red (HCC 724) with salmon glow. *B*

Langley Park (van Nes), deep red. *B*

Langworth (Slocock), white, chocolate blotch, dark throat. *B*

Last Chance (R. Henny), *R. eriogynum* × 'Mars.'

Lavender Girl (Slocock), pale lavender, margins rose, center white. *B*

Leaburg (Phetteplace), blood red (HCC 820/3).

Lee's Best Purple (Lee), deep purple; good habit.

Lee's Dark Purple (Lee), large purple trusses; dark wavy leaves. *A*

Lee's Scarlet (Lee), rosy crimson; fading. Will flower before Christmas. *B*

Lem's Goal (Halfdan Lem, USA), cream yellow.

Lenape (Nearing), pale yellow. *R. Keiskei* × *pubescens.*

Leopold (Seidel), dark purple-violet, brown marks.

Letty Edwards (S. Clarke), pale sulphur (HCC 1/3), shaded darker. *B***XX**

RHODODENDRON CLONES AND GROUPS—*Continued*

Lewis Carroll (Bagshot), white with pink edges. *C*

Lily No. 1 (Endre Ostbo, USA), large; white; lily-like flowers. *B*

Linswegeanum g. (Hobbie), deep scarlet; Repens hybrid. *B*

Lionel's Triumph (Rothschild), dresden yellow (HCC 64/3), crimson markings.

Little Ben (Scrase-Dickins), deep scarlet; dwarf; waxy. *B*

Little Pudding (R. Henny), camellia rose (HCC 622/1), throat (HCC 614/2).

Little Sheba (R. Henny), 'Fabia' hybrid x *repens.*

Lodauric g. (Slocock), clone 'Iceberg'; large; white. *B*

Loderi g. (Sir E. Loder), *R. Fortunei* × *Griffithianum* ♀. White or pink. *C*XX

    There are many clones, all preceded by name 'Loderi.'

Loderi King George (Loder), huge white flowers; fragrant. *C*XX

Loderi Sir Edmund (Loder), waxy; blush pink; scented. *C*X

Loderi Venus (Loder), pale pink; scented. *C*X

Loder's White (Mangles), large delicate pink mauve, fading to white. *C*X

Logan Damaris (Stevenson), dresden yellow (HCC 64/3).

Lord Armstrong (Waterer?), darker than 'Lady Armstrong'; white anthers.

Lord Roberts (B. Mason), dark red, black blotch.

McIntosh, analine red; vigorous.

Madame Carvalho (J. Waterer), white, yellowish green spots. *A*

Madame Masson (Bertin, 1849), white, yellow blotch. *ponticum* hybrid.

Madonna (Gable), white, yellow throat.

Mariloo g. (Rothschild), pure yellow. 'Dr. Stocker' × *lacteum.* *C*XX

Mariloo Eugenie (Rothschild), large clear yellow, small crimson spots. *C*XX

Mariloo Gilbury (Rothschild), pale creamy pink, pink stripe on back. *C*X

Marinus Koster (Koster), deep pink, lighter shadings. *B*X

Mars (Bagshot), deep red; *Griffithianum* hybrid. *B*X

Martin Hope Sutton (Waterer), red, blotched.

Mary Swaythling (Swaythling), 'Gladys' grex; soft yellow. *B*

Mary Waterer (Knap Hill), bright rich pink, paler center, buff spots. *B*

Matador (Aberconway), dark orange red (HCC 721/1); tubular. *B*

May Day (Williams), cerise scarlet; loose clusters. Also grex. *C*XX

May Templar (van Nes), bright scarlet. *B*

Meadowbrook (Paul Vossberg, USA) bright pink; crenate petals. *A*

Merle Lee (Esch), pink. 'Azor' selfed.

Mevrouw P. A. Colijn (Koster), dark carmine red. *A*

Mexiko (Seidel), red.

Michael Waterer (Waterer), dark red, spotted; *ponticum* hybrid. *B*

Midsummer (Bagshot), rose pink; a *maximum* hybrid. *A*

Minnie (Standish), bluish white, chocolate blotch.

Modesty (Waterer), pale blush, fading.

Mohamet (Rothschild), red (HCC 19/1). *C*

Montchanin (Nearing), white; *R. pubescens* × *Keiskei.*

Moonstone (Williams), cream or ivory (grex); pink-edged. *C*

Moontide (R. Henny), white.

Moser's Maroon (Moser et Fils), red maroon flowers, dark spots. *B*X

Mother of Pearl (J. Waterer), sport of 'Pink Pearl.' blush to white. *B*

Mount Everest (Slocock), pure white, speckled brown on upper lobe. *B*

Mouton Rothschild (Rothschild), blood red, brown spots; *Elliotti* hybrid.

Mrs. A. C. Kendrick (Koster), deep rose pink, spotted deeper. *B*

Mrs. A. F. McEwan (Univ. of Washington Arboretum), fuchsine pink (HCC 627/3).

RHODODENDRON CLONES AND GROUPS—*Continued*

Mrs. A. M. Williams (Schulz–van Nes), cardinal red (HCC 122/2), spotted. *B*

Mrs. Anthony Waterer (Knap Hill), pale cream, rose tinge, saffron blotch. *A*

Mrs. Arthur Fawcus (Knap Hill), pale yellow. Synonym: 'Mrs. A. Evans.' *A*

Mrs. Ashley Slocock (Slocock), cream, suffused apricot; *campylocarpum* hybrid. *B*

Mrs. A. T. de la Mare (van Nes), white with green spot; fragrant. *C*

Mrs. Betty Robertson (Koster), pale yellow, pink flush, red center. *B*

Mrs. Carter Glass (Gable), white; 'Catalgla' × *decorum*. *A*

Mrs. C. B. van Nes (van Nes), rosy red, fading to deep pink. *B*

Mrs. Charles E. Pearson (Koster), pale blush mauve, brown spots. *B*XX

Mrs. Charles S. Sargent (Waterer, 1888), best "ironclad" deep rose. *A*

Mrs. Charles Thorold (Waterer), pink, yellow center. *A*

Mrs. Davies Evans (Waterer), light mauve (HCC 33/1); fine truss. *A*

Mrs. Donald Graham (Endre Ostbo), spinel red (HCC 0023/1) and (HCC 24/2).

Mrs. E. C. Stirling (J. Waterer), blush pink. *B*

Mrs. Furnival (Waterer), pink, heavily blotched crimson; funnel-shaped. *B*XX

Mrs. G. W. Leak (Koster), light pink, brown purple blotch. *B*X

Mrs. Helen Koster. (Koster), light lilac, large purplish blotch. *A*

Mrs. J. C. Williams (Waterer), white or blush white, spotted red. *A*

Mrs. J. G. Millais (Waterer), white, prominent yellow blotch. *A*

Mrs. John Clutton (Waterer), white, small yellowish green blotch. *A*

Mrs. John Waterer (Waterer), rosy crimson. *A*

Mrs. Lindsay Smith (Koster), white, slightly spotted on upper lobe. *B*

Mrs. Lionel de Rothschild (Waterer), bright pink, paler at maturity. *B*

Mrs. Mary Ashley (Slocock), salmon pink, shaded cream. *B*

Mrs. Mendel (Waterer), pink, rayed white, yellow center.

Mrs. P. den Ouden (den Ouden), deep crimson.

Mrs. P. D. Williams (Waterer), ivory with brown-yellow eye. *A*X

Mrs. Philip Martineau (Knap Hill), rose pink; fading; yellow blotch. *B*XX

Mrs. Powell Glass (Gable), white; 'Catalga' × *decorum*.

Mrs. R. G. Shaw (Waterer), blush, dark eye. *A*

Mrs. R. S. Holford (Waterer), rosy salmon. *B*

Mrs. Tom Agnew (J. Waterer), white with lemon blotch. *A*

Mrs. Tom H. Lowinsky (Waterer), blush to white, reddish brown blotch. *B*

Mrs. Walter Burns (Lowinsky), pink with bright red blotch. *B*

Mrs. W. C. Slocock (Slocock), apricot pink, shaded to yellow. *B*X

Mrs. William Agnew (J. Waterer), pale rose, purple blotch. *B*

Mrs. William R. Coe (Dexter–Vossberg), deep bright pink, crimson throat.

Mrs. Wm. Watson (Waterer), white, reddish (violet?) markings.

Mum (J. Waterer), white, lemon eye; compact; a good Maximum hybrid. *A*

Myrtifolium (*R. minus* × *hirsutum*) lilac pink.

Naomi (Rothschild), large pink, yellow undertone; scented. Also grex. *B*X

Naomi Nereid (Rothschild), lavender and yellow. *C*

Nellie, an Azaleodendron; white, yellow eye. *B*

New Moon (Slocock), white flushed primrose yellow (HCC 601/2); buds pink. *B*X

N. N. Sherwood (Sibray), pink, gold center. *B*

Nobleanum Album (Waterer), white. *B*

Nobleanum Coccineum (Waterer), bright red. *B*

Norman Shaw (Rothschild), rich pink.

Nuneham Park (van Nes), bright red.

Odoratum (Thompson), blush or pale lilac; an Azaleodendron. *C*

RHODODENDRON CLONES AND GROUPS—*Continued*

Oldewig (Seidel), crimson with lighter center.
Old Port (Waterer), deep plum color.
Omega (Seidel), pure carmine rose.
Opal Fawcett (Endre Ostbo), pale pink to white.
Orbwill (Gable), *R. orbiculatum* × *Williamsianum*.
Orion (Bagshot), rose pink, red eye. *A*
Parsons Gloriosum (Waterer–Parsons), large light rose-lilac; very hardy.
Parsons Grandiflorum (Waterer–Parsons), large dark purplish rose; very hardy.
Paulina, a selection of *R. pseudoyanthinum.*
Pauline g. (Lowinsky), crimson (HCC 821/3), black eye. *C*
Peggy (Bagshot), phlox pink (HCC 625/1). *A*
Penjerrick (S. Smith), large pale pink cream or white campanulate fls. *C*XX
Peter Koster (Koster), bright magenta red, edged lighter. *B*
Philip Waterer (J. Waterer), rose pink, soft rose.
Picotee (Waterer), white, picotee-edged. *A*
Pierre Moser (Moser et Fils), light pink; early; *caucasicum* hybrid. *B*
Pilgrim (Johnston), rich pink, few dark markings. Also grex. *B*X
Pink Mermaid (Esch), pink, darker edge and throat.
Pink Pearl (J. Waterer), soft pink, deeper in bud. *B*X
Pink Perfection (van Houtte), pale pink, lilac tinge. *B*
Polar Bear (Stevenson), pure white, narrow green throat; fragrant. *C*X
Praecox (Davis, 1860), purple or rosy lilac. A grex. *B*X
Prelude (Rothschild), primrose yellow (HCC 601/3), darker base. *B*
Prince Camille de Rohan (Verschaffelt, 1865), rosy pink, deep blotch; frilled. *B*
Prince of Wales (Bagshot), rose pink, lighter center; medium height; strong. *B*
Princess Elizabeth (Bagshot), deep crimson; strong grower. *B*
Professor F. Bettex (den Ouden), red.
Professor Hugo de Vries (Endtz), pink, deeper than its parent, 'Pink Pearl.' *B*
Professor J. H. Zaayer (Endtz), light red. *B*
Prometheus (C. Noble), scarlet crimson. *A*
Purple Emperor (Knap Hill), near Doge purple (HCC 732/3), paler throat. *A*X
Purple Gem (Hardgrove), purplish violet. *R. carolinianum* × *fastigiatum.*
Purple Splendour (Waterer), very deep violet-purple; most popular purple. *A*X
Purpureum Elegans (Waterer), lilac purple. *A*
Purpureum Grandiflorum (Waterer), lilac purple. *A*
Pygmalion (Bagshot), crimson-scarlet, spotted black. *B*
Quapp (Seidel), purplish pink.
Queen Mary (Felix & Dijkhouis), rose bengal (HCC 25/2). *A*
Queen of Hearts (Rothschild), crimson (HCC 824), spotted black above. *C*
Queen o' the May g. (C. Smith), white. *C*
Queen Souriya (Slocock), dusky sulphur and pink; edge mauve, pale ochre. *B*
Queen Wilhelmina (Schulz–van Nes), scarlet, fading to rosy pink. *C*
Querida, bright red: *Elliottii* hybrid. Also grex. *D*
Racil (N. S. Holland), shell pink; *R. racemosum* × *ciliatum. B*
Rainbow (Slocock), carmine with light center, darker edges. *B*
Ramapo (Nearing), bright, light violet; *R. fastigiatum* × *carolinianum.*
Raphael (Seidel), dark lilac red.
Ray (D. W. James), dresden yellow (HCC 64/3).
Red Cap g. (Stevenson), blood red or deep plum red. *C*
Red Cat (Gable), red Catawba seedling.

RHODODENDRON CLONES AND GROUPS—*Continued*

Red Cloud (R. Henny), claret rose (HCC 021), inner tube scarlet overlay.
Red Riding Hood (Slocock), bright red. 'Atrosanguineum' × *Griffithianum. B*
Renhaven (James), dark red; *Elliottii* hybrid.
Repose (Rothschild), creamy yellow. *C*
Rickshaw g. (Rothschild), biscuit colored, suffused orange, deeper at throat. *C*
Romany Chai (Rothschild), rich red terra cotta, brown spots. Also grex. *B*
Romany Chal (Rothschild), scarlet maroon, darker spots. Also grex. *C***X**
Ronald (*R. Hodgsonii × sinogrande*), whitish, stained rosy purple; large.
Rosamundi (Standish & Noble), pale rose. *A*
Rosamund Millais (Koster), cerise, blotched purple. *B*
Roseann, fuchsine pink.
Rose Elf (Lancaster), white, flushed violet pink.
Rose Perfection (Gill), deep red bud, opening pink. *B*
Roseum Elegans (Waterer, 1851), rose lilac. Said to be three forms in trade. *A*
Roseum Pictum (H. Waterer, 1851), rose, yellow spots; Catawba hybrid. *A*
Roseum Superbum (Waterer, 1865), purplish rose; Catawba hybrid. *A*
Roslyn (Paul Vossberg), lavender blue; white stamens. *A*
Rosy Bell (Davies), old rose or soft pink. *C*
Rosy Morn (Rothschild), Loderi group; pink, lightly spotted. *C*
Rouge (Rothschild), large reddish carmine; spotted throat. Also grex. *C*
Royal Flush g. (Williams), pink and orange; *R. cinnabarinum × Maddenii. D*
Royal Purple (White), purple, yellowish blotch.
Rubens (Waterer), rich deep red. *D*
Rubina g. (Crosfield), dark maroon red. *B*
Ruby Bowman (Druecker), Tyrian rose, blood red base.
Ruddy, deep red.
St. George g. (Bagshot), pale crimson (HCC 22/1) fading; veined. *C***X**
Sapphire (Knap Hill), light blue; dwarfish. *A*
Sappho (Waterer c. 1867), white, heavily spotted black maroon. *A*
Saracen (Waterer), deep red, black blotch. *B*
Saturn (Bagshot), cerise, shading to pink, white interior. *C*
Scandinavia (Koster), cardinal red on rose red base, black blotch. *B***X**
Scharnhorst (Seidel), crimson.
Scintellation (Dexter–Vossberg), luminous pink flowers in large trusses.
Scipio (Waterer), purplish red. *A*
Sefton (Waterer), deep crimson red; late; straggling habit; hardy. *A*
Seta (Aberconway), pink flushed. *B*
Sharon (James), white, crimson blotch; Loderi hybrid.
Shilsonii (Gill), scarlet to crimson; *R. Thomsonii × barbatum. C*
Sigismund Rucker (Waterer), magenta, with black center.
Sir Charles Butler (G. Paul), pale mauve to pearl rose. Syn: 'Mrs. Butler.' *B*
Sir Charles Lemon (Aberconway), white; Arboreum hybrid, or selection. *B*
Sir Frederick Moore (Rothschild), clear pink, crimson spots at base. Also grex. *B*
Sir James (Gable), pink; Fortunei hybrid.
Sir John Ramsden (Bagshot), outside carmine, pale margins, rose inside. *B***XX**
Smithii Aureum (Smith c. 1830), an Azaleodendron; orange yellow. *C*
Snow Lady (Rothschild), pure white; Leucaspis selection.
Snow Queen (Loder), buds rose, turning white when open; red base. *B***X**
Solent Queen (Rothschild?), Angelo g.; pale rose to white, green spots. *C*
Souvenir de Anthony Waterer, salmon red, orange blotch. *B*

RHODODENDRON CLONES AND GROUPS—*Continued*

Souvenir de D. A. Koster (Koster), medium, profuse, dark red flowers. *B*

Souvenir de Dr. S. Endtz (Endtz), bright rose pink, dotted crimson. *B*

Souvenir of W. C. Slocock (Slocock), primrose yellow, apricot buds. *B***X**

Spinulosum (Kew), apricot pink; *R. racemosum* × *spinuliferum. C*

Spitfire (Kluis), dark red (HCC 824/1), dark brown blotch. *B*

Spring Glory (Shammarello, USA), pink.

Stanley Davies (Davies), red.

Starfish (Bagshot), bright pink; star-shaped; *Griffithianum* hybrid. *A*

Stella (Waterer), lilac rose, spotted dark chocolate.

Stoplight (R. Henny), scarlet; Griersonianum hybrid.

Strategist (J. Waterer), light red; *Griffithianum* hybrid. *A*

Sulfmeg (Magor), pale sulphur yellow (HCC 1/3).

Sun of Austerlitz (Methven), brilliant crimson; early. *B*

Suomi g. (Hobbie), bright red, partly deeper borders. *A*

Susan (Williams–Slocock), amethyst violet (HCC 35/2 and 35/3); spotted. *B***XX**

Sweet Simplicity (Bagshot), white, edged rose pink. *A*

Symphonie (Slocock), cream center, almond pink edges. *B*

Tally Ho (Crosfield), bright orange scarlet, black anthers. *D*

Tan (Dexter–H. F. du Pont), biscuit color; *Fortunei* hybrid.

Temple Belle g. (Kew), soft pink; semi-dwarf. *C*

The Bride (Standish & Noble), white, greenish spots. *A*

The Don (Lowinsky), intense rosy scarlet. *C*

The Hon. Jean Marie de Montague (van Nes), bright scarlet red.

The Hon. Joyce Montague (van Nes), scarlet, showing white stripes. *C*

Thelma (Lem), geranium lake (HCC 20/1); large; *Griersonianum* hybrid.

The Queen (Noble), blush, changing to white.

The Warrior (J. Waterer), light crimson.

Three Star (Gable).

Thunderstorm (Slocock), very dark red (HCC 022); stamens white; margins wavy. *B*

Tony Willis Flemming (Slocock), deep red; 'Doncaster' seedling. *B*

Towhee (James), scarlet.

Trilby (van Nes), deep crimson, dark blotch. *A***X**

Tulyar (Waterer), red, black blotch. *B*

Tumalo (James), white, suffused pink.

Tyermannii (Tyerman), white or cream lily-like flowers; tender. *F***XX**

Unique (Slocock), pale yellow, tinged peach; *Campylocarpum* hybrid. *B***X**

Unknown Warrior (van Nes), light red; early. *B*

Ursela Siems g. (Hobbie), intense scarlet carmine; translucent; fleshy. *B*

Van der Hoop (den Ouden), dark crimson rose.

Vanessa (Aberconway), soft pink. *C***X**

Vanessa Pastel (Aberconway), cream shell pink (HCC 516/2), stained scarlet. *C*

Van Nes Sensation (van Nes), pale lilac, white center; fragrant. *B*

Van Weerden Poelman (den Ouden), crimson.

Vesuvius (J. Waterer), bright orange scarlet, shaded violet above; Syn: 'Grand Arab.' *B*

Violet Parsons (Parsons), salmon pink. *B*

Virgin (Abbott), white.

Von Oheimb Woislowitz (Seidel), purplish rose.

Voodoo (R. Henny), scarlet.

Vulcan (Bagshot), bright red (HCC 820/3). *B. Griersonianum* hybrid.

RHODODENDRON CLONES AND GROUPS—*Continued*

War Paint (D. James), crimson scarlet; *Elliottii* selection.
Waterer's Caucasicum (Waterer), blush pink. *B*
Waterer's Hybridum (Waterer), *R. ferrugineum* hybrid; rose pink. *A*
Wellesleyanum (Waterer), white, tinged rose; *R. catawbiense × maximum. A*
Werei (S. Smith), rose pink. *C*
Westbury (Dexter–Vossberg), lively pink, gold throat; compact.
Westward Ho! (Slocock), deep pink, crimson throat. *B*
Wheatley (Dexter–Vossberg), delicate pink; upstanding trusses.
White Cloud (Slocock), pure white. *B*
White Pearl, Synonym of 'Halopeanum.'
White Samite, a white Loderi derivative. *C*
White Swan (Bagshot), white with green eye; large flower. *C***X**
Wilgen's Ruby (van Wilgen, Boskoop), bright deep red (HCC 721–724). *B*
William Austin (J. Waterer), dark purplish crimson; spotted.
Wilsoni, synonym of 'Laetevirens.'
Windbeam (Nearing), apricot, fading to pink and white; *carolinianum* hybrid.
Windsor Lad (Knap Hill), blush lilac with bold blotch. *A*
Winkfield (Windsor Great Park), pinkish yellow, throat marked crimson.
W. S. Reuthe g. (Hobbie), delicate rose; porcelain-like. *B*
Wyanokie (Nearing), white; *carolinianum* hybrid.
Yellow Hammer (Knap Hill), small yellow flowers; also grex. *B*
Yvonne Opaline (Rothschild), pink; buds darker; loose trusses. *C*
Yvonne Pride (Rothschild), pale pink, fading white; six in truss. *C*
Zuiderzee (Koster), creamy yellow, small red spots on throat. *B*

JAVANESE HYBRID RHODODENDRONS

Balsaminaeflorum Album, Aureum, Carneum, Rajah, Roseum (all double).
Baroness Henry Schroeder, white, finely spotted.
Brilliant, bright scarlet, large flowers.
Clorinda, dull rose pink.
Diadem, orange scarlet.
Duchess of Edinburgh, light crimson, lighter center.
Eos
Favourite, pinky yellow to salmon.
Flame, rich orange scarlet.
Hercules, apricot yellow, tinted rose.
Indian Yellow, orange yellow.
Jasminiflorum Carminatum, carmine.
King Edward VII, deep yellow.
Little Beauty, carmine scarlet.
Lord Wolseley, red orange.
Luteo Roseum, pinky yellow to salmon.
Maiden's Blush, cream and pink.
Mrs. Heal, shaded pink.
Primrose, yellow.
Princess Alexandra, white, waxy, scented.
Princess Beatrice, light yellow and pink.
Princess Christian, nankeen yellow.

JAVANESE HYBRID RHODODENDRONS—*Continued*

Princess Frederica, yellow.
Princess Royal, pale pink, shaded yellow.
Souvenir de J. H. Mangles, chrome orange.
Sybil, rose pink.
Taylori, pink.
The Queen, blush changing to white.
Thetis, yellow to yellow-orange.
Triumphans, crimson scarlet.

AZALEODENDRONS

Broughtonii Aureum (B), bronzy yellow with persistent leaves. Syn: *R. norbitonense* var. *aureum* Rehder.
Dot, rose crimson.
Dr. Masters, pink, tinged lilac.
Fragrans, pale rose; scented.
Galloper Light, soft salmon rose, spotted deeper.
Gemmiferum (B), bright magenta rose.
Glory of Littleworth (B), yellow with a dark orange blotch.
Govenianum (A), lavender purple.
Jackie (B), deep rose, spotted.
Nellie (B), white, yellow eye.
Odoratum (B), pale lilac; scented.
Smithii Aureum (C), orange yellow.
Torlonianum (C), purple with yellow eye.

GHENT HYBRID AZALEAS

Bartholo Lazzari, deep yellow; double.
Beauté Celeste, syn: 'Cardinal.'
Bouquet de Flore, bright pink, striped white.
Buttercup, bright yellow, orange eye.
Cardinal, bright pink.
Charlemagne, orange, yellow blotch.
Coccinea Speciosa, brilliant orange red.
Corneille, pink; double.
Daviesii, white, pale yellow eye.
Dr. Charles Baumann, deep blood red.
Fanny, magenta pink, tinted purplish.
Fenélon, apricot yellow; double.
Flamingo, reddish pink.
Gloria Mundi, bright orange, yellow lobe.
Graf von Meran, rose pink; double.
Grandeur Triomphante, violet red.
Hollandia, orange yellow.
Ignea Nova, carmine red, yellow lobe.
Joseph Baumann, deep salmon pink, tinted orange.
Josephine Klinger, salmon pink, yellow lobe.

GHENT HYBRID AZALEAS—*Continued*

Leibnitz, yellow; double.
Mrs. Harry White, white, rose tinted, yellow eye; late.
Nancy Waterer, golden yellow, deeper eye; large.
Narcissiflora, pale yellow; double.
Orange Man, orange yellow.
Orpheus, reddish orange, deep blotch.
Pallas, jasper red (HCC 018), orange yellow blotch.
Prince Henry de Pays-Bas, tangerine orange and orange red eye.
Quentin Metsys, white, flushed orange-red, blotch empire yellow.
Rosetta, double; rosy red and yellow.
Sang de Ghentbrugge, signal red (HCC 719/3).
Souvenir du President Carnot, cadmium orange and brick red.
Standishii, deep yellow.
Tangerine, terra-cotta, orange eye.
Teniers, maize yellow, flushed venetian pink; double.
Thisbe, rose pink, orange blotch.
Unique, tangerine orange (HCC 9/1).
Vulcan, blood red, blotch cadmium orange.
Willem III, nasturtium red, yellowish orange blotch.

MOLLIS HYBRID AZALEAS

Adelaide, orange yellow, red blotch.
Admirable, orange pink, orange blotch.
Afterglow, syn: 'Thérèse.'
Alice de Stuers, salmon pink, deep orange blotch.
Alma Tadema, soft pink, red blotch.
Alphonse Lavallée, orange flushed pink.
Altaclarense, orange yellow, blotched.
Altaclarense Sunbeam, yellow, flushed apricot, orange blotch; large.
Annie Laurie, orange red, saffron yellow blotch.
Anthony Koster, rich yellow, flushed orange.
Babeuff, salmon orange.
C. B. van Nes, fire red.
Chicago, light orange red.
Christopher Wren, chrome yellow, orange blotch.
Cinderella, pale orange red.
Clara Butt, salmon pink.
Colonel F. R. Durham, bright yellow.
Comte de Gomer, spinel pink (HCC 625/2), yellow blotch.
Comte de Papadopoli, porcelain rose, tangerine orange blotch.
Comte de Quincy, light chrome yellow (HCC 605/2).
Consul Cérésole, syn: Comte de Gomer.
Dante G. Rossetti, white with orange-yellow blotch.
David Teniers, orange rose.
Directeur Moerlands, golden yellow, deeper within.
Dr. Jacobi, deep red.
Dr. M. Oosthoek, mandarin red (HCC 17/1), lighter blotch.
Dr. Reichenbach, yellowish orange.

MOLLIS HYBRID AZALEAS—*Continued*

Duchess of Portland, light salmon pink.
Dulcinae, salmon red, yellow blotch.
Elizabeth, bright pink, yellow spots.
Emil Liebig, cadmium yellow with orange blotch.
Evening Glow, brilliant deep red.
Fairy Queen, salmon pink.
Favorite, red.
Floradora, nasturtium orange, burnt orange blotch.
Flying Enterprise, soft yellow, shaded pink.
Frans Hals, deep pinkish red.
Frans van der Bom, pale apricot (HCC 609/1) to (HCC 013).
Fraternité, salmon pink.
Fred de Connick, maize yellow, edges salmon pink, orange blotch.
Frisia, reddish salmon, shaded orange.
Guillaume Caillet, light yellow, edged rose.
Gypsy Lass, orange with some pink.
Hamlet, Chinese coral (HCC 614), blotch reddish orange.
Hortulanus H. Witte, light orange-yellow, cadmium yellow blotch.
Hugo de Groot, deep salmon orange; late.
Hugo Hardijzer, begonia red (HCC 619), burnt orange blotch (HCC 014).
Hugo Koster, poppy red (HCC 16/2) with orange blotch.
Imperator, orange; late.
Indian Chief, orange and yellow shades, blended.
Irish Lass, pastel pink, orange and yellow.
J. C. van Tol, porcelain rose (HCC 620), marigold orange blotch.
John Ball, rose red, early midseason.
John Kersbergen, salmon red, shaded orange.
John Ruskin, bright pink; late.
Koningin Emma, orange yellow, suffused orange red; blotch orange.
Koningin Sophia, carmine rose.
Koningin Wilhelmina, light salmon orange, bittersweet orange blotch.
Koster's Brilliant Red, glowing reddish orange.
Lemonora, apricot yellow, tinted rose.
Liberty, deep pink.
Lord Lister, pink.
Marconi, reddish orange (HCC 16/1) blotch, marked orange (HCC 013).
Marmion, yellow.
Mathilda, orange red and rose doree shaded spectrum red; frilled.
Mina den Ouden, deep carmine rose.
Mme. Arthur de Warelles, light salmon orange.
Mme. Jules Buyssens, orange.
Mr. D. Webster, light golden yellow, tinted pink.
Mrs. A. E. Endtz, dark golden yellow.
Mrs. G. van Noordt, salmon pink.
Mrs. H. den Ouden, orange red.
Mrs. Helen Koster, deep orange.
Mrs. J. Dijkhuis, salmon orange; late.
Mrs. J. Patterson, light rose, deeper edges, golden blotch.
Mrs. L. J. Endtz, clear yellow.
Mrs. Norman Luff, orange, yellow blotch.

MOLLIS HYBRID AZALEAS—*Continued*

Mrs. Oliver Slocock, rich orange yellow, suffused terra cotta.
Mrs. Peter Koster, scarlet (HCC 19) with burnt orange blotch.
Multatuli, orange, yellowish blotch.
Nicolaas Beets, apricot to maize yellow.
Oranea, deep orange red.
Orange Princess, orange.
Peter Kersbergen, orange with yellow ochre blotch.
Prins Frederick, neyron rose, blotched yellow ochre.
Prinses Juliana, lemon yellow, edged salmon pink.
Prof. Amundsen, soft rose, red border, yellow blotch.
Prof. Donders, light red.
Queen Emma, syn: 'Koningin Emma.'
Queen Sophia, syn: 'Koningin Sophia.'
Radiant, deep orange red.
Robespierre, orange red, paler toward edges.
Rosy, apple blossom pink, light yellow blotch.
Rudyard Kipling, reddish orange, dark spots.
Salmon Glow, deep salmon orange.
Salmon Queen, apricot.
Samuel Taylor Coleridge, rose pink, cadmium orange blotch.
Shakespeare, maize yellow, buttercup yellow blotch.
Signal Light, deep reddish orange.
Snowdrift, cream, shaded greenish, fading to white, yellow spots.
Southgate Wonder, light orange red.
Spek's Brilliant, orange red, conspicuous yellow anthers.
Spek's Orange, reddish orange, greenish blotch.
Spinoza, orange, tinted rose; golden center blotch.
Thérèse, pink with darker pink stripes.
T. J. Seidel, pale orange, darker blotch.
Von Gneist, orange red, salmon glow.
W. E. Gumbleton, orange yellow, faint greenish blotch.
Willem Hardijzer, deep red.
Winston Churchill, mandarin red (HCC 17), signal red blotch (HCC 719).

RUSTICA FLORE PLENO (DOUBLE MOLLIS) HYBRID AZALEAS

Aida, faintly tinged pink.
Byron, hose-in-hose; white, tinged red. Syn: 'Dir. C. Ohrt.'
Freya, hose-in-hose; reddish orange, tipped carmine rose.
Il Tasso, scarlet, paler edges.
Milton, white, orange yellow blotch.
Murillo, carmine rose, salmon glow.
Norma, carrot red, edged old rose.
Phebe, sulphur yellow.
Phidias, mimosa yellow (HCC 602/3).
Ribera, camellia rose (HCC 622/2).
Velasquez, cream tinged pink, fading to white.

ALBICANS (OCCIDENTALE *) HYBRID AZALEAS

Advance, rose, yellow blotch.
Bridesmaid, late; white, yellow blotched.
Delicatissima, cream, flushed rose; yellow blotch.
Exquisita, white, flushed rose; orange-yellow blotch; scented.
Graciosa, orange yellow, suffused red, tangerine orange blotch.
Irene Koster, white, flushed dawn pink; scented.
Magnifica, neyron rose (HCC 623/2), cadmium orange blotch.
Primavera, rose and cream.
Rosea, pure pink.
Superba, pale pink, orange blotch; fringed.
Westminster, delicate pink; sweet scented; late.

KNAP HILL HYBRID AZALEAS †

Albatross, white tinged pink, orange blotch.
Altair, cream, yellow blotch.
Annabella, orange.
Ann Callingham, deep crimson.
Aurora, salmon pink, orange blotch.
Avocet, white and pink.
Ballerina, white, yellow blotch.
Balzac, orange-red.
Barbara Jenkinson, orange-apricot.
Basilisk, cream, yellow blotch.
Beaulieu, pink, yellow blotch.
Berryrose, pink, yellow blotch.
Brazil, tangerine.
Bride's Bouquet, pale pink.
Bright Forecast, salmon, deep orange blotch.
Bright Straw, deep yellow, deeper blotch.
Brimstone, pale yellow, orange blotch.
Bullfinch, deep vermilion, suffused orange blotch.
Canasta, orange yellow.
Caprice, deep pink.
Cecile, salmon-pink, yellow blotch.
Chaffinch, salmon-pink; often semi-double.
Clarice, pale salmon, orange blotch.
Cockatoo, flame apricot.
Colin Kenrick, pale flesh-pink; double.
Coronation Lady, marigold-orange, suffused poppy-red.
Corringe, flame.
Cresta, yellow.

* The natural forms of *R. occidentale* bear little resemblance to the clone under that name grown in Holland, which I suspect of hybridity. If the Dutch clone is the source of *occidentale* genes in the so-called 'Occidentale Hybrids,' I consider this group designation of doubtful validity. Hence, I prefer to use the name 'Albicans,' which goes back to the original Waterer cross of *R. occidentale* × *molle*.

† Including Exbury, Goldsworth, etc., Azaleas.

KNAP HILL HYBRID AZALEAS—*Continued*

Crinoline, white, flushed pink; frilled.
Curacao, orange.
Dairymaid, creamy yellow.
Danger, orange-scarlet.
Daybreak, marigold-orange, suffused fire-red.
Debutante, light carmine, orange eye.
Desert Pride, pale pink, orange blotch.
Devon, bright red.
Drift, white.
Eisenhower, fire-red, orange blotch.
Eva Goude, sulphur yellow.
Exbury White, large white.
Exbury Yellow, primrose yellow, orange eye.
Fancy Free, pink, yellow blotch.
Favor Major, orange yellow.
Fawley, white flushed pink.
Fireball, deep red.
Firecracker, currant red.
Firecrest, deep red, orange blotch; early.
Firefly, deep orange.
Fireglow, orange-vermilion.
Flaming June, deep red.
Flarepath, deep red.
Florence Pilkington, cream, tinted red.
Frances Jenkinson, orange-apricot.
Frills, orange-red; double.
Gallipoli, orange-scarlet.
Gannet, pale straw-yellow, suffused pink, orange blotch.
George Reynolds, buttercup yellow, deeper blotch.
Gibraltar, orange.
Ginger, brownish orange.
Glowing Embers, red, orange blotch.
Gog, orange-red.
Goldcrest, bright yellow, blotched.
Gold Dust, bright yellow.
Golden Eagle, bright orange.
Golden Eye, deep vermilion, bold orange blotch.
Golden Girl, yellow, deep blotch.
Golden Gleam, yellow.
Golden Glory, bright yellow.
Golden Hind, Indian yellow, orange blotch.
Golden Horn, golden yellow.
Golden Oriole, deep Chinese yellow, orange blotch.
Golden Sunset, light yellow, orange blotch.
Goldfinch, rich yellow; compact.
Goldilocks, pale yellow, orange eye.
Gwenda Kitcat, pink and white.
Gwyneth, light orange.
Gwynnid Loyd, white, flushed pink, yellow blotch.
Harvest Moon, pale yellow.

KNAP HILL HYBRID AZALEAS—*Continued*

Hawfinch, pale pink.
Heron, deep red.
Hiawatha, orange-red, orange blotch.
Homebush, semi-double; neyron rose on a base of rose madder.
Honeysuckle, flesh-pink, orange blotch.
Hotspur, orange-scarlet, yellow blotch.
Hugh Wormald, yellow.
Icarus, salmon orange.
Inspiration, pink.
Iora, yellow.
J. Jennings, red.
Jock Coutts, white, tinged pink.
Joy Bentall, rich orange, flushed apricot.
Kestrel, rich orange.
Kipps, tangerine.
Klondyke, golden yellow.
Knap Hill Apricot, yellow-apricot.
Knap Hill Pink, carmine-rose, orange blotch.
Knap Hill Red, deep red.
Knap Hill White, white shaded carmine-rose.
Knap Hill Yellow, rich canary yellow.
Knighthood, bright orange.
Krakatoa, fiery red.
Lady Derby, pale yellow, flushed pale pink, orange blotch.
Lady Roseberry, scarlet, dull suffused orange blotch.
Langley, pink, yellow blotch.
Lapwing, pale yellow, tinged pink, orange blotch.
Leander, pink.
Leo Kelly, orange-apricot.
Linnet, double; carmine, faint yellow flush.
Madeleine, pale pink, yellow blotch.
Mariclare, pink, yellow blotch.
Marina, pale yellow, deep yellow blotch.
Marionette, pink, orange blotch.
Marion Marriman, pale yellow, tinged pink, orange blotch.
Mazurka, coral-apricot.
Mephistopheles, bright red.
Merlin, salmon-pink.
Middle East, deep orange.
Moonshine, golden yellow.
Mrs. Anthony Waterer, pale yellow, saffron blotch.
Muriel Watson-Jones, rich pink.
Mustard, Indian yellow.
Nancy Buchanan, white, yellow blotch.
Nathaniel, salmon, orange blotch.
Old Gold, golden yellow.
Orient, brick-red, orange blotch.
Oxydol, white, faint yellow blotch.
Pavane, peach-pink.
Peach Blossom, carmine-rose, orange blotch.

KNAP HILL HYBRID AZALEAS—*Continued*

Penguin, salmon pink.
Peregrine, rich orange.
Persil, white, yellow blotch.
Pink Delight, peach-pink, yellow eye.
Pink Lady, apricot-pink, yellow eye.
Pink Ruffles, carmine-rose, orange eye.
Polonaise, peach-pink, orange blotch.
Pompadour, carmine, bold orange blotch.
Princess, pale pink, yellow blotch.
Princess Royal, cream, yellow blotch.
Quaker Maid, white, edged carmine.
Radiance, nasturtium-red.
Red Indian, intense orange-red.
Redshank, orange-red, yellow blotch.
Redstart, deep red.
Rocket, light orange, suffused red.
Rosella, pale pink.
Royal Command, vermilion.
Royal Lodge, red.
Royal Ruby, nasturtium-red.
Ruddy Duck, salmon-pink, orange blotch.
Rumba, bright orange.
Ruth Davies, bright orange.
Sand Dune, pink, orange blotch.
Sandpiper, pale pink, flushed pale yellow.
Satan, scarlet.
Scarlet Pimpernel, red.
Scarlett O'Hara, red.
Serenade, apricot-yellow, buds coral.
Seville, intense orange.
Silver Slipper, white, flushed pink.
Soft Lips, flesh-pink, yellow blotch.
Sonia, white, flushed pink.
Spoonbill, white, tinged pink.
Strawberry Ice, pale pink.
Sugared Almond, pale pink.
Sun Chariot, buttercup-yellow, deep orange eye.
Sunset Boulevard, pale pink.
Sunset Pink, pink, yellow blotch.
Surprise, cream, flushed pink.
Sydney Firth, deep pink, orange blotch.
Tangiers, tangerine.
Toucan, cream, fading white, yellow blotch.
Troupial, orange.
Tunis, orange-red.
Verulam, orange-yellow.
Whitethroat, pure white; double.
Wryneck, yellow, edged pink.

KURUME AZALEAS *
(1936 List)

Agemaki (Jose), carmine.
Aioi (Fairy Queen), almond blossom (h).
All Aglow (Sakua Tsukasa), rosy mauve.
Admiration, pure pink (h) hose-in-hose.
Amoena, purplish crimson (h).
Amoena Superba, rich dark purple (h).
Apple Blossom (Hoo), white, tinged pink.
Asagasumi (Rosy Morn), rose pink.
Augigasana, pale pink.
Avalanche, pure white.
Aya Kammuri (Pinkie), rose color.
Azuma Kagami (Pink Pearl), deep pink.
Benifude (Sunbeam), salmon.
Benigiri, deep red.
Betty (Suga No Ito), bright red.
Bijinsui (Little Imp), pale pink.
Bridesmaid, bright salmon.
Brilliant, salmon rose, shaded deeper.
Bouquet Rose, rose pink, darker center.
Cardinal (Tsuta Momiji), bright red.
Carmine Queen (Kurai No Himo), carmine (h).
Cattleya, white, tinted lilac (h).
Cengalto, clear pink.
Cheerfulness, dark vermilion red, lighter center.
Cherry Blossom (Takasago), cherry blossom pink (h).
Cherry Pink, bright pink.
Cherub (Kimigayo), pink.
Christmas Cheer, brilliant red (h).
Coral Bells, shell pink, shaded darker (h).
Dainty (Irohayama), white, margined pale lavender.
Dame Lavender (Omoine), pale lavender.
Daphne, lavender, light center.
Daybreak (Kirin), deep rose, shading silvery.
Debutante, salmon pink, splashed red.
Delicatissima, white, shaded lilac.
Elf (Kasumi Gaseki), pale pink.
Esmeralda, bright pink.
Exquisite, salmon.
Fairy, blush pink.

* Seedlings and variants of the Kurume azaleas and their allies and derivatives have become so numerous that the present author does not pretend to list them all in this work. A very adequate list of these, with full descriptions under classified headings, may be found in Mr. Frederic P. Lee's recent work (*The Azalea Book*, 1958). In trade catalogues, forms other than true Kurume azaleas are frequently intermingled. In this book the Kurume clones from the first edition are now being reprinted, supplemented by a new list of more recent introductions, including AMOENA and BELTSVILLE (Yerkes) azaleas and some of their allies. The letter (h) after some of the following descriptions indicates hose-in-hose or semi-double flowers. Japanese and English synonyms are given in parentheses.

KURUME AZALEAS—*Continued*

Fairy Queen (Aioi), almond blossom pink (h).
Fancy (Tamafuyo), white, striped peach color.
Fascination (Ima Shojo), bright red (h).
Firebrand, vivid red.
Flame (Suetsumu), crimson.
Flamingo (Tama No Utena), pale salmon.
Frieda, rosy purple.
Fude Tsuka, bright pink.
Fudesute Yama (Poppy), light red.
Gosho Zakura (Vanity), white, striped peach.
Hachika Tsugi (Prudence), white, suffused lavender.
Hana Osibi (Sultan), bright pink.
Hatsu-Giri, purplish crimson.
Haya Otomi, bright pink.
Hinodegiri, bright ruby red.
Hinode No Taka (Ruby), crimson.
Hinomayo, soft pink.
Hoo (Apple Blossom), white tinged pink.
Hortensia, soft pink.
Ima Sho Jo (Fascination), bright red (h).
Ivette, salmon pink.
Jose (Agemaki), carmine.
Koshitisibu, bright pink.
Kurume Blood Red, blood red.
Kurume Pink, pink.
Kurume White, white.
Lavender Queen, light lavender.
Little Imp (Bijinsui), pale pink.
Macrostemon, small fls. and long exserted stamens.
Madonna (Seikai), white (h).
Maiden's Blush (Otone), blush pink.
Mauve Beauty, mauve.
Melody (Oino Mezame), deep rose.
Morning Glow, bright rose pink, darker blotch.
Mountain Laurel, white, tinged pink.
Obtusum Album, a white form, introduced in 1846.
Old Ivory (Shin Seikai), cream white (h).
Orange Beauty, orange pink.
Painted Lady (Nani Wagata), white, suffused salmon pink.
Peachblossom (Saotome), rose.
Peach Blow, pink.
Penelope (Osaraku), white, tinged and margined lavender.
Pinkie (Aya Kammuri), rose color.
Pink Pearl (Azuma Kagami), deep pink (h).
Poppy (Fudesute Yama), light red.
Prince Delight (Ukamuse), vermilion (h).
Prudence (Hachika Tsugi), white, tinged lavender.
Purity (Yorozuyo), white.
Ramentacea, pure white.
Red Hussar (Hinodegiri) (see Hinodegiri).

KURUME AZALEAS—*Continued*

Red Robin (Waka Kayede), red.
Rosa, rose (h).
Rosita (Kasane Kagaribi), dull salmon red.
Rosy Morn (Asagasumi), rose pink (h).
Ruby (Hinode No Taka), crimson.
Ruth (Katsura No Hana), rose.
Salmon Beauty, salmon pink.
Salmon Prince (Kumo No Uye), pure salmon.
Santoi (Shin Utena), pale salmon.
Scarlet Prince (Yayehiryu), bright scarlet.
Senge Tauren Kana, bright pink.
Seraphim (Tancho), flesh color (h).
Snow, snow white (h).
Snowflake (Kureno Yuki), white (h).
Spirite (Suiyohi), flesh color.
Sukata, red.
Sultan (Hana Asobi), red.
Sunbeam (Benifude), salmon.
Sunstar, rose pink, striped carmine.
Tauten, bright pink.
Twilight (Kiritsubo), rosy mauve.
Vanity (Gosho Zakura), white, striped peach.
Vesuvius, bright salmon, dark center.
Winsome (Osaraku seedling), white, suffused lavender.
Yayegiri (Yayehira), bright salmon red (h).

DERIVATIVES OF RHODODENDRON OBTUSUM AMOENA

Caldwellii, pale pink.
Carminata Splendens, deep pink.
Coccineum, crimson, small.
Forsterianum, blood red, semi-dbl.
Hexe (see Sander Hybrids).
H. O. Carre, bright pink.
Illuminata, rosy purple.
Mrs. Carmichael, rosy purple.
Princess Maud, rich rosy pink.
Splendens, soft pink.

SUPPLEMENTARY LIST OF KURUME AZALEAS

Akebonar Ruykin, white, flushed pale mauve.
Animation, scarlet, spotted throat; hose-in-hose.
Blush, light pink, tinted lavender; hose-in-hose.
Brasier, bright red.
Carol, white, wavy petals; hose-in-hose.
Cheniston, bright mahogany-crimson.
Cindy, rose, tinted lavender, spotted red; hose-in-hose.
Concurrent, clear pink.
Frosty, white, hose-in-hose, petals wavy.
Fukuhiko, clear pink.

KURUME AZALEAS—*Continued*

Guy Yerkes, salmon-pink, hose-in-hose.
Gyokuko, small flower; veined pink.
Haru No Kyokii, white.
H. H. Hume, white, faintly yellowish throat; hose-in-hose.
Innocence, white, greenish throat; hose-in-hose.
Koran Yuki, orange-red; small flowers.
La France, pink, flushed vermilion, fading pink.
Lark, white; hose-in-hose; spreading; prolific.
Lucia, pure white; crimped; hose-in-hose.
Majestic Pink, clear rose-pink, throat faintly marked.
Pink Profusion, pink; hose-in-hose.
Placid, white with greenish tint; hose-in-hose.
Polar Bear, white; for forcing.
Purple Glory, purple-lavender; hose-in-hose.
Regullus, salmon; hose-in-hose.
Rose Banner, rose, pink spots; hose-in-hose.
Rose Glory, rose, red spots; hose-in-hose.
Roxanne, vivid pink to salmon; hose-in-hose.
Sakata Red, fiery red.
Salmon Hinomayo, salmon-pink.
Salmon Kirin, salmon-pink.
Salmon Sander, salmon.
Salmon Spray, salmon-pink.
Shi No Ue, shell pink.
Snow White, white, yellowish-green throat; hose-in-hose.
Surprise, light orange-red.
Toreador, bright red.
Twilight, shell pink; hose-in-hose.
White Cloud, white; hose-in-hose.
White Habit, pure white; hose-in-hose.
White Mountain, white; floriferous.

KAEMPFERI HYBRID AZALEAS *

Aartje, bright red.
Addy Wery, bright scarlet.
Alice, orange red.
Anny, orange red.
Atalanta, light purple.
Audrey Wynniatt, cerise.
Augusta, rosy red.
Beethoven, magenta lilac.
Betty, rosy pink.
Billy, bright red; single.
Boudoir, watermelon pink.
Briarcliffe, violet red.

* This list includes representatives from several sub-races within the general heading, such as: Ahrendsii, Arnoldianum, Chisholm-Merritt, Coolidge, Deerfield, De Wilde, Feldyk, Gable, Hexe, Malvatica, Mayo, Sherwood and Vuyk azaleas.

KAEMPFERI HYBRID AZALEAS—*Continued*

Cameo, soft pink; double.
Cameroon, mulberry red.
Cardinalis, phlox pink.
Carmen, rose color.
Carol, bright pink; hose-in-hose (Gable).
Caroline Gable, radiant pink.
Charlotte, lavender with red spots.
Chinook, red; hose-in-hose.
Chloris, pink.
Claret, bronze, claret red.
Cleopatra, light pink; early; tall.
Corsage, orchid; large.
Dexter's Pink, violet red (Phlox pink HCC 625/2).
Diana, salmon pink.
Early Dawn, violet red (Fuchsia purple HCC 26/2).
Edna, bright pink; hose-in-hose.
Elisabeth, pale salmon pink.
Elizabeth Gable, rose pink; late.
Ethelwyn, light pink; single.
Eva, rosy violet.
Favorite, deep rosy pink.
Fedora, large; salmon rose.
Fidelio, deep rosy pink.
Frigid, white.
Fringed Beauty, pink; single; fringed.
Garden Beauty, soft pink.
Glow, orange.
Grenadier, bright scarlet; single.
Gretchen, dark mauve.
Hanny, brick red.
Helena, pink.
Herbert, dark crimson purple.
Howard Anderson, single; blush pink; red spotted.
Ivory, white.
James Gable, vivid blood red.
Jessie Coover, salmon pink; double.
Jimmie Coover, red; single; late.
Johann Sebastian Bach, purple violet.
Johann Strauss, deep rose.
John Cairns, Indian red; large flowers.
Kathleen, rosy red.
Lady Elphinstone, carmine rose.
Lakme, pink; tall.
La Roche, magenta red; single; early.
Leo, orange pink; late.
Lilac Time, bright lilac.
Little Indian, similar to 'Claret.'
Lohengrin, dark pink.
Louise Gable, salmon pink; double.
Marie, cerise.

KAEMPFERI HYBRID AZALEAS—*Continued*

Mary, deep rose.
Maryann, pink double.
Mary Dalton, salmon red; hose-in-hose.
Mary F. Hawkins, pink; hose-in-hose.
May King, carmine.
May Queen, clear pink.
Mello-Glo, violet red (HCC 26/2).
Mildred May, lavender, red spots; early.
Miriam, bright rose pink.
Mme. Butterfly, white, flushed lavender.
Mossieanum, violet red (HCC 627/1).
Mother's Day, red; semi-double.
Mozart, rosy pink.
Naomi, salmon pink; late.
Nome, double Hinomayo.
Norma, violet red.
Normandy, fiery red.
Oberon, soft pink.
Old Faithful, orchid pink; single.
Orange Favorite, pinkish orange.
Orange King, orange red.
Orion, salmon pink.
Othello, bright red.
Palestrina, pure white, faint green eye.
Pekoe, pink.
Pink Treasure, pink.
Pippa, pale mauve.
Prins Bernhard, vermilion red.
Prinses Irene, pale geranimum lake.
Psyche, pure pink.
Purple King, light purple; large.
Purple Splendor (Gable), dark purple.
Purple Triumph, deep purple.
Queen Wilhelmina (Vuyk), Syn. of 'Koningin Wilhelmina.' Deep vermilion.
Red Pimpernel, orange red.
Rosebud, rose; double.
Rose Greely, white; hose-in-hose; hardy (Gable).
Royalty, bright purple; double; large.
Salmon King, salmon orange.
Schubert, bright rose.
Sibelius, orange red.
Springtime, clear pink; single.
Sunrise, deep red.
Susan, salmon pink; single.
Swan, white; large.
Viola, lavender, red spots.
Vuyk's Rosyred, rose red.
Vuyk's Scarlet, deep red.
Willy, clear pink.
Zampa, orange red.

JAPANESE INDICUM (MACRANTHA) HYBRID AZALEAS *

(Mostly variegated, spotted, blotched, striped or margined)

Ai-No-Tomo, purplish crimson on white.
Chu-Ai, lilac purple on white.
Daiki, scarlet crimson on white.
Dainankow, purple variegation.
Ei-Kow, purple on white.
Fuji No Koshi, violet purple on white.
Fukuju, lilac purple on white.
Fuku-Musume, purple on white; wavy petals.
Fuku-Ryo, deep violet on blush and white.
Ginkon, blushed lilac on white.
Gomi-Nishiki, two-toned crimson on white.
Haru-No-Hikari, purple on white; thick round petals.
Haru-No-Umi, wavy variegation purple on white.
Hoshi-No-Umi, purple with big white spots.
How-Raku, purple on white.
Kansei, crimson on white, wavy.
Keibow, pure purple on white.
Keisetsu, scarlet crimson, white throat.
Keishuku, lilac-purple on white.
King of Yamamoto, white, variegated purple; 12–15 petals.
Kisaragi, purple dappling on white ground.
Kongow, purple on white.
Ko-Ei, blushed violet purple, lined deeper.
Kow-Ka, crimson on white.
Kowkow, crimson and blush on white.
Kumo-Asobe, deep violet on light violet.
Kuni-No-Megumi, crimson variegation on white ground.
Musow, rosy crimson and blush on white.
Nishiki-Den, white, blotched and spotted crimson.
Otohime, variegated purple.
Raku-How, lilac purple on white.
Rimpu, variegated leaves; low habit.
Rokugo-Nishiki, white blushed crimson.
Row-Getsu, clear rose, white throat.
Ryo-Jyo, white, striped lilac; large.
Ryugu, crimson and white.
Sakon, purple on white, white margins and throat.
Sakura-Gari, cherry pink, margined crimson.
Sakura-Shigure (Comet), crimson blushed. F_1 hybrid.
Secchu-No-Matsu, white bell-shaped flower; small leaves.
Seihow, dark purple on light; white throat.
Seiraku, purple on white.
Shinnyo-No-Tsuki, dark crimson with white throat. F_1
Shizuka-No-Mai, purple with white margins and throat.
Takara-Bune, scarlet-crimson stripes on white.
Tama-Ginu, purple, semi-dbl. "chrysanthemum" flowers.
Tenju, purple-crimson on white.

* Old list, printed without change from first edition (1936).

JAPANESE INDICUM (MACRANTHA) HYBRID AZALEAS—*Continued*

Tsuki-No-Umi, light lilac, white throat.
Ukon, deep lilac on white.
Zangetsu, pinkish crimson, white throat; large.

SATSUKI AZALEAS *

Bungoishiki, terra-cotta; late.
Bunkwa, white, with orange-red.
Chichibu, white; large.
Eddie, scarlet.
Fujinishiki, white; frilled.
Gumpo (*R. indicum* var. *eriocarpum*), white; large flowers.
Gumpo Fancy, white, flushed deep pink.
Gumpo Red, pale pink.
Gunbi, white with rose.
Gyokushin, white with violet.
How-raku, white with chartreuse; frilled.
Jindai, white, chartreuse throat, sometimes flaked red.
Keisetsu, Jasper red.
Kingetsu, white, margined or flecked rose.
Kow-koku, white, frilled, flaked red.
Mai-hime, red, darker blotch.
Shinnyo-no-tsuki, white, violet-red margin.

GLENN DALE HYBRID AZALEAS †

Abbot, rose color with few dots tyrian-rose.
Acme, pale rosaline-purple to rose near margins.
Advance, rose-red, very floriferous. Twiggy.
Alabaster, white with few flakes spinel-pink.
Aladdin, salmon-pink, few dots rose. Erect.
Alight, spinel-pink with purple blotch. Spreading.
Allegory, white with a few purple stripes.
Allure, pale rose-pink freely produced.
Altair, white with few dots and flakes purple.
Ambrosia, begonia-pink to pale apricot. Distinct.
Anchorite, rose-pink with undertone of orange.
Andros, pure mallow-pink. Resembles rosebuds.
Angela Place, pure white, almost no blotch.
Anthem, between rose-pink and deep rose-pink.

* Including MACRANTHA or *R. Indicum* forms, CHUGAI, DAWSON, GUMPO, LEDI-FOLIA (*R. mucronatum*), WADA and B & A Hybrids, and Miscellaneous Japanese Azaleas.
† There are approximately 400 named clones belonging to this group, with more introductions to follow. Until they are tested more widely, there can be no standard evaluations made. Only a mere name-list can be given here, omitting some, of clones known to be in the trade, accompanied with terse commercial descriptions. A printed bulletin giving a descriptive list of all available clones, with details, entitled "The Glenn Dale Azaleas," may be procured from the Superintendent of Documents, U.S. Government Printing Office, Washington, D.C.

GLENN DALE HYBRID AZALEAS—*Continued*

Antique, pure white striped purple. Flowers large.
Aphrodite, pale rose-pink, blotch upper lobe.
Araby, Jasper-red with tyrian-rose blotch.
Arcadia, deep rose-pink with tyrian-rose blotch.
Arctic, white with greenish blotch. Very large.
Argosy, geranium-pink, large tyrian-rose dots. Large.
Astarte, pink with showy rose blotch. Large.
Astra, mallow-purple, white at base of tube.
Ave Maria, white, greenish blotch, flaked purple.
Aviator, white greenish blotch, striped red. Large.
Bacchante, red with purple blotch. Large.
Bagatelle, begonia-rose. Flowers 2¾ to 3¼ in.
Bagdad, dark rose-pink. Large flowers in clusters.
Ballet Girl, Jasper red, purple dots.
Baroque, white, striped and sanded purple.
Beacon, rose-doree, scarlet effect.
Bettina, carmine flowers freely produced.
Bishop, rose with an undertone of yellow.
Blizzard, white, chartreuse throat, purple stripes.
Blushing Maid, pink, large flowers, tall growing.
Bohemian, rose colored flowers, broad spreading.
Bolivar, deep rose-pink, tyrian-rose dots.
Bonanza, purple with rose blotch, brilliant.
Bopeep, white, tinted pink, early flowering.
Bountiful, phlox-purple, frilled flowers.
Bowman, carmine-pink flowers, purple dots.
Brangaene, delicate rose with yellow undertone.
Bravo, pink rose blotch, scarlet tube.
Buccaneer, brilliant orange-red.
Burgundy, a deep brownish-red. Vigorous.
Cadenza, ruffled white, flaked and striped magenta.
Camelot, tyrian-pink, deeper at margin.
Campfire, purple, tube red.
Cantabile, white, freely produced. Early.
Caraval, spinel-pink flushed purple. Brilliant.
Carmel, brownish-red effect. Large.
Carrara, white with yellowish blotch. Large.
Cascade, white flaked rose-pink, hose-in-hose.
Catawba, pink with rose dots. Spreading.
Cathay, little darker than geranium-pink.
Cavalier, a beautiful orange-red.
Cavatina, white, striped purple. Spreading.
Celestial, rose pink, yellow undertone.
Challenger, salmon washed pale lavender.
Chamelon, white, yellow blotch, striped purple.
Chanticleer, purple, rose tube. Very brilliant.
Cherry Spot, purple with pink blotch.
Chloe, brilliant rose, margins ruffled.
Chum, white, striped red, sometimes all red.
Clarion, brilliant red, orangetone at base tube.

GLENN DALE HYBRID AZALEAS—*Continued*

Cocktail, white with red stripes, some spots.
Commando, purple with rose blotch. Freely produced.
Commodore, scarlet-red, large flowers, spreading.
Con Amore, deep rose-pink, lighter at margins.
Concordia, bright pink, a little yellow at base tube.
Conquest, white with few lines purple.
Constance, rose color, large flowers. Vigorous.
Consuela, deep rose-pink. Large.
Content, pale amparo-purple. Large.
Copperman, brilliant red.
Coquette, pink conspicuous red pistil.
Coralie, salmon-pink, hose-in-hose.
Coral Sea, pink with showy rose dots.
Cordial, pink with red blotch, frilled. Large.
Corsair, deep rose-pink. Large.
Corydon, deep rose-pink. Spreading.
Cranford, deep rose-pink. Late May.
Cremona, vivid rose, purple dots.
Crusader, geranium-red, blotch rose-red.
Cygnet, white with pale yellow blotch.
Cythera, white.
Damask, white washed with chartreuse.
Damozel, geranium-pink, white at base.
Daphnis, tyrian-pink, yellow at base.
Dawning, lavender-pink. Freely produced.
Dayspring, center white shading to pink. Early.
Defiance, white, striped red. Starry flowers.
Delilah, begonia-rose. Leaves narrow glistening.
Delos, rose-pink. Large double flowers.
Demure, rose, red dots. Dark green leaves.
Desire, pale rose-pink toned salmon.
Dimity, white, flaked and striped red.
Dowager, white flaked and striped magenta.
Dragon, rose-red. Brilliant and floriferous.
Dream, deep rose-pink, frilled.
Driven Snow, white, large. End of May.
Dulcimer, rose-doree, purple dots.
Effective, rose, large. Early.
Egoist, white, striped and sanded purple.
Elizabeth, begonia-rose. Late May; large.
Emblem, scarlet-red. A very good red one.
Enchantment, geranium-pink, hose-in-hose.
Epicure, deep rose. Late May, early June.
Epilogue, orange-salmon. Early June.
Eros, pink, heavy substance. Late May.
Eucharis, frilled, white with chartreuse blotch.
Evensong, starry rose-colored flowers.
Everest, white, chartreuse blotch.
Fairy Bells, pink, like a Christmas cactus.
Fakir, rose with yellow undertone.

GLENN DALE HYBRID AZALEAS—*Continued*

Fandango, purple, red throat, brilliant.
Fanfare, pink, rose-red blotch. Narrow leaves.
Fashion, begonia-rose, base almost white.
Favorite, pale salmon effect. Late April.
Fawn, white center, pink margins, self-pink.
Festive, white sanded and striped old rose.
Folly, white striped tyrian-pink.
Fountain, rose-pink with rose-red blotch.
Freedom, geranium-pink, shaded rose.
Frivolity, white, yellow blotch, red stripes.
Furbelow, white, sanded, striped or flaked red.
Gaiety, light rose-pink blotch rose-red.
Galathea, acajou-red, few dots on upper petals.
Galaxy, white sanded bright purple.
Gallant, creamy-white with red flakes.
Ganymede, pink, large. Late April.
Gawain, lavender with dark purple blotch.
Geisha, white, flaked and striped purple.
Glacier, white with a faint green tone.
Gladiator, nopal-red with darker red dots.
Glamour, brilliant rose-red, freely produced.
Gnome, white, green blotch, striped red.
Gracious, pink to rose, blotch rose.
Granat, bright red, blotch rose.
Grandam, white, sanded and striped purple.
Grandee, pink, blotch rose. Large. May.
Greeting, coral-rose, lobes ruffled.
Guerdon, purple, rose blotch, orange tube.
Gypsy, purple. Very striking. Large flowers.
Harlequin, white flaked and striped purple.
Helen Fox, red, margins irregularly white.
Helen Gunning, white center, pink margins.
Herald, white, magenta stripes and dots.
Hopeful, rose color. Late April early May.
Illusion, deep rose pink darker blotch. Starry.
Isolde, red with purple dots. Large. Early May.
Ivory, pure white, very large. Late April.
Jamboree, scarlet red, spreading. Late April.
Janet Noyes, rose with scarlet tube and throat.
Jeannin, deep rose-pink, pomegranate dots.
Jessica, deep rose-pink. Large. Late May.
Jingle, rose-red, freely produced. Mid-April.
Jongleur, deep rose-pink, undertone old rose.
Joya, very brilliant rose-pink.
Jubilant, striking salmon-pink color. Late April.
Jubilee, pink with few dots rose in blotch.
Kashmir, begonia-rose. Large. Mid-April.
Kathleen, rose colored flowers. Mid-May.
Katinka, rose-pink, lightly suffused orange.
Kenwood, deep tawny-rose. Late April.

GLENN DALE HYBRID AZALEAS—*Continued*

Killarney, white, chartreuse blotch purple flakes.
Kobold, reddish-purple. A very striking color.
Kohinoor, ruffled white, chartreuse blotch, few red stripes.
Ladylove, rose-pink, darker at margins.
Leonore, deep rose-pink to almost white.
Lilliemaude, clear tyrian-pink. Frilled.
Litany, deep lavender-pink. Late April.
Louise Dowdle, brilliant tyrian-pink. Large.
Lucette, tyrian-pink, slightly waved margins.
Lullaby, rose-doree, hose-in-hose. Late April.
Luminary, salmon, rose in throat, yellow base of tube.
Lustre, rose color. Early May. Spreading.
Lyric, white, chartreuse blotch, many clusters.
Madcap, white, flaked and striped red.
Madrigal, begonia-rose, covered with red.
Magic, rose-doree, tyrian-rose blotch.
Mandarin, geranium-pink, rose dots in blotch.
Manhattan, pink, large, freely produced.
Marjorie, rose with yellow tone at base.
Marmora, pure white, abundant. Mid-April.
Martha Hitchcock, white, margined magenta. Large.
Marvel, deep rose-pink, shaded rose. Mid-April.
Mary Helen, white with chartreuse blotch.
Mary Margaret, a glowing-orange. Mid-May.
Mascot, begonia-rose, vigorous. Mid-April.
Masquerade, white, sanded, flaked, striped pink.
Masterpiece, pink with rose blotch. Very large.
Matins, pale lavender. Mid-April.
Mavis, tyrian-pink, tube yellowish. Spreading.
Mayflower, La France-pink, hose-in-hose.
Megan, amaranth-pink. Mid to late May.
Melanie, rose-pink freely produced.
Memento, white, striped and flaked purple.
Merlin, rosy-lavender. Early to mid-May.
Meteor, purple with scarlet tube.
Minuet, white, flaked with magenta.
Modesty, rose, darker from center. Semidouble.
Moonbeam, white, frilled margins. Very large.
Morgana, large lavender flowers. Early May.
Mother of Pearl, white washed pink.
Motley, white, sanded and striped pink.
Nectar, rose-doree, paler at edges.
Nerissa, deep rose-pink, lighter to edges.
Niagara, white, with chartreuse blotch. Frilled.
Niphetos, white, green blotch, striped purple.
Nobility, purple, white margins, purple dots.
Nocturne, purple, blotch rose, tube scarlet.
Noreen, rose-pink, hose-in-hose. Anthers dark.
Novelty, white, with few purple stripes.
Omen, white, with chartreuse blotch. Mid-May.

GLENN DALE HYBRID AZALEAS—*Continued*

Opera, begonia-rose, with small carmine dots.
Oracle, deep rose-pink, rose dots in blotch.
Oriflamme, tyrian-rose, irregular white margin.
Orison, white, flaked and striped magenta.
Paladin, ruffled mallow-purple. Mid-May.
Paprika, white, with red flakes and stripes.
Parade, purple, rose blotch, scarlet tube. Frilled.
Paradise, rose-doree. Late April.
Pastel, white, striped pink. Hose-in-hose.
Patriot, white, green in blotch, striped purple.
Pearl Bradford, deep rose-pink. Large.
Peerless, brilliant geranium-pink, red blotch.
Peter Pan, rose-pink, almost white in center.
Phoebe, Jasper-pink, flushed old-rose.
Picador, orange-red with darker blotch.
Picotee, white center, purple edge.
Pilgrim, deep rose-pink, spreading.
Pink Star, begonia-rose. Large.
Pinocchio, white with stripes lacquer-red.
Pippin, pink to rose, base of tube almost white.
Pirate, a little lighter than scarlet-red.
Pixie, white, rayed pink, blotch red.
Polar Sea, frilled, white, chartreuse blotch.
Polonaise, white with magenta stripes.
Prelate, deep rose-pink with rose dots.
Presto, red, sanded and striped darker red.
Prodigal, white, sanded and striped purple.
Progress, mallow-purple, toward white at center.
Prosperity, purple, large. Freely produced.
Prudence, rose color flowers. Late April.
Puck, white, sanded, striped red, yellow blotch.
Quest, lavender-pink, large, prolific.
Radiance, deep rose-pink, rose blotch.
Red Bird, scarlet-red.
Red Hussar, rose, tube red.
Refrain, white, suffused pink, hose-in-hose.
Refulgence, rose color, yellow at base.
Regina, deep rose-pink. Large.
Remembrance, violet-rose with tiny rose dot.
Requiem, white chartreuse blotch, magenta stripes.
Revery, pale rose, freely produced.
Reward, lavender-pink, large. Mid-April.
Rhapsody, rose-pink, red blotch, frilled.
Rising Sun, dark pink with blotch, large.
Robinhood, deep rose-red, pistil scarlet.
Rogue, white, chartreuse blotch, purple flakes.
Rosalie, brilliant pink, large.
Rose Ash, geranium-pink, large. Late May.
Roselight, clear pink, large. Mid-April.
Rosette, red, large, double. Mid-April.

GLENN DALE HYBRID AZALEAS—*Continued*

Roundelay, white with few purple stripes.
Safrano, white with a touch of chartreuse.
Sagittarius, brilliant pink, salmon undertone.
Sambo, purple to brownish-red. Mid-May.
Samite, pure white. A very early bloomer.
Samson, rose with yellow undertone. Large.
Sappho, rose-purple with purplish blotch.
Sarabande, white center, edged purple.
Satin Robe, pink, hose-in-hose. Late April.
Satyr, white, purplish flakes, yellow blotch.
Scherzo, white with violet stripes. Late May.
Scholar, white, green blotch, lavender stripes.
Scout, pale rose-pink flowers freely produced.
Seafoam, white, frilled, yellow in throat.
Seashell, deep rose-pink, almost white at base.
Sebastian, rose, hose-in-hose. Early April.
Seneca, very large, purple, red marks, white base.
Sentinel, amaranth-pink with tyrian-rose.
Serenade, salmon-pink, blotch of tyrian-rose.
Serenity, rose-pink, large. Mid-April.
Shannon, pale orange. Flowers large.
Sheila, amaranth-purple to pink on margins.
Shimmer, white, sanded, striped and flaked rose.
Signal, rose, starry. Large. Mid-April.
Silver Lace, white, green blotch, purple stripes.
Silver Mist, white, sanded and flaked magenta.
Sligo, pale rose. Early to mid-April.
Snowclad, white, chartreuse blotch, ruffled.
Snowscape, greenish white. Late.
Snowwreath, pure white, chartreuse blotch.
Sonata, ruffled white, banded and striped purple.
Sorcerer, white, sanded and striped purple.
Souvenir, salmon-pink, hose-in-hose.
Sprite, mallow-pink, large. Mid-April.
Stampede, rose-doree, purple dots in blotch.
Sterling, deep rose-pink. Early June.
Susannah, white with broad purple edges.
Suwanee, rose-pink, large. Late April.
Swagger, white, sanded, striped red. Variable.
Swansong, white with yellow blotch. Large.
Swashbuckler, rose-doree, blotch red.
Taffeta, white, sanded and striped purple.
Talisman, white, sanded and striped red.
Tanager, brilliant red with red blotch.
Tango, pink with salmon shadings.
Tartar, red, hose-in-hose. Early. Freely produced
Templar, mallow-purple, white base tube.
Temptation, pink, darker at tip of petals.
Thisbe, geranium-pink, blotch begonia-pink.
Treasure, white.

GLENN DALE HYBRID AZALEAS—*Continued*

Trilby, amaranth-pink, large, late April.
Trinket, white with few pale pink flakes.
Tristan, rose with yellow undertone. Brilliant.
Trophy, pink, clear rose blotch. Large.
Trouper, nopal-red. Early to mid-April.
Twinkles, rose color, yellow suffusion at base.
Undine, white with green dots. Mid-May.
Ursula, La France-pink, darker at margins.
Valkyrie, self mallow-purple, deeper at edges.
Vanguard, white, yellow blotch, rose stripes.
Vanity, deep rose-pink, starry. Mid-season.
Velvet, very brilliant begonia-rose. Late April.
Vespers, white, chartreuse throat. Frilled. Large.
Vestal, white with chartreuse blotch.
Viking, light mallow-purple. A *poukhanese* hybrid.
Vintage, pale rosaline-purple. Late April.
Violetta, light mallow-purple. Mid-April.
Warrior, mallow-purple, blotch rose-red.
Wavelet, white with yellow blotch. Large.
Whimsical, white, very little chartreuse blotch.
Whirlwind, pale rose-pink, hose-in-hose.
Winedrop, white, sanded and striped purple.
Winner, pink, hose-in-hose. Late April.
Wisdom, pure white with chartreuse blotch.
Witchery, clear pink, large. Mid-April.
Yoeman, white, striped red. Large.
Youth, purple with very little dotting.

BELGIAN HYBRID AZALEAS

Brillanta, double; red.
Columbine, single; orange red.
Dr. Bergmann, semi-double; orange red.
Eric Schaeme, double; orange red.
Ernest Eeckhaute, double; red; frilled.
Etoile de Belgique, semi-double; red.
Gloire de Loochristi, double; orange red.
Hexe de Saffelaere, red; hose-in-hose; frilled.
Jubilee, double; red.
Mme. Chas. Vuylsteke, double; red; dense.
Mme. Petrick, double; red.
Mme. Petrick Alba, white mutant.
Mme. Petrick Superba, mutant, flaked.
Mons. Millaut, single; red.
Niobe, double; white, tinted chartreuse; frilled.
Perle de Swynaerde, double; white.
Rubis, semi-double; red.
Souvenir de Theophile Piens, double; orange red.
Vervaeneana, double; red. Color variations in mutants.

RUTHERFORD HYBRID AZALEAS

Alaska, white, chartreuse blotch.
Albion, semi-double; white.
Constance, single; violet red; frilled.
Dorothy Gish, orange-red; hose-in-hose.
Firelight, red; hose-in-hose.
L. J. Bobbink, reddish-violet; semi-double.
Mrs. A. W. Mueller, reddish-violet, red blotch.
Purity, single; white; hose-in-hose.
Rose Queen, double, rose with white throat; spreading.
Salmon Glow, red with darker blotch; hose-in-hose.
Snowbank, semi-double; white, chartreuse throat.

DAWSON HYBRID AZALEAS

Hazel Dawson, single; cyclamen-purple; large.
Helen Dawson, single; lilac-purple; large.

PERICAT HYBRID AZALEAS

Alphonse Pericat, red; hose-in-hose.
Anne Chenee, white, flushed violet.
Augusta Belle, white, flushed spinel-pink.
Dawn, violet-red, white center, darker blotch.
Emile Russave, red, darker blotch; frilled; semi-double.
Flanders Field, blood-red.
Fortune, red; semi-double.
Gardenia Supreme, white, chartreuse throat, violet-red blotch.
Gem, carmine-rose, darker blotch; hose-in-hose.
Gloriana, violet-red, darker blotch.
Glory, orange-red; semi-double; hose-in-hose.
Hampton Beauty, carmine-rose, darker blotch.
Hampton Rose, rose bengal, hose-in-hose.
Hiawatha, red.
Maiden's Blush, neyron rose.
Melody, claret-rose.
Orchid, rose bengal; semi-double.
Marjorie Ann, carmine.
Pride, claret-rose.
Princess Augusta, flushed neyron rose.
Sensation, violet-red.
Splendor, violet-red; semi-double.
Spring Dawn, white, faintly flushed pink; semi-double.
Sunset, delft rose; semi-double.
Sweetheart, delft rose; frilled.
Sweetheart Supreme, camellia-rose; semi-double.
Symphony, camellia-rose.
Twenty Grand, violet-red; semi-double.
Willie Belle Mayo, violet-red; frilled.

SANDER HYBRID AZALEAS

RHODODENDRON SANDERI = R. OBTUSUM FORMS × INDIAN AZALEAS

Alice Sargent, bright salmon rose.
Black Hawk, very deep scarlet.
Brookline, carmine.
Firefly (see Hexe).
Havemeyer, rose red.
Hebe, white, striped red.
Helena, rose pink.
Hermione, deep salmon red.
Hexe, crimson red, (h) (Syn: Firefly).
Hiawatha, salmon rose.
Hilda Hedlund, deep pink.
Holm Lea, crimson maroon.
Jupiter, fiery red.
Mars, intense scarlet.
Muriel, rose-red.
Natalie, salmon.
North Star, deep scarlet.
Rose Queen, deep rose.
Ruby, crimson maroon, richest red.
Suzuki, scarlet maroon.
Uncas, dark scarlet.
Venus, cerise.
Vivid, scarlet.
Vulcan, salmon-red.

INDIAN AZALEAS *

RHODODENDRON SIMSII HYBRIDS

Single Flowers

Antigone, white, striped and spotted violet.
Apollo, vermilion red.
Blushing Bride, pale rose. Large flowers.
Charmer, amaranth pink.
Comtesse de Beaufort, rose, blotched crimson.
Criterion, salmon pink, bordered white, blotched red.
Diamond, white, blotched crimson.
Duc de Nassau, rich rosy purple. Large flowers.
Easter Greetings, small crimson; sometimes semi-double.
Eclatante, deep crimson, tinged rose.
Emil Liebig, pink.
Fanny Ivery, salmon-scarlet, blotched purple.
Fielder's White, pure white; early.
Flambeau, crimson.
Fuerstin Bariatinsky, white, red stripes.
Haeren's Lorraine, bright pink. Small flowers.

* This is not a complete list of all the varieties, but represents some of the leading clones in use during recent years. See also the lists of Miscellaneous Non-Hybrid Azalea Clones.

INDIAN AZALEAS—*Continued*

Jean Vervaene, salmon, with white stripes and border.
John Gould Veitch, lilac rose, red stripes, white border.
La Victoire, reddish, light at edges, spotted dark red.
Louise Von Baden, pure white, sometimes speckled pink.
Mme. Charles Van Eeckhaute, white, crisped edges.
Mme. L. Van Houtte, scarlet rose, bordered white.
Marquis of Lorne, fine scarlet.
Miss E. Jarret, pure white, crisped edges.
Mrs. Turner, bright pink, bordered white, spotted red.
Mons. Thibaut, vermilion red.
Perle de la Belgique, large; white.
President Victor Van Den Hecke, white, crimson markings, yellow center.
Princess Alice, white; excellent.
Princesse Clementine, white, greenish yellow spots.
Professor Wolters, pink with darker blotch.
Reine des Pays-Bas, violet-rose, bordered white.
Roi de Hollande, dark red, spotted black.
Sigmund Rucker, rich rose, white border; showy.
Stella, scarlet, tinged rose.
Wilson Saunders, white, striped and blotched vivid red.

Double Flowers

Alice, deep rose, blotched vermilion.
Baron N. de Rothschild, large purple violet.
Bernard Andre, dark purple violet.
Bernard Andre Alba, white.
Borsig, pure white.
Charles Leirens, dark salmon, blotched purple.
Charles Pynaert, salmon, bordered white.
Chicago, deep carmine, bordered white.
Comtesse Eugenie de Kerchove, white, flaked red.
Deutsche Perle, early; white.
Dominique Vervaene, bright orange-red (1865).
Dr. Moore, deep rose, marked white and violet.
Eggebrechtii, bright crimson.
Empereur du Bresil (Emperor of Brazil), rose, red and white markings.
Empress of India, salmon rose, bordered white, spotted red.
Ernest Eeckhaute, deep carmine.
Francois de Vos, deep crimson.
Frau Herman Seidel, white, red stripes.
Fred Sanders, salmon pink.
Helene Thelemann, rosy pink.
Imbricata, white, sometimes flaked pink.
Imperitrice des Indes (see Empress of India).
Johanna Gottschalk, white.
John Haerens, carmine-rose; late (Jean Haerens).
John Llewelyn, soft pink.
Louise Pynaert, white.
Madeleine, large; white; semi-dbl.

INDIAN AZALEAS—*Continued*

Mme. Camille Van Langenhove, white, striped rose.
Mme. Iris Lefebvre, orange red, shaded purple, blotched brown.
Mme. Joseph Vervaene, large pink and white variegated.
Mme. Petrick, bright rose, almost cerise; compact.
Mme. Petrick Superba, light pink; large; compact.
Mme. Van der Cruyssen, pink; semi-double.
Mrs. Frederick Sanders, salmon pink; large; spreading habit.
Niobe, white, fine form.
Pharailde Mathilde, white, spotted red.
President Ghellinck de Walle, bright rose, upper lobe spotted yellow.
President Comte de Kerckhove, pink and white variegated (see following p. 142).
Raphael, white.
Sakuntala, white.
Simon Mardner, light pink, large fls.
Souvenir du Prince Albert, rose-peach, white margins.
Theodore Reimers, large; lilac.
Vervaeneana, fine rose-salmon, variegated, white margins.
Vervaeneana Alba, white; otherwise like the above.
Vuylstekeana, deep crimson; hose-in-hose.

CULTIVARS GROWN IN THE SOUTH

The following clonal varieties are commonly listed as "Indian Azaleas" and are cultivated in the southeastern United States, from Charleston southward to Florida and the Gulf of Mexico. Some of the varieties are old-fashioned sorts which have been out of commerce for many years and have recently been re-introduced. Others are seedlings of recent introduction. The origin of many is not clear, and some, notably those in the orange-red class, are obviously confused with varieties of *Kaempferi* and *calendulaceum* extraction. The author presents the list with the explanation that further study is needed before these varieties are accepted as "Indian Azaleas." For fuller descriptions of many, see Hume (1931), "Azaleas and Camellias."

Lilac or Purple

Concinna, rosy lilac, mid-season, strong grower.
Formosa, mallow purple, early, robust, best of its color—*R. pulchrum* hybrid.
Phoenicea, a clone of *R. pulchrum*.
Rosea Purpurea, dark rosy purple, mid-season.
Voilacea Rubra, dark violet purple, crenate margins.

Orange-Red

Aurantiaca Splendida, scarlet, late, very dwarf.
Coccinea Major, probably a derivative of *R. calendulaceum*.
Daphne Red, orange-red, with purple spots.
Glory of Sunninghill (Gloriosa), orange-scarlet.
Moss Point Red.
Pluto, orange-scarlet, late, dwarf.
President Claeys, orange-red, purple spot, early.

INDIAN AZALEAS—*Continued*

Prince of Orange, a derivative of *R. Kaempferi.*
Rosaeflora (synonym of Balsaminaeflora).

Rose or Pink

Brilliant, deep rose pink.
Croemina, violet pink, mid-season.
Elegans Superba, deep rose pink; syn. Pride of Mobile, watermelon pink.
George Franc, pink with dark blotch.
Harry Veitch, light pink, crisped petals, bushy.
Miltonii, pink, rounded petals, dwarfish.
Model de Marc, rosy pink, late, medium size.
Perfection, large light rose.
Praestantissima, deep rose pink.
Pride of Dorking, deep carmine, late.
Pride of Mobile (see Elegans Superba), an old-time variety of great merit.
Prince of Wales, rose red, upright, early.
Reine des Roses, large bright rose fls.
Rosea Elegans, clear light pink.
Watermelon Pink (see Elegans Superba).

Salmon

Cavendishiana, large, very late.
Comte de Thole, large, tall, early.
Daphne Salmon, pleasing salmon, mid-season.
Duc de Rohan, fine salmon, free flowering.
Duke of Wellington, rosy salmon, dark center.
Frederick the Great, low, late, floriferous.
Madame Frey, medium, late, rosy salmon.
President, salmon pink with dark throat.
Symmetry, large; tall; early.
Vicomte de Neuport, large flowered; dwarf.
Wm. Bull, open-branched picturesque habit; small dbl. fls.; late.

White

A. Borsig, double; white; late; dwarf.
Alba Maculata, large; white; late; medium height.
Flag of Truce, double; white.
Laterita Alba, compact; white; late.

Variegated

Alba Multiflora, white with lilac markings; late.
Alba Punctata, white, striped pink; dwarf.
Anthenon, rose-pink centers and light edges; sport of Iveryana.
Iveryana, fine large white with faint rose stripes; compact.
Louise Margottin, white, striped pink; late.
Perfection de Rentz, white, striped pink; late.
Vittata Fortunei (Vittata Punctata), white and lavender; long season.

MISCELLANEOUS NON-HYBRID AZALEA CLONES *

Clones of *Rhododendron indicum*

Balsaminaeflorum, dbl., salmon-red; needs light soil.
Beni Kirishima, large flowered pink.
Charles Encke, light pink.
Criterion, variegated pink and white; form of Variegata.
Iveryana, variegated pink and white; form of Variegata.
Kinnozai, similar to Balsaminaeflorum but less dbl.
Laciniatum (Shide-Satsuki), laciniate corolla.
Mrs. Carmichael, pink.
Macrantha (Macranthum), synonym for *R. indicum;* perhaps a clone.
Osakazuki, rose pink; large flowered.
Polypetalum, petaloid calyx and no corolla; abnormal.
Satsuki No. 77087, pink, dark blotch.
Satsuki No. 77104, large pink flowers.
Satsuki No. 77145, few large pink flowers; good ground-cover.
Tama-No-Ito, light rosaline purple.
Variegata (Matsushima), white and red striped form of *R. indicum.*
Waraigishi, deep rose; erect habit.
Yozakura, large rose-purple flowers; plant like a Kurume azalea.

Clones of *Rhododendron macrosepalum*

Dianthiflorum, double; purple.
Hanaguruma (see Oyeyama).
Kocho-Zoroi (see Rhodoroides).
Linearifolium (*R. linearifolium*), monstrous form with lance-shaped petals.
Oyeyama, rose-purple; deeply cleft corolla.
Rhodoroides, greenish white, tinged rose; smallish.
Seikan (see Rhodoroides).

Clones of *Rhododendron mucronatum*

Amethystinum, white, delicately flushed lilac, few faint spots (Syn: *A. japonica alba*).
Damask Rose (see Sekidera).
Fujimanyo, double; rose-purple (*R. mucronatum* f. *plenum*).
Gulf Pride, light purple.
Indica Alba (Ledifolia), *R. mucronatum* type species.
Indica Rosea (see Sekidera).
Mattapan (Syn: America), white, yellowish blotch, fringed.
Narcissiflorum (Shiro Manyo), double; white.
Noordtianum, large white (Liukiu Azalea).
Sekidera, white, spotted crimson rose (similar and possibly inferior clones are known as Damask Rose, Magnifica and Indica Rosea).
Viola, violet mauve form of Sekidera.

Clones of *Rhododendron poukhanense*

Yodogawa (*R. yedoense* Maxim), double lilac.

* Reprinted without change from first edition (1936).

MISCELLANEOUS NON-HYBRID AZALEA CLONES—*Continued*

Clones of *Rhododendron pulchrum*

Maxwellii, carmine red (Aka-Yodogawa); large fls.
Omurasaki, rose-purple, spotted crimson; large fls.
Semiduplex, semi-double (*R. pulchrum semiduplex*).
Smithii, purple (*R. pulchrum Smithii*).
Splendens, purple (*R. pulchrum splendens*).
Tebotan, double fls. with green leaves in center.

Clones of *Rhododendron Kaempferi*

Cryptopetalum (Kinshibe), abortive corolla; no garden value.
Komatsui, petaloid calyx; hose-in-hose flowers.
Mikado.
Monstrosum, white; hose-in-hose; abnormal pistil.
Plenum, double; small; salmon-red flowers.
Prince of Orange.

PART III

SPECIAL LISTS, KEYS, REFERENCES AND CHARTS

CHAPTER XXIV

SELECTIONS FOR SPECIAL AREAS AND PURPOSES

SELECTED CLONES AND SPECIES ORDINARILY AVAILABLE AND WORTH TRYING IN CERTAIN GEOGRAPHICAL REGIONS

New England, New York State and the Interior Northeastern States

Rhododendrons *

ABRAHAM LINCOLN

ALBUM ELEGANS **X**

ALBUM GRANDIFLORUM **X**

ARBUTIFOLIUM (*R. ferrugineum × minus*)

ATROSANGUINEUM **X**

BOULE DE NEIGE

CARACTACUS

CATAWBIENSE ALBUM **X**

CHARLES DICKENS **X**

DELICATISSIMUM

EVERESTIANUM **X**

HENRIETTA SARGENT **X**

LA BAR'S WHITE

LADY ARMSTRONG **X**

MRS. CHARLES S. SARGENT **X**

MYRTIFOLIUM (*R. hirsutum × minus*)

PURPUREUM ELEGANS **X**

PURPUREUM GRANDIFLORUM **X**

ROSEUM ELEGANS **X**

WILSONII (syn. LAETEVIRENS)

R. brachycarpum
R. carolinianum
R. carolinianum var. *album*
R. Degronianum (?)
R. catawbiense
R. lapponicum (?)

R. maximum
R. micranthum
R. minus
R. racemosum
R. Smirnowii
Selected clones of Fortunei series

Azaleas

BOUQUET DE FLORE

COCCINEA SPECIOSA

DAVIESII

DULCINEE

FANNY (syn. PUCELLE)

GLORIA MUNDI

KNAP HILL HYBRIDS (?) †

IGNEA NOVA

LOUISA HUNNEWELL

NANCY WATERER

NARCISSIFLORA

PALLAS

SANG DE GENTBRUGGE

UNIQUE

WHITE FIND (*Vaseyi* clone)

* E. H. Wilson's "best dozen" clones for New England are indicated here by **X** marks.

† Includes Improved Knap Hill Hybrids known also as Exbury and Goldsworth Hybrid Azaleas. To be accepted experimentally at present.

R. *arborescens*
R. *atlanticum*
R. *Bakeri* (syn. cumberlandense)
R. *calendulaceum*
R. *canadense*
R. *japonicum*
R. *Kaempferi* (to 10° below zero)
Mollis hybrids or seedlings

R. *mucronulatum*
R. *nudiflorum*
R. *poukhanense*
R. *roseum*
R. *Schlippenbachii*
R. *Vaseyi*
R. *viscosum*

*Metropolitan New York, Cape Cod, Long Island, New Jersey, Philadelphia
and elsewhere along the Atlantic Coast where boxwood grows outdoors* (light
protection being required in exposed sites)

All clones and species listed above, plus the following:

Rhododendrons

AMERICA
CHARLES BAGLEY
DR. H. C. DRESSELHUYS
DR. V. H. RUTGERS
DEXTER HYBRIDS in variety
EDWARD S. RAND
F. D. GODMAN
FASTUOSUM FLORE PLENO
GENERAL GRANT
GIGANTEUM
HERBERT PARSONS
INGATIUS SARGENT

J. H. VAN NES
KETTLEDRUM
LEE'S DARK PURPLE
MEADOWBROOK
MRS. P. DEN OUDEN
MUM
PARSONS GLORIOSA
PARSONS GRANDIFLORA
PRESIDENT LINCOLN
PURPLE SPLENDOUR
ROSEUM SUPERBUM
SEFTON

Also the following less common or old clones:

ALBUM NOVUM
AMPHION (syn. F. L. AMES)
CUNNINGHAM'S WHITE
FLUSHING
GOMER WATERER
GUYENCOURT HYBRIDS
KATE WATERER
LADY CLERMONT
LADY GREY EDGERTON
LORD ROBERTS

MADAME DE BRUIN
MADAME MASSON
MIDSUMMER
MRS. R. S. HOLFORD
NOVA ZEMBLA
OLD PORT
PRINCE CAMILLE DE ROHAN
PROF. F. BETTEX
ROSLYN
VAN WEERDEN POELMAN

Most of the following species need some protection:

R. *auriculatum*
R. *decorum*
R. *discolor*
R. *Fargesii*
R. *ferrugineum*
R. *Fortunei* (hardy clones)

R. *hippophaeoides*
R. *impeditum*
R. *Keiskei*
R. *racemosum*
R. *russatum* (experiment only)
R. *Williamsianum* (experiment only)

Also the following, for very sheltered positions, usually near the sea, are suggested for experiment only:

BLUE PETER

BOWBELLS

BRITANNIA

CYNTHIA

DUKE OF YORK

GOLDSWORTH YELLOW

JEAN MARY MONTAGUE

LADY CLEMENTINE MITFORD

MRS. CHARLES E. PEARSON

MRS. FURNIVALL

PINK PEARL

PURPLE SPLENDOUR

TEMPLE BELLE

Azaleas

AMOENUM

GABLE HYBRIDS

GHENT HYBRIDS (own roots)

GLENN DALE HYBRIDS in part

HINODEGIRI

J. T. LOVETT

KAEMPFERI HYBRIDS

KNAP HILL (EXBURY & GOLDSWORTH) HYBRIDS

KURUME AZALEAS in part (protect)

MAXWELLII (protect)

MOLLIS HYBRIDS (own root)

MUCRONATUM (syn. LEDIFOLIA ALBA)

VUYK HYBRIDS

YODOGAWA (syn. yedoense)

R. Kaempferi

R. luteum (syn. flavum)

R. macrosepalum

R. mucronatum (syn. *indica alba*)

Delaware, Maryland, Virginia and the Southern Highlands

Most of the rhododendrons and azaleas previously listed, except *R. Albrechtii*, *R. canadense* and *grafted* plants of Ghent and Mollis azaleas. Also the following are suggested for trial in these areas; some of them are already growing somewhere in the region:

Rhododendrons

BAS DE BRUIN

BIANCHI

BETTY WORMALD

CHINTZ

CUNNINGHAM'S SULPHUR

DONCASTER

DR. ARNOLD W. ENDTZ

EARL OF ATHLONE

ELIZABETH

GARIBALDI

KLUIS SENSATION

KLUIS TRIUMPH

LADY ANNETTE DE TRAFFORD

MARS

MOSER'S MAROON

MRS. P. D. WILLIAMS

MRS. R. S. HOLFORD

MRS. W. C. SLOCOCK

SAPPHO

SCANDINAVIA

THE BRIDE

THUNDERSTORM

UNIQUE

Azaleas

All of the preceding azaleas, except *R. Albrechtii* and *R. canadense,* also these:

GLENN DALE HYBRIDS (all)

HEXE

KURUME AZALEAS (all)

MAXWELLII

OMURASAKI

PERICAT HYBRIDS

SATSUKI AZALEAS (general)

TEBOTAN

R. alabamense

R. austrinum

R. canescens

R. indicum

R. Mariesii

R. molle

R. Oldhamii

R. prunifolium

R. serpyllifolium album

R. serrulatum

R. Simsii in its clones

R. speciosum

R. Weyrichii

Atlantic Coastal Regions of the Carolinas, Georgia, Florida and the Lower South and Gulf Coast

R. Chapmanii is the only true rhododendron presently suggested.

Azaleas

Native species of the Lower South, including *R. canescens, R. serrulatum* and *R. speciosum.* "Indian" azaleas, including clones of *R. Simsii, R. phoeniceum* and forms such as 'Formosa,' as well as 'Kurume Azaleas' and other azaleas of the Obtusum series.

Midwestern United States (St. Louis, Mo.)

Mostly the "ironclad" rhododendrons recommended for New England, plus the native American azalea species, a few Ghent and Mollis hybrids and certain Kurume azaleas, such as 'Snow,' 'Hinodegiri' and 'Hinemayo.'

The American West Coast: Washington, Oregon and Adjacent Areas

Along the Pacific Coast, from San Francisco northward to British Columbia, nearly all the species and hybrids grown in Great Britain will flourish. Most kinds that have a hardiness rating of A, B, or C from the Royal Horticultural Society are suitable for the northern part of this range, while many of the Burmese sorts and others that cannot endure more than a few degrees of frost appear happy in the San Francisco Bay area and in northern California. Southern California is generally too arid for them.

It is only within comparatively recent years that extensive growing of exotic species and hybrids has been taking place. While the British ratings furnish a fair guide to the behavior of the plants generally, these should not be regarded as parallel. Very recently, unusual cold and exceptional winter weather has made it necessary to reappraise former hardiness records for rhododendrons and azaleas grown in Washington and Oregon, and it is scarcely possible to regard existing ratings as final. Accordingly, precise recommendations are not attempted in this work, and readers are referred to present and future publications of the American Rhododendron Society for up-to-date information.

In the list of hybrids, current British and American hardiness ratings tend to coincide rather well, while in the lists of species some sharp differences exist, but in no consistent direction. It has seemed wise in the present work to retain the British hardiness ratings, but only for the sake of comparing one kind against another, since the growing of large collections in one location, as is done in Britain, offers a more accurate basis for comparison than do the smaller and more scattered collections in America.

As for merit ratings, these in both instances are colored by personal tastes and climatic divergencies and hence should not be given too much weight. Generally, however, agreement is reached regarding the very finest clones and species. In view of the fact that approximately the same sorts can be grown both in Britain and on the American West Coast, and that these involve nearly all the good horticultural kinds, the general catalogue of species and clones presented elsewhere in this work is considered adequate without the addition of a full special listing here. For ready reference, however, we are inserting a concise list of hybrid clones of A, B and C hardiness having the highest merit ratings in the current handbook of the Royal Horticultural Society, for the benefit of readers in both lands.

RHODODENDRONS OF HIGH MERIT AND A, B OR C HARDINESS
(BRITISH)

BEAUTY OF LITTLEWORTH	LODER'S WHITE
BLUE DIAMOND	MARILOO
BRITANNIA	MAY DAY
CORONA	MRS. CHARLES E. PEARSON
ELIZABETH	MRS. FURNIVALL
GLADYS	MRS. PHILIP MARTINEAU
LADY BESSBOROUGH	PENJERRICK
LADY CHAMBERLAIN	POLAR BEAR
LADY ROSEBERRY	PURPLE SPLENDOUR
LETTY EDWARDS	SIR J. RAMSDEN
LODERI KING GEORGE	SUSAN

OTHER POPULAR SORTS

AZOR	MATADOR
BETTY WORMALD	MOSER'S MAROON
BLUE TIT	MRS. ASHLEY SLOCOCK
CYNTHIA	MRS. P. D. WILLIAMS
EARL OF ATHLONE	ROMANY CHAL
FABIA A. M.	SAPPHO
FAGGETTER'S FAVORITE	TALLY HO (rating D)
FASTUOSUM FLORE PLENO	TEMPLE BELLE
FIRE BIRD	THUNDERSTORM
GLORY OF LITTLEWORTH (Azaleodendron)	UNIQUE
IDEALIST	VULCAN
MARS	

SOME BRITISH CHOICES

Except for fanciers and those who live in the exceptional climates of Cornwall and "tropical" West Scotland, the British consensus is perhaps best expressed in the foregoing R.H.S. lists of high-rating rhododendrons. British authorities, however, differ markedly in points of taste in picking out their favorite kinds. Frederick Street, who favors hybrids over species, chooses clones both old and new, such as 'Garibaldi,' 'Kluis Sensation,' 'Bianchi,' 'Everestianum,' 'Purple Splendour,' and 'Goldsworth Yellow.' F. Kingdon Ward, on the other hand, prefers species, although he lists some hybrids, too. E.H.M. and Peter Cox offer a well-balanced series of lists covering both species and hybrids, set up for various places and purposes, as moist, dry, cool, warm, large, small or sheltered sites, and give selections of dwarf kinds, tall kinds, etc., for such places. Other writers have still different inclinations. It is well that they do not all agree, yet most seem to concur in a common feeling that the following popular and available clones should be on a preferred list:

BETTY WORMALD	LODERI clones
BRITANNIA	MRS. FURNIVALL
CHRISTMAS CHEER	PINK PEARL
GOLDSWORTH YELLOW	PURPLE SPLENDOUR

FLORISTS' PLANTS FOR FORCING

INDIAN AZALEAS—EARLY FLOWERING SORTS

× *Rhododendron Simsii*

MADAME PETRICK. Double, bright rose pink, beautiful flowers. Habit compact.

MADAME PETRICK SUPERBA. Double, large, light pink, compact.

MRS. FREDERICK SANDERS. Double, large, salmon-pink flowers. Large foliage with a spreading habit.

PRESIDENT OSWALD DE KERCHOVE. Double, bright pink, bordered white, blotched carmine.

SIMON MARDNER. Double, large, light pink.

VERVAENEANA. Double, rose, bordered white, striped salmon. One of the most popular forcing varieties. Foliage good. Flowers very double.

VERVAENEANA ALBA. Double, white, but otherwise resembling Vervaeneana.

INDIAN AZALEAS—LATER FLOWERING SORTS

× *Rhododendron Simsii*

BLUSHING BRIDE (Syn: Daybreak, Lady Roosevelt). Double, large soft pink.

EMPRESS OF INDIA. Double, salmon-rose, suffused with white and carmine.

JEAN HAERENS. Very double, carmine-rose.

MADAME VAN DER CRUYSSEN. Semi-double, carmine-rose. Somewhat smaller.

PROFESSOR WOLTERS. Single, pink with darker center, fringed petals.

SANDER AZALEAS OR "BABY INDICAS"

(RHODODENDRON SANDERI = INDIAN AZALEAS × OBTUSUM VARIETIES)

BLACK HAWK. Deep scarlet.

HEXE (Syn: Firefly). Rich red, hose-in-hose flowers. A compact grower and one of the most popular for forcing at the present time. Not one of Sander's hybrids, but belonging in this general class.

HIAWATHA. Salmon-rose.

LORRAINE. Semi-double, deep rose. A sport of Hexe.

NORTH STAR. Deep scarlet.

RUBY. Crimson maroon, very rich. An original Sander production.

UNCAS. Dark scarlet. Also produced by Sander.

VUYLESTEKEANA. Hose-in-hose, deep crimson.

KURUME AZALEAS

(*Rhododendron obtusum*)

BRIDESMAID. Bright salmon-pink with prominent stamens; large clusters.

CHERRY BLOSSOM (Syn. Takasago). Large, light pink flowers, white toward the center.

CHRISTMAS CHEER. Brilliant red with glossy foliage. Slow growing, compact.

CORAL BELLS. Shell pink, deeper in the center; dainty. Compact grower.

HINODEGIRI. Bright crimson, almost scarlet.

PINK PEARL. Salmon-rose with light centers, large trusses. This is not the well-known evergreen rhododendron by the same name, often forced.

SALMON BEAUTY. Salmon-rose with large flowers. Slow, compact grower.

SNOW. White flowers on a compact growing plant. Very free flowering.

GROOTENDORST'S LIST OF RHODODENDRONS FOR FORCING

Excellent for forcing	*Early, Medium or Late*
BLUE PETER, pale lavender, dark blotch	E
CATAWBIENSE BOURSAULT, lilac, tinged rose	M
CATAWBIENSE GRANDIFLORUM, lilac	M–L
CHEVALIER FELIX DE SAUVAGE, light red, dark blotch, fringed	E
DR. ARNOLD W. ENDTZ, carmine, tinted lilac, fringed	M
HOLLANDIA, carmine	M
PETER KOSTER, bright magenta-red, edged lighter	E–M
SOUVENIR DE DR. S. ENDTZ, deep pink	M

	Early, Medium or Late
Very good for forcing	
EL ALAMEIN, deep red	M–L
ENGLISH ROSEUM, rose, tinted lilac	M
IRENE, pink	M
KLUIS SENSATION, bright scarlet, vermilion glow, dark blotch	L
LOUIS PASTEUR, light red, pink center	L
MADAME DE BRUIN, bright red	M–L
MARCEL MOSER, bright red	M
MARINUS KOSTER, deep pink, shaded to lighter pink	M
MAX SYE, dark red, black blotch	vE
PINK PEARL, light pink	M
QUEEN MARY, deep pink	E
RED EAGLE, deep scarlet	M
SCHUBERT, light orchid, fringed	E
SOUVENIR DE D. A. KOSTER, dark scarlet	M
WILGEN'S RUBY, bright deep red	E–M

Good for forcing	
ALICE, pink	E–M
ANTOON VAN WELIE, bright deep pink	L
BAGSHOT RUBY, bright red	M
BRITANNIA, bright scarlet	M
CATAWBIENSE ALBUM, white	L
CATHERINE VAN TOL, carmine rose	M–L
CYNTHIA, light carmine red	E
DONCASTER, scarlet-crimson	M
EVERESTIANUM, lilac	M
GOMER WATERER, white, blushed	L
JOHN WALTER, crimson	M
KATE WATERER, pink, yellow blotch	L
LEE'S DARK PURPLE, deep purple	L
MADAME JEANNE FRETS, rose, red blotch	E
MARION, deep pink	M
MARS, dark true red	M
MRS. CHARLES E. PEARSON, pale mauve, brown spots	M
MRS. E. C. STIRLING, blush pink, fringed	M
PELOPIDAS, light red	M
PINK PERFECTION, light pink, tinged lilac	M
PRINCE CAMILLE DE ROHAN, light pink, dark red blotch	E
PROF. HUGO DEVRIES, pink	M
PROF. J. H. ZAAYER, bright light red	M
PURPLE SPLENDOUR, deep purple, black blotch	M
ROSEUM ELEGANS, rose-lilac	M
VAN WEERDEN POELMAN, crimson red	M

BELGIAN, RUTHERFORD, DAWSON AND PERICAT HYBRID AZALEAS

Lists of these will be found in the notes on available clones, Chapter XXIII, pages 435–436.

CHAPTER XXV

KEYS

I. A KEY TO THE CULTIVATED AZALEA SPECIES

AZALEA SERIES

a. Flowers and leaves from same bud; flowers never yellow; corolla smooth outside, 5 to 10 stamens; species exclusively Asiatic.
   b. Leaves never in whorls; persistent and frequently dimorphic *; appressed hairs on branchlets ....Subser. *Obtusum*.
   bb. Leaves in whorls.
     c. Leaves deciduous, in whorls of 2–5; corolla rotate-funnelform, 5–10 stamens
                                   Subser. *Schlippenbachii*.
     cc. Leaves persistent, in whorls of 2–3; corolla campanulate, 10 or 12 stamens
                                     Subser. *Tashiroi*.
aa. Flowers from separate terminal buds, leaves and branchlets from separate lateral buds below.
   b. Stamens 5; flowers often yellow or yellow-blotched; corolla funnelform
                                     Subser. *Luteum*.
   bb. Stamens more than 5; flowers never yellow.
     c. Corolla rotate-campanulate, deeply lobed...Subser. *Canadense*.
     cc. Corolla tubular-campanulate, lobes short; 10 stamens.......................Subser. *Nipponicum*.

SUBSERIES OBTUSUM
(SECT. TSUTSUTSI, G. DON)

a. Diameter of flowers ¾ in. to 2 in., corolla funnelform-campanulate.
   b. Style smooth (glabrous).
     c. 5 stamens (except in *R. tosaense* and some forms of *R. obtusum*).
       d. Leaves narrowly lance-shaped, ½ to 1½ in. long, persistent.
         e. Leaves slightly saw-toothed (crenate-serrulate); flowers rose to red, more than 1 in. across ....*R. indicum*.
         ee. Leaves entire; flowers lilac; 5–10 stamens...*R. tosaense*.
       dd. Leaves more oval than lance-shaped; over ½ in. long.
         e. Bud scales not sticky (non-viscid) ; leaves dimorphic.
           f. Plant loosely branched, above 3 ft. tall, usually deciduous.................*R. Kaempferi*.

---

* In azaleas, the term "dimorphic leaves" refers to the two forms of leaves with which certain species are equipped. The leaves which ordinarily develop in early spring are known as the "spring leaves" and persist during the summer, but fall in autumn. They are usually somewhat larger than the "summer leaves" which develop later in the season and persist all winter, in most species, not falling from the plant until the next season's spring leaves unfold.

    ff. Plant compact, dwarfish, less than 3 ft. tall, usually semi-evergreen, with dimorphic leaves ....*R. obtusum.*
  ee. Bud scales sticky (viscid).
    f. Leaves deciduous, 1–2½ in. long; dimorphic; ovary glandular-bristly
                                B. linearifolium var. *macrosepalum.*
    ff. Leaves persistent, 2–3½ in. long; ovary with reddish brown bristles, glandless
                                        R. rivulare.
  dd. Leaves small, oval, less than ½ in. long..................................*R. serpyllifolium.*
cc. 7 to 10 stamens.
  d. Leaves conspicuously dimorphic; many appressed hairs on shoots.
    e. Usually deciduous; corolla, lilac or magenta..................*R. poukhanense.*
    ee. Leaves persistent; tender or half-hardy.
      f. Flowers scarlet to rose red; calyx lobes oval; leaves very slightly saw-toothed
                                      R. scabrum.
      ff. Flowers rose-purple and magenta; calyx lobes lance-shaped; leaves entire
                                      R. pulchrum.
      fff. Flowers white; calyx lobes minute................................*R. boninense.*
  dd. Leaves not conspicuously dimorphic; persistent.
    e. Leaves oval or elliptic, not narrow.
      f. With many appressed, flattened hairs on shoots.
        g. Stamens as long or longer than corolla.
          h. Flowers about 1½ to 2 in. across.....................................*R. Simsii.*
          hh. Flowers less than 1 in. across; short tube..................*R. boninense.*
        gg. Stamens shorter than corolla.
          h. Flowers less than 1 in. long...*R. Nakaharai.*
          hh. Flowers more than 1 in. long; appressed hairs on both sides of leaves
                                       R. longiperulatum.
      ff. With a few appressed hairs and more spreading or glandular hairs on the shoots.
        g. Corolla 1½ to 2 in. long.
          h. Flowers white or purple; ordinarily 3–6 ft. tall; fairly hardy
                                       R. mucronatum.
          hh. Flowers red; leaves and shoots with red-brown glandular hairs; to 10 ft. tall; tender ....*R. Oldhamii.*
        gg. Corolla only ¾ in. long, red; no glandular hairs..................*R. rufo-hirtum.*
    ee. Leaves narrowly lance-shaped.
      f. Flowers about 1¾ in. long..*R. annamense.*
      ff. Flowers about 1¼ in. long..*R. hainanense.*
bb. Style hairy at base.
  c. 5 stamens (both species imperfectly known and not yet in cultivation).
    d. Style hairy below the middle..*R. Sasakii.*
    dd. Style hairy only at extreme base..................................*R. breviperulatum.*
  cc. 7 to 10 stamens.
    d. Leaves obovate, conspicuously dimorphic..................*R. lasiostylum.*
    dd. Leaves persistent, not dimorphic, not obovate.
      e. Leaves oval or elliptic, entire.
        f. Flowers lilac or magenta..*R. subsessile.*
        ff. Flowers pink ....*R. rubropilosum.*
      ee. Leaves narrowly lance-shaped, slightly saw-toothed..................*R. Kanehirai.*
aa. Diameter of flowers ¾ in. or less.
  b. Style and corolla smooth.
    c. 5 stamens (sometimes 4).
      d. Leaves deciduous; flowers ⅝ in. across, white..................*R. Tschonoskii.*
      dd. Leaves persistent.
        e. Corolla rose-purple to white; flowers ½ to ¾ in. across; leaves ⅕ to 1½ in. long
                                       R. microphyton.
        ee. Corolla lilac, ¾ in. across; leaves 1¼ to 3½ in. long..................*R. Mariae.*
  bb. Style with soft hairs at base, corolla bristly outside.
    c. Leaves 2½ in. long; corolla white to rose, ⅗ in. across..................*R. Seniavinii.*

Subseries Schlippenbachii
(sect. sciadorhodion rehd. & wils.)

a. Leaves broadest at or above the middle.
  b. Leaves obovate (inverted egg-shaped), sometimes broadly elliptic, in whorls of 4 or 5 at the ends of branchlets; stamens 10, unequal.
    c. Leaves 2 to 4 in. long, broadly obovate; flowers usually shell pink, style smooth
                                                                 R. Schlippenbachii.
    cc. Leaves 1 to 2 in. long; flowers white, style glandular; leaves in whorls of 5
                                                                 R. quinquefolium.
  bb. Leaves rhombic; fruit cylindric.
    c. Flowers almost brick red, stamens 6 to 10, corolla rotate-funnelform........*R. Weyrichii.*
    cc. Flowers rose-purple to magenta, stamens 5 to 10, unequal, corolla rotate-campanulate
                                                                 R. reticulatum.
aa. Leaves broadest below the middle; stamens 8 to 10, nearly equal.
  b. Flowers pale lilac, stamens shorter than corolla; leaves ovate 1–1¼ in. long, on very short (1/12 in.) petioles..*R. Farrerae.*
  bb. Flowers rose purple, stamens as long as corolla; leaves 1½–3 in. long and manifestly petioled ....*R. Mariesii.*

Subseries Tashiroi

Leaves persistent, in whorls of 2–3; branchlets with appressed flattened hairs; flowers and leafy branchlets from the same terminal winter floral buds; corolla campanulate, stamens 10 or 12; flowers pale rose-purple, spotted with maroon; 1 species only................................*R. Tashiroi.*

Subseries Luteum
(sect. pentanthera g. don)

a. Flowers yellow, orange or vermilion, or conspicuously blotched with yellow or orange on the upper lobe.
  b. Corolla large and wide-funnelform, 2–2½ in. across, with gradually expanding tube (type No. 44), blotch divided into dots.
    c. Leaves without hairs beneath, except on the veins; winter buds without hairs (glabrous); stamens sometimes shorter than the corolla; hardy outdoors at Boston or its equivalent; flowers of typical form orange or apricot........................*R. japonicum.*
    cc. Leaves soft pubescent (downy) beneath; winter buds pubescent; smaller and less bristly calyx than R. japonicum; stamens as long as the corolla; not hardy outdoors at Boston or its equivalent (except in hybrid varieties); flowers more often yellowish than orange ....*R. molle.*
  bb. Corolla smaller, funnelform with cylindric tube, not more than 2 in. across, more abruptly expanding (types No. 41 and No. 42); blotch not divided into dots.
    c. Flowers white (or sometimes pinkish) with prominent yellow blotch, up to 2 in. across, bearing fine glands on the outside; leaves without hair, except on the midrib
                                                                 R. occidentale.
    cc. Flowers orange, or sometimes lemon or scarlet or intermediate shades between yellow, orange and red.
      d. Flowers appearing as the leaves unfold or later; scales of the winter buds smooth on the back.
        e. Corolla tube glandular on the outside, as long as the lobes or shorter; yellow, orange or scarlet.
          f. Blooms midseason; tetraploid....................................*R. calendulaceum.*
          ff. Blooms at least two weeks later than above; diploids; fls. usually in round trusses, often deep orange to deep vermilion ....*R. Bakeri.*
        ee. Corolla tube pubescent on the outside, not glandular, longer than the lobes; scarlet or orange-red.. *R. speciosum.*

dd. Flowers appearing before the leaves unfold; scales of the winter buds pubescent on the back; corolla tube longer than the lobes (type No. 41).

 e. Leaves almost smooth beneath, glandular while young; winter buds sticky; corolla yellow, 1¾ to 2 in. across; flowers very fragrant; native of Europe
R. luteum.

 ee. Leaves downy beneath, not glandular; corolla yellow and orange, with purplish or striped tube sometimes; flowers about 1½ in. across; scarcely fragrant; Florida ....*R. austrinum.*

aa. Flowers white, pink to deep rose or crimson, without large yellow blotch but sometimes having two smaller yellow blotches.

 b. Flowers appearing before or as the leaves unfold.

  c. Shrubs usually upright and more than 2 or 3 ft. tall, much branched.

   d. Corolla tube distinctly longer than the lobes (type No. 41), southern plants.

    e. Winter buds pubescent; corolla pinkish, sometimes almost white, with a very slender tube which is abruptly expanded into the limb; not fragrant
R. canescens.

    ee. Winter buds smooth; corolla white, more gradually expanded tube
R. alabamense.

   dd. Corolla tube about as long as the lobes (type No. 42); northern plants primarily.

    e. Scarcely fragrant with insipid sweet odor, not spicy: leaves smoothish and green beneath, not pubescent; flowers generally impure pink, often whitish, with dark carmine at base of tube; tube not so gradually expanded as in *R. roseum*
R. nudiflorum.

    ee. Very fragrant with spicy odor resembling cloves; leaves very finely pubescent beneath and with distinctly bluish green color beneath; flowers a clear pink color, deep rose in some, without dark carmine at base of tube; corolla tube gradually expanded and wider than that of *R. nudiflorum,* more openly tubular; habit sometimes spreading, almost stoloniferous...*R. roseum.*

  cc. Low shrub, 18 in. high, distinctly stoloniferous, having a horizontal underground stem and forming colonies; flower buds with 5 rows of stipitate glands at apex; flowers white or pink, delicately rose scented..*R. atlanticum.*

 bb. Flower clusters not appearing until after the leaves are fully expanded.

  c. Twigs strigose (with appressed hairs) or pubescent.

   d. Calyx lobes short, semi-orbicular.

    e. Twigs pale; leaves usually smooth; very fragrant with clove-like scent, northern plant ....*R. viscosum.*

    ee. Twigs red-brown; leaves often pubescent beneath; many bud-scales; very fragrant; Florida plant ....*R. serrulatum.*

   dd. Calyx lobes oblong to oblong-lance-shaped; plant from Arkansas to Texas
R. oblongifolium.

  cc. Twigs free from hair (glabrous).

   d. Corolla white or pinkish, tube glandular-pubescent; very fragrant with heliotrope scent; northern plant ....*R. arborescens.*

   dd. Corolla crimson, tube glabrous; southern plant, blooming in July........*R. prunifolium.*

SUBSERIES CANADENSE
(SECT. RHODORA G. DON)

a. Corolla not divided to the base.

 b. Stamens 10; not spotted; leaves in whorls of 5.

  c. Flowers 3 to 6, magenta or red-purple, blooming in June or July; leaves obovate or oblanceolate; pubescent beneath ....*R. Albrechtii.*

  cc. Flowers 1 to 2, bright rose or magenta-rose, blooming in April before the leaves appear; leaves elliptic, glabrescent beneath, in whorls of 5...................*R. pentaphyllum.*

 bb. Stamens 5–7; flowers spotted; leaves not whorled, smooth and green beneath; blooms before the leaves appear ....*R. Vaseyi.*

aa. Corolla partly divided to the base, 2-lipped: stamens 10; blooms before the leaves appear; flowers lilac ....*R. canadense.*

Leaves deciduous, large resembling those of R. Schlippenbachii; flowers tubular or tubular-campanulate, with included style and stamens, distinct for the Series Azalea; flowers white, less than ½ in. long; 1 species only...*R. nipponicum.*

2. A KEY TO THE NATIVE NORTH AMERICAN RHODODENDRONS

a.   Leaves evergreen; stamens 10..Subgenus EURHODODENDRON.
  b.   Leaves not lepidote (not scaly) beneath..Section Leiorhodion.

Ponticum Series

  c.   Bud scales not conspicuously long; leaves not tomentose; calyx lobes wider than long; pedicels not sticky; blooms before new foliage is fully developed (usually June).
    d.   Leaves rounded at both ends; pedicels pubescent; ovary glandular pubescent
                                                                  R. catawbiense.
    dd. Leaves acute at ends; pedicels glabrous; ovary rusty-hairy; not so hardy as the preceding ....*R. macrophyllum*
  cc. Bud scales conspicuously long and pointed, especially those at the base of buds; branchlets, buds, pedicels and corolla sticky; leaves elliptical or lance-oblong, narrowed toward base; blooms 3–4 weeks later than R. catawbiense, usually about first of July ....*R. maximum.*
bb. Leaves lepidote (scaly) beneath..Section Lepipherum
  c.   Upright shrubs, 3–20 ft. high.
    d.   Leaf blades acute or acuminate; flowers appearing after the leafy shoots of the season; habitat Blue Ridge region.

Carolinianum Series

    e.   Corolla lepidote outside; calyx lobes ovate; flowers bloom in late June or July; leaves more acuminate than acute, and frequently not symmetrical toward apex and twisted; loose habit of growth; 6 to 20 ft. tall......................................*R. minus.*
    ee. Corolla not lepidote; calyx lobes deltoid; blooms 4 to 6 weeks earlier than above, usually May; never more than 6 ft. tall, except in var. *foliatum*
                                                                  R. carolinianum.
  dd. Leaf blades obtuse or retuse; flowers appearing before the leafy shoots of the season; 6 ft. or less high; habitat low pine lands, Florida.........................*R. Chapmanii.*

Lapponicum Series

  cc. Procumbent shrub, a few inches tall; stamens 5–8; flowers violet-purple
                                                                  R. lapponicum.
aa. Leaves deciduous, never lepidote.
  b.   Flowers from leafless buds; stamens 5–10.

Albiflorum Series

  c.   Flowers from lateral buds clustered at end of branchlets....Subgenus AZALEASTRUM.
    d.   Stamens 5; flowers white, nodding; from Rocky Mt. region only.............*R. albiflorum.*

Azalea Series

cc. Flowers from terminal buds; stamens 5–10...................Subgenus ANTHODENDRON.
(See separate key to Azalea series)
The following species are native American azaleas:

R. alabamense	*R. oblongifolium*
R. arborescens	*R. occidentale*
R. atlanticum	*R. prunifolium*
R. austrinum	*R. roseum*
R. Bakeri	*R. serrulatum*
R. calendulaceum	*R. speciosum*
R. canadense	*R. Vaseyi*
R. canescens	*R. viscosum*
R. nudiflorum	

Camtschaticum Series

bb. Flowers from a leafy-bracted peduncle; 10 stamens........Subgenus THERORHODION.
c. Small procumbent shrub; Alaska...*R. camtschaticum.*

3. SERIES GROUPS LISTED ACCORDING TO POSSIBLE RELATIONSHIPS *

I. Series Having Scaly Leaves (Lepidote)

Dauricum—Flowers magenta or pink; 1–2 fls. in an inflorescence.
Trichocladum—Flowers yellow; 2–4 fls. in an inflorescence.
Triflorum (in part)—Flowers funnel-shaped.
} Often deciduous and approaching azalea character.

Anthopogon—Calyx large; corolla tubular with wide spreading limb.
Cephalanthum—Calyx smaller, but well developed; tubular corolla as above.
} Dwarf alpines having tubular corolla with wide spreading limb.

Campylogynum—Corolla nodding, solitary, purple or blackish.
Glaucum—Corolla campanulate; leafy calyx.
Lapponicum—Corolla open funnelshaped.
Lepidotum—Corolla short and openly tubular.
Saluenense—Corolla wide open, from short tube; large calyx.
} Mostly dwarf shrubs (2 ft.) from very high altitudes, 10,000–14,000 ft.; also a few dwarf species from the arctic.

Boothii—Inflorescence terminal; large calyx, corolla campanulate; some epiphytic.
} Related to preceding groups, but 3–4 ft. tall. Some are from lower altitudes.

Scabrifolium—Leaves pubescent beneath.
Virgatum—Leaves glabrous beneath.
} Inflorescence axillary; 2–8 ft. tall.

*Only by careful research with original specimens can an accurate key to the series be developed. The present list is only a crude grouping of series into their supposed natural divisions, worked out from the literature and not intended as a scientific basis of classification. It is included here only for the purpose of furnishing general information to hybridists and growers who wish to know something of the probable natural affinities of the series as an aid to their work. Botanical keys to the species within most of the series may be found in "The Species of Rhododendron" (1930) and the R.H.S. Rhododendron Handbook, 1956.
Reprinted without change from first edition (1936).

Heliolepis—6–30 ft. tall; leaf scales very densely arranged. ⎫
Triflorum—Mostly 3–8 ft. tall; leaf scales not so densely ⎬ Funnel-shaped flowers with very
arranged. ⎭ small calyx.

Camelliaeflorum—Corolla short and broadly tubular; scaly ⎫
outside. ⎮ Medium-sized to large shrubs, suit-
Maddenii—Corolla large, funnelshaped or campanulate, ⎬ able for the cool greenhouse; often
scaly or pubescent; several flowers in one truss. ⎮ epiphytic in natural habitats.
Moupinense—Corolla not scaly outside; branchlets bristly. ⎭

Edgeworthii—Both woolly hairs and scales on lower leaf ⎫ Cool greenhouse subjects; often
surfaces. ⎭ epiphytic.

Vaccinioides—Seeds with elongated threadlike tails; from ⎫ Usually epiphytic.
lower and warmer habitats. ⎭

Javanicum, etc.—Large group of tropical species, suitable ⎫ Very tender, medium-sized shrubs;
only for growing in a warmhouse. ⎭ many are epiphytic.

Cinnabarinum—Corolla tubular-cylindric; flowers fleshy. ⎬ A very distinct group from the
Himalayas.

Carolinianum—An American series with probably no close ⎫ 6–20 ft. tall and notably hardy.
Asiatic relatives. ⎭

Ferrugineum—A series from the European Alps with no ⎫ Usually under 6 ft. and hardy.
close affinities. ⎭

Micranthum—Small, white flowers like those of a ⎫
Spiraea or Ledum. A very distinct and hardy outlier ⎬ Unlike any other rhododendron and
from northern China and Manchuria, up to 4 ft. tall. ⎭ very hardy, but of little floral value.

II. Series Which do Not Have Scales Beneath
Their Leaves (Elepidote)

Albiflorum—Inflorescence axillary with flowers alone or ⎫ A deciduous outlier from the
in pairs; unlike any other species in many characters. ⎭ Rocky Mountains.

Camtschaticum—Flowers borne on young leafy shoots; ⎫ A deciduous outlier from the arctic
plant very dwarf, few inches tall. ⎭ region.

Azalea—Inflorescence terminal and never axillary; leaves ⎫
dimorphic in some semi-evergreen sorts. Evergreen ⎮
species all have more than 5 stamens. ⎮
Ovatum—Axillary inflorescence; leaves evergreen; flowers ⎮ Mostly deciduous, azalea-like spe-
solitary; calyx lobes large and broad; 5 stamens, all of ⎮ cies, with some evergreen forms,
equal length. ⎬ especially those from the South.
Semibarbatum—Small solitary flowers from lateral buds ⎮ Ovatum and Stamineum series are
below terminal leaf buds; 5 stamens of unequal length. ⎮ regularly evergreen. Some of the
Stamineum—Evergreen; 10 stamens; only rudimentary ⎮ species have dimorphic leaves.
calyx; flowers narrowly funnelshaped; plants up to 40 ft. ⎮
tall. ⎭

Falconeri—With cup- or funnel-shaped hairs on upper layer of leaf indumentum.

Grande—Without cup-shaped hairs on the indumentum; both series are distinguished by very large leaves.

The "big leaved" rhododendrons; large shrubs or trees. The leaves have a 2-layered indumentum. Need much shelter.

Arboreum—Tree-like habit; dense trusses with many flowers.

Barbatum—Tree-like habit; bears bristles and coarse hairs; deep red flowers with conspicuous nectar pouches.

Irroratum—Usually shrubby habit; the indumentum tends to disappear, usually becoming absent at maturity.

Mostly soft-leaved species, tender except in very mild climates. Large shrubs or trees with rather dense trusses of campanulate or tubular-campanulate flowers. The leaves are mostly acute at apex.

Campanulatum—Rounded leaves; flower truss not elongated; ovary smooth.

Fortunei—Funnelform flowers, large, with 6 to 8 corolla lobes; often fragrant.

Fulvum—Narrow obovate leaves; flowers in open trusses; long thin pedicels; long narrow smooth ovary which becomes a sickle-shaped seed capsule.

Lacteum—Indumentum thin; ovary tomentose.

Neriiflorum—Flowers not spotted; flower truss loose; ovary hairy or glandular.

Ponticum—Elongated flower truss; flowers on long pedicels, funnelshaped or campanulate, with lobes cut equal to length of corolla tubes. Contains many species from northern and colder regions, mostly lying outside main rhododendron center of Asia.

Taliense—Pointed leaves; thick felty indumentum; spotted flowers borne in dense truss.

Thomsonii—Leaves cordate at base; 5 corolla lobes; not very hardy.

Mostly shrubs 6 to 20 ft. tall, many from relatively high, cold or northern latitudes, including several very hardy garden species, such as catawbiense and maximum. Generally medium-sized shrubs with medium-sized leaves and an upright habit of growth.

Auriculatum—Long narrow leaf buds and lanceolate leaves; hairs on the shoots; glandular or woolly tomentum; corolla with long narrow tube below and hairs on the outside.

A distinct group, with one species an August bloomer.

4. A CONDENSED TRANSLATION OF SLEUMER'S SYSTEMATIC ARRANGEMENT OF THE GENUS RHODODENDRON *

SUMMARY OF THE SUBGENERA AND SECTIONS

I. Inflorescence terminal.
  A. Lepidote.
    1. Leaves evergreen (rarely deciduous).   Subgenus I. RHODODENDRON
      a) Seeds without proper marginal appendages.
        i. Stamens 10, erect, projecting out of tubular or campanulate corolla.
        Trichomes (scales of the indumentum) discoid, with margins
        entire.   Section 1. RHODODENDRON
        ii. Stamens 5–10, with short filaments included within the perianth.
                   Section 2. POGONANTHUM

      b) Seeds with more or less long, caudate appendages at both ends.
      Trichomes discoid with margins entire, or irregularly indented in
      the margins to form star-rays.   Section 3. VIREYA

    2. Leaves usually deciduous, occasionally semipersistent. Flowers appear-
      ing in spring before the leaves.   Subgenus II. PSEUDAZALEA
  B. Elepidote.
    1. Flowers from *terminal* buds, but the leafy branchlets (new foliate
      shoots) from *lateral* buds, i.e. from the axils of the leaves of the
      past season.
      a) Leaves evergreen.   Subgenus III. HYMENANTHES
                     Section 1. HYMENANTHES

      b) Leaves deciduous.   Subgenus IV. PENTANTHERA
        i. Stamens 8–10 (rarely 7; very rarely 5–6).
          α Corolla rotate-campanulate, deeply lobed (almost to the base),
          wide open; stamens well visible. Mostly blooming before or as
          the leaves unfold in spring.   Section 1. RHODORA

          β Corolla tubular-campanulate; stamens included in the corolla.
          Flowers appearing with or after the leaves.   Section 2. VISCIDULA
        ii. Stamens always 5; corolla funnel-shaped.   Section 3. PENTANTHERA

    2. Flowers *and* leafy branchlets (new foliate shoots) from the same
      terminal bud, i.e. the latter from the axils of the lowest scale-like
      bracts of the same bud (of the recent season). Stamens 5–10 (often
      varying in number within the same species).   Subgenus V. ANTHODENDRON

      a) Leaves more or less deciduous.
        i. Branches smooth or hairy, but generally hairy; leaves in whorls at
        tips of branches, usually smooth when mature or with hairs only on
        the back of midrib or nerves. Blooms with or just before the leaves
        appear.   Section 1. BRACHYCALYX

        ii. Branches and leaves with flattened adpressed setose hairs. Leaves
        scattered on the branches, dimorphic. The spring leaves broad, thin
        and deciduous, followed by smallish, thick, more or less persistent
        winter leaves.   Section 2. ANTHODENDRON

---

* Freely translated from the German text of: Sleumer, H.: Ein System der Gattung Rhododendron L. Bot. Jahrb. 74(4): 511–553. Stuttgart, 1949. A great amount of detail has been
omitted in this abbreviated translation. Emended and enlarged as to the Malaysian groups of the
genus in harmony with the recent work of Sleumer: The genus Rhododendron L. in Indochina
and Siam, Blumea, Suppl. IV: 39–59. 1958, and: The genus Rhododendron in Malaysia, Rein-
wardtia 5(2):45–231. 1960. The author is greatly indebted to Prof. Dr. H. Sleumer, Rijksher-
barium, Leyden, Holland, for his valuable cooperation in making this new material available.

b) Leaves always evergreen, coriaceous, arranged in 2 to 3 whorls at
   the ends of the twigs (except on vigorous branches where they may
   appear scattered).   Section 3. Tsusiopsis
II. Inflorescence lateral, e.g., only in the axils of the upper leaves, or in the
    axils of deeper leaves of the previous year's growth. The uppermost leaf
    or flower buds "pseudoterminal" when in the axil of upper foliage leaves.
  A. New leaf growth from pseudoterminal buds, or out of lower leaf-bud
     axils.
    1. Elepidote.   Subgenus VI. AZALEASTRUM
      a) Leaves evergreen.
        i. Stamens 5, calyx lobes large and broad. Seeds without marginal
           appendages.   Section 1. Azaleastrum
        ii. Stamens 10, calyx minute. Seeds with rather short spindle-shaped
            marginal appendages at both ends. Style remaining attached to seed
            capsule after maturity.   Section 2. Choniastrum
      b) Leaves deciduous; flowers after the leaves appear.
        i. Stamens 10 (to 12), all of equal length.   Section 3. Candidastrum
        ii. Stamens 5, the upper two shortened.   Section 4. Mumeazalea
    2. Lepidote; leaves evergreen.   Subgenus VII. PSEUDORHODORASTRUM
      a) Leaves soft-hairy to hispid, at least on upper sides; undersides
         rarely glaucous. Stamens 8–10. Seeds without marginal appendages.
                                                 Section 1. Trachyrhodion
      b) Leaves always glabrous, often glaucous on lower side. Stamens 10.
        i. Flowers always solitary in each leaf axil. Seeds with long marginal
           appendages.   Section 2. Pseudorhodorastrum
        ii. Flowers more than one (1–5) in a single leaf axil.   Section 3. Rhodobotrys
  B. New leaf growth always out of foliage occurring below the inflores-
     cence. Flowers, often solitary, from pseudoterminal buds or axils of
     foliage leaves immediately beneath, appearing before new growth.
                                             Subgenus VIII. RHODORASTRUM

SYNOPSIS OF THE SUBGENERA, SECTIONS
AND SUBSECTIONS *

Subgenus I. RHODODENDRON
Section 1. Rhododendron

A. Pistil short, thick, mostly incurved.
  B. Trichomes (scales) of two kinds: small yellow and dark brown.
                                              Subsect. *Glauca* Sleum.
                                      Series and subseries GLAUCOPHYLLUM
  BB. Trichomes (scales) of only one kind.
    C. Pedicels shorter than corolla; flowers yellow or white.   Subsect. *Boothia* Sleum.
                                                       Series BOOTHII

---

* A synopsis, such as this, is devised primarily for the study of relationships between the
various taxa and is not ordinarily intended for purposes of identification. The translation here
included makes available in English a useful framework for studying the various series of
rhododendron in their presumed relationships. In Sleumer's paper the material was presented
in the form of a bracketed key. Since most American horticulturists are unfamiliar with the
style and form of bracketed keys, the translator has taken the liberty of transposing Sleumer's
original bracketed key into the more familiar form of a yoked key. Although the descriptions
have been shortened and abbreviated greatly, an effort has been made to follow the main points
of the German text. Since there has been no opportunity for the present writer to study herbarium
material involved, he takes no credit and assumes no responsibility in the matter. The numerals
preceding subgenera and sections are mine.—C.G.B.

CC. Pedicels longer than the corolla.

    D. Inflorescence of 1–3 fls., corymbose. Lvs. small (0.4–2.6 cm.).

        E. Corolla campanulate, often hoary; otherwise without scaly
           indumentum.   Subsect. *Campylogyna* Sleum.
                                        Series CAMPYLOGYNUM

        EE. Corolla expanding from broad tubular base, densely lepidote
            outside.   Subsect. *Lepidota* Sleum.
                        Series and subseries LEPIDOTUM

    DD. Inflorescence of 4–18 fls., short or racemose. Lvs. large (3–15 cm.
        long).

        E. Trichomes (indumentum scales) crenulate, overlapping.   Subsect. *Baileya* Sleum.
                                          Series LEPIDOTUM
                                        Subser. BAILEYI

        EE. Trichome margins entire, scales separated by ½–10 diameters.
                          Subsect. *Genestieriana* Sleum.
                          Series GLAUCOPHYLLUM
                          Subser. GENESTIERIANUM

AA. Pistil long as stamens, slender, rather straight.

    B. Inflorescence of 1–2 (or 3) fls.; lvs. small (1.2–3.8 cm.); corolla thick-
        hairy outside (except *R. monanthum*); dwarf shrubs.   Subsect. *Uniflora* Sleum.
                                        Series UNIFLORUM

    BB. Inflorescence of 3–14 fls. Corolla sparsely hairy outside; mostly bare
        or lepidote.

        C. Leaves thick-woolly beneath, lepidote; bullate on upper surface.
            Ovary woolly.   Subsect. *Edgeworthia* Sleum.
                                      Series EDGEWORTHII

    CC. Leaves not woolly; lepidote only.

        D. Pistil both lepidote and woolly in lower third (except *R. ciliatum*).
            Stamens not over 10.

            E. Corolla proportionately small, lobes 2–3 cm. long, often yellow
                or yellowish white to rose.   Subsect. *Tephropepla* Sleum.
                                    Series BOOTHII
                              Subser. TEPHROPEPLUM

            EE. Corolla proportionately large, lobes 3.2–4.8 cm. long, often
                white and waxy.   Subsect. *Maddenia* Sleum.
                                    Series MADDENII

        DD. Pistil elepidote.

            E. Stamens 12–16, pubescent; corolla short and broad, tubular with
                spreading limb, scaly outside, villous inside.   Subsect. *Camelliaeflora* Sleum.
                                    Series CAMELLIAEFLORUM

            EE. Stamens 10 (rarely fewer), occasionally differing in length.

                F. Flowers very small, scarcely 5–6 mm., scaly outside. Inflo-
                    rescence a many-flowered raceme.   Subsect. *Micrantha* Sleum.
                                    Series MICRANTHUM

                FF. Flowers essentially larger; generally borne in few-flowered
                  trusses.

                    G. Calyx large and distinct, rarely short as 4 mm., otherwise
                      at least 6 mm. long; often persistent with capsule more or
                      less enclosed.

                      H. Low, dwarf shrubs, often prostrate or only a few inches
                        high; never epiphytic. Corolla small, seldom over 2 cm.;
                        style almost always glabrous. Trichomes (scales)
                      crenate.   Subsect. *Saluenensia* Sleum.
                                    Series SALUENENSE

HH. Smallish shrubs, generally epiphytic. Corolla medium, 3 cm. long; fragrant. Trichome margins entire.

Subsect. *Moupinensia* Sleum.

Series MOUPINENSE

GG. Calyx short and small (3 mm.), often insignificant (except in *RR. cuneatum, intricatum,* and *setosum* in Lapponicum series and *RR. Hanceanum* and *Searsii* in Triflorum series, where calyx lobes are 6–8 mm. long).

H. Corolla fleshy, tubular-cylindric, glabrous outside; corolla lobes short and erect; style pubescent.

Subsect. *Cinnabarina* Sleum.

Series CINNABARINUM

HH. Corolla not so fleshy, generally broadly campanulate or funnelform, or tubular below, broadening above.

I. Leaf margins prominently crenate; shrubs smallish to medium-tall; corolla somewhat tubular, 12–16 mm. long; pedicels 6–16 mm. long.

Subsect. *Ferruginea* Sleum.

Series FERRUGINEUM

II. Leaf margins not crenate.

J. Low dwarf or carpet-like shrubs (not over 1.5 m.) with spreading habit of growth. Leaves small to very small. Flowers almost sessile or with very short petioles (2–3 mm.), except in *R. parvifolium* and *R. ravum* (4–6 mm.) and *R. cuneatum* and *R. lapponicum* (10–12 mm.).

Subsect. *Lapponica* Sleum.

Series LAPPONICUM

JJ. Medium-sized shrubs, from 1.8 and 2.4 m. to 10 m., with larger leaves.

K. Calyx lobes unequal, 5-lobed, ciliated. North American species.

Subsect. *Caroliniana* Sleum.

Series CAROLINIANUM

KK. Calyx lobes, if distinct, equal, 5-lobed, occasionally ciliated. Eastern Asia.

L. Trusses of 4–6 flowers.

Subsect. *Heliolepida* Sleum.

Series HELIOLEPIS

LL. Trusses of 3 flowers only. Corolla glabrous outside (rarely lepidote); stamens mostly unequal; leaves evergreen (except semievergreen in *R. chartophyllum* and *R. yunnanense*).

Subsect. *Triflora* Sleum.

Series TRIFLORUM

Section 2. POGONANTHUM G. Don

Small evergreen shrubs, leaves with lacerate scales. Includes the species formerly classified under 'Cephalanthum Series' now combined under one series head.

Series ANTHOPOGON

Section 3. VIREYA (Bl.) Copel. f.

A. Scales "disk-shaped," i.e. their marginal zone entire or nearly so.

B. Corolla short-tubular in general, rarely funnelform or (tubular-) campanulate, the lobes straight or spreading. E. Asia, Malaysia.

Subsect. *Pseudovireya* (Clarke) Sleum.

Series VACCINIOIDES

BB. Corolla trumpet-like or salver-shaped, the tube elongate and ± narrow, the lobes spreading ± horizontally. New Guinea.

Subsect. *Siphonovireya* Sleum.

AA. Scales "star-shaped," i.e. their marginal zone distinctly lobed, dented or
    incised (lacerate) to various degree.
 C. Scales in general markedly "dendroid," and each scale on top of a
    distinct and permanent epidermal tubercle, the leaves ± rough to
    the touch. Celebes, New Guinea.   Subsect. *Phaeovireya* Sleum.
 CC. Scales usually "sessile," rarely "subdendroid." Tubercles, if any,
    subinconspicuous, not permanent; leaves smooth.
  D. Scales of two obviously different sizes, i.e. very many smaller and
    few much larger ones irregularly mixed (all touching or overlap-
    ping each other, the center dark chestnut or blackish-brown).
    W. Malaysia, Celebes, Ceram, Buru.   Subsect. *Malayovireya* Sleum.
  DD. Scales all equal in size (very spaced to very dense, the center
    never very dark).
   E. Scales very dense, touching or slightly overlapping each other,
    rather large in general, still forming a coherent layer on the
    undersurface of ± mature leaves. Malaysia.   Subsect. *Albovireya* Sleum.
   EE. Scales lax to subdense, always distinctly spaced, rather small in
    general.
    F. Corolla trumpet-like or salver-shaped, the ± straight tube
    elongate and narrow, the lobes relat. short, equalling one
    fourth or less of the total length of the corolla and ± spread-
    ing horizontally. Malaysia.   Subsect. *Solenovireya* Copel. f.
    FF. Corolla tubular, campanulate or funnelform, the tube in gen-
    eral wider and shorter than in Subsect. Solenovireya, the
    lobes equalling one fourth or more of the total length of the
    corolla, erect or ± funnelform-expanded. Subsect. *Euvireya* Copel. f.
     G. Leaves very small, in general, 0.3–1 by 0.2–0.6 cm. New
    Guinea.   Series LINNAEOIDEA Sleum.
     GG. Leaves larger.
      H. Compact dwarf shrub, forming tussocks or mats. New
    Guinea.   Series SAXIFRAGOIDEA Sleum.
      HH. Erect shrub or treelet.
       I. Leaves linear to narrow-lanceolate, not exceeding 7
    mm. in width generally.
        J. Leaves 20 or more in each pseudowhorl, 1–1.5 mm.
    wide. Luzon.   Series TAXIFOLIA Sleum.
        JJ. Leaves opposite or 3–8(–15) in each pseudowhorl,
    3–7 mm. wide generally. Borneo, New Guinea.
         Series STENOPHYLLA Sleum.
       II. Leaves not linear or narrow-lanceolate, generally much
    wider.
        K. Stamens 5. Sumatra, Java, Bali   Series CITRINA Sleum.
        KK. Stamens (7–)10(–14).
         L. Leaves medium-sized, in general 1–4 cm.
    long. Malaysia.   Series BUXIFOLIA Sleum.
        LL. Leaves larger in general. Indochina, Malaysia.
         Series JAVANICA Sleum.

Subgenus II. PSEUDAZALEA Sleum.

          Series TRICHOCLADUM

Subgenus III. HYMENANTHES (Bl.) Endl.

Section 1. HYMENANTHES

A. Leaf-buds and flower-buds long and pointed, with small and long-acu-
    minate outside bracts. Leaves lanceolate. Gland-tipped strigose hairs on
    shoots and petioles. Corolla funnelform with glandular or floccose hairs
    on outside of tube toward base.   Subsect. *Auriculata* Sleum.
          Series AURICULATUM

AA. Leaf-buds roundish or ovoid, outer bracts rather short.
  B. Leaves glandular with bristly hairs, often woolly beneath.
    C. Calyx conspicuous (5–25 mm. long). Flower trusses mostly compact.
      Young leaves also often woolly-haired. Twigs with bristly glandular
      hairs.   Subsect. *Barbata* Sleum.
                                                          Series BARBATUM
                              Subser. BARBATUM, GLISCHRUM AND CRINIGERUM

    CC. Calyx very small (except *R. longesquamatum*) ; flower trusses lax.
      Glandular bristles only on the undersides of the leaf midribs (except
      in *R. strigillosum* where they occur over the whole under-side).
      Young twigs without bristles.   Subsect. *Maculifera* Sleum.
                                                          Series BARBATUM
                                                      Subser. MACULIFERUM

  BB. Leaves and shoots without bristly hairs.
    C. Prominent nectar pouches, often dark colored, in base of corolla.
      D. Chiefly trees with regular boles. Leaves oblong-acuminate with
        numerous parallel lateral nerves, somewhat depressed on the
        upper side ; on the under side a thin filmlike indumentum varying
        to thick-felty, rust-brown or whitish. Trusses compact. Pedicels
        thickish, up to 1 cm. long. Corolla tubular, campanulate, often
        dark red.   Subsect. *Arborea* Sleum.
                                                      Series and subser. ARBOREUM

      DD. Shrubs without regular trunks or boles.
        E. Leaves broad, rounded at both ends, often cordate at base,
          rather bluish green, appearing glabrous ; the under sides (seen
          under a lens) vested with fine hairs or clusters of glandular
          hairs or their traces. Few flowers to a truss. Corolla campanu-
          late or tubular funnelform, always 5-parted ; partly spotted in
          the throat. Peduncle often glandular. Ovary glabrous or glandu-
          lar, never simply hairy.   Subsect. *Thomsonia* Sleum.
                                                      Series and subser. THOMSONII

      EE. Leaves oblong-elliptic to broad-obovate, acuminate or rotund,
          the base never really cordate ; glabrous or pubescent on under
          side. Trusses more or less lax. Corolla variable in form, not
          spotted. Ovary pubescent or pilose and glandular or only
          glandular.   Subsect. *Neriiflora* Sleum.
                                                          Series NERIIFLORUM

    CC. Corolla without nectar pouches.
      D. Corolla lobes as long as the tube. Leaves oblong, glabrous on
        the under side, generally with a depressed midrib on the upper
        side ; or sometimes with a heavy tomentose or woolly (rarely
        stellate) indumentum on the under side. Trusses generally with
        a long flower-axis or candelabroid inflorescence. The pedicel
        becomes elongated at the time of bloom, later rigidly erect under
        capsule.   Subsect. *Pontica* Sleum.
                                                          Series PONTICUM

      DD. Corolla lobes shorter than the tube.
        E. Leaves, even when young, never hairy ; more or less stalked
          glands sometimes occurring, however, most frequently on
          under sides of young leaves.
          F. Flowers 5-lobed.
            G. Corolla funnelform. Capsule very slender, sickle-shaped.
              Leaves thin-leathery, oblong to elliptical.   Subsect. *Selensia* Sleum.
                                                          Series THOMSONII
                                                          Subser. SELENSE

GG. Corolla cup-shaped to campanulate.
  H. Capsule cylindrical, rather fat, slightly curved.
    I. Style covered to the top with glands. Leaves thick-
      leathery, elliptical to orbiculate.   Subsect. *Souliea* Sleum.
                                               Series THOMSONII
                                           Subser. SOULIEI

    II. Style glabrous, or bearing glands only toward the
      base. Leaves thin-leathery, rigid, small, elliptical.
                                Subsect. *Martiniana* Sleum.
                                           Series THOMSONII
                                     Subser. MARTINIANUM

  HH. Capsule sickle-shaped, slim. Leaves leathery, roundish
     to elliptical.   Subsect. *Campylocarpa* Sleum.
                                         Series THOMSONII
                                 Subser. CAMPYLOCARPUM

FF. Flowers generally 6(–8)-lobed.   Subsect. *Fortunea* Sleum.
                                         Series FORTUNEI

EE. Leaves more or less densely tomentose (to woolly-felty), later
  sometimes becoming glabrate.
  F. Leaves sparsely hairy underneath, becoming glabrate later.
    G. Leaves tomentose only when young, glabrous later.
      H. Young leaves thin-hairy, later almost glabrous with
        only marks of hairs appearing as small dots. Leaves
        more or less oblong, mostly acuminate, with cartilag-
        inous leaf margins often obscurely notched and rough
        to the touch. Corolla generally spotted. Ovary never
        stellate-hairy.   Subsect. *Irrorata* Sleum.
                                  Series and subser. IRRORATUM

      HH. Leaves stellate-pilose when young, later glabrous,
        mostly large, oblong-oval, thin, blunt or rounded at apex.
        Ovary stellate-pilose.   Subsect. *Parishia* Sleum.
                                   Series IRRORATUM
                                   Subser. PARISHII

  GG. Leaves with silvery indumentum when mature.
    H. Under-sides of leaves covered with a thin, rather silvery
      (to yellow-brown) plaster-like or parchment-like indu-
      mentum composed of stellate hairs, never woolly or
      thick-felty. Trusses lax (except five species under
      Subsect. *Floribunda*).   Subsect. *Argyrophylla* Sleum.
                                    Series ARBOREUM
                                 Subser. ARGYROPHYLLUM

    HH. Under-sides of leaves covered with a thin whitish to
      cinnamon-brown indumentum, like glove leather, com-
      posed of radiate hairs. Trusses umbellate with a very
      short rachis.   Subsect. *Lactea* Sleum.
                                    Series LACTEUM

FF. Leaves regularly dense woolly-felty underneath.
  G. Woolly indumentum consisting of two layers. Leaves very
    large. Corolla mortar-shaped, of 7–10 lobes. Stamens
    12–18.
    H. Upper layer of indumentum on under-sides of leaves
      (made up of distinctive cup- or funnel-shaped hairs)
      falling off, leaving a thin-skinned indumentum layer
      beneath.   Subsect. *Falconera* Sleum.
                                   Series FALCONERI

HH. Upper layer of indumenum made up of rosulate, dendroid or ramiform hairs united at their base. Lower layer thin and parchment-like, similar to that of Subsection *Falconera.* Subsect. *Grandia* Sleum.
Series GRANDE

GG. Indumentum of only one layer. Leaves medium-sized. Corolla more or less campanulate, 5-lobed. Stamens 10.
H. Capsule small, sickle-shaped. Ovary glabrous, slender. Leaves slim, oblong to obovate. Trusses lax, 15–20 flowered, with pedicels long and slender. Subsect. *Fulva* Sleum.
Series FULVUM

HH. Capsule cylindric, oblong. Ovary glabrous or pilose.
I. Leaves more or less blunt at both ends. Ovary almost always glabrous. Subsect. *Campanulata* Sleum.
Series CAMPANULATUM

II. Leaves more or less acuminate.
J. Rachis much shortened. Subsect. *Taliensia* Sleum.
Series TALIENSE

JJ. Rachis elongated. (Here belong only *R. denudatum, R. floribundum, R. Hunnewellianum, R. Rockii* and *R. farinosum.*) Subsect. *Floribunda* Sleum.
Series ARBOREUM
Subser. ARGYROPHYLLUM

Subgenus IV. PENTANTHERA (G. Don) Sleum.
Section 1. RHODORA G. Don

Series AZALEA
Subser. CANADENSE

Section 2. VISCIDULA Matsumura et Nakai

Series AZALEA
Subser. NIPPONICUM

Section 3. PENTANTHERA

Series AZALEA
Subser. LUTEUM

Subgenus V. ANTHODENDRON (Reichenbach) Endl.
Section 1. BRACHYCALYX Sweet

Series AZALEA
Subser. SCHLIPPENBACHII

Section 2. ANTHODENDRON

Series AZALEA
Subser. OBTUSUM

Section 3. TSUSIOPSIS Sleum.

Series AZALEA
Subser. TASHIROI

Subgenus VI. AZALEASTRUM Maxim.
Section 1. AZALEASTRUM

Series OVATUM

Section 2. CHONIASTRUM Franchet

Series STAMINEUM

Section 3. CANDIDASTRUM Sleum.

Series ALBIFLORUM

Section 4. MUMEAZALEA Makino

Series SEMIBARBATUM

Subgenus VII. PSEUDORHODORASTRUM Sleum.
Section 1. TRACHYRHODION Sleum.

Series SCABRIFOLIUM

Section 2. PSEUDORHODORASTRUM

Series VIRGATUM

Section 3. RHODOBOTRYS Sleum.

Example: *R. racemosum*

Subgenus VIII. RHODORASTRUM (Maxim.) C. B. Clarke

Series DAURICUM

NOTE: Keys to the separate species within many of the Subsections or Series groups may be found in Stevenson's "The Species of Rhododendron." Additional keys for certain groups recently reclassified by Cowan and Davidian are presented in the R.H.S. Rhododendron Handbook, Part I, 1956. Keys to all species of the subsect. Maddenia (ciliicalyx group) and Irrorata, and of the sect. Choniastrum are published by Sleumer in Blumea, Suppl. IV: 39–59. 1958.

BIBLIOGRAPHY

For recording original sources and historical material, the bibliography of 1935, which was presented in the first edition of this work, is being reprinted here in full. Since that time, however, most of the significant literature on this genus has been channeled into a relatively few publications, consisting mainly of periodicals and a few notable books, plus a limited number of scattered technical papers. Material printed in the regular publications, bulletins, year-books, etc., of the rhododendron societies, such as those of the Royal Horticultural Society, the American Rhododendron Society and the Deutsche Rhododendron-Gesellschaft, and other organizations such as the American Horticultural Society, have covered most of the purely horticultural information published on these plants. To these, then, the reader is referred without special citation to the scores of articles appearing through these media. And I shall make no attempt to enumerate the names of many fine authors who have been responsible for these valuable papers. In addition, the indices of the various scientific abstract journals, such as Biological Abstracts, will yield references to most of the research papers of the world and to new species as they appear.

For further information, existing plant collections and herbaria are of considerable value. Perhaps the largest herbarium collection of rhododendrons and azaleas is that maintained by the Royal Botanic Garden in Edinburgh, Scotland. A large collection of living plants is perpetually maintained in Edinburgh, and through the herbarium there most of the new species are ultimately cleared.

A notable rhododendron collection is maintained also by the Royal Horticultural Society at their Wisley Gardens in Surrey, England. A new but rapidly expanding American test garden for rhododendrons is that supervised by the American Rhododendron Society at Portland, Oregon, and another fine collection on the West Coast is at the University of Washington Arboretum in Seattle. More limited collections in colder climates are maintained at the Arnold Arboretum, Boston, the Planting Fields Arboretum at Glen Cove, Long Island, at Swarthmore College near Philadelphia, The Morris Arboretum, Philadelphia, The Biltmore Estate, Biltmore, North Carolina, Longwood Gardens, Kennett

Square, Pennsylvania, and at the United States National Arboretum in Washington, D.C. Private collectors and commercial nurserymen here and abroad are sources of ordinary and special kinds of rhododendrons and no attempt will be made to list them here. Information concerning these is usually available through the offices of the larger horticultural societies. Important collections also exist in Holland and Germany.

The author feels that to cover the more recent publications adequately, it is necessary to list here only the more important books, publications and periodicals, plus a few miscellaneous but significant special papers that have appeared occasionally over the last twenty-five years. These, therefore, with the old original references, constitute the revised bibliography here presented.

RECENT BOOKS

BERG, J. and G. KRUESSMANN. Freiland-Rhododendron, pp. 1–164 (Deutsche Rhododendron-Gesellschaft). Eugen Ulmer in Stuttgart, z.Z. (presently at) Ludwigsburg, Koernerstrasse 16, West Germany, 1951.

BOWERS, CLEMENT GRAY. Winter-hardy azaleas and rhododendrons, pp. 1–112. Massachusetts Horticultural Society, Boston, 1954.

CHITTENDEN, F. J., P. M. SYNGE, et al. Article on Rhododendrons in Royal Hort. Soc. Dictionary of Gardening, vol. IV. Clarendon Press, Oxford, 1951.

CLARKE, J. HAROLD, Editor, and Members of the American Rhododendron Society. Rhododendrons, pp. 1–231. Amer. Rhod. Soc., 3514 North Russet St., Portland, Ore., 1956.

COWAN, JOHN MACQUEEN. The rhododendron leaf, pp. 1–120. Oliver & Boyd, Edinburgh and London, 1950.

COX, E. H. M. and P. A. COX. Modern rhododendrons, pp. 1–193. Thomas Nelson & Sons, Edinburgh and New York, 1956.

FLETCHER, H. R. The international rhododendron register. R.H.S., London, 1958.

GROOTENDORST, HERMAN J. Rhododendrons en azalea's, pp. 1–216. Vereniging voor Boskoopse Culturen, Boskoop, Holland, 1954.

HUME, H. HAROLD. Azaleas, kinds and culture, pp. 1–199. Macmillan, New York, 1949.

IHRIG, HERBERT G. and JOHN H. HANLEY, et al. University of Washington Arboretum handbook of rhododendrons, pp. 1–198. The Arboretum Foundation, Seattle, Wash., 1944.

KELLOGG, CHARLES E. Our garden soils, pp. 1–232. Macmillan, New York, 1952.

LEE, FREDERICK P. The azalea book, rev. ed., pp. 1–328. American Horticultural Society, Washington 2, D.C., 1958.

STREET, FREDERICK. Hardy rhododendrons, pp. 1–192. Collins, St. James Place, London, 1954.

WARD, F. KINGDON. Rhododendrons, pp. 1–128. Purnell & Sons, Ltd., London, and Pellegrini & Cudahy, New York, 1950.

WELLS, JAMES F. Plant propagation practices, pp. 1–344. Macmillan, New York, 1955.

SERIAL PUBLICATIONS

AMERICAN RHODODENDRON SOCIETY. Quarterly Bulletin, 3514 N. Russet St., Portland, Oregon. 1947 et seq.

AMERICAN RHODODENDRON SOCIETY. Yearbook, Vols. I to V, 1945–1949. Portland, Oregon.

DEUTSCHE RHODODENDRON-GESELLSCHAFT. Jahrbuch (Rhododendron und immergruene Laubgehoelze). German Rhododendron Society, Bremen (c/o J. Berg, Rhododendron-Park, Bremen-Horn, Marcusallee 60, West Germany), 1953.

ROYAL BOTANIC GARDEN, EDINBURGH. Notes. Edinburgh, Scotland.

ROYAL HORTICULTURAL SOCIETY. Rhododendron (and Camellia) Yearbook. London, 1946 et seq.

ROYAL HORTICULTURAL SOCIETY. The Rhododendron Handbook, Parts I and II. London, 1956. (New editions published about every five years. Part I contains terse enumeration and description of species; Part II contains stud book and listing of hybrids.)

ROYAL HORTICULTURAL SOCIETY. Journal. A monthly publication, containing frequent articles on rhododendrons and reports of plants to which awards have been made. Roy. Hort. Soc., Vincent Square, London, S.W. 1, England.

MISCELLANEOUS PAPERS

BOWERS, CLEMENT GRAY. Possibilities for improving hardy rhododendrons and azaleas. Proceedings of the Fifth American Horticultural Congress, 1950, pp. 60–63. Amer. Hort. Council, Inc., Bailey Hortorium, Ithaca, N.Y., 1951.

BOWERS, CLEMENT GRAY. Rhododendron Fortschritte der letzten Jahre in Amerika (Recent Rhododendron progress in America). Deutsche Rhododendron-Gesellschaft Jahrbuch, 1954, 32–36. Bremen, 1954.

BOWERS, CLEMENT GRAY. How good is a species? Horticulture Magazine XXXV (5):258, 274 (May); How good is a hybrid? Ibid. XXXV (6):317, 331 (June). Boston, 1957.

BOWERS, CLEMENT GRAY. On the importance of the clone. Quar. Bull. Amer. Rhod. Soc. 12 (4):211–215. 1958.

BROWN, J. C. and R. S. HOLMES. Iron the limiting element in a chlorosis. Plant Physiology 30:451–462. 1955.

COLGROVE, M. S. and A. N. ROBERTS. Growth of the azalea as influenced by ammonium and nitrate nitrogen. Quar. Bull. Amer. Rhod. Soc. 11 (4):184–196. Portland, Ore., 1957.

CORY, E. N. and H. A. HIGHLAND. Control of azalea pests. Univ. of Maryland Ext. Bull. 154: 1–8. 1955.

COWAN, J. M. and H. H. DAVIDIAN. A review of rhododendrons in their series. R.H.S. Rhododendron Yearbook, London. I. The Anthopogon alliance, 2: 55–86. 1947. II. The Boothii, Glaucum, Lepidotum alliance, 3: 51–112. 1948. III. The Campanulatum and Fulvum series, 4: 159–182. 1949. IV. The Thomsonii series, 6: 116–183. 1951.

CREECH, JOHN L. Sphagnum moss for plant propagation. U.S. Dept. Agr. Publication F2015. 1955.

DAVIDIAN, H. H. and J. M. COWAN. A revision of the Lacteum series. R.H.S. Rhododendron Yearbook *10*: 122–156. London, 1956.

DAVIDSON, HAROLD C. and C. L. HAMNER. Photoperiodic responses of selected woody ornamental shrubs. Quart. Bull. Mich. Agr. Exp. Station *40*: (2): 327–343. E. Lansing, Mich., 1957.

DOORENBOS, J. Shortening the breeding cycle of rhododendron. Euphytica *4*: 141–146. Wageningen, Holland, 1955.

FRISBIE, LEONARD F. Rhododendron macrophyllum D. Don ex G. Don. Jour. Arnold Arb. XXXVI: 115–117. Cambridge, Mass., 1955.

JANAKI-AMMAL, E. K. et al. Chromosome numbers in species of rhododendrons and polyploidy in the genus Rhododendron. R.H.S. Rhododendron Yearbook *5*: 78–98. London, 1950.

LI, HUI-LIN. Chromosome studies in the azaleas of eastern North America. Am. Jour. Bot. *44* (1): 8–14. 1957.

LUNT, H. A. The use of woodchips and other wood fragments as soil amendments. Bull. Conn. Agr. Exp. Sta. *593*: 1–48, Storrs, Conn. 1955.

MORRISON, B. Y. The Glenn Dale azaleas. Monograph 20, U.S. Dept. Agr., Washington, D.C.

NEARING, GUY G. Rhododendron Fortunei and its allies. Quar. Bull. Amer. Rhod. Soc. *11* (3): 155–160. 1957.

NEARING, GUY G. and CHARLES H. CONNORS. Rhododendrons from cuttings. New Jersey Agr. Expt. Station Bull. 666. 1939. (See also Quar. Bull. Amer. Rhod. Soc. *6*: 186–205 and *7*: 11–28. 1953).

PISEK, A. Zur Kenntnis der frosthaerte alpinen Pflanzen. (Contributions to the study of frost-hardiness of Alpine plants). Naturwiss. *39* (4): 73–78, Innsbruck, 1952.

SKINNER, HENRY T. In search of native azaleas. Morris Arb. Bull. (Univ. of Pa.) *6* (1): 3–10, (2): 15–22, Philadelphia, 1955.

SLEUMER, HERMANN. Ein System der Gattung Rhododendron L. (A systematic treatment of the genus Rhododendron). Engler's Botanische Jahrbücher *74* (4): 511–553. E. Schweizerbartische Verlagsbuchhandlung (Erwin Naegale), Stuttgart, 1949.

TICKNOR, ROBERT L. Gibberellic acid—its effect on the growth of rhododendron seedlings with and without supplemental light. Quar. Bull. Amer. Rhod. Soc. *12* (2): 78–80. 1958.

TOD, HENRY. Rhododendrons and lime. R.H.S. Rhododendron and camellia yearbook, 1959 *13*: 19–24. Roy. Hort. Soc., London, 1959.

VARIOUS AUTHORS. A symposium on rhododendrons and azaleas. Plants & Gardens (n.s.) *5* (1): 1–64. Brooklyn Botanic Garden Record, Brooklyn, N.Y., 1949.

GENERAL REFERENCES

(from the first edition of this book)

ARNOLD ARBORETUM, Bulletin of Popular Information.—Current and back numbers contain numerous notes on rhododendrons.

ARNOLD ARBORETUM, Journal of the.—Occasional contributions on rhododendrons.

BAILEY, L. H. Standard Cyclopedia of Horticulture, vol. *5*. New York, 1916.—
Valuable information on propagation and general culture, with descriptions of
species by A. Rehder.

BAILEY, L. H. The cultivated evergreens, pp. 335–412. New York, 1923.

BAILEY, L. H. Hortus. New York, 1934.

BALFOUR, I. BAILEY. New species of rhododendrons. Notes from the Royal Bot.
Gard. Edinburgh *9* : 207–320; *10* : 79–166; *11* : 19–154; *12* : 85–186. 1915–1922.

BEAN, W. J. Trees and shrubs hardy in the British Isles, vol. *2* (1915) ; vol. *3*
(1934).

(BIBLIOGRAPHY) Rhododendrons and azaleas. Nat. Hort. Mag. *6* : 51. Washington, D.C. 1927.

BOTANICAL MAGAZINE, CURTIS's. London 1787 to date.—Best colored figures.

BOWERS, CLEMENT G. Praising and raising rhododendrons. Cornell Countryman,
25 (7) : 208–209, 219. 2 figs. Ithaca, N.Y., 1928.

BOWERS, CLEMENT G. Azaleas at the [N.Y.] flower show. Jour. N.Y. Bot. Gard.
19 : 105–108. 1928.

BOWERS, CLEMENT G. The blooming dates for rhododendrons and azaleas. Jour.
N.Y. Bot. Gard. *30* : 18–20. 1929.

BOWERS, CLEMENT G. Articles on "Rhododendron" and "Azalea" in The Garden
Encyclopedia, William H. Wise & Co., New York [1935].

CHITTENDEN, F. J. Rhododendron lapponicum and its allies. Jour. Royal Hort.
Soc. *59* (2) : 227–229. 1 col. plate. London, 1934.

CLARKE, S. R. Rhododendron notes, 1918. Rhododendron Society Notes *2* : 24–25.
1920.

CONNORS, CHARLES H. Rhododendrons and their kin. Circular 210, N.J. Agr.
Exp. Sta. New Brunswick, 1928.

COX, E. H. M. Rhododendrons for amateurs, pp. 1–112. London, 1924.

COX, E. H. M. Dwarf rhododendrons. House and Garden *59* (5) : 130, 132, 136.
3 figs. New York, 1931.

CURTIS, RALPH W. Rhododendron planting tables. Horticulture *17* : 670–671.
Boston, 1913.

CURTIS, RALPH W. and DONALD WYMAN. Woody plants that tolerate shade.
Cornell Extension Bull. 268, Cornell Univ., Ithaca, 1933.

DE ROTHSCHILD, LIONEL. Some new rhododendrons of quality. New Flora and
Silva *4* (1) : 5–10. London, 1931.

DE ROTHSCHILD, LIONEL. Notes on the series of Rhododendron. Yearbook Rhodo.
Association (1933), 54–62; (1934), 93–111; (1935), 79–94. London.—The
series are discussed in alphabetical order and those cited above proceed as far
as Ser. Glaucum.

DE ROTHSCHILD, LIONEL. The rhododendron rock garden at Exbury. Jour. Roy.
Hort. Soc. *59* (3) : 325–329. 12 figs. London, 1934.

DRUDE, O. Ericaceae. In ENGLER and PRANTL's Die natülichen Pflanzenrfamilien
4 : 15–16. Leipzig, 1889.

DUNBAR, JOHN. How to grow rhododendrons. Jour. N.Y. Bot. Gard. *22* : 184–190.
1921.

EDINBURGH BOTANIC GARDEN. Notes. 1915 to date.—Original descriptions of
many new oriental species appear here.

HARKNESS, BERNARD. Rhododendron atlanticum. Nat. Hort. Mag. *11* (1) : 54–55. 1 fig. Washington, D.C., 1932.

HOOKER, J. D. Rhododendrons of Sikkim Himalaya. London, 1851.—Magnificent color plates of Himalayan species.

HUME, H. HAROLD. Azaleas and camellias, pp. 1–90. New York, 1931.

HUTCHINSON, J. A. REHDER and H. J. TAGG. The species of Rhododendron. The Rhododendron Society, London and Edinburgh, 1930.—This large taxonomic work of 861 pages sets the prevailing standard for rhododendron nomenclature and arrangement which is followed by the Rhododendron Association and other horticultural groups. It is the best present reference work for the Asiatic species in general. Hybrids and horticultural varieties are not treated. New ed., 1938.

KOSTER, P. M. Hardy azaleas for garden color notes. House and Garden *61* (5) : 64–65, 90, 92. 5 figs. New York (May), 1932.

KOSTER, P. M. Growing rhododendrons for magnificent effects. House and Garden *62* (5) : 36–37, 74, 76. 4 figs. New York (Nov.), 1932.

MAGOR, E. J. P. Rhododendrons for the rock garden. Jour. Roy. Hort. Soc. *50* (2) : 192–200. 8 plates. London, 1925.

McADAM, THOMAS. Azaleas, the showiest spring-flowering shrubs. Country Life in America *11* : 495–500. Illus. 1907.

MILLAIS, J. G. Rhododendrons and the various hybrids, vol. *1* (1917) ; vol. *2* (1924). Many plates, several in color. London.—An elaborate monograph in two large volumes, richly illustrated.

MORRISON, B. Y. Rhododendron viscosum. Nat. Hort. Mag. *9* (4) : 229. 1930.

NAKAI, T. Trees and shrubs of Japan. Tokyo, 1922.

NATIONAL HORTICULTURAL MAGAZINE. Amer. Hort. Soc., Washington, D.C.—Occasional notes on American cultivation, with illustrations.

NEARING, G. G. Undeveloped possibilities in the new Asiatic rhododendrons. Florists' Exchange *76* (7) : 27–38 ; (16) : 27 ; *77* (2) : 23 ; (8) : 25 ; 30 ; (10) : 23, 31 ; (13) : 28 ; *79* (21) : 17 ; (22) : 20. 8 figs. New York, 1931–1932.

RAND, E. S. The rhododendron, pp. 1–176. Cambridge, Mass., 1876.

REHDER, ALFRED. Manual of cultivated trees and shrubs hardy in North America, pp. 679–702. New York, 1927.—A leading work.

RHODODENDRON ASSOCIATION (London). Yearbook, 1930 to date.—Current issues and supplements thereto contain information on new species and varieties cultivated in England, plus reports and articles of contemporary interest.

RHODODENDRON SOCIETY NOTES, vols. *1–4*. Edinburgh, 1916–1928.

ROYAL HORTICULTURAL SOCIETY, JOURNAL. London.—Current and past volumes contain descriptions of new varieties, hybrids and species ; also results of tests, awards of merit and reports of the Joint Rhododendron Committee.

SARGENT, C. S. American azaleas and their hybrids. Rhod. Soc. Notes (1917) : 119–121.

SARGENT, C. S. Trees and Shrubs, vol. *2*. Boston, 1907.

SARGENT, C. S., E. H. WILSON and A. REHDER. Plantae Wilsonae. Boston, 1913.

SCHNEIDER, CAMILLO. Neue Rhododendron-wildarten. Gartenschönheit *7* : 123–125. 1926.

SMALL, JOHN K. Manual of the southeastern flora, pp. 993–999. New York, 1933.—Authority for native species south of Mason and Dixon's line. Uses special nomenclature.

..

STAPF, O. Index Londinensis. Azaleas, vol. *1*; Rhododendrons, vol. *5*. London, 1928.—Contains references to all plates and figures of flowering plants from 1753 to 1920.

T., Malayan rhododendrons and their hybrids. Garden *56*: 62. 1899.

VAN HOUTTE, L. Flores des Serres et des Jardins de l'Europe. 23 volumes. Ghent, 1845–1880.—Descriptions and many colored plates of horticultural varieties, especially Ghent azaleas.

WALTHER, ERIC. Rhododendron tephropeplum. Nat. Hort. Mag. *13* (2) : 197–198, 1 fig. 1934.

WARD, F. KINGDON. Rhododendrons for everyone, pp. 1–115. Illus. London, 1926.

WARD, F. KINGDON. The worth of hybrid rhododendrons. Gard. Chron. *81*: 411. London, 1927.

WATSON, WILLIAM. Azaleas and rhododendrons. London, 1911.

WILDING, E. H. Rhododendrons; their names and addresses, pp. 1–105. London, 1923.—Gives brief data, including names of those who discovered the various species.

WILSON, E. H. The Indian azaleas at Magnolia Gardens. Jour. Arnold Arb. *2*: 159–160. 1921.

WILSON, E. H. The brilliant gaiety of azaleas. House and Garden *46* (1) :56. 1924.

WILSON, E. H. Rhododendrons of Hupeh. Jour. Arnold Arb. *5*: 84–107. 1924.

WILSON, E. H. The rhododendrons of northeastern Asia. Jour. Arnold Arb. *4*: 33–56. 1923.

WILSON, E. H. The rhododendrons of eastern China, the Bonin and Liukiu Islands and of Formosa. Jour. Arnold Arb. *6*: 156–186. 1925.

WILSON, E. H. Hardy azaleas. Country Life (London) *57*: 339–340; 444–445. Illus. 1925.

WILSON, E. H. Aristocrats of the garden, pp. 244–274. Boston, 1926.

WILSON, E. H. Azaleas in the Arnold Arboretum. Rhod. Soc. Notes *3* (2) : 73–76. Edinburgh, 1926.

WILSON, E. H. The magnificence of rhododendrons. House and Garden *50* (5) : 57–58, 150. 1926.

WILSON, E. H. The coming of Kurume azaleas. House and Garden *49* (4) : 112–113, 142. New York, 1926.

WILSON, E. H. Azaleas for southern gardens. House and Garden *57* (6) : 80, 134, 142. 4 figs. New York, 1930.

WILSON, E. H. A new greenhouse rhododendron (*R. burmanicum*). Horticulture *8* (14) : 349–350. Boston, 1930.

WILSON, E. H. and ALFRED REHDER. A monograph of azaleas. Publication of the Arnold Arboretum, No. 9, pp. 1–219. Cambridge, Mass. 1921.—The most complete and detailed botanical work on the Azalea series; written to fit American gardening conditions. It is naturally somewhat technical. Contains no illustrations.

HISTORICAL

ANDRÉ, ÉDOUARD. Plantes de terre de Bruyeres. Paris (Librairie Agricola de la Maison Rustique), 1865.

FOCKE, W. O. Die Pflanzen-mischlinge, pp. 233–245. Berlin, 1881.—Lists all species and hybrids known at that time.

FORSTER, O. Azalea amoena hybrids. Garden *42* : 156. London, 1893.

GOWEN (J. R.?). Hybrid azaleas. Edwards' Botanical Register, 1830.—Abstract in Gardener's Magazine *7* : 62, 471. See also abstracts of articles on hybrid rhododendrons in Gardener's Magazine (London) *7* : 205 and 341, by anonymous authors, 1831.

MANGLES, H. J. (Article on crossing rhododendron species.) Gardeners' Chronicle (London), 2nd series, *12* : 136. Aug. 2, 1879.

PLANCHON, J. E. Sur l'histoire botanique et horticole des plantes dites azalées de l'Inde. Revue Horticole (1854) : 42–49, 61–68. Paris. Reprinted in Flore des Serres, *23* : 230–240. Ghent, 1882.

RODIGAS, E. Nouveaux hybrides : Azaleodendron. L'Illustration Horticole *39* : 53. Ghent, 1892.

STANDISH and NOBLE. A chapter in the history of hybrid rhododendrons. Jour. Roy. Hort. Soc., *5* : 271. London, 1850.

WILDING, E. H. Hybrid rhododendrons in 1855. Rhod. Soc. Notes *3* (2) : 134–136. Edinburgh, 1926.

WILSON, E. H. The story of Azalea indica. Horticulture *8* (10) : 244–245, 1 fig. Boston, 1930.

CULTURE AND PROPAGATION

BAHR, FRITZ. Azaleas and rhododendrons for Easter. Florists' Exchange *76* (11) : 25. 1931.—Commercial forcing.

BALFOUR, I. BAILEY. Observations on rhododendron seedlings. Trans. and Proc., Bot. Soc. Edinburgh, *27* : 221–227. Edinburgh, 1917.

BODDINGTON, ARTHUR T. Don't neglect azalea opportunities. Florists' Exchange *81* (14) : 20. 1933.—Commercial forcing.

BLOWER, S. Root-grafting rhododendrons. Jour. Roy. Hort. Soc. *57* (2) : 352–353. 1 plate. London, 1932.

COMBER, JAMES. Rhododendrons for medium-sized gardens. Yearbook Rhod. Assoc., pp. 48–53. London, 1933.—Includes also information on culture and planting.

DUNBAR, JOHN. How to grow rhododendrons. Jour. N.Y. Bot. Gard., *22* : 184–191. New York, 1921.—As practiced successfully in the collection of Highland Park, Rochester, N.Y.

DUNBAR, JOHN. The leading broad-leaved evergreens and their adaptation. In : L. H. Bailey's The Cultivated Evergreens, pp. 345–353. New York, 1923.

GABLE, JOSEPH B. Growing rhododendrons from seeds. Horticulture *9* (9) : 200. Boston, 1931.

HITCHCOCK, A. E. Effect of peat moss and sand on rooting response of cuttings. Bot. Gaz. *86* : 121–148. 1929. Reprinted in Contributions of the Boyce Thompson Institute, *1* (7) : 439–466. 3 plates. Yonkers, 1928.

KACHE, PAUL. Die Praxis des Baumschulbetriebes. 7th volume of Parey's Handbücher des praktischen Gartenbaues. Paul Parey, Berlin, 1929.—Vegetative propagation in Germany.

KNIGHT, F. P. Propagation of rhododendrons by cuttings. Gard. Chron. (London), *85* : 79, 99. 5 figs. 1929.

MALLINSON, J. W. Grafting rhododendrons in winter (and other methods of vegetative propagation). Florists' Exchange *61* : 555, 651, 749, 837, 939, 1139. New York, 1926.—Propagation of rhododendrons and azaleas by grafting, cuttings, etc., is discussed and illustrated.

MORRISON, B. Y. Azaleas and rhododendrons from seed. U.S. Dept. Agr. Circ. *68*. 8 pp., 3 figs. Washington, 1929.

ROCKWELL, F. F. Azaleas and rhododendrons. House and Garden, *45* (5) : 126. New York, (May) 1924.

TAYLOR, A. D. Plants for ground cover among rhododendrons. The Complete Garden, p. 209. New York, 1925.

WILKINSON, A. E. (Commercial) azalea growing (in Germany). Florists' Exchange, *70* (17) : 30. New York, 1929.

PHYSIOLOGY, SOIL RELATIONS, ECOLOGY, MORPHOLOGY

ARTOPOEUS, A. Über den Bau und Öffnungsweise der Antheren und die Entwickelung der Samen der Erikaceen. Flora, *92* : 309–345. 1903.

BIRKNER. Soil treatment for broad-leaved evergreens. Florists' Exchange, *61* : 648. 1926.

BOWERS, CLEMENT G. How hardy are azaleas? Florists' Exchange, *73* (7) : 47. New York, 1930.

BOWERS, CLEMENT G. Thermotropism and tenderness in Rhododendron ponticum. Florists' Exchange, *78* (15) : 31. 1 fig. New York, 1931.

BURBIDGE, F. W. Cultivated plants, their propagation and improvement, p. 292. Edinburgh and London, 1877.—Hints on propagation and historical data on hybrids.

CAIN, STANLEY A. and J. D. OLIVER MILLER. Leaf structure of Rhododendron catawbiense grown in Picea-Abies forest and in heath communities. Am. Midland Nat. *14* (2) : 69–82. 5 figs. 1933.—Anatomical differences between leaf structure of wild forms found in open bald habitats and others inhabiting forests.

COTTON, A. D. Flower-bud formation in rhododendrons. Rhod. Soc. Notes, *3* (3) : 176–178. Edinburgh, 1927.

COUNCILMAN, W. T. The root system of Epigaea repens and its relations to the fungi of the humus. Washington, D.C., 1923.—Mycorrhiza in the trailing arbutus.

COVILLE, F. V. Use of acid soil for raising seedlings of Epigaea repens. Science n.s. *33* : 711. New York, 1911.

COVILLE, F. V. The formation of leaf-mold. Jour. Wash. Acad. Sci., *3* : 77–89. 1913.

COVILLE, F. V. Soil acidity. Annual Report, Smithsonian Institution, 1920, pp. 247–268. Gov't Printing Office, Washington, 1922.

COVILLE, F. V. Effect of aluminum sulphate on rhododendron seedlings. Am. Hort. Soc. Bull. *1* : 1–6. Washington, 1923.

COVILLE, F. V. Buttermilk as a fertilizer for blueberries. Science n.s., *64* : 94–96. New York, 1926.

COVILLE, F. V. The effect of aluminum sulphate on rhododendrons and other acid-soil plants. Publication 2897 of the Smithsonian Institution, Gov't Printing

Office, Washington, 1927. Reprinted in Florists' Exchange, *66*: 1257, 1285, 1361. New York, 1927.

COVILLE, F. V. Acid soils for certain broad-leaved evergreens. In: L. H. Bailey's The Cultivated Evergreens, pp. 336–341. New York, 1923.

DENNY, F. E. and E. N. STANTON. Chemical treatments for shortening the rest period of pot-grown woody plants. Am. Jour. Bot. *15*: 327–336. 1928. Reprinted in Contributions of the Boyce Thompson Institute, *1*: 355–364. 1 fig.; 2 pl. Yonkers, 1928.—Blooming of *R. nudiflorum* was accelerated by treatment of potted greenhouse plants, with ethylene chlorhydrin in December.

DEXTER, CHARLES O. Proper soil acidity for rhododendrons. Horticulture *9* (15): 333. Boston, 1931.—Mr. Dexter's soil tests pH 4.32, is sandy and well drained.

FUKUDA, YASONA. Hygronastic curling and uncurling movement of the leaves of Rhododendron micranthum with respect to temperature and resistance to cold. Jap. Jour. Bot., *6*: 191–224, 14 figs. Tokyo, 1932.

GROVE, A. Rhododendrons and lime. Gard. Chron. (London) *82*: 426–428. 1927.

HARSHBERGER, J. W. Thermotropic movement of the leaves of Rhododendron maximum. Proc. Acad. Nat. Sci., pp. 219–224. Philadelphia, 1899.

HICKS, HENRY. Plants from East Asia and Western Europe on Long Island. Proceedings Internat. Conference on Plant Hardiness and Acclimatization (1907). Memoir II, Hort. Soc. N.Y., pp. 103–109. New York, 1910.

JOHNSTONE, GEORGE W. The effect of tree-stumps upon rhododendrons. Rhod. Soc. Notes, *3* (2): 108–110. Edinburgh, 1926.

KNUDSON, LEWIS. Non-symbiotic development of seedlings of Calluna vulgaris. The New Phytologist, *32* (2): 115–127; 6 figs. London, 1933.—Reviews work on mycorrhiza of ericaceous plants, presenting new experimental data.

MACLAGAN, J. F. A. Date of flowering as affected by climatic temperature. Plant Physiol. *8* (3): 395–423; 8 figs. 1933.—Rhododendron flowering records at Edinburgh.

MATTHEWS, J. R. and E. M. KNOX. Comparative morphology of the stamen in the Ericaceae. Trans. and Proc. Bot. Soc. Edinburgh, *29*: 243–281; figs. Edinburgh, 1926.

MOLISCH, HANS. Über die Ursachen der Wachstumsrichtungen bei Pollenschläuchen. Sitzungsanz. Kais. Akad. Wiss., Wien, *17*: 11–13. Vienna, 1889.—Acid medium for germinating pollen.

NEARING, G. G. Rhododendrons as thermometers. Horticulture, *6*: 51. Boston, 1928.

NEARING, G. G. A good way to hold down a winter mulch. Horticulture, *6*: 65. Boston, 1928.

RIVETT, MAUD F. The anatomy of Rhododendron ponticum and of Ilex aquifolium in reference to specific conductivity. Annals of Botany *34*: 525–550. 1920. Abstracted in Bot. Abstracts *7*: 1297.

SPENCER, E. L. The nutrition of rhododendrons. Nursery Disease Notes N.J. Agr. Exp. Sta. *2* (3): 1–4. New Brunswick, 1929.

SPENCER, E. L. and J. W. SHIVE. The growth of Rhododendron ponticum in sand cultures. Bull. Torrey Bot. Club, *60*: 423–439. New York, 1933.—The most comprehensive technical report to date on rhododendron nutrition.

STERN, F. C. Rhododendrons on lime soil. Yearbook Rhod. Assoc., pp. 73–76. London, 1933.

STOKER, FRED. The resistance of rhododendrons to drought. Yearbook Rhod. Assoc., pp. 25–42. London, 1935.—Alpine rhododendrons are considered the most resistant.

WHERRY, EDGAR T. Soil reaction in relation to horticulture. Amer. Hort. Soc., Bull. 4. Washington, D.C., 1926.—Contains a list of plants preferring acid soils.

WHERRY, EDGAR T. Remarks to Pennsylvania nurserymen's meeting. Florists' Exchange 79 (7) : 25, 31. New York, 1932.—Soils.

WHITE, RICHARD P. Soil treatments for rhododendron wilt. Florists' Exchange, 77 (4) : 23. New York, 1931.

WHITE, RICHARD P. Leaf mold experiments with rhododendrons. Florists' Exchange, 77 (9) : 23. New York, 1931.

HYBRIDIZATION, GENETICS, CYTOLOGY, STERILITY

BOWERS, CLEMENT G. The development of pollen and viscin strands in Rhododendron catawbiense. Bull. Torrey Bot. Club, 57 : 285–314. 5 pl., 3 figs. New York, 1931.

BOWERS, CLEMENT G. Rhododendrons and azaleas for breeding purposes in America. Jour. N.Y. Bot. Gard., 28 : 81–86. New York, 1927.

BOWERS, CLEMENT G. Hybrid seedling rhododendrons versus grafted plants. Florists' Exchange, 66 : 1445, 1454. 1 fig. New York, 1927.

BOWERS, CLEMENT G. Preservation, storage and artificial germination of rhododendron pollen. Proc. Sixth Internat. Cong. Genetics, 2 : 10. Ithaca, 1932.

COMBER, H. F. Self-sterility in the rhododendrons. Gard. Chron. (London), 3rd Series, 77 : 300–301. London, 1925.

DE ROTHSCHILD, LIONEL. Notes on hybrid rhododendrons. Yearbook Rhod. Assoc. (London), (1933) : 63–72; (1934) : 112–119; (1935) : 95–101.

GABLE, JOSEPH B. Unusual rhododendron hybrids. Nat. Hort. Mag. 12 (3) : 257–258. Washington, D.C., 1933.

GRAHAM, R. J. D. The question of the inbreeding of rhododendrons. Garden 88 : 110–111. 1924.

HERBERT, W. Amaryllidaceae, with a treatise upon cross-bred vegetables. London, 1837.

HERBERT, W. On hybridization amongst vegetables. Jour. Roy. Hort. Soc. 2 : 98. London, 1843.

HURST, C. C. Notes on some experiments in hybridization and cross breeding. Jour. Roy. Hort. Soc. 24 : 90–126. 1900.

IKENO, S. Some crossing experiments with rhododendron species (in German). Studia Mendeliana, pp. 104–111, 1 pl. 1 fig. Brünn, Czechoslovakia, 1923. English abstract in Botanical Abstracts, 14 : 510. 1925.—Genetical investigations on three abnormal flower types in R. obtusum.

MIYAZAWA, B. Rhododendron indicum Sweet var. obtusum Max. Idengaku Zassi (Japanese Journal of Genetics) 1 : 153–157. 1922. Abstract in Botanical Abstracts 14 : 512. 1925.

Noguchi, Yakichi. Studies on the species crosses of Japanese rhododendrons. 1. On the crossability between various species and the cotyledon color of F_1 seedlings. Japanese Journal of Botany, *6* (1) : 103–124. 2 pl. Tokyo, 1932. Abstract in Biological Abstracts.

Report of the Conference on Hybridization. Rhododendrons. Jour. Roy. Hort. Soc. *24* : 22. London, 1900.

Rhododendron Stud Book, included in Yearbooks of the Rhododendron Association (London), beginning 1934. Comprises records of parents and progeny from known crosses between species.

Sax, Karl. Chromosome stability in the genus Rhododendron. Am. Jour. Bot., *17* (4) : 247–251. 1 pl. 1930.

PATHOLOGY AND INSECT PESTS

Felt, E. P. and W. H. Rankin. Insects and diseases of ornamental trees and shrubs. New York, 1932.

Seymour, A. B. Host index of the fungi of North America. Cambridge, Mass., 1929.

Slocock, O. C. A. The lacewing fly. Yearbook Rhod. Assoc., pp. 89–92. London, 1934.

White, Richard P. Nursery Disease Notes, N.J. Agr. Exp. Sta. *1* (11) : 1–5; *2* (4) : 1–4; (5) : 1–4; *3* (12) : 1–4; *4* (3) : 1–4; (4) : 1–4. New Brunswick, 1929–1931.

White, Richard P. Progress with rhododendron wilt. Florists' Exchange *70* (13) : 37–50. New York, 1929.

White, Richard P. Pathogenicity of Pestalotia spp. on rhododendron. Phytopathology, *20* (1) : 85–91. 1930.

White, Richard P. The insects and diseases of rhododendrons and azaleas. Jour. Econ. Ent., *26* (3) : 631–640. 1933.—A brief survey, the most complete report to date on rhododendron pests.

Wilson, G. Fox. The rhododendron white fly. Jour. Roy. Hort. Soc. *54* (1) : 214–217 (1929) and (later report) *60* (6) : 264–271. London, 1935.—*Dialeurodes chittendeni*, a new sucking insect, destructive in England.

Wilson, G. Fox. Rhododendron pests: A key to symptoms of attack. New Flora and Sylva, *6* (1) : 36–44. London, 1933.

Wilson, G. Fox. Insect pests of rhododendrons. Jour. Roy. Hort. Soc. *50* (1) : 46–54. 7 pl. London, 1925.

TYPES OF INFLORESCENCE

Figures *a* to *zz* in the accompanying black and white plates indicate certain general types of inflorescence and are referred to under the index figures (a) to (zz) respectively in chapters XXII and XXIII as illustrating these general types of inflorescence in the description of species. The following species are represented in the figures:

a. *catawbiense*
b. *Nuttallii*
c. *Maddenii*
d. *minus*
e. *trichostomum* var. *ledoides*
f. *micranthum*
g. *Davidii*
h. *virgatum*
i. *triflorum*
j. *japonicum*
k. *calendulaceum*
l. *roseum*
m. *dauricum*
n. *Kaempferi*

o. *mucronatum*
p. *obtusum*
q. *setosum*
r. *intricatum*
s. *spinuliferum*
t. *Keysii*
u. *hirsutum*
v. *lepidotum*
w. *albiflorum*
x. *camtschaticum*
y. *pendulum*
z. *cantabile*
zz. *Forrestii*

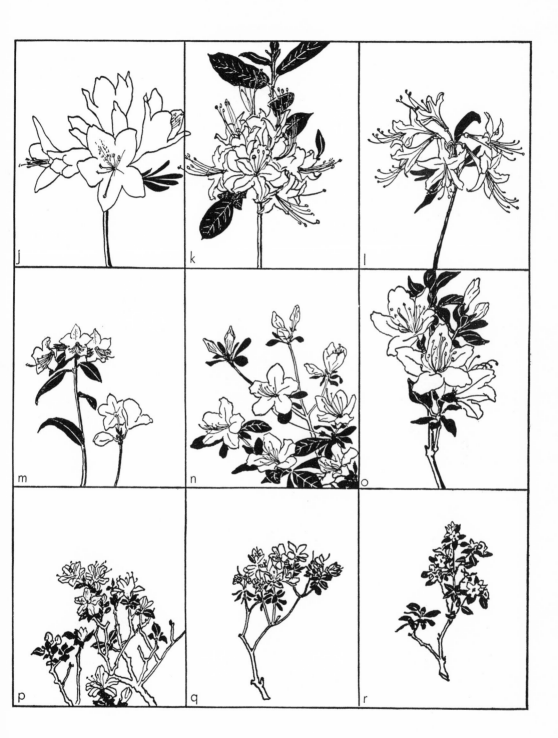

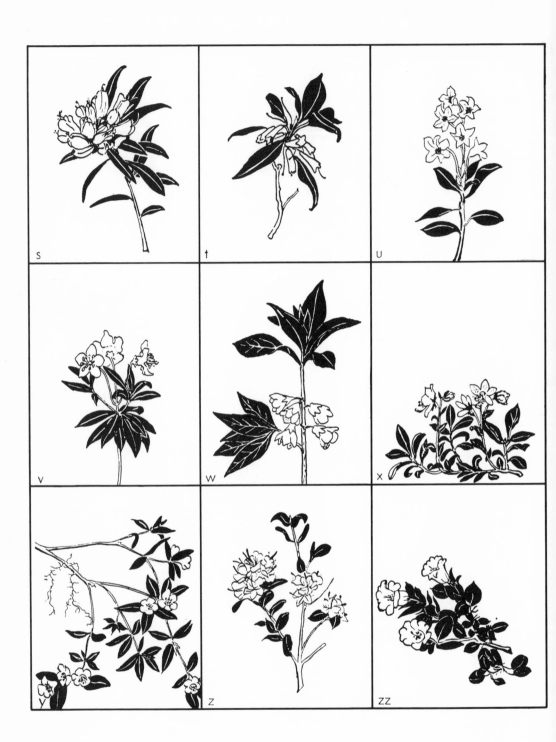

FLOWER FORM OUTLINES

Figures 1 to 76 in the accompanying diagrams indicate the approximate shape of the flowers referred to under the index figures (1) to (76) respectively in the descriptions of species included in Chapter XXII. It should be understood that these are approximations only. The figures as numbered represent types of the following species of Rhododendron:

1. (a) *Keysii*
   (b) *spinuliferum*
2. (a) *ferrugineum*
   (b) *cinnabarinum*
3. *nipponicum*
4. *barbatum*
5. (a) *scabrifolium*
   (b) *myrtilloides*
6. *racemosum*
7. (a) *anthopogon*
   (b) *Tschonoskii*
8. *ledoides*
9. *camelliaeflorum*
10. *lepidotum*
11. *semibarbatum*
12. *sulfureum*
13. *ovatum*
14. *dauricum*
15. *camtschaticum*
16. *canadense*
17. *microphyton*
18. *setosum*
19. *triflorum*
20. *rubiginosum*
21. *micranthum*
22. *albiflorum*
23. *campylogynum*
24. *Sargentianum*
25. *brachyanthum*
26. *cantabile*
27. *lapponicum*
28. *pumilum*
29. *citriniflorum*
30. *polyandrum*
31. *Forrestii*
32. *haematodes*
33. *dichroanthum*
34. *calostrotum*
35. *Brookeanum*
36. *oreotrephes*

37. *oleifolium*
38. *Tashiroi*
39. *Vialii*
40. *obtusum* AMOENA (hose-in-hose)
41. *viscosum*
42. *roseum*
43. X *mixtum* (double)
44. *japonicum*
45. *mucronatum*
46. *Kaempferi*
47. *Schlippenbachii*
48. *reticulatum*
49. *Vaseyi*
50. *ponticum*
51. *Smirnowii*
52. *maximum*
53. V. ATROSANGUINEUM
54. V. MRS. CHAS. SARGENT
55. *carolinianum*
56. V. BOULE DE NEIGE
57. V. EVERESTIANUM
58. *Fargesii*
59. *sutchuenense*
60. *apodectum*
61. *irroratum*
62. *glischrum*
63. *Griffithianum*
64. *Maddenii*
65. *arboreum*
66. *Davidii*
67. *decorum*
68. *campylocarpum*
69. *Falconeri*
70. *orbiculare*
71. *simiarum*
72. *auriculatum*
73. *lacteum*
74. *occidentale*
75. *linearifolium*
76. *ciliicalyx*

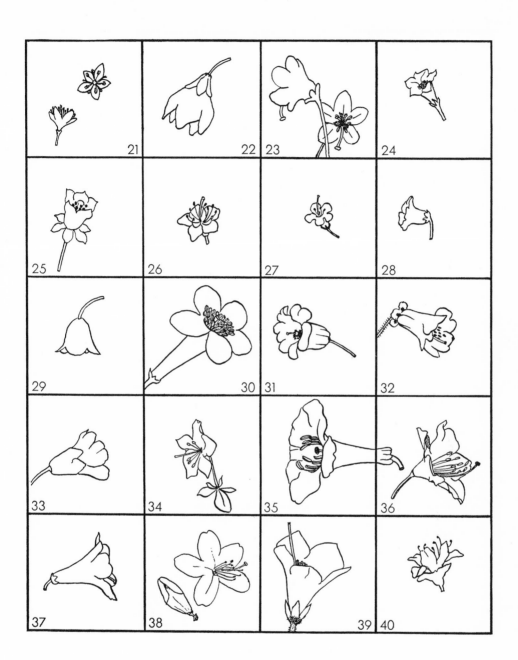

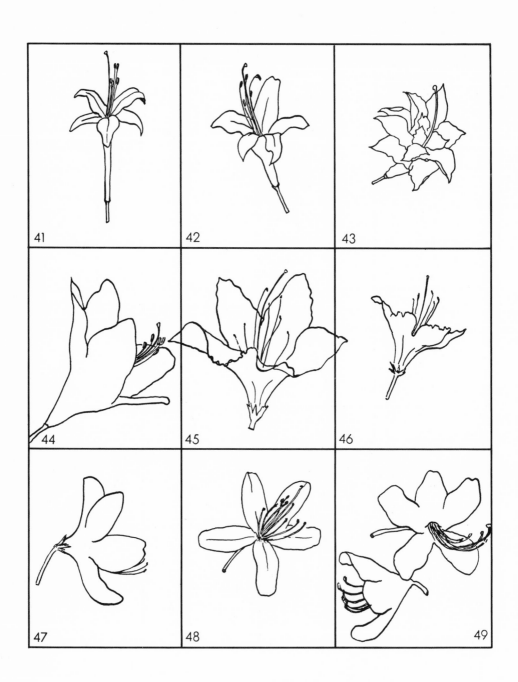

41 42 43
44 45 46
47 48 49

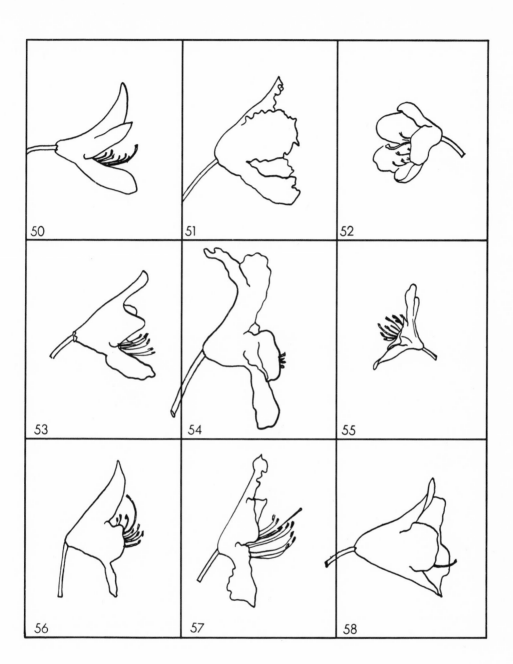

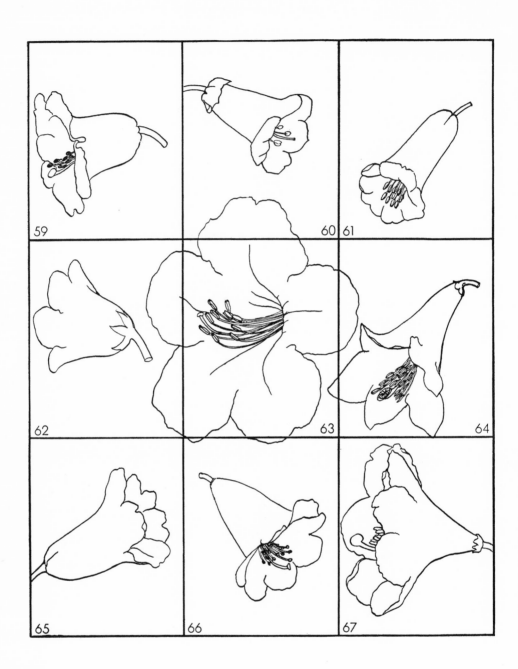

68   69   70

71   72   73

74   75   76

ERRATA

The following species, with descriptions, inadvertently omitted from their proper places elsewhere in this book, are here presented along with references to the page numbers on which they should have appeared:

Rhododendron bivelatum Balfour f. (twice covered). *D.* 6 ft., with evergreen leaves. Small rose-colored flowers about 1 in. long. Dry hills in N.E. Yunnan, up to 8,000 ft. Not in general cultivation. TRIFLORUM SERIES, SUBSERIES AUGUSTINII. Page 383.

Rhododendron hypophaeum Balfour f. & Forrest (gray beneath). *B.* 4–5 feet. Flowers about 1 in. long, white, faintly tinged rose. Open situations in and on margins of pine forests, S.W. Szechuan, 11,000 ft. TRIFLORUM SERIES, SUBSERIES YUNNANENSE. Page 388.

Rhododendron Mayebarae (after the collector, K. Mayebara). A little known shrub with the leaves arranged 2–3 together at the ends of the branchlets; the flowers are large, purple with deeper purple spots. AZALEA SERIES, SUB-SERIES SCHLIPPENBACHII. Page 270.

Rhododendron Potaninii Batalin (after G. N. Potanin, Russian traveler in N. China). Height 15 ft. Flowers broadly campanulate, 1 in. long, white or whitish. Eastern Kansu. TALIENSE SERIES. SUBSERIES NOT PLACED. Probably page 369.

Rhododendron recurvoides (like *recurvum*). *B.* Height 2–3 ft., habit compact. Flowers whitish or rose, spotted. Leaves narrow, dark green and felted beneath. TALIENSE SERIES, SUBSERIES ROXIEANUM. Page 368.

SUBJECT INDEX

SPECIES INDEX

Recognized species are italicized. Cultivar names are usually initialed in capitals. Synonyms are shown in roman type, sometimes followed by legitimate name in parentheses. Where two or more cultivars bear the same name, distinctions are shown by indicating azaleas, e.g. (az), or group names, e.g. (Mollis az).

Aartje, 424
Abbot, 428
A. Bedford, 399
Aberconwayi, 310
aberrans, 318
A. B. Mitford, 399
A. Borsig, 440
Abraham Lincoln, 399
accuminatum, 315
achroanthum, 322
Acme, 428
acraium, 232
Adamsii, 232
Addy Wery, 424
Adelaide, 414
adenogynum, 365
adenophorum, 365
adenopodum, 349
adenostemonum (see *pogonostylum*), 312
admirabile, 311
Admirable, 414
Admiration, 421
adoxum, 301
Adriaan Koster, 399
adroserum, 311
Advance (Glenn Dale az), 428
Advance (Occid. az), 417
aechmophyllum, 387
aemulorum, 340
aeruginosum (*Campanulatum*), 280
Afghan, 399
afghanicum, 384
Afterglow, 399
Afterglow (az), 414
aganniphum, 368
agapetum, 313
agastum, 310
agathodaemonis, 315
Agemaki, 421
agetum, 342
agglutinatum, 318, 368
Ahrendsii Azaleas, 424
Aida, 416
Aileen Henderson, 399
Ai-no-tomo, 427
Aioi, 421
aiolopeplum, 318

aiolosalpinx (*Stewartianum*), 379
aischropeplum, 368
aizoides, 345
Ajax, 399
Akebonar Ruykin, 423
Alabama Azalea, 246
alabamense, 246
Alabaster, 428
Aladdin, 428
Alarm, 399
Alaska, 436
Alba Maculata, 440
Alba Multiflora, 440
Alba Punctata, 440
Albatross, 399, 417
Albert, 399
Albert Close, 399
Albertsenianum, 341
albicans, 251
albicaule (*decorum*), 299
albiflorum, 231
Albion, 436
albipetalum, 345
Albrechtii, 242
Albrecht's Azalea, 242
album, 315
Album Elegans, 399
Album Grandiflorum, 399
Album Novum, 399
Alfred, 399
Alice, 399
Alice (Indian az), 424, 438
Alice Martineau, 399
Alice Sargent, 437
Alice Street, 399
Alice de Stuers, 414
Alight, 428
All-a-glow, 421
Allah, 399
Allegory, 428
Allure, 428
Alma Tadema, 414
Alphonse Lavallée, 414
Alphonse Pericat, 436
alpicola, 322
Alpine Rose Rhododendron, 295
Altaclarense, 414

nanothamnum, 375
nanum (*polycladum*), 326
Naomi, 408
Naomi (az), 426
Naomi Nereid, 408
Narcissiflora (Ghent az), 414
Narcissiflora (*mucronatum*), 441
Natalie, 437
Nathaniel (az), 419
nebrites (*himertum*), 345
Nectar, 432
Nellie, 408, 413
nepalense (*arboreum*), 235
neriiflorum, 341
neriifolium, 316
Nerissa, 432
New Moon, 408
nhatrangense, 316
Niagara, 432
Nicolaas Beets, 416
Nieuwenhuisii, 316
nigropunctatum, 325
nikoense, 243
niko-montanum (*chrysanthum*), 351
nilagiricum, 236
ningyuenense, 311
Niobe, 435, 439
niphargum, 303
Niphetos, 432
niphobolum, 379
nipponicum, 255
Nishiki-den, 427
nitens, 360
nitidulum, 325
nitidum (*viscosum*), 254
nivale, 325
niveum, 236
nmaiense, 233
N. N. Sherwood, 408
Nobility, 432
Nobleanum Album, 408
Nobleanum Coccineum, 408
Nocturne, 432
nodosum, 316
Nome, 426
Noordtiana, 441
Noreen, 432
noriakianum (unplaced)
Norma, 416, 426
Norman Shaw, 408
Normandy, 426
North Star, 437
Nortoniae, 316
notatum, 331
Novelty, 432
nubicola, 316
nudiflorum, 251
nudipes, 270
Nuneham Park, 408
Nuttallii, 334

Oberon, 426
oblongifolium, 252
oblongum (*Griffithianum*), 301
obovatum, 328

obscurinervium, 316
obscurum, 388
obtusum, 264, 422
occidentale, 252
ochraceum, 276
Oconee Azalea, 254
Odoratum, 408, 413
odoriferum, 333
officinale, 351
Oi-no-mezane (Melody), 422
Old Faithful, 426
Old Gold, 419
Oldewig, 409
Old Ivory, 422
Old Port, 409
Oldhamii, 265
oleifolium, 392
ombrochares, 312
Omega, 409
Omen, 432
Omoine (Dame Lavender), 421
Omurasaki, 442
Opal Fawcett, 409
Openshawianum, 297
Opera, 433
oporinum, 309
Oracle, 433
Oranea, 416
Orange Beauty, 422
Orange Favorite, 426
Orange King, 426
Orange Man, 414
Orange Princess, 416
orbiculare, 302
Orbwill, 409
Orchid, 436
oreadum, 316
oreinum (*alpicola*), 322
oreodoxa, 303
oreotrephes, 384
oreotrephoides, 384
oresbium (*Edgarianum*), 324
oresterum, 377
Orient, 419
Oriflamme, 433
orion, 316, 409, 426
Orison, 433
Orpheus, 414
orthocladum, 325
Osakazuki, 441
Osaraku (Penelope), 422
osmerum (*russatum*), 326
Oswald de Kerkhove (syn.), 439
Othello, 426
Otohime (Macrantha az), 427
Otome (Maiden's Blush), 422
oulotrichum, 381
ovatosepalum, 265
ovatum, 347
Oxydol, 419
oxyphyllum, 363
Oyeyama, 262, 441

pachypodum, 332
pachysanthum, 276

The
RHODODENDRON REGIONS
of the New World

C.G.Bowers, del.